Teen Health

Teachers & Students

health.glencoe.com

New Student Edition Includes

- Content based on the latest health research
- Guide to Reading and Graphic Organizers
- Spanish Edition
- Student Edition Online
- TIME Health News

Reading Skills and Assessment

- Reading Skills Reinforcement
- Writing Support
- Activating Prior Knowledge Strategies
- Academic Vocabulary
- Comprehensive Reading Tutor
- Standardized Test Practice

Health Online Resources

- Complete Student Edition Online
- Audio Summaries (English and Spanish)
- Study Guides with Interactive Vocabulary
- Education Resources, Conferences, and Grants
- Professional Development Articles
- Correlations to National and State Standards

New Technology Resources

- Teen Health PowerPoint®
- TeacherWorks™
- StudentWorks™ Plu
- ExamView® Test Ge
- Vocabulary PuzzleM (English and Spanish)

D1158097

Improving Active Reading and Study Skills

Dinah Zike's FOLDABLES™

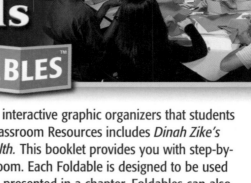

Foldables™ are easy-to-make, three-dimensional, interactive graphic organizers that students create out of plain sheets of paper. The Teacher Classroom Resources includes *Dinah Zike's Reading and Study Skills Foldables™ for Teen Health.* This booklet provides you with step-by-step instructions for using Foldables in your classroom. Each Foldable is designed to be used as a study guide for the main ideas and key points presented in a chapter. Foldables can also be used for a more in-depth investigation of a concept, idea, opinion, event, or a person or place studied in a chapter. These unique hands-on tools for studying and reviewing were created exclusively for Glencoe by education specialist Dinah Zike.

Why Use Foldables in Health?

Because they

- organize, display, and arrange information, making it easier for students to grasp health skills concepts, theories, facts, opinions, questions, research, and ideas.

- are student-made study guides that are compiled as students listen for main ideas, read main ideas, or conduct research.

- integrate language arts into the study of health.

- replace teacher-generated writing or photocopied sheets with student-generated print.

- incorporate the use of such skills as problem solving, comparing and contrasting, recognizing cause-and-effect, and finding similarities and differences.

- continue to immerse students in previously learned vocabulary, concepts, information, generalizations, ideas, and theories, providing them with a strong foundation that they can build upon with new concepts and knowledge.

- can be used by students or teachers to easily communicate data through graphs, tables, charts, models, and diagrams, including Venn diagrams.

- can be used as alternative assessment tools by teachers to evaluate student progress or by students to evaluate their own progress.

- provide a sense of student ownership or investiture in the health curriculum.

▼ *Student Edition, p. 31*

FOLDABLES™ Study Organizer

As You Read

Make this Foldable™ to record what you learn about positive self-concept in Lesson 1. Begin with a plain sheet of 8½" x 11" paper.

1 Fold the sheet of paper in half along the long axis.

2 Turn the paper and fold it into thirds.

3 Unfold and cut the top layer along both fold lines. This makes three tabs.

4 Draw two overlapping ovals, and label as shown.

Positive Self-Concept | Both | Positive Self-Esteem

Under the appropriate tab, take notes on what you learn about positive self-concept and high self-esteem. Under the middle tab, write down what the two have in common.

Teen Health

COURSE 1

Teacher Wraparound Edition

Mary H. Bronson, Ph.D.

Michael J. Cleary, Ed.D., C.H.E.S.

Betty M. Hubbard, Ed.D., C.H.E.S.

Contributing Authors

Dinah Zike, M.Ed.

TIME®

Glencoe

New York, New York   Columbus, Ohio   Chicago, Illinois   Peoria, Illinois   Woodland Hills, California

Meet the Authors

Mary H. Bronson, Ph.D., recently retired after teaching for 30 years in Texas public schools. Dr. Bronson taught health education in grades K–12, as well as health education methods classes at the undergraduate and graduate levels. As Health Education Specialist for the Dallas School District, Dr. Bronson developed and implemented a district-wide health education program. She has been honored as Texas Health Educator of the Year by the Texas Association for Health, Physical Education, Recreation, and Dance and selected Teacher of the Year twice, by her colleagues. Dr. Bronson has assisted school districts throughout the country in developing local health education programs. She is also the coauthor of the *Glencoe Health* textbook.

Betty M. Hubbard. Ed.D., C.H.E.S., has taught science and health education in grades 6–12, as well as undergraduate- and graduate-level courses. She is a professor at the University of Central Arkansas, where, in addition to teaching, she conducts in-service training for health education teachers in school districts throughout Arkansas. In 1991, Dr. Hubbard received the university's teaching excellence award. Her publications, grants, and presentations focus on research-based, comprehensive health instruction. Dr. Hubbard is a fellow of the American Association for Health Education and serves as the contributing editor for the Teaching Ideas feature of the *American Journal of Health Education*.

Michael J. Cleary, Ed.D., C.H.E.S., is a professor at Slippery Rock University where he teaches methods courses and supervises field experiences. Dr. Cleary taught health education at Evanston Township High School in Illinois and later served as the Lead Teacher Specialist at the McMillen Center for Health Education in Fort Wayne, Indiana. Dr. Cleary has published widely on curriculum development and assessment in K-12 and college health education. Dr. Cleary is also coauthor of the *Glencoe Health* textbook.

Contributing Authors

Dinah Zike, M.Ed., is an international curriculum consultant and inventor who has designed and developed educational products and three-dimensional, interactive graphic organizers for over thirty years. As president and founder of Dinah-Might Adventures, L.P., Dinah is author of over 100 award-winning educational publications. Dinah has a B.S. and an M.S. in educational curriculum and instruction from Texas A & M University. Dinah Zike's *Foldables*™ are an exclusive feature of McGraw-Hill textbooks.

TIME is the nation's leading news and information magazine. With over 80 years of experience, TIME provides an authoritative voice in the analysis of the issues of the day, from politics to pop culture, from history-making decisions to healthy living. TIME Learning Ventures brings the strength of TIME and TIME For Kids' editorial and photographic excellence to educational resources for school and home.

 **Glencoe**

The *McGraw-Hill* Companies

Printed in the United States of America.

Send all inquiries to:
Glencoe/McGraw-Hill
21600 Oxnard Street, Suite 500
Woodland Hills, California 91367

ISBN-13: 978-0-07-869760-9 (Course 1 Student Edition)
ISBN-10: 0-07-869760-3   (Course 1 Student Edition)

ISBN-13: 978-0-07-869763-0 (Course 1 Teacher Wraparound Edition)
ISBN-10: 0-07-869763-8   (Course 1 Teacher Wraparound Edition

1 2 3 4 5 6 7 8 9 071 10 09 08 07 06 05

Health Consultants

Alia Antoon, M.D.

Chief of Pediatrics
Shriners Hospital for Children
Assistant Clinical Professor, Pediatrics
Harvard Medical School
Boston, Massachusetts

Elissa M. Barr, Ph.D., C.H.E.S.

Assistant Professor of Public Health
University of North Florida
Jacksonville, Florida

Beverly Bradley, Ph.D., R.N., C.H.E.S.

School Health Consultant
Retired Assistant Clinical Professor
University of California, San Diego
San Diego, California

Roberta L. Duyff, M.S., R.D., C.F.C.S.

Food and Nutrition Consultant/President
Duyff Associates
St. Louis, Missouri

Kristin Danielson Fink, M.A.

National Director
Community of Caring
Salt Lake City, Utah

Kathryn J. Gust, M.A.

Instructional Technology Specialist
Freedom High School
Morganton, North Carolina

Christine A. Hayashi, M.A. Ed., J.D.

Attorney at Law, Special Education Law
Adjunct Faculty, Educational Leadership
and Policy Studies Development
California State University, Northridge
Northridge, California

Tinker D. Murray, Ph.D., FACSM

Professor
Texas State University
San Marcos, Texas

Don Rainey, M.S., C.S.C.S.

Director, Physical Fitness and Wellness
Texas State University
San Marcos, Texas

Michael Rulon, M.S.

Instructional Coach
Health Instructor
Albuquerque Public Schools
Albuquerque, New Mexico

Robin Scarcella, Ph.D.

Director, Academic English/ESL
University of California, Irvine
Irvine, California

Peter T. Whelley, M.S., N.C.S.P.

School Psychologist
Moultonborough School District
Adjunct Faculty
Plymouth State University
Plymouth, New Hampshire

David C. Wiley, Ph.D.

Professor of Health Education
Texas State University
San Marcos, Texas

Teen Health

Table of Contents

Your Partner for K-12 Health and Fitness........................ TM2

The *Teen Health* Program at a Glance............................ TM4

Student Edition.. TM6

Teacher Wraparound Edition.. TM8

Reading to Succeed..TM10
> Strengthen Student Reading and Writing
> Active Reading and Study Skills
> Generate High Achievers
> Enhance Student Learning
> Academic Integration
> Tips for Teaching Academic Vocabulary

Program Resources..TM16

Technology Solutions...TM18

Assessment Options..TM20

Meeting the Needs of All Students............................... TM22

Spanish Resources..TM24

Education Partners... TM25

National Health Education Standards...........................TM26

Professional Health Series..TM28

Teacher Appendix
> Physical Activity and Fitness Guidelines 357
> *Healthy People 2010* 358
> 40 Developmental Assets...360

Your Partner for K-12 Health & Fitness

McGraw-Hill, the leader in health education, offers a comprehensive and sequential K-12 health education program designed to assist schools in developing and implementing a coordinated school health education curriculum.

Start with a Healthy Foundation

Macmillan/McGraw-Hill presents *Health & Wellness* for grades K-5. This easy-to-manage program provides integrated curriculum strategies tailored for the elementary classroom. The easy-to-do, student-guided activities are structured for success, which helps lay the foundation for building lifelong health skills.

Promote Healthy Behaviors with *Teen Health*

Teen Health, offered by Glencoe/McGraw-Hill is a three book series designed specifically for students in grades 6-8. The inviting style, easy to read format, and motivating activities engage middle school learners. *Teen Health* combines scientifically accurate, age-appropriate health content with extensive practice and application of skills. Colorful and informative photos, visuals, charts, and diagrams engage student interest and facilitate learning.

> "Quality physical education and health education programs in all K-12 schools provide the foundation for healthy, active lifestyles that support all learning and help ensure success in future pursuits."
>
> —American Association for Health, Physical Education, Recreation and Dance, 2005

Foster Lifelong Health and Wellness Behaviors

A comprehensive approach to health and fitness is essential in motivating teens to develop healthy behaviors. *Glencoe Health*, *Health & Wellness*, and *Foundations of Personal Fitness* provide flexible formats to improve health and wellness among high school students. Real-life application of health skills helps students apply what they learn in health class toward practicing healthy behaviors for a lifetime. Hands-on features are integrated with technology, embedded assessments, and up-to-date health content.

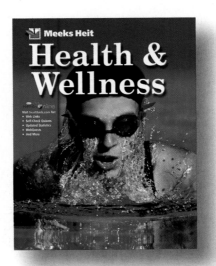

Glencoe's Online Learning Centers: Offering Technology Solutions

At **health.glencoe.com,** you and your students will find a variety of interactive features and study tools to enhance the print programs.

The Teen Health Program at a Glance

Teen Health, the three-book series for students in grades 6, 7, and 8, provides middle school students with the foundation of concepts and skills necessary for lifelong health. Current health concepts are integrated with nationally recognized, health-based skills.

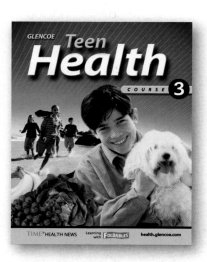

Teen Health Course 1

Chapter

1. Your Health and Wellness
2. Mental and Emotional Wellness
3. Healthy Relationships
4. Nutrition
5. Physical Activity
6. Personal Health
7. Your Body Systems
8. Growth and Development
9. Tobacco
10. Alcohol and Other Drugs
11. Preventing Diseases
12. Safety and the Environment

Teen Health Course 2

Chapter

1. Understanding Health and Wellness
2. Taking Charge of Your Health
3. Physical Activity and Fitness
4. Nutrition
5. Mental and Emotional Health
6. Building Healthy Relationships
7. Resolving Conflicts and Preventing Violence
8. Tobacco
9. Alcohol
10. Drugs
11. Personal Health and Consumer Choices
12. Growing and Changing
13. Communicable Diseases
14. Noncommunicable Diseases
15. Personal Safety
16. The Environment and Your Health

Teen Health Course 3

Chapter

1. Understanding Your Health
2. Skills for a Healthy Life
3. Mental and Emotional Health
4. Mental and Emotional Problems
5. Relationships: The Teen Years
6. Promoting Social Health
7. Conflict Resolution
8. Violence Prevention
9. Physical Activity and Fitness
10. Nutrition for Health
11. Your Body Image
12. Alcohol
13. Tobacco
14. Drugs
15. Personal Care and Consumer Choices
16. Your Body Systems
17. Growth and Development
18. Communicable Diseases
19. Noncommunicable Diseases
20. Safety and Emergencies
21. Environmental Health

Dynamic Instruction Motivates Students

Dynamic Instructional Strategies present a clear and comprehensive coverage of health.

- Engaging lesson introductions include Guide to Reading, Key Terms, Reading Strategy, and Quick Write.
- Hands-On Health, Media Watch, and TIME® Health News provide real-life application to the study of health concepts and behaviors.
- Chapter summary and Reading Review offer concise summaries of chapter topics and can be used to preview, review, or summarize chapter content.

A Research-Based Reading Strand encourages active reading and learning for students of all reading levels.

- Foldables™ help students organize and process key concepts as they read.
- Analyzing Graphics, Photos, Charts, and Tables questions ask students to interpret and evaluate a visual.
- Reading Checks help students check their reading comprehension.

Differentiated Instruction makes *Teen Health* accessible to students of all learning levels.

- Differentiated Instruction activities and strategies are designed for students of differing abilities and learning challenges.
- How Do I Use My Textbook? Teaches students how to approach the text to retain course information and get the most value out of the Student Edition.

Standardized Test Practice gives students the opportunity to practice for state and national exams.

- Chapter assessments and workbooks provide a variety of standardized test practice, including multiple choice, open-ended short response, and open-ended extended response.
- Test-Taking Tips help students learn how to successfully approach test questions.

A Variety of Interdisciplinary Activities and Features are essential for student success and get students excited about health.

- Connect To...Math, Science, Language Arts integrates core curriculum.
- Developing Good Character emphasizes character traits in teens.
- Media Watch guides students to develop critical media literacy skills.

Teacher Resources provide convenient strategies for new and experienced teachers.

- The Planning Guide in each chapter provides background information to help you prepare for each chapter's key topics.
- *Fast Files* chapter resources contain important reproducible masters.
- Chapter Resources help teachers organize their daily lessons.

Technology provides time-saving software products to help you creatively engage students and reduce prep time.

- Teen Health PowerPoint® Presentation
- TeacherWorks™
- StudentWorks™ Plus
- Health Online at **health.glencoe.com** provides additional study tools and activities

Energize Your Students...

Teen Health introduces students to vital health concepts and provides opportunities to practice health skills that can lead to health-enhancing behaviors

Chapter Opener

Engage students at the beginning of every chapter with motivational start-up activities.

IM Express challenges students to think about health issues in this newest feature.

HEALTH INVENTORY evaluates teens' healthy behaviors—with additional interactive inventories at **health.glencoe.com**.

HEALTH QUIZ peaks curiosity and quickly assesses prior knowledge.

Working with the Photo visually introduces the chapter and guides students with an engaging question to help them interpret the meaning.

Guide to Reading introduces each lesson's key concepts and builds vocabulary and reading skills.

Building Vocabulary activities enhance vocabulary development.

Focusing on the Main Ideas previews the learning outcome for students.

Reading Strategy and Foldables™ provide lesson-specific study tools so students can effectively organize content and increase comprehension.

to make Real-Life Connections

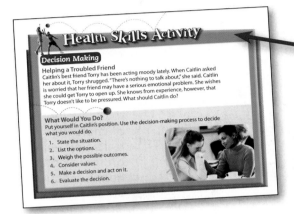

Health Skills Activity

These activities reinforce health skills that are taught with each lesson. They emphasize healthy decision making, communication, goal setting, accessing information, practicing healthy behaviors, analyzing influences, and advocacy.

Building Health Skills

Standards-based Health Skills features connect skills to real life.

- **Model** presents positive modeling of the skill

- **Practice** gives students a chance to practice the skill in a realistic situation.

- **Apply** lets students personalize and perform the skill on their own and evaluate performance.

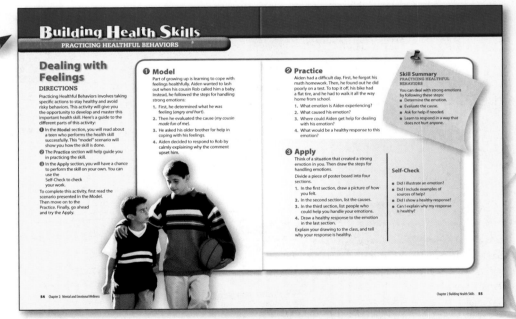

Additional Features

Hands-On Health features in selected chapters present students with another chance to create a product or demonstration to show what they have learned.

Career Corner gets students thinking about their future with health career options.

Power Your Classroom...

Find a variety of teaching strategies coded to the student text with Glencoe's easy-to-follow lesson cycle — *Focus, Teach, Assess, Close* — in this Teacher Wraparound Edition.

Activating Prior Knowledge

Foldables™ Study Organizers

Quick Write

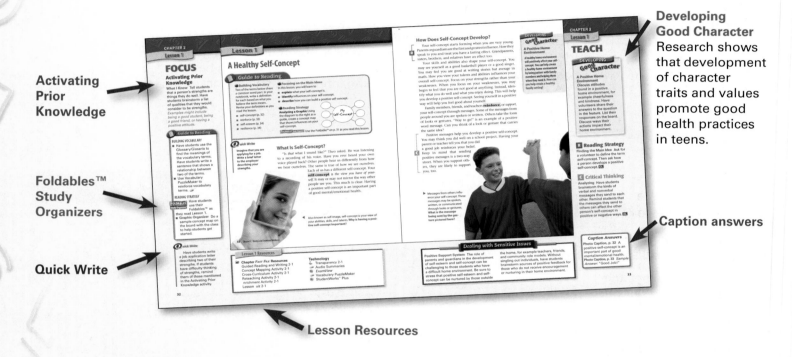

Lesson Resources

Developing Good Character Research shows that development of character traits and values promote good health practices in teens.

Caption answers

Teaching Strategies for all features

Highlighted discussion answers

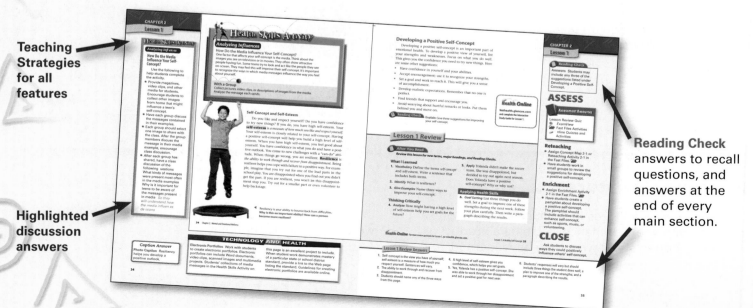

Reading Check answers to recall questions, and answers at the end of every main section.

with Flexible, Focused, and Fully Accessible Teaching Strategies

Reading Strategies and Writing Support to aid student comprehension of concepts and skills.

Strategies are coded for differentiated learning throughout the text.

Point-of-use coding matches strategies with student edition content.

U Universal Access

Support for Teaching Reading

R Reading Support   **Health Online**   Academic Integration For additional academic integration strategies, visit the Teacher Center at health.glencoe.com.

Reading Preview

Activating Background Vocabulary Ask students what comes to mind when they hear the term "self-esteem." Guide students in a discussion to help them recognize the meaning of self-esteem as the measure of how much a person likes and respects him- or herself. Explain that this chapter will help students to develop their positive self-esteem.

FOLDABLES Study Organizer *Dinah Zike's Reading and Study Skills for Teen Health* provides interactive graphic organizers that help students comprehend and retain health concepts as they read. Use the Foldables™ on page 31 or find more Foldables™ activities for the chapter on **Mental and Emotional Wellness** in the separate booklet, available in the TCR.

Lesson 1 A Healthy Self-Concept
Predicting Read aloud the introduction to the lesson on Self-Concept. Have students scan the rest of the lesson, paying attention to pictures, lists, and words in bold. Ask them to predict in writing one thing they think they will learn from reading this lesson. After students complete the reading, have them confirm or revise their predictions.

Lesson 2 Your Character Counts
Organizing Information Tell students that each boldface head is a main idea. The text under the head gives details about the main idea. Have students list each boldface head in Lesson 2 on the front of an index card. As students read each section on developing good character, have them write notes on the back of the index card.

Lesson 3 Expressing Emotions
Interactive Reading Have students write three questions on sticky notes regarding emotions. The questions should begin with why, how, when, or where. As they read about types of emotions and expressing emotions, they should use their questions to discuss the content with a partner.

Lesson 4 Coping with Stress
Double-entry Notes Have students fold a sheet of paper in half lengthwise. As they read **Strategies for Managing Stress** (pages 48–49) have them write the bold-faced headings on the left side. On the right side, they should make notes about the important ideas in each section as they read.

Lesson 5 Emotional Problems
Clarifying Text Have students read the section on **Anxiety Disorders, Mood Disorders,** and **Depression** (page 51). Ask: Are any of the concepts unclear? Write student responses on the board. Model ways to clarify the text, such as referring to the illustrations and definitions of terms to find supporting facts. Encourage volunteers who understand the concepts to explain them in their own words to the class.

Post Reading
Technology Based Presentations Have students describe strategies for maintaining mental and emotional wellness. Encourage students to develop a presentation of these concepts for younger students using a variety of media including technology, art, and music. Have them share their presentations with the class.

Key for Using the Teacher Wraparound Edition

Use this key to help you identify the different types of prompts found in the Teacher Wraparound Edition.

R Reading Strategies activities help you teach reading skills and vocabulary.

C Critical Thinking strategies help students apply and extend what they have learned.

U Universal Access activities provide differentiated instruction for students learning to speak English, along with suggestions for teaching various types of learners.

HS Health Skills Practice activities reinforce Health Skills concepts and help students apply these skills in their everyday lives.

W Writing Support activities provide writing opportunities to help students comprehend the text.

AL Active Learning strategies provide a variety of activities for presenting lesson content, including Quick Demos and engaging classroom projects that get students actively involved.

Key to Ability Levels

Teaching Strategies and activities have been coded for ability level and appropriateness.

AL Activities for students working above grade level
OL Activities for students working on grade level
BL Activities for students working below grade level
EL Activities for English Learners

Symbols
Transparencies
CD-ROM
health.glencoe.com
Print Resources

30D

CHAPTER 2
Lesson 4

TEACH

U Universal Access
Learning Disabled Organize the lesson in an outline format. Use the major headings in the lesson as the main ideas (Sources of Stress, Types of Stress). Use one or two bullet points under each heading. Model outlining for students:
1. Sources of Stress
   a. small events
      • forgetting something
   b. major events
      • moving
      • starting new school
   c. anxiety
      • worrying **BL**

HS Health Skills Practice
Goal Setting Tell students that positive stress can help them to reach their goals. Have students identify one health-related goal, such as improving performance in their favorite sport. Have them fold a piece of paper into three horizontal sections. In the top section, have students write their goal. In the middle section, have students list steps to reach their goal, for example, by increasing their practice time. In the bottom section, have students record ways in which positive stress might help them achieve their goals. **OL**

Sources of Stress

Many different things can cause stress. It can result from small events, like forgetting your locker combination. Stress can also come from major events. These include life-changing situations—for example, moving to a new city or starting a new school. People sometimes respond to stressful events with anxiety. **Anxiety** is *feelings of uncertainty or worry over what may happen.*

People may view different events as stressful. You may feel stress when trying out for a part in the school play. Your friend may find this situation exciting rather than stressful. What has happened to you in the past may affect your views on what is stressful. For example, maybe you forgot some of your lines when performing in the school play. This might make you more anxious in similar situations. Your beliefs, attitudes, and values also influence what you think of as stressful.

Types of Stress

Stress can be positive or negative. For example, Jay was really excited about the race. When the signal to start sounded, he felt a burst of energy and took the lead. Jay was experiencing what is known as *positive stress*. Positive stress has many benefits. It can help you reach goals and accomplish tasks. It also provides needed energy to help you escape danger.

Caption Answer
Photo Caption Use the extra energy to accomplish a goal.

TECHNOLOGY AND HEALTH

Digital Tools to Ease Stress Students can feel stress when busy schedules do not allow time for studying, family activities, or relaxation. Today's teens may not recognize how much more efficient many tasks have become with recent advances in technology. People use these tools to make better use of their time, such as cell phones and e-mail to keep in touch with family and friends, PDAs for keeping assignments and reminders, and the Internet for quick research. Ask students to add examples of ways technology can be used to relieve stress.

46   Chapter 2: Mental and Emotional Wellness

...in your way and holds you back. Sources ...n out of your control. They may include ...hool. Too much negative stress can be ...

Reading Check Analyze Compare and contrast positive and negative stress. Give an example of each.

The Stress Response

The stress response is how nature prepares the body to deal with threats of harm. This is also known as the *fight-or-flight response*. Your body is preparing to *fight* the threat or take *flight* from it. During the stress response, your body undergoes a series of physical changes, which are summarized in **Figure 2.1.**

Reading Check Recall Name two physical changes that occur during the fight-or-flight response.

FIGURE 2.1

R THE FIGHT-OR-FLIGHT RESPONSE
This illustration shows some of the physical changes stress can cause.

1 The brain detects a source of stress.

2 The brain signals the adrenal (uh-DREEN-uhl) glands to send out **adrenaline**, a hormone that prepares the body to respond to stress.

3 The heart receives the message from the brain and beats faster. Blood vessels expand, allowing more blood to flow to the brain and muscles.

4 The muscles tighten and become ready for action.

5 Breathing deepens and speeds up as passages in the lungs widen. This brings extra oxygen to the muscles.

6 To make more energy available to the muscles, other body activities slow down. This includes the activities of the stomach and intestines.

Lesson 4: Coping with Stress   47

CHAPTER 2
Lesson 4

Reading Check
Answer Positive stress is the energy you feel when you are excited about something, such as a race or a music recital. It can help you reach goals or accomplish tasks. Negative stress gets in your way and holds you back. Stress over problems at home is an example of negative stress.

R Reading Strategy
Analyzing a Graphic. Have students read Figure 2.1. Divide the class into six groups. Assign each group one of the body parts discussed. Tell students that you are an "on-the-scene" news reporter. Conduct interviews with each group about its assigned body part's action during a fight-or-flight response. **OL**

Reading Check
Answer Two physical changes that occur during the fight-or-flight response are muscles tightening and heart rate increasing.

U Universal Access
Visually Impaired Have visually able students describe Figure 2.1 to visually impaired students. Have students discuss the impact of the fight-or-flight response on each part of the body. If the school has models of the human body, make the models available for use during this lesson. **OL**

HEALTH LITERACY

Alcohol and Other Drugs Remind students that using alcohol or other drugs is not a healthy way to cope with stress. Encourage student discussion by asking: What additional short- and long-term problems will drug or alcohol use create? List student responses on the board. Then ask: Do these seem like problems that will reduce or increase an individual's overall level of stress? Conclude the discussion by asking volunteers for ways to communicate the dangers of substance abuse to mental and emotional health.

47

Bottom Column Boxes provide supplemental information related to the lesson.

Strengthen Student Reading and Writing...

Teen Health is designed to enhance students' health literacy while providing tools to improve reading comprehension.

In the Student Edition

Guide to Reading at the beginning of each lesson provides an overview of main ideas, vocabulary building exercise, and reading strategies, often with graphic organizers that work with the lesson.

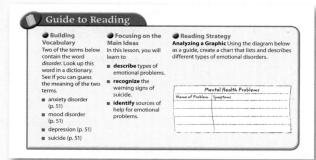

Foldables™ Study Organizers open each chapter to help students organize and process information as they read through the chapter.

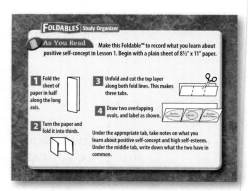

Writing Activities at the beginning of each lesson start students thinking about the topic with a quick writing activity that can be done independently.

Reading Checks at the end of every main section stimulate quick recall and keep students focused on the main ideas.

Reading Check Explain What are hormones? How do they affect emotions during the teen years?

▶ Positive stress gives athletes the motivation they need to perform. How can you use positive stress to your own benefit?

Caption Questions for every photo and infographic offer a visual approach to learning. Students are asked to apply what they have read by interpreting the visual.

Reading Review at the end of each chapter provides students with a quick overview of the material they have just read.

with Active Reading and Study Skills

In the Teacher Edition

- **Support for Reading** section at the start of every chapter in the Teacher Wraparound Edition provides specific, proven prereading, during reading, and post-reading strategies for every lesson.

- **Reading Strategy** at point of use provides activities to help teach reading within the health content.

- **Writing Support** strategies throughout the Teacher Wraparound Edition offer writing opportunities to aid comprehension while developing writing skills.

- **Academic Vocabulary** provides added information for teachers to explain common words used in textbooks that every successful student should know. Includes a description of each word and an exercise to help students grasp the meaning.

- **Teaching Tips** features at the end of each chapter include additional effective reading techniques.

Reading Support Materials

Reading Tutor Designed to help students strengthen reading skills, this booklet provides essential lesson content in a condensed format. The book includes vocabulary terms and definitions and activities to guide students in applying their knowledge of health concepts and skills. This resource is developed for the reluctant reader and can be a help to learning disabled and English language learners as well.

Also available in the Chapter *Fast Files*

- Guided Reading and Writing Activities
- Concept Mapping Activities

Online Learning Center

- eFlashcards and crossword puzzles
- Online Audio Summaries

Generate High Achievers...

Teen Health incorporates the most current educational research in health literacy while reinforcing academic skills essential for student success.

No Child Left Behind: Building Academic Skills

The emphasis on student achievement in basic academic skills is an important part of the No Child Left Behind Act. These academic skills are reinforced throughout the *Teen Health* program. Teaching strategies and support give you the tools you need to reinforce academic skills while teaching health content.

- **Activating Prior Knowledge** *Teen Health* encourages students to use their prior knowledge from all subject areas by adding relevance to the material they read in the health text. Students are referred back to other parts of the text or to their own real-life experiences as they are introduced to new content.

- **Using Proven Study Strategies** Through the use of graphic organizers, highlighting, outlining, note-taking, summarizing, and other strategies, students can monitor their own progress and organize information more effectively.

- **Integrating Academics** Activities connecting health to core curriculum areas are featured in every chapter. Students apply math concepts, examine science principles, develop critical language arts skills, and use technology tools in every chapter as they develop essential skills for lifelong learning.

- **Using Visuals to Communicate, Organize, and Reinforce Learning** High-quality, visually engaging photos, art, and graphics throughout the text communicate concepts more efficiently and reinforce learning, while allowing students to organize and comprehend information.

- **Developing Decoding and Reading Comprehension Strategies** Throughout the text, students are supplied with caption questions, reading checks, discussion starters, and other strategies to aid in comprehension.

Research-Based Learning Strategies

The *Teen Health* White Paper outlines the educational strategies on which this program was based. This document provides specific examples from the Student Edition, Teacher Wraparound Edition, ancillary program, and technology resources, highlighting extensive use of educationally sound strategies that help students learn health concepts and practice academic skills. The White Paper is available online in the Teacher Center at **health.glencoe.com**.

...and Enhance Student Learning

Learning healthy behaviors is a complex process that requires students to bridge the gap between reading the text and mastering the subject matter. Glencoe provides a series of scientifically based reading strategies that enhance students' access to the text, no matter what their reading level. In the Teacher Wraparound Edition, each chapter planning guide includes the following reading support components.

Before You Read

Vocabulary is a key component of reading comprehension, especially in the health area. Many students acquire a superficial understanding of vocabulary terms but fail to grasp the complex associations, applications, or facets of the key concepts they represent. Research reveals that students must have multiple exposures to a word to comprehend its meaning, so Glencoe has provided activities and strategies in each section to guide teachers in helping students unlock vocabulary before they begin to read. By examining new vocabulary through structural analysis, activating prior knowledge and /or explicit instruction, students will learn more than new words—they will learn strategies for future encounters with difficult vocabulary. Once students develop an understanding of health concepts through word study, they will be introduced to additional strategies during and after reading to fully incorporate the concept described by the word. Instructional techniques such as word webbing, brainstorming, previewing, and setting a purpose for reading will ensure that students are prepared to comprehend the text.

Reading Check

Reading is constructing meaning from text. Teachers can help students construct meaning during reading by providing systematic instructional techniques that increase comprehension as students internalize strategies that hone their cognitive skills. Teachers and students will practice activities that build strong comprehension skills such as identifying cause and effect, making inferences, and drawing conclusions. Students will also learn when and how to use graphic organizers, charts, and notes to summarize, categorize, and clarify. Students will learn to rely on such tools when comprehension breaks down. A combination of individualized activities, cooperative learning, and meaningful dialogue will provide the differentiated instruction necessary to meet the needs of each student.

After You Read

Because reading is an active process, comprehension questions at the end of each chapter are not enough to ensure mastery of the content. Interactive projects in which students work together to gain deeper understanding, written responses that stimulate reflection, and extended learning based on practicing and applying will engage students and encourage them to own the concepts provided in the text.

Academic Integration

How Can I Help My Students Learn Academic Vocabulary?

By Robin Scarcella, Ph.D.

What Is Academic English?

Academic English is the language used by the educated and by leaders in business, academic, and other professional disciplines. It is the type of English used in professional books, including textbooks, and it contains specific linguistic features that are associated with academic disciplines including health. Proficiency in reading and using academic English is especially related to long-term success in all aspects of life.

Academic vocabulary is the basis for academic English. By reinforcing academic vocabulary and academic English, teachers help learners to access authentic, academic texts—not simplified texts that dummy down the content. In this way they can provide information that will help build their students' background knowledge rapidly.

What Is Academic Vocabulary?

By the time children have completed elementary school, they must have acquired the knowledge needed to understand academic vocabulary. How many words should they acquire to be able to access their textbooks? A basic 2,000 word vocabulary of high-frequency words makes up 87 percent of the vocabulary of academic texts. Eight hundred other academic words comprise an additional 8 percent of the words. Three percent of the remaining words are technical words. The remaining two percent are low-frequency words. There may be as many as 123,000 low-frequency words in academic texts.

Why Should Students Learn Academic Vocabulary?

English learners who have mastered a basic 2,000-word vocabulary are ready to acquire the majority of general words found in their academic texts. Knowledge of academic words combined with continued acquisition of general words can significantly boost an English learner's comprehension level of academic texts. English learners who learn and practice these words before they graduate from high school are likely to be able to master academic material with more confidence and speed. They waste less time and effort in guessing words or consulting dictionaries than those who only know the basic 2,000 words that characterize general conversation.

Also consider academic success in terms of measurement and assessment—state standards-based assessments, the SAT, the ACT, and the GRE—with regards to word mastery. All demand an understanding of academic vocabulary.

How Do I Include Academic Vocabulary and Academic English in My Teaching?

Teachers can provide their students with rich samples of academic vocabulary and help students understand and attend to the academic English of their texts.

To develop academic English, learners must have already acquired a large amount of basic proficiency in the grammar of everyday English.

Academic English should not be taught overtly, but rather within contexts that make sense. In terms of instruction, teaching academic English includes providing students with access to core curriculum—in this case in the health classroom.

Academic English arises not only from knowledge of a linguistic code and cognition but also from social practices in which academic English is used to accomplish communicative goals. The acquisition of academic vocabulary and grammar is necessary to advance the development of academic English.

Tips for Teaching Academic Vocabulary:

- **Expose Students to Academic Vocabulary** Do not teach it. You do not need to call attention to words students are learning because they will acquire them subconsciously.

- **Do Not Correct Students' Mistakes When Using the Vocabulary Words** All vocabulary understanding and spelling errors are developmental and will disappear once the student reads more.

- **Help Students Decode the Words Themselves** Once they learn the alphabet, they should be able to decode words. Decoding each word they don't recognize will help them more than trying to focus on sentence structure. Once they can recognize the words, they can read "authentic" texts.

- **Do Not Ignore the English Learner in This Process** They can learn academic vocabulary before they are completely fluent in oral English.

- **Helping Students Build Academic Vocabulary Leads to Broader Learning** Students who have mastered the basic academic vocabulary are ready to continue acquiring words from the rest of the groups. To help determine which words are in the 2,000-word basic group, refer to *West's General Service List of English Words*, 1953. The list is designed to serve as a guide for teachers and as a checklist and goal list for students. For additional information about the list, visit **health.glencoe.com** Teacher Tools and Resources.

There are a number of guidelines that teachers can follow when teaching academic English and vocabulary:

Guidelines for Teaching Academic Vocabulary
1. Direct and planned instruction
2. Models—that have increasingly difficult language
3. Attention to form—pointing out linguistic features of words
4. Practice
5. Motivation
6. Instructional Feedback
7. Assessment—on a regular basis

Robin Scarcella is a professor and Director Academic English/ESL, University of California at Irvine, Irvine, CA

Classroom Activity: Writing About Health and the Environment
Advice from Robin Scarcella

Give students an impromptu writing assignment. Ask them to write a short essay about one of the topics listed below in the left column. Have students use as many of the academic vocabulary words in the right column as they can in their essay. Give students a time limit for their writing. When completed, ask student volunteers to share their writing. Note what academic vocabulary words they use.

Topic	Academic Vocabulary
The challenges of reducing waste products in America	recycle
	environment
	conserve
Recent technological advances in health	computers
	technology
	laptop
	desk station
	digital
	transmit

FAST FILE

Teen Health comes with an extensive variety of easy-to-use resources and support materials designed for your convenience.

Chapter Resource masters contain all the materials you need for the chapter, together in one convenient booklet, with answer keys and reproducible lesson plans.

Reproducible Student Resources include

- **Chapter Summary and Activity** is a complete overview of the chapter content.
- **Performance Assessment Activity** for outcome-based projects to challenge students.
- **Building Health Skills Activity** further reinforces skill development.
- **Concept Mapping Activity** helps students preview or review lesson content.
- **Reteaching Activity** helps students who need to review key concepts.
- **Enrichment Activity** extends the lesson for those who have mastered the content.
- **Guided Reading and Writing** guides students to organize and comprehend what they read.
- **Chapter Test** includes true-false, multiple choice, matching, and short-answer assessment items.
- **Lesson Quizzes** provide additional assessment of lesson concepts.
- **Hands-on Health:** Cross-Curriculum Activity, Decision-Making Activity, and Health Lab worksheets provide further extension of lesson content.
- **Student Activities Workbook** is a separate booklet that includes study guide, health inventory, and an activity sheet for each chapter.

Teacher Support and Planning

- Parent Letter and Activities
- Universal Access Activities
- Performance Assessment and Rubrics
- Transparency Preview
- Answer Keys
- Reproducible Lesson Plans

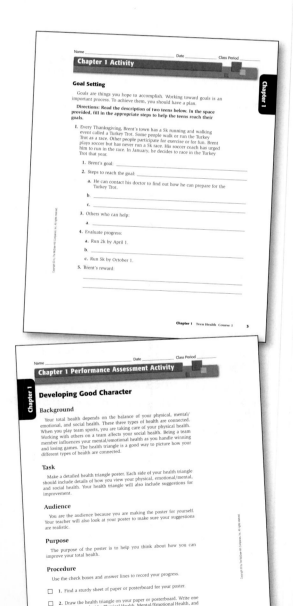

Transparencies with Instructor Guide

A booklet with 52 full-color overhead transparencies and teaching strategies for each lesson facilitates classroom discussion of key ideas.

Modules

Healthy Relationships and Sexuality Relevant and valuable information on relationships and sexuality is discussed in this module, which emphasizes the importance of abstinence from sexual activity before marriage.

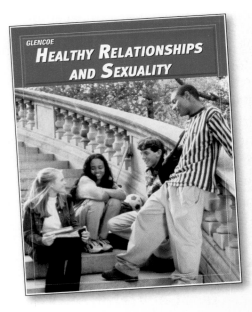

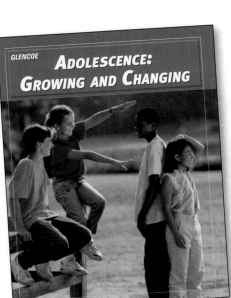

Adolescence: Growing and Changing This module provides teens with age-appropriate information on the physical, mental/emotional, and social changes of adolescence.

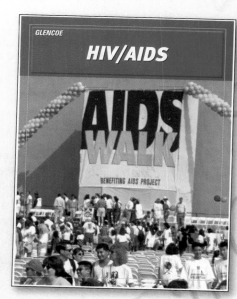

HIV/AIDS Clear, accurate, up-to-date information on HIV/AIDS is presented in this full-color text designed to help students recognize and abstain from risk behaviors associated with the spread of this disease.

Seize the Possibilities

Teen Health's time-saving digital tools and software give teachers options for organizing materials, presenting concepts and skills, and tracking student progress.

This all-in-one teacher resource center helps you personalize lesson plans, access resources right from the Teacher Wraparound Edition, connect to the Internet, or create a to-do list. Many other features assist you in planning and organizing lessons for the health classroom.

Also includes:

- Calendar feature
- Access to all blackline masters
- Standards Correlations

(with Audio Summaries in Spanish)

This is a valuable resource for students to access content online and use online resources to learn more about chapter concepts.

Includes:

- Complete Student Edition on CD-ROM
- Audio read of the Student Edition
- Links to online activities and resources
- Access to all student worksheets

ExamView® Test Generator

- Create, edit, and customize tests
- Create multiple versions of tests
- Translate tests from English to Spanish and vice versa
- Build tests aligned with state and national standards

Vocabulary PuzzleMaker

Build vocabulary skills with custom-designed puzzles. Create word searches and crossword puzzles using vocabulary words from each lesson. Includes English and Spanish.

Online Accessibility

Announcing—Premium Online Access to *Teen Health* Student Edition available to students with adoption of the *Teen Health* program.

Student Center

- At **health.glencoe.com** click on *Teen Health Course 1 2007* Click on **Online Student Edition** 📖 to access the entire text of *Teen Health*
- Building Health Skills Activities
- Audio English/Spanish Chapter Summaries
- Study Guides with Interactive Vocabulary
- Health Inventories
- Interactive Games with Body Systems, eFlashcards, Crossword Puzzles
- Self-Check Quizzes
- Student Web Activities

Teacher Center

- Correlations to National and State Health Standards
- Inclusion Strategies for Teachers
- Lesson Plans
- Teaching Today
- Professional Development
- State Resources
- Student Web Activities Teacher Version

Lighten the Backpack Load by directing your students to *Teen Health* Online Student Edition

STUDY TO GO Study-to-Go lets students download free content to their PDA and gain instant mobile access to quizzes and eFlashcards directly from the *Teen Health* Web site at **health.glencoe.com**. Students can study anytime and anywhere — between classes, during work breaks, or while waiting for the bus.

Sharpen Your Approach

Throughout the *Teen Health* program, assessment options are provided for teachers to measure students' progress and knowledge of concepts and skills presented in the text.

Student Edition Assessment

- **Lesson Review** Students are asked to recall facts and vocabulary, answer critical thinking questions, and apply health skills they are learning. Answers to each question are provided in the Teacher Wraparound Edition.

- **Health Skills Activities** These skills assessments can be found wherever a key concept is presented. These engaging activities give students a chance to demonstrate their understanding of the lesson content by applying the skills to health concepts.

- **Chapter Assessment** Each chapter is followed by a review page and a two-page assessment. The test includes vocabulary, multiple choice, modified true-false, fill-in-the-blank, and short-answer questions.

- **Standardized Test Practice** At the end of each chapter, health-related questions connected to Language Arts, Math, or Science enable students to test their knowledge while practicing for state and national standardized testing.

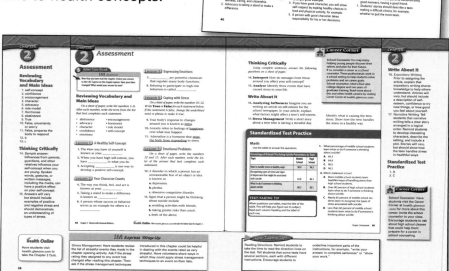

Chapter Fast Files Assessment Resources

- Lesson Quizzes and Chapter Tests
- Performance Assessment

Technology Assessment Options

- Online Quizzes
- ExamView® Test Generator

Help Students Make Health-Enhancing Choices

Health skills are identified by health educators across the nation as essential for students to make responsible decisions. They are included in the National Standards for Health Education to provide professionals with a framework to help determine the content of health education curricula. These skills can be developed and practiced by your students.

Teen Health presents these skills in a unique way that guides students through the learning process. Each skill is modeled for the student. Then students have the opportunity to practice the skill. Finally, students apply the skill to their own lives. They can then use these skills to promote their own health and the health of others.

Rubrics and Teaching Tips are provided for each skill in the Teacher Wraparound Edition to help you assess student mastery of the health behavior being taught.

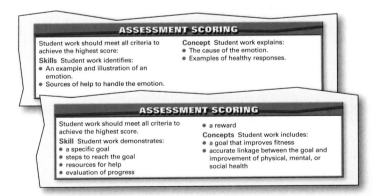

ASSESSMENT SCORING

Student work should meet all criteria to achieve the highest score:

Skills Student work identifies:
- An example and illustration of an emotion.
- Sources of help to handle the emotion.

Concept Student work explains:
- The cause of the emotion.
- Examples of healthy responses.

ASSESSMENT SCORING

Student work should meet all criteria to achieve the highest score.

Skill Student work demonstrates:
- a specific goal
- steps to reach the goal
- resources for help
- evaluation of progress

- a reward

Concepts Student work includes:
- a goal that improves fitness
- accurate linkage between the goal and improvement of physical, mental, or social health

Accessing Information
This skill addresses the important steps to take to get valid health information and appropriate health services.

Stress Management
This skill involves the use of techniques that reduce and manage stress.

Conflict Resolution
This skill involves specific strategies to resolve conflicts peacefully.

Analyzing Influences
This skill involves analysis of the dynamic factors of families, media, peers, personal interests, and pressures that affect health decisions.

Communication
This skill is an interactive process between and among individuals to clarify ideas, thoughts, needs, and feelings.

Self-Management and Practicing Healthful Behaviors
This skill is the actual practice of healthful behavior. It includes the steps and procedures used to promote wellness.

Refusal Skills
This skill involves strategies to refuse involvement in behaviors that may put one's health at risk.

Decision Making
This skill requires speculation into the future based on a particular action.

Goal Setting
This skill is an interactive process for individuals. It requires planning and revision throughout the application of the process.

Advocacy
This skill calls for the use of persuasion to promote positive health choices personally and for others.

Differentiated Learning

Glencoe addresses the national concern for access to learning for all students in the differentiated classroom. Students from diverse cultural backgrounds, students with different learning styles, students with special needs, and gifted or advanced students must learn the important concepts and skills to ensure healthy behaviors.

Each of the teaching strategies in the Teacher Wraparound Edition is coded for teaching students at a variety of levels. Look for the following codes following the appropriate materials in every lesson.

- **AL** Activities for students working above grade level
- **OL** Activities for students working on grade level
- **BL** Activities for students working below grade level
- **EL** Activities for English Learners

Lesson 5

W Writing Support
Expository Writing Ask students to prepare a brief article for the school newspaper explaining how to recognize warning signs of suicide. Be sure students include resources for getting help. Students should proofread their first drafts and make corrections before turning in their final articles. Review students' work for accuracy and appropriate before they are submitte the school paper. **AL**

U Universal Access
Visually Impaired Have visually able students describe Figure 2.1 to visually impaired students. Have students discuss the impact of the fight-or-flight response on the each part of the body. If the school has models of the human body, make the models available for use during this lesson. **OL**

Universal Access

Strategies for differentiated learning are provided throughout the Teacher Wraparound Edition to help you target your lessons to each students' preferred learning style. Many of these activities will be helpful for a variety of students in your classroom. You will find strategies labeled specifically for

- students with vision impairments
- students with hearing impairments
- students with learning impairments
- students with physical impairments
- students with speech or language impairments
- gifted students
- at-risk students
- students with behavioral problems

In addition, each Chapter *FAST FILE* booklet contains a variety of Universal Access activity worksheets developed especially for teaching students in the differentiated classroom.

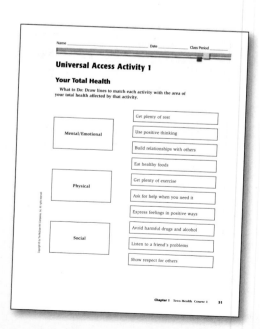

Multiple Learning Styles

The needs of individual students are addressed in a broad range of Universal Access activities. You will find appropriate strategies and activities for all students, including students with these learning styles:

- Kinesthetic learners learn through touch, movement, and manipulation of objects.
- Visual-Spatial learners think in terms of images, illustrations, and models.
- Interpersonal learners understand and work well with other people.
- Intrapersonal learners can analyze their own strengths and weaknesses and may prefer to work on their own.
- Linguistic learners write clearly and easily understand the written word.
- Logical-Mathematical learners understand numbers easily and have highly developed reasoning skills.

U Universal Access

Learning Styles Tell students that the nervous system carries messages about sounds, sights, smells, feel, and tastes to the brain. Review with students the five senses (hearing, sight, smell, touch, taste). Spray some air freshener in the air. Tell [stud]ents that their nervous [syst]em carries the message [abo]ut the smell from their [nose] to their brain. Then clap [loud]ly, and explain that the [nerv]ous system carries the [mess]age about the sound [from] their ear to their brain.

U Universal Access

Learning Disabled Provide students with magazine pictures showing a wide range of physical activities. Have students discuss the activities. Use some of the questions about activities provided in the text to extend the discussion of each activity. Have students choose several of the pictures to use in a physical activity collage. **BL**

Dealing with Sensitive Issues

Special features in the Teacher Wraparound Edition of **Teen Health** are designed to equip teachers with background ideas, techniques, and suggestions for dealing with sensitive issues that often arise when teaching important health concepts.

Dealing with Sensitive Issues

Uninsured Students Some students may have limited access to health care due to lack of health insurance. Many states offer low- or no-cost health insurance to children in families with incomes below a certain threshold. If your state offers such a program, gather relevant information, then incorporate this information into the lesson content. The school nurse may be able to assist you with this. Be certain all students have access to the materials you provide. **OL**

Dealing with Sensitive Issues

Is Everyone's Family Picture-Perfect? Teens can feel self-conscious or embarrassed by their families, particularly if their families are a different type than most families in their community or peer group. As you teach the lesson, be certain to give equal time to the positive aspects of all family types. Stress the similarities of all families, rather than differences between family types. Have students make a poster showing many types of families using magazine pictures, photos, drawings, or written words. They can include aspects and characteristics associated with all types of families.

La salud de los jóvenes

A complete Spanish translation of the **Teen Health** student edition is available for your Spanish-speaking students. The dynamic photo and illustration program, engaging infographics, and fun hands-on activities will motivate English language learners as they develop health knowledge and skills.

Health *Online*

Spanish Online Student Edition

Spanish Resources Booklet includes worksheets in Spanish

- Chapter Summary
- Chapter Activity
- Chapter Test
- Lesson Quizzes
- Parent Letter
- Answer Key

Technology Options for the English Language Learner

Spanish Audio Summaries on StudentWorks™

Chapter and Lesson summaries provide the English language learner with additional practice to comprehend the key ideas in each lesson and apply what they have learned. Also available at **health.glencoe.com**.

ExamView® and Vocabulary Puzzlemaker

Each of these CD-ROM programs include a Spanish version, making assessment components and vocabulary practice accessible to students who are English language learners.

TIME *health news*

TIME health news features health-related topics in the news, developed by Time magazine to capture the interests of today's middle school students. Teaching Strategies make connections to media, technology, and culture, encouraging students to understand their own culture and the culture of others in the ways that media and technology impact their health.

TIME *health news*

How to Stay FIT FOR LIFE

Getting the right amount of exercise is key to staying healthy.

GOOD FOR YOUR MIND AND BODY

Along with building muscle and preventing health problems, staying fit can give you more energy to keep up with your packed daily schedule. Experts suggest that young people get a total of 60 minutes of exercise most days. Exercise can help you relax, respond better to stress, and boost your self-confidence.

You don't need to play competitive sports to stay in shape. Riding a bike or inline skating with your friends will provide results, too. Choose activities that are fun—you'll be more likely to keep doing them in the future!

BENEFIT	AMOUNT
Aerobic exercise increases your heart rate and makes you breathe harder. This strengthens your heart and lungs.	Thirty minutes of aerobic exercise most days
...e strength is the ability of your muscles to ...a force. Muscle endurance is the ability to ...up a physical activity without becoming overly ...Building both improves overall fitness.	Two or three days a week
Jog or warm up for five to 10 minutes before you do light stretching. After exercise, do more stretching. This helps ...protect you from injury.	Before and after any workout

TIME *health news*

Schoolroom TORMENT

Do you have the wrong idea about bullies?

...ut bullies.

...t can young people do about bullies ...bullying?

...shouldn't be easy targets for ...es. Look the bully in the eye and ...away confidently. Bullies want ...urt your feelings. Even if they're ...g really mean, act as if they're not ...eeding and don't get into a fight.

Did you know that you have an internal biological clock that regulates the timing of ...so, tell a parent or ...acher. They want to ...w what is happening ...how you ...about it. ...e bullying ...pened at ...ol, have ...rent talk ...er with ...teacher. ...nts ...ldn't call ...parents ...e bully.

TIME *health news*

The Mystery of SLEEP

You'll spend a third of your life sleeping, but that helps keep your body in shape.

Everyone knows that you can't live without sleep, but no one knows exactly why or precisely how sleep works. Some researchers, such as Dr. Terrence Sejnowski, are working on a theory. He says the brain uses deep slumber to "shut off" so that it can process memories of the day. "It's like when you move out of your house so workers can renovate the kitchen," Dr. Sejnowski says. According to Sejnowski, sleep gives your brain time to refresh itself. In the morning, your brain is ready to go to work.

Scientists such as Dr. Sejnowski may have different ideas about how sleep works to keep your organs in good working order. All scientists agree, however, that just as eating right and getting enough exercise are important, sleep is something your body needs to keep going strong. During sleep many of your body's major organs and regulatory systems continue to work actively. Some parts of your brain actually increase their activity while you are making zzzz's, and your body produces more of certain hormones that you need.

Did you know that you have an internal biological clock that regulates the timing of sleep? It programs each person to feel sleepy during nighttime hours and to be active during the day. Natural light sets your biological clock to the 24-hour cycle of day and night. And like some clocks, you wind down at the end of the day. That's when your body says it's time to get a good night's rest.

SLEEP TIPS

A good night's sleep can help you do your best in school and at other activities. Use these tips to get the most out of snooze time.

- Set a regular time for bed each night, and stick to it.
- Follow a relaxing bedtime routine, like listening to quiet music or reading a book.
- Don't exercise too close to bedtime.
- Skip anything with caffeine, such as cola drinks, six hours before going to bed.
- Turn off your TV, computer, video game, and other noisy gadgets 30 minutes before bedtime.

196 Chapter 7: Your Body Systems

Activity Media, Technology, and Culture

Developing a PSA Have students brainstorm ways to encourage others to recognize the importance of sleep to good health. Have them work in small groups to write scripts for 30-second public service announcement (PSA) promoting sleep. The PSAs should include the benefits of sleep and tips for getting a good night's sleep. Allow time for students to rehearse. Allow each group to present its PSA for the class. If possible, make a video recording of the presentations and share them with other students in the school.

TIME
health news

The Mystery of Sleep

Objectives

After completing this activity, students will be able to
- Describe how different body systems benefit from sleep
- Identify ways to get a good night's sleep

Motivator

Write the word sleep on the board. Ask students to describe how a good night's sleep makes them feel. Record their responses on the board.

Teaching The Activity

- Have students read the feature. Encourage them to think beyond the text and use inference to consider the following. Explain that people who travel to other time zones often experience a set of symptoms called jet lag. Ask: Why does jet lag affect travelers who cross into different time zones? *(because their body's 24-hour sleep cycle is disrupted when adapting to a new time zone)* **OL**

- Have each student draw a large health triangle on a blank sheet of pape. and label sides physical health, mental/emotional health, and social health. Have students identify ways sleep can positively affect each side of the health triangle. Have them record answers on the appropriate sides of their triangles. **OL**

196

The Teen Health program meets the National Health Education Standards

The *National Health Education Standards* were created with the goal of improving educational achievement for students and improving health in the United States through the promotion of health literacy. The Health Standards for middle school students highlight eight key components of health knowledge and skills.

Health Education Standard 1

Students will comprehend concepts related to health promotion and disease prevention to enhance health.

1.1 Explain the relationship between positive health behaviors and the prevention of injury, illness, disease and premature death.

1.2 Describe the interrelationship of mental, emotional, social and physical health during adolescence.

1.3 Explain how health is influenced by the interaction of body systems.

1.4 Describe how family and peers influence the health of adolescents.

1.5 Analyze how environment and personal health are interrelated.

1.6 Describe ways to reduce risks related to adolescent health problems.

1.7 Explain how appropriate health care can prevent premature death and disability.

1.8 Describe how lifestyle, pathogens, family history, and other risk factors are related to the cause or prevention of disease and other health problems.

Health Education Standard 2

Students will analyze the influence of family, peers, culture, media, technology, and other factors on health behaviors.

2.1 Describe the influence of cultural beliefs on health behaviors and the use of health services.

2.2 Analyze how messages from media and other sources influence health behaviors.

2.3 Analyze the influence of technology on personal and family health.

2.4 Analyze how information from peers influences health.

Health Education Standard 3

Students will demonstrate the ability to access valid information and products and services to enhance health.

3.1 Analyze the validity of health information, products, and services.

3.2 Demonstrate the ability to utilize resources from home, school, and community that provide valid health information.

3.3 Analyze how media influences the selection of health information and products.

3.4 Demonstrate the ability to locate health products and services.

3.5 Compare the costs and validity of health products.

3.6 Describe situations requiring professional health services.

Health Education Standard 4

Students will demonstrate the ability to use interpersonal communication skills to enhance health and avoid or reduce health risks.

4.1 Demonstrate effective verbal and nonverbal communication skills to enhance health.

4.2 Describe how the behavior of family and peers affects interpersonal communication.

4.3 Demonstrate healthy ways to express needs, wants, and feelings.

4.4 Demonstrate ways to communicate care, consideration, and respect of self and others.

4.5 Demonstrate communication skills to build and maintain healthy relationships.

4.6 Demonstrate refusal and negotiation skills to enhance health.

4.7 Analyze the possible causes of conflict among youth in schools and communities.

4.8 Demonstrate strategies to manage conflict in healthy ways.

Health Education Standard 5

Students will demonstrate the ability to use decision-making skills to enhance health.

5.1 Demonstrate the ability to apply a decision-making process to health issues and problems individually and collaboratively.

5.2 Analyze how health-related decisions are influenced by individuals, family, and community values.

5.3 Predict how decisions regarding health behaviors have consequences for self and others.

Health Education Standard 6

Students will demonstrate the ability to use goal setting skills to enhance health.

6.1 Apply strategies and skills needed to attain personal health goals.

6.2 Describe how personal health goals are influenced by changing information, abilities, priorities, and responsibilities.

6.3 Develop a plan that addresses personal strengths, needs, and health risks.

Health Education Standard 7

Students will demonstrate the ability to practice health-enhancing behaviors and avoid or reduce health risks.

7.1 Explain the importance of assuming responsibility for personal health behaviors.

7.2 Analyze a personal health assessment to determine health strengths and risks.

7.3 Distinguish between safe and risky or harmful behaviors in relationships.

7.4 Demonstrate strategies to improve or maintain personal and family health.

7.5 Develop injury prevention and management strategies for personal and family health.

7.6 Demonstrate ways to avoid and reduce threatening situations.

7.7 Demonstrate strategies to manage stress.

Health Education Standard 8

Students will demonstrate the ability to advocate for personal, family, and community health.

8.1 Analyze various communication methods to accurately express health information and ideas.

8.2 Express information and opinions about health issues.

8.3 Identify barriers to effective communication of information, ideas, feelings, and opinions about health issues.

8.4 Demonstrate the ability to influence and support others in making positive health choices.

8.5 Demonstrate the ability to work cooperatively when advocating for healthy individuals, families, and schools.

Glencoe's Professional Health Series

Planning a Coordinated School Health Program increases awareness of the need for coordinated school health programs throughout the United States.

Dealing with Sensitive Issues provides background information and teaching strategies to guide health educators in presenting sensitive issues to students.

Promoting Character Education outlines the principles of character education and includes activity ideas for the teacher.

Home, School and Community Involvement designed to involve family and community members in students' health education, including service learning projects.

CHAPTER 1

Your Health and Wellness

Lesson 1 **Your Total Health** 4

Lesson 2 **Influences on Your Health** 8

Lesson 3 **Building Health Skills**...12

    Health Skills Activity: Too Good To Be True? 14

Lesson 4 **Making Responsible Decisions**...16

    Health Skills Activity: A Test of Friendship 19

Lesson 5 **Setting Health Goals** 20

Building Health Skills: Evaluating Influences on Your Health
                      (Analyzing Influences) 24

HANDS-ON HEALTH: Your Personal Health 26

Chapter 1 Reading Review 27

Chapter 1 Assessment...28

Table of Contents

v

Mental and Emotional Wellness

Lesson 1 **A Healthy Self-Concept** 32

  Health Skills Activity: How Do the Media Influence Your Self-Concept?...... 34

Lesson 2 **Your Character Counts** 36

Lesson 3 **Expressing Emotions** 41

Lesson 4 **Coping with Stress** 45

  Health Skills Activity: Relaxation Exercises 48

Lesson 5 **Emotional Problems** 50

  Health Skills Activity: Helping a Troubled Friend.................................. 53

Building Health Skills: Dealing With Feelings
              (Practicing Healthful Behaviors) 54

HANDS-ON HEALTH: Developing Good Character 56

Chapter 2 Reading Review...57

Chapter 2 Assessment...58

Healthy Relationships

Lesson 1 **Communication Skills** 62

  Health Skills Activity: Safety Online 64

Lesson 2 **Your Family** 67

  Health Skills Activity: Family Meetings 70

Lesson 3 **Your Friends and Peers**..73

Lesson 4 **Refusal Skills** 78

  Health Skills Activity: Saying No 79

Lesson 5 **Resolving Conflicts** 81

Building Health Skills: Working Things Out *(Conflict Resolution)* 86

TIME **Health News:** School Torment 88

Chapter 3 Reading Review 89

Chapter 3 Assessment..90

CHAPTER 4

Nutrition

Lesson 1 **Your Body's Nutrient Needs** 94

Lesson 2 **Following a Healthful Eating Plan** 98

Lesson 3 **Making Healthful Food Choices** 102

    Health Skills Activity: Mastering Nutrition Facts 104

Lesson 4 **Managing Your Weight** 108

    Health Skills Activity: Help for a Friend with an Eating Disorder............... 111

Building Health Skills: Choosing Health-Promoting Foods
        (Decision Making) 112

HANDS-ON HEALTH: Keeping a Food Diary 114

Chapter 4 Reading Review 115

Chapter 4 Assessment...116

CHAPTER 5

Physical Activity

Lesson 1 **Physical Activity and Your Health** 120

    Health Skills Activity: Fun for the Family................................122

Lesson 2 **Creating a Personal Fitness Plan** 126

    Health Skills Activity: Exercise with "Eye Appeal" 130

Lesson 3 **Safety in Sports and Physical Activities** 132

Building Health Skills: Developing a Personal Fitness Plan *(Goal Setting)* 136

TIME **Health News:** How to Stay Fit for Life 138

Chapter 5 Reading Review 139

Chapter 5 Assessment..140

CHAPTER 6

Personal Health

Lesson 1 **Your Teeth, Skin, and Hair** 144

Lesson 2 **Protecting Your Eyes and Ears** 151

Lesson 3 **Choosing Health Products** 155

    Health Skills Activity: Persuasive Advertising 157

Lesson 4 **Using Medicines Responsibly** 159

Lesson 5 **Health Care in Your Community** 163

    Health Skills Activity: Doing Your Part for Community Health 166

Building Health Skills: Buyer Beware! *(Accessing Information)* 168

HANDS-ON HEALTH: Observing the Eye 170

Chapter 6 Reading Review 171

Chapter 6 Assessment 172

Your Body Systems

Lesson 1 **From Cells to Body Systems** 176

Lesson 2 **Bones and Muscles** 181

Health Skills Activity: Building Strong Bones 183

Lesson 3 **Digestion and Excretion** 185

Lesson 4 **Heart, Blood, Lungs, and Nerves** 188

Building Health Skills: Maintaining Healthy Body Systems
(Practicing Healthful Behaviors) 194

TIME **Health News:** The Mystery of Sleep 196

Chapter 7 Reading Review 197

Chapter 7 Assessment 198

Growth and Development

Lesson 1 **Adolescence: A Time of Change** 202

Lesson 2 **Human Reproduction** 206

Health Skills Activity: Care of the Reproductive System 209

Lesson 3 **Heredity and the Life Cycle** 210

Building Health Skills: Coping With Changes During Puberty
(Accessing Information) 214

HANDS-ON HEALTH: Looking Ahead 216

Chapter 8 Reading Review 217

Chapter 8 Assessment 218

CHAPTER 9

Tobacco

Lesson 1 **Tobacco: A Harmful Drug** 222

Lesson 2 **Teens and Tobacco** 227

Lesson 3 **Staying Tobacco Free** 230

    Health Skills Activity: Spreading the Word About Tobacco 233

Building Health Skills: Taking A Stand Against Tobacco *(Refusal Skills)* 234

TIME **Health News:** Kick Butts...236

Chapter 9 Reading Review 237

Chapter 9 Assessment...238

CHAPTER 10

Alcohol and Other Drugs

Lesson 1 **The Dangers of Alcohol Use** 242

Lesson 2 **Alcoholism and Addiction**..246

Lesson 3 **What Are Illegal Drugs?** 249

Lesson 4 **Drug Abuse**...253

Lesson 5 **Staying Alcohol-and-Drug-Free**..................................256

    Health Skills Activity: Getting SADD About Substance Abuse 257

Building Health Skills: Avoiding Drug Abuse *(Decision Making)* 260

HANDS-ON HEALTH: "Say No to Drugs" Skit 262

Chapter 10 Reading Review 263

Chapter 10 Assessment...264

Preventing Diseases

Lesson 1 **What Causes Disease?** 268

Lesson 2 **Communicable Diseases** 272

    Health Skills Activity: Handwashing for Health 276

Lesson 3 **Understanding STDs** 277

    Health Skills Activity: Accurate Information on HIV and AIDS 281

Lesson 4 **Noncommunicable and Hereditary Diseases** 282

Building Health Skills: Protecting Your Health *(Goal Setting)* 288

TIME **Health News:** Don't Panic! 290

Chapter 11 Reading Review 291

Chapter 11 Assessment 292

Safety and the Environment

Lesson 1 **Personal Safety Habits** 296

    Health Skills Activity: Building Safe Habits 299

Lesson 2 **Safety at Home and Away** 300

    Health Skills Activity: Fire Escape Plan 302

Lesson 3 **Safety Outdoors** 305

Lesson 4 **Safety In Severe Weather** 308

Lesson 5 **First Aid for Emergencies** 312

Lesson 6 **Protecting Your Environment** 318

Building Health Skills: Reduce Waste *(Advocacy)* 322

HANDS-ON HEALTH: Are You Earth Friendly? 324

Chapter 12 Reading Review 325

Chapter 12 Assessment 326

Getting the most out of *Teen Health*

Making healthy and responsible choices is easy with Teen Health. Follow the guidelines below to make the most out of each lesson.

Review Key Terms
Complete the Building Vocabulary activity to become familiar with the key terms before you read the lesson. Vocabulary terms are highlighted in yellow to make them easy to find.

Do the Quick Write
This feature will help you start thinking about the information in the lesson.

Preview the Lesson
Get a preview of what's coming by reading the lesson objectives in Focusing on the Main Ideas. You can also use this feature to prepare for quizzes and tests.

Strengthen Your Reading Skills
Complete the Reading Strategy activity to help you understand the information in the lesson.

Health Online

Use Glencoe's *Online Learning Center* to Boost Your Health Smarts!

- Rate your health by taking the Health Inventories for each chapter. Jump-start your goals by filling out a Personal Wellness Contract.
- Check out Student Web Activities for fun and interactive learning.
- Learn about different health-related careers at Career Corner.
- Get ready for tests by using the different Online Study Tools to review vocabulary terms and chapter content. E-flashcards, crossword puzzles, review questions, and online quizzes make studying fun!
- Building Health Skills features give you another chance to master important skills for good health.

Look at the Reading Checks

When you see a Reading Check, stop and answer the question to make sure that you understand what you have just read.

Study the Infographics

First, think about the overall message that the infographic is presenting. Then read each callout carefully and determine what part of the image it is referring to.

Try the Health Skills Activities

Develop valuable health skills by completing the Health Skills Activities that appear in each chapter.

Complete the Lesson Reviews

Completing the lesson reviews can help you see how well you know the material you just read. It also gives you a chance to apply what you've learned to different situations, as well as practice a health skill.

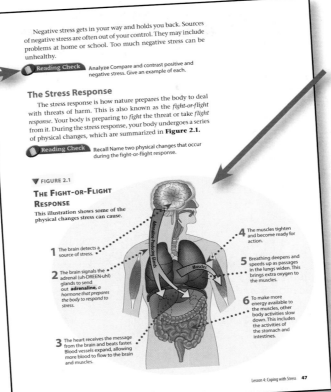

Negative stress gets in your way and holds you back. Sources of negative stress are often out of your control. They may include problems at home or school. Too much negative stress can be unhealthy.

Reading Check Analyze Compare and contrast positive and negative stress. Give an example of each.

The Stress Response

The stress response is how nature prepares the body to deal with threats of harm. This is also known as the *fight-or-flight response*. Your body is preparing to *fight* the threat or take *flight* from it. During the stress response, your body undergoes a series of physical changes, which are summarized in **Figure 2.1.**

Reading Check Recall Name two physical changes that occur during the fight-or-flight response.

▼ FIGURE 2.1

THE FIGHT-OR-FLIGHT RESPONSE
This illustration shows some of the physical changes stress can cause.

1 The brain detects a source of stress.

2 The brain signals the adrenal (uh-DREEN-uhl) glands to send out **adrenaline,** *a hormone that prepares the body to respond to stress.*

3 The heart receives the message from the brain and beats faster. Blood vessels expand, allowing more blood to flow to the brain and muscles.

4 The muscles tighten and become ready for action.

5 Breathing deepens and speeds up as passages in the lungs widen. This brings extra oxygen to the muscles.

6 To make more energy available to the muscles, other body activities slow down. This includes the activities of the stomach and intestines.

Lesson 4: Coping with Stress **47**

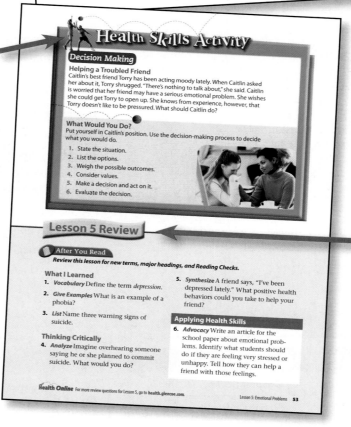

Health Skills Activity

Decision Making

Helping a Troubled Friend
Caitlin's best friend Torry has been acting moody lately. When Caitlin asked her about it, Torry shrugged. "There's nothing to talk about," she said. Caitlin is worried that her friend may have a serious emotional problem. She wishes she could get Torry to open up. She knows from experience, however, that Torry doesn't like to be pressured. What should Caitlin do?

What Would You Do?
Put yourself in Caitlin's position. Use the decision-making process to decide what you would do.

1. State the situation.
2. List the options.
3. Weigh the possible outcomes.
4. Consider values.
5. Make a decision and act on it.
6. Evaluate the decision.

Lesson 5 Review

After You Read
Review this lesson for new terms, major headings, and Reading Checks.

What I Learned
1. *Vocabulary* Define the term *depression*.
2. *Give Examples* What is an example of a phobia?
3. *List* Name three warning signs of suicide.

Thinking Critically
4. *Analyze* Imagine overhearing someone saying he or she planned to commit suicide. What would you do?

5. *Synthesize* A friend says, "I've been depressed lately." What positive health behaviors could you take to help your friend?

Applying Health Skills
6. *Advocacy* Write an article for the school paper about emotional problems. Identify what students should do if they are feeling very stressed or unhappy. Tell how they can help a friend with those feelings.

Health Online For more review questions for Lesson 5, go to health.glencoe.com.

Lesson 5: Emotional Problems **53**

1

CHAPTER 1 pp. 2–29	Standards		Skills and Activities
	National	**State/Local**	
	National Health Education Standards 6.1, 6.2, 6.3		**HEALTH INVENTORY**, *p. 3* **HANDS-ON HEALTH** Your Personal Health, *p. 26* **BUILDING HEALTH SKILLS** *Analyzing Influences* Evaluating Influences on Your Health, *pp. 24–25*
Lesson 1 Your Total Health pp. 4–7	National Health Education Standards 1.1, 1.2, 1.4, 1.5, 3.2, 4.2, 4.4		
Lesson 2 Influences on Your Health pp. 8–11	National Health Education Standards 1.1, 1.4, 1.5, 1.8, 2.1, 2.2, 2.3, 2.4, 3.3, 4.2, 5.2		**DEVELOPING GOOD CHARACTER** *Setting a Good Example, p. 9*
Lesson 3 Building Health Skills pp. 12–15	National Health Education Standards 1.1, 1.2, 2.2, 2.4, 3.1, 3.2, 3.3, 4.5, 7.1, 7.2, 7.4, 7.5, 8.5		**Connect To... LANGUAGE ARTS** An Ounce of Prevention, *p. 13* **HEALTH SKILLS ACTIVITY** *Analyzing Influences* Too Good to Be True? *p. 14*
Lesson 4 Making Responsible Decisions pp. 16–19	National Health Education Standards 2.2, 5.1, 5.2, 5.3, 7.1		**MEDIA WATCH** Decisions, Decisions, *p. 17* **HEALTH SKILLS ACTIVITY** *Decision Making* A Test of Friendship, *p. 19*
Lesson 5 Setting Health Goals pp. 20–23	National Health Education Standards 6.1, 6.2, 6.3		**DEVELOPING GOOD CHARACTER** *Setting Goals in a Group, p. 22*

PACING THE CHAPTER

Lesson 1 45 min	**Lesson 4** 90 min	**Chapter Review** 45 min
Lesson 2 45 min	**Lesson 5** 45 min	**Hands On Health** 20 min
Lesson 3 90 min	**Building Health Skills** 45 min	

BLOCK SCHEDULING

For block scheduling, assign students Building Health Skills feature *Evaluating Influences on Your Health*, pages 24-25, and have them complete Guided Reading and Writing. 📁

Planning Guide

StudentWorks Plus

Glencoe Exclusive!
TeacherWorks™
All-In-One Planner and Resource Center

Reproducible Resources	Assessment	Media and Technology
Chapter FAST FILE Resources 　Chapter Summaries and Activities REVIEW 　Building Health Skills Activity TEACH 　Performance Assessment Activity EXTEND 　Universal Access Activities TEACH 　Parent Letter and Activities **Student Activities Workbook** TEACH **Reading Tutor** TEACH	Building Health Skills Activity, *pp. 24–25* Chapter 1 Assessment, *pp. 28–29* **Chapter FAST FILE Resources** 　Performance Assessment Activity, 　*pp. 4–5* 　Chapter 1 Test, *p. 7* 　*ExamView® Test Generator*	**Teacher Works™** includes: 　• Interactive Teacher Edition 　• Lesson Planner with Calendar 　• Access to all blackline masters 　• Correlations to standards 　StudentWorks™ Plus 　Online Student Edition Dinah Zike's Teaching Health with Foldables™
Chapter FAST FILE Resources 　Concept Mapping Activity 1-1 REVIEW 　Decision-Making Activity 1-1 EXTEND 　Enrichment Activity 1-1 EXTEND 　Guided Reading and Writing 1-1 TEACH 　Lesson Plan 1-1 　Reteaching Activity 1-1 REVIEW	Lesson 1 Review, *p. 7* 　Vocabulary PuzzleMaker 　*ExamView® Test Generator*	Vocabulary PuzzleMaker *ExamView® Test Generator* StudentWorks™ Plus Transparency 1-1 **Health Online**
Chapter FAST FILE Resources 　Concept Mapping Activity 1-2 REVIEW 　Cross-Curriculum Activity 1-2 EXTEND 　Enrichment Activity 1-2 EXTEND 　Guided Reading and Writing 1-2 TEACH 　Lesson Plan 1-2 　Reteaching Activity 1-2 REVIEW	Lesson 2 Review, *p. 11* 　Vocabulary PuzzleMaker 　*ExamView® Test Generator*	Vocabulary PuzzleMaker *ExamView® Test Generator* StudentWorks™ Plus Transparency 1-2 **Health Online**
Chapter FAST FILE Resources 　Concept Mapping Activity 1-3 REVIEW 　Health Lab 1-3 EXTEND 　Enrichment Activity 1-3 EXTEND 　Guided Reading and Writing 1-3 TEACH 　Lesson Plan 1-3 　Reteaching Activity 1-3 REVIEW	Lesson 3 Review, *p. 45* 　Vocabulary PuzzleMaker 　*ExamView® Test Generator*	Vocabulary PuzzleMaker *ExamView® Test Generator* StudentWorks™ Plus Transparency 1-3 **Health Online**
Chapter FAST FILE Resources 　Concept Mapping Activity 1-4 REVIEW 　Cross-Curriculum Activity 1-4 EXTEND 　Enrichment Activity 1-4 EXTEND 　Guided Reading and Writing 1-4 TEACH 　Lesson Plan 1-4 　Reteaching Activity 1-4 REVIEW	Lesson 4 Review, *p. 19* 　Vocabulary PuzzleMaker 　*ExamView® Test Generator*	Vocabulary PuzzleMaker *ExamView® Test Generator* StudentWorks™ Plus Transparency 1-4 **Health Online**
Chapter FAST FILE Resources 　Concept Mapping Activity 1-5 REVIEW 　Decision-Making Activity 1-5 TEACH 　Enrichment Activity 1-5 EXTEND 　Guided Reading and Writing 1-5 TEACH 　Lesson Plan 1-5 　Reteaching Activity 1-5 REVIEW	Lesson 5 Review, *p. 23* 　Vocabulary PuzzleMaker 　*ExamView® Test Generator*	Vocabulary PuzzleMaker *ExamView® Test Generator* StudentWorks™ Plus Transparency 1-5 **Health Online**

Chapter and Lesson Resources

The *Teen Health* resources are designed for differentiated learning abilities. You may want to use the coded items in this way:

REVIEW—activities to review or reinforce content
TEACH—activities to teach basic concepts
EXTEND—activities to extend or enrich lesson content

 OUT OF TIME?

Use Health Skills Activities *Too Good to Be True?* page 15 and *A Test of Friendship*, page 19 or Developing Good Character, page 23.

Health in the 21st Century

Lifestyle choices, including diet, exercise, and risk behaviors, are a major influence on health. Health education plays a key role in reinforcing the positive behaviors that can prevent illness and injury and promote a healthy life. Health education also has an important role in teaching the detrimental effects of risky behaviors.

National trends in youth health behaviors have shown some encouraging statistics. Cigarette use has decreased among teens over the past five to seven years. National antismoking campaigns aimed at teens may have some part in this trend. Marijuana and alcohol use also decreased in the same time period.

Safety-belt use among teens increased during this time period.

Some risk behaviors have shown no change over the past five to seven years, despite increased awareness in the role of lifestyle choices in overall health. For example, as compared to 1993, there has been no significant change in the percentage of students who participate in exercise or physical activity three or more times a week.

Involving Parents and Guardians in Health Education

Staying connected with parents and guardians is important throughout the school year. At the beginning of each chapter, send home the Parent Letter and Activity provided in the Chapter *Fast File* Resources. This resource is also available in Spanish. In addition to the Parent Letters, use the following tips for maintaining active parent and guardian involvement throughout the school year.

- **Be Accessible** Let parents and guardians know the best way to reach you. Include your contact information in a beginning-of-the-year newsletter.

- **Use E-mail** Send regular e-mail updates to inform parents and guardians of upcoming projects, major assignments, and tests.

- **Have Students Write Home** Occasionally, assign students to write a brief letter home explaining the topics they are studying in health class.

- **Maintain a Teacher Web page** If your school district Web site features teacher Web pages, be sure yours is up to date and contains your contact information.

- **Ask for Help** Ask parents and guardians to volunteer throughout the school year. In particular, parents who work in health-related fields may be able to provide resources or serve as guest speakers.

- **Communicate Achievements** Take note of students who complete quality work, serve as role-models to other teens, or assist special needs students in the classroom. Take the time to report the good news, not just the problems.

Support for Teaching Reading

Reading Support   **Health Online**   **Academic Integration** For additional academic integration strategies, visit the Teacher Center at **health.glencoe.com**.

Reading Preview

Word Association Introduce the chapter by saying one of the new vocabulary words. Ask students to write whatever comes to mind when they hear the word. For example, when you say *health* students could write *how a person feels or being well or sick.* Such associations help students deepen their understanding of new words.

FOLDABLES Study Organizer *Dinah Zike's Reading and Study Skills for Teen Health* provides interactive graphic organizers that help students comprehend and retain health concepts as they read. Use the Foldable™ on page 3 or find more Foldables™ activities for the chapter on **Your Health and Wellness** in the separate booklet, available in the TCR.

Lesson 1   Your Total Health

Determining Main Ideas Ask students to read **What is Health?** Have them create a statement using the headings on pages 4-6. They might write "Your health is your physical, mental/emotional, and social health." Students can answer heading questions as a way to determine main ideas.

Lesson 2   Influences on Your Health

Setting a Purpose Create a chart with columns titled *What I know, What I think I know, What I think I'll learn,* and *What I learned.* Have students preview the lesson and complete the first two columns to identify any misconceptions they may have about what influences their health. Have them complete the rest of the columns as they read the lesson.

Lesson 4   Making Responsible Decisions

Pairs Reading Direct student pairs to take turns reading aloud to one another. One student takes the role of the coach and the other the reader. After the reader reads the section **The Decision-Making Process**, have the coach paraphrase the main ideas. Then, have the reader clarify any questions. Have students reverse roles and continue reading.

Lesson 5   Setting Health Goals

Learning Logs Stop students after reading the section titled **Reaching Your Goals.** Ask: Which of the text passages in this lesson has been the most interesting so far? Have students consider their responses, explain their reasoning, and write in their learning logs for five minutes.

Post Reading

Extending the Content Ask students to choose a concept from this chapter that interests them. Have them describe a real-world situation in which they can use this information.

Key for Using the Teacher Wraparound Edition

Use this key to help you identify the different types of prompts found in the Teacher Wraparound Edition.

R **Reading Strategies** activities help you teach reading skills and vocabulary.

C **Critical Thinking** strategies help students apply and extend what they have learned.

U **Universal Access** activities provide differentiated instruction for students learning to speak English, along with suggestions for teaching various types of learners.

HS **Health Skills Practice** activities reinforce Health Skills concepts and help students apply these skills in their everyday lives.

W **Writing Support** activities provide writing opportunities to help students comprehend the text.

AL **Active Learning** strategies provide a variety of activities for presenting lesson content, including Quick Demos and engaging classroom projects that get students actively involved.

Key to Ability Levels

Teaching Strategies and activities have been coded for ability level and appropriateness

AL Activities for students working above grade level

OL Activities for students working on grade level

BL Activities for students working below grade level

EL Activities for English Learners

Symbols

Transparencies

CD-ROM

health.glencoe.com

Print Resources

Your Health and Wellness

Chapter at a Glance

Lesson 1 identifies the three parts of the health triangle, explains the relationship between health and wellness, and explains how to balance physical, mental/emotional, and social health.

Lesson 2 identifies factors that influence health and explains the role of behavior, choices, and attitudes in health.

Lesson 3 identifies health skills and explains why health skills are skills for life.

Lesson 4 identifies ways to make healthy, responsible decisions and explains how to distinguish between important and less important decisions.

Lesson 5 explains why having goals is important and describes how to set goals.

R Reading Strategy

Interpreting the Photo
Ask students to brainstorm a list of ways that the students in the picture are demonstrating good health. Remind students that health includes more than just physical health. **OL**

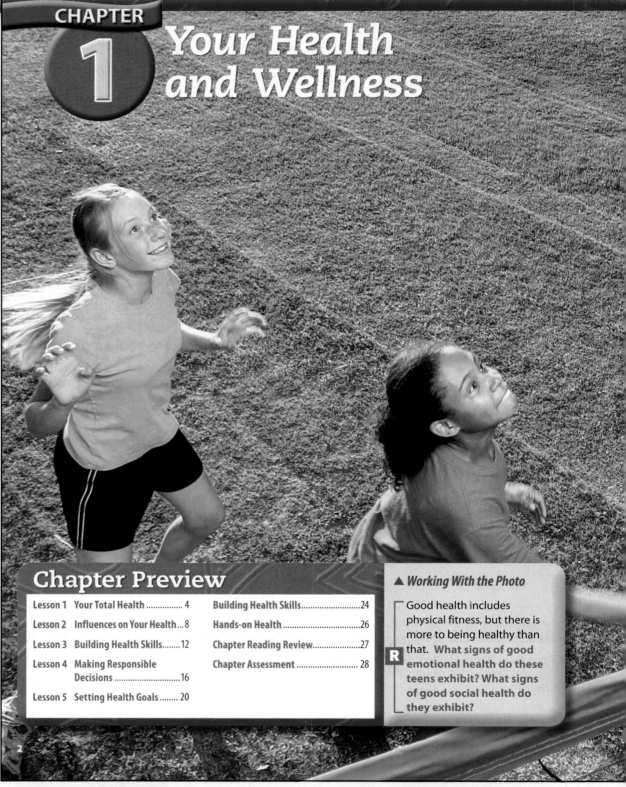

CHAPTER

1

Your Health and Wellness

Chapter Preview

Lesson 1 Your Total Health 4

Lesson 2 Influences on Your Health ... 8

Lesson 3 Building Health Skills 12

Lesson 4 Making Responsible
          Decisions 16

Lesson 5 Setting Health Goals 20

Building Health Skills 24

Hands-on Health 26

Chapter Reading Review 27

Chapter Assessment 28

▲ **Working With the Photo**

Good health includes physical fitness, but there is more to being healthy than that. **What signs of good emotional health do these teens exhibit? What signs of good social health do they exhibit?**

Universal Access

Differentiated Learning Glencoe provides teacher support and student materials for all learners in the health classroom.

● Spanish *Glosario* and chapter summaries for the English Language Learners.
● *Reading Tutor* and related worksheets support reluctant readers.

● Universal Access strategies throughout the Teacher Wraparound Edition and Fast Files help you present materials for gifted students, at-risk students, physically impaired and those with behavior disorders or learning disabilities.

Start-Up Activities

Before You Read What do you do to take care of your health? Find out by taking the short health inventory on this page. Keep a record of your answers.

HEALTH INVENTORY

1. I try to stay physically active.
(a) always   (b) sometimes   (c) never

2. I am aware of what influences my health.
(a) always   (b) sometimes   (c) never

3. I think about my health before making decisions.
(a) always   (b) sometimes   (c) never

4. I set realistic goals for myself.
(a) always   (b) sometimes   (c) never

FOLDABLES™ Study Organizer

As You Read Make this Foldable™ to help you organize the main ideas on health and wellness in Lesson 1. Begin with a plain sheet of 8½" × 11" paper.

1 Line up one of the short edges of a sheet of paper with one of the long edges to form a triangle. Fold and cut off the leftover rectangle.

2 Fold the triangle in half, then unfold. The folds will form an X dividing the paper into four equal sections.

3 Cut along one fold line, and stop at the middle. This forms two triangular flaps. Draw an X on one tab, and label the other three as shown.

4 Fold the X flap under the other flap, and glue together to make a three-sided pyramid.

Write the main ideas about the three parts of health on the back of the appropriate side of the pyramid.

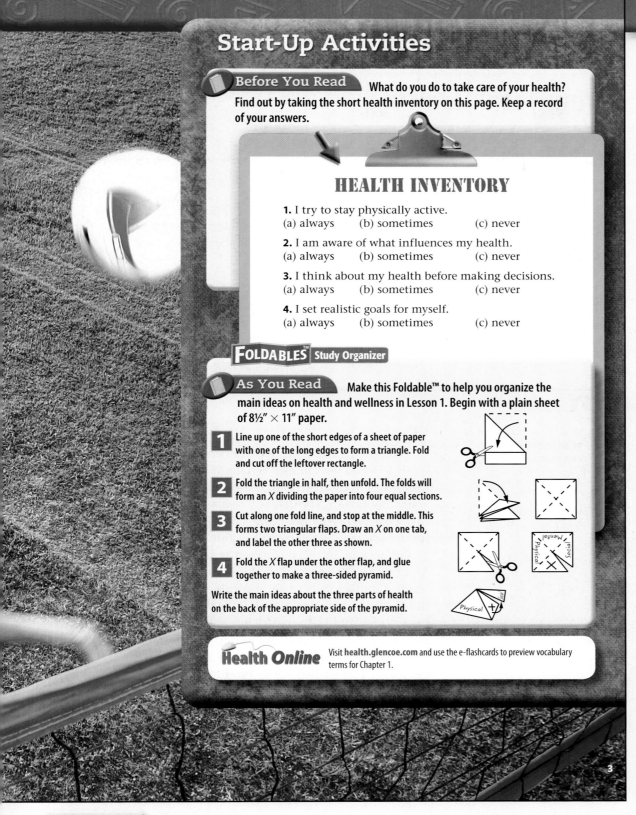

Health Online Visit health.glencoe.com and use the e-flashcards to preview vocabulary terms for Chapter 1.

HEALTH INVENTORY

Your Health and Wellness Have students complete the health inventory. Tell students that they may keep their answers confidential. Explain that each topic in the inventory is covered in the chapter. Have students identify health strengths and weaknesses. Students will have a chance to complete the survey again after reading the chapter.

No Child Left Behind

Classroom Management Small group activities require careful planning and management. Establishing a set format for group activities will allow group work to proceed smoothly. Use the following tips for successful group work: Groups should be teacher-assigned and consist of students with varied abilities. A time period should be specified in advance. Work areas should be planned in advance. Each member of the group should have an assigned task that is vital to the group's success.

Health Online

Have students visit **health.glencoe.com** and complete the Health Inventory for Chapter 1.

FOLDABLES™ Study Organizer

Dinah Zike Foldables™

Developing Main Ideas As students read Lesson 1, have them write down definitions and main ideas on the sides of the Foldable™. The pyramid can be made into a mobile to illustrate the concept of balanced health. Have students write down or draw examples of each part of the health triangle on small cards. Direct them to sort the cards into physical, mental/emotional, and social health and attach the cards in each category to one piece of string. Then have them hang each string from the appropriate side of the Foldable™. **BL**

FOCUS

Activating Prior Knowledge

What I Know Ask students to describe one choice they have made today that positively affects their health.

Guide to Reading

BUILDING VOCABULARY

- Have students use the Glossary/ Glosario to find the definitions of the vocabulary terms. Then have students write a sentence that explains how *habits* are related to *health* and *wellness*.
- Use Vocabulary PuzzleMaker to reinforce vocabulary terms.

READING STRATEGY

 Have students use their Foldables™ as they read Lesson 1.

- **Classifying** Have the class identify the three sides of the health triangle before beginning the Reading Strategy.

Quick Write

Have students write a definition of what the word *health* means to them. Point out that the word *health* may have different meanings to different students. Have students review their definitions after reading Lesson 1.

Your Total Health

Guide to Reading

Building Vocabulary
As you read this lesson, write each highlighted term and its definition in your notebook.

- health (p. 4)
- wellness (p. 7)
- habit (p. 7)

Focusing on the Main Ideas
In this lesson, you will learn to

- **identify** the three parts of the health triangle.
- **describe** the relationship between health and wellness.
- **explain** how to balance your physical, mental/emotional, and social health.

Reading Strategy
Classifying Using the diagram to the right as a guide, create a concept map that gives examples of each of the three types of health.

 Use the Foldable™ on p. 3 as you read this lesson.

Quick Write

Write an explanation of what the word *health* means to you.

What Is Health?

What sports and other activities do you participate in? What kinds of foods do you eat? What kind of people do you spend time with? Your answers to these and similar questions reflect your total health. **Health** is *a combination of physical, mental/ emotional, and social well-being.* These parts of your health work together to build good overall health.

Often, good health is pictured as a triangle with equal sides. As shown in **Figure 1.1,** one side of the triangle is your physical health. Another side is your mental/emotional health, and the third side is your social health. Like the sides of a triangle, the three "sides" of health meet. They are connected. If you ignore any one side, your total health suffers. By the same token, if you make improvements to one side, the others benefit. For example, when you participate in physical activities, you improve your physical health. This helps you feel good about yourself, benefiting your mental health. Activities can also improve your social health when you share them with family and friends.

Lesson 1 Resources

📁 **Chapter** *Fast File* **Resources**
Guided Reading and Writing 1-1
Concept Mapping Activity 1-1
Decision-Making Activity 1-1
Reteaching Activity 1-1
Enrichment Activity 1-1
Lesson Quiz 1-1

Technology
🔦 Transparency 1-1
💿 Audio Summaries
💿 *ExamView*
💿 Vocabulary PuzzleMaker
💿 StudentWorks™ Plus

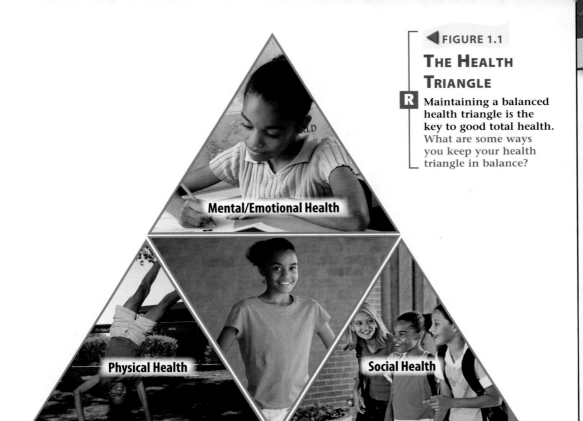

◀ FIGURE 1.1

THE HEALTH TRIANGLE

R Maintaining a balanced health triangle is the key to good total health. What are some ways you keep your health triangle in balance?

Mental/Emotional Health

Physical Health

Social Health

Physical Health

Do you stay active? Do you get plenty of rest each night? Do you eat healthy snacks? Your answers to these questions will tell you something about your physical health. Physical health is the condition of your body.

Physical health is measured by what you *do* as well as what you *don't* do. Teens who want to be healthy avoid harmful substances such as tobacco, alcohol, and other drugs. They balance the amount of time they spend watching TV or playing computer games with physical activity. Physical activity includes things such as playing sports, hiking, aerobics, swimming, dancing, and taking a walk. By avoiding harmful substances and being physically active, you can stay physically healthy. In other words, being physically healthy means taking care of your body.

Health *Online*

Topic: Creating Healthy Habits

Visit **health.glencoe.com** for Student Web Activities on creating healthy habits.

Activity: Using the information provided at the link above, make a checklist of five activities you can do every day to maintain your health.

Lesson 1: Your Total Health **5**

TEACH

R Reading Strategy

Analyzing a Graphic Have students examine the infographic in Figure 1.1. Divide the class into three groups. Assign each group one part of the health triangle. Have each group develop a list of actions and activities that could improve that particular area of health. **OL**

C Critical Thinking

Synthesizing Encourage a discussion in which students communicate understanding of the interrelationship between the three areas of health demonstrated in the health triangle. Ask students to imagine a balanced triangle. Ask: What happens to a three-legged stool when one side is cut short or removed? *Students may say it will tip over or fall.* Have volunteers explain why maintaining each side of health will help balance overall wellness. **AL**

Academic Vocabulary

Physical On this page, students learn about physical health as one part of the health triangle. In this case, *physical* refers to the body. Have students volunteer phrases that use the word *physical.* Samples: *physical fitness, physical education*

Caption Answer

Figure Caption Students may mention sports or physical activities, clubs, musical groups, or other extracurricular activities.

Dealing with Sensitive Issues

Physical Health The statement "you can stay physically healthy by taking care of your body" can be challenging to those students who have chronic medical conditions. Many factors that affect physical health are under the control of the individual, but other factors are not. Habits such as healthy diets and avoiding tobacco are beneficial to everyone, but they do not guarantee good health. Stress that some illnesses and physical conditions are not the result of poor health habits but may be caused by genetic factors, bacteria, or viruses.

R **Reading Strategy**

Analyzing a Graphic Have students examine Figure 1.2 on page 7. Have each student generate a list of three actions that would allow a person to improve his or her rating on the wellness scale. Ask volunteers to share their ideas with the class. **OL**

AL **Active Learning**

Learning Stations Have students read the sections on Physical Health, Mental/Emotional Health, and Social Health. Set up three learning stations, each with an index card labeled with one of the three aspects of total health. Divide the class into three groups. Have the groups rotate through the stations at 5-minute intervals. At each station, have students generate and record three healthy habits that could improve that aspect of health. Discuss the results. Ask: What steps can you take to keep your health triangle in balance? **OL**

Reading Check

Answer The three sides of total health are physical health, mental/emotional health, and social health. Examples: physical—eats a healthy diet; mental/emotional—manages stress well; social—communicates well with others.

Caption Answer

Photo Caption They are working on social and mental/emotional health by talking with friends.

▲ Physical activity is a good choice for improving your health. **What other parts of the health triangle are these teens working on?**

Health Online

Visit **health.glencoe.com** and complete the Interactive Study Guide for Lesson 1.

Mental/Emotional Health

Do you feel good about who you are? Do you know how to handle stressful situations? Do you have a positive attitude about life? Your answers to these questions will tell you something about your mental/emotional health. Mental/emotional health is measured by the way you think and express your feelings.

You can develop good mental/emotional health by learning to think positively and to express your feelings in healthy ways. Positive thinking is a good strategy to use when you are feeling sad or down. Try focusing your attention on all of the good things in your life, such as your friends, family, and activities you enjoy. Then the cause of your sadness might not seem so bad. Likewise, recognizing and building your strengths will help you feel good about yourself. When negative thoughts and feelings come up, look to express them in ways that won't hurt you or others. If problems feel overwhelming, don't be afraid to talk to adults you trust. Knowing when to ask for help is a sign of good mental/emotional health.

AL

Social Health

How well do you get along with others? Can you work through problems with others peacefully? Are you a good listener? Your answers to these questions will help you measure your social health. Good social health means communicating well with and having respect for family, friends, and acquaintances. It also means building relationships with people you can trust and who can trust you in return. You might build a relationship with a counselor or coach, someone you trust and can go to when you have a problem. A close friend at school may need you to listen to them if they have a problem or need advice. Think about the people in your life. With whom do you feel the most comfortable and why? Can you imagine reaching out to them to offer or ask for support?

AL

Reading Check

Identify What are the three sides of total health? Name a trait or characteristic found on each of the three sides.

Cultural Perspectives

Fast Food and Good Health Habits Due to busy schedules, many families rely on fast food for a part of their diets in today's culture. According to a Harvard study, every day more than 30 percent of American children eat fast food. Fast-food consumption is generally correlated with increased fat and sugar consumption. Brainstorm with students some healthy options, such as green salads, which are available at fast-food restaurants. Remind students that restaurants can provide nutrition information to help them make healthy choices.

Healthy Habits and Wellness

When you are taking care of your health triangle and all three sides are balanced, wellness is achieved. **Wellness** is *a state of well-being, or total health.* You can improve your wellness by developing good health habits. A **habit** is *a pattern of behavior that you follow almost without thinking.* Good health habits include:

- choosing healthy foods.
- participating in regular physical activity.
- learning how to handle stress.
- getting along with others.

By taking a look at all the parts of your health triangle, you can get a snapshot of how healthy you are right now. (See **Figure 1.2.**) This will let you know if any areas need work. The pages ahead will help you develop positive health behaviors that will aid in the prevention of injury, illness, disease, and other health problems.

 Reading Check **Define** What is *wellness*?

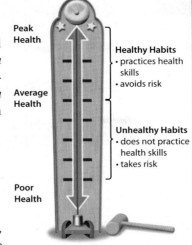

Peak Health

Healthy Habits
- practices health skills
- avoids risk

Average Health

Unhealthy Habits
- does not practice health skills
- takes risk

Poor Health

▲ **FIGURE 1.2**

R THE WELLNESS SCALE

Your health habits affect your wellness. Where do you fit in on the wellness scale?

 **Lesson 1 Review**

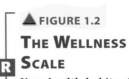 **After You Read**

Review this lesson for new terms, major headings, and Reading Checks.

What I Learned

1. *Vocabulary* What is *health*?

2. *List* What are two measures of good social health?

3. *Recall* Identify three positive health habits.

Thinking Critically

4. *Hypothesize* Jordan spends most of his time getting together with friends. They play video games and skateboard. Jordan is not doing very well in school. What do you think his health triangle would look like?

5. *Evaluate* Alexandra is feeling upset because she didn't do well in her piano recital. Does this mean that she does not have good total health? What can she do to keep her mental/emotional health in balance?

Applying Health Skills

6. *Analyzing Influences* Name a positive health habit that you recently started practicing. Who or what influenced you to begin this health habit?

Health Online For more review questions for Lesson 1, go to **health.glencoe.com**.

Lesson 1: Your Total Health **7**

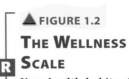 **Reading Check**

Answer Wellness is a state of well-being, or total health.

ASSESS

Assessment Resources

Lesson Review Quiz
- *ExamView*
- Fast Files Activities
- Online Quizzes and Activities

Reteaching

- Assign Concept Map 1-1 or Reteaching Activity 1-1 in the Fast Files. 📁
- Have students work in pairs to review the definitions of the vocabulary terms. Randomly call on students to give the terms.

Enrichment

- Assign Enrichment Activity 1-1 in the Fast Files. 📁
- Have students create a poster that depicts good health habits for one selected area of the health triangle.

CLOSE

Ask students to give examples of why making healthy choices is important for each area of health.

Lesson 1 Review Answers

1. Health is physical, mental/emotional, and social well-being.

2. *Any two:* feeling good about yourself, building strengths, managing stress, expressing feelings, and seeking help with problems

3. *Any three:* choosing healthy foods; avoiding tobacco, alcohol, and other drugs; exercising; handling stress; getting along with others

4. *Sample answer:* Since Jordan is not doing well at school, his health triangle is lacking on the mental/emotional health side.

5. She needs to improve her mental/emotional health. She could express her feelings to a friend.

6. Responses will vary but should include the following: a positive health habit, for example healthy eating or regular exercise, and what or who influenced the student to start this habit.

7

FOCUS

Activating Prior Knowledge

What I Know Ask students to think about what they ate for lunch yesterday. Then ask what determined their choice.

Guide to Reading

BUILDING VOCABULARY
- Have students write each vocabulary word on a sheet of paper. As they encounter a word in the lesson, have them record the definition next to the word.
- Use Vocabulary PuzzleMaker to reinforce vocabulary terms.

READING STRATEGY
Skimming Instruct students to skim the major and minor headings in the lesson. Then ask for volunteers to identify the topics that are covered.

Quick Write

After students do the Quick Write, have them choose one item from each list and write sentences describing how their families and friends influence them. Discuss how the influence of family and friends might change as they get older.

Caption Answer

Photo Caption A person may choose to participate in sports that require running.

Influences on Your Health

Guide to Reading

Building Vocabulary
Read the terms below. Define each in your notebook as best you can. As you read the lesson, make changes where needed.

- heredity (p. 8)
- environment (p. 9)
- culture (p. 9)
- peers (p. 9)
- media (p. 10)
- technology (p. 10)
- behavior (p. 11)
- attitude (p. 11)

Focusing on the Main Ideas
In this lesson, you will learn to

- **identify** factors that influence your health.
- **explain** the role that your behavior and choices play in your health.
- **describe** how your attitudes affect your health.

Reading Strategy
Skimming Look over the major and minor headings in this lesson. Write a brief paragraph explaining what you think the lesson is about.

Quick Write

Make a list of your likes and dislikes. Explain which of these are shared by your family and which are shared by your friends.

Factors that Affect Your Health

What foods do you like to eat? What are your hobbies and favorite activities? Your answers to these questions reflect your personal tastes, your likes and dislikes. Your health is influenced by your personal tastes. It is also influenced by outside factors. These include heredity, environment, family, culture, the media, and technology.

Heredity

Heredity is *the process by which biological parents pass traits to their children.* These include physical traits, such as eye, hair, and skin color, and body type and size. You may also inherit a musical or athletic ability. The risk of developing certain diseases such as diabetes or allergies can also be passed along through heredity.

◄ The ability to run fast is sometimes passed along through heredity. **What health choice might you make based on inheriting this ability?**

Lesson 2 Resources

📁 **Chapter *Fast File* Resources**
Guided Reading and Writing 1-2
Concept Mapping Activity 1-2
Cross-Curriculum Activity 1-2
Reteaching Activity 1-2
Enrichment Activity 1-2
Lesson Quiz 1-2

Technology
🔋 Transparency 1-2
💿 Audio Summaries
💿 *ExamView*
💿 Vocabulary PuzzleMaker
💿 StudentWorks™ Plus

Environment

Think about where you live and go to school. These are part of your environment. **Environment** (en·VY·ruhn·muhnt) is *the sum total of your surroundings.* It includes the air you breathe and the water you drink. It also includes the neighborhood you live in and the people around you.

Your environment can both positively and negatively affect your personal health. If you live in a warm climate, you may have more opportunities to participate in outdoor activities. You will also have to be extra careful in the sun. How does the environment where you live affect your health?

Family and Culture

Two related influences on your health are your family and your culture. **Culture** is *the collected beliefs, customs, and behaviors of a group.* Family and culture can influence many aspects of your health including eating habits, physical activity, and the use of health services. Some cultures, for example, eat special foods on special occasions. Some eat no food at all during religious celebrations. Bessem's family observes the holiday of *Ramadan.* During this holiday, members of the family fast until sundown. Your family might also celebrate certain holidays and observe special cultural traditions. These traditions might include dances, foods, ceremonies, songs, and games.

Peers

Peers are an especially important influence during your teen years. **Peers** are your *friends and other people in your age group.* Peer pressure can influence healthful choices. For example, Dena's friend Shawn began volunteering at the animal shelter. Shawn invited Dena to go with him one day, and now they volunteer at the animal shelter together.

Peers can also have a negative influence on your health. If your friends take part in risky behaviors, such as smoking or drinking, you might feel pressure to join in.

▲ Your tastes in food may be a reflection of your family's preferences and your culture. **What other factors might influence your food choices?**

W Writing Support

Persuasive Writing Explain that some advertising is directed at young children in an attempt to influence their health decisions. Have students write a persuasive paragraph stating their opinions of advertising aimed at young children. Remind students to include examples and supporting evidence. Students should prepare a rough draft, then proofread and revise their work before they turn it in. **AL**

HS Health Skills Practice

Analyzing Influences Discuss ways that the media can be a positive influence, for example, by providing information on new medicines. Then ask students to discuss ways that the media can be a negative influence, such as commercials for unhealthy food choices. Make a T-diagram on the board with students' responses. Have students evaluate whether media has more positive or more negative impact on their health choices. **OL**

 Reading Check

Answer Environmental factors may include school, neighborhood, climate, and people around you.

▲ The media influence the health choices we make. **Have you bought a health product based on an advertisement? Were you satisfied with your purchase?**

Media

Troy realized how much the media could influence him when he saw a TV ad. As soon as he saw it, he knew he wanted the video game it advertised for his birthday. Have you had an experience similar to Troy's? The **media** is *the various methods of communicating information, including newspapers, magazines, radio, television, and the Internet.* It is often used by companies to encourage us to buy their products, such as the video game Troy saw on TV. **W**

Messages from media and other sources influence health behavior. Through the media, it's possible to quickly find information on almost any health topic. The media also provides us with advertisements for health products and services. However, not all media sources are equally reliable. Later in this chapter, you will learn how to judge whether a source is reliable. **HS**

Technology

Technology is *the use of scientific ideas to improve the quality of life.* The use of computer technology in planes has made it easier and safer to fly. A variety of technologies for health information are now available. E-mail and the Internet are only two examples. These resources influence your health because they can provide you with fast and easy access to valid health information. The control of diseases is another area that technology has impacted.

One area in which technology has had a huge impact is in detecting illnesses. For example, MRI machines give a view of the inside of any area of the body. Finding early evidence of diseases can help doctors treat them successfully. Can you give another example of technology that has made your health and life better?

 Reading Check

List Name four factors that affect your health. Give an example of each.

Caption Answer

Photo Caption Students should relate an experience of buying a health product and whether they were satisfied.

10

TECHNOLOGY AND HEALTH

Medical Technology MRI, or magnetic resonance imaging, is a technology that is used to diagnose illness and injury. An MRI scanner works because the hydrogen atoms in a patient's body align to the strong magnetic field produced by the scanner. A radio wave is then used to move the hydrogen atoms out of alignment. The hydrogen atoms send out radio waves as they move back into alignment with the strong magnetic field. A computer uses these radio waves to produce an image of an organ or body part. MRI is used to diagnose problems without surgery.

Your Health Choices and Behaviors

Some of the factors that influence your health, such as heredity, are out of your control. You do, however, have control over your behavior and the choices you make. Your **behavior** is *the way you act in the many different situations and events in your life.* Many of the choices you make affect your health. For example, choosing to eat healthy foods will affect your physical health. Knowing the consequences of your choices and behaviors can help you take responsibility for your health.

Personal Attitudes

An **attitude** is *what you believe or feel about someone or something.* Individual, family, community, and cultural attitudes play a role in your health. For example, if you have a positive feeling about wearing safety belts, you'll probably wear one when riding in a car. Teens who have positive attitudes toward healthy habits usually encourage others to do the same.

 **Reading Check**

Recall Give one example of a choice that can affect your health.

Health Online

Visit **health.glencoe.com** and complete the Interactive Study Guide for Lesson 2.

 Reading Check

Answer Choosing healthy foods affects my physical health.

ASSESS

Assessment Resources

Lesson Review Quiz
- *ExamView*
- Fast Files Activities
- Online Quizzes and Activities

Reteaching

- Assign Concept Map 1-2 or Reteaching Activity 1-2 in the Fast Files.
- Randomly ask students to identify factors that influence health.

Enrichment

- Assign Enrichment Activity 1-2 in the Fast Files.
- Have students prepare a poster that uses words and images to show one way in which the media influence health decisions.

CLOSE

Have students discuss ways that a person's attitudes can affect their health behavior.

Lesson 2 Review

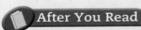 **After You Read**

Review this lesson for new terms, major headings, and Reading Checks.

What I Learned

1. ***Vocabulary*** Define *culture* and *media.* Explain how each influences health.

2. ***Describe*** How has medical technology improved life?

3. ***Explain*** How does your attitude affect your health?

Thinking Critically

4. ***Synthesize*** Which side of the health triangle do you think is most affected by outside influences?

5. ***Apply*** Think of a positive health habit or behavior you learned from your family. Think of another you learned from a peer.

Applying Health Skills

6. ***Analyzing Influences*** Our country has people from many different cultures living within its borders. Identify cultures in your own community. With a group, discuss ways in which these cultures influence the lifestyle of community members. Think about celebrations, food, music, and the like.

Health Online For more review questions for Lesson 2, go to **health.glencoe.com**.

Lesson 2: Influences on Your Health **11**

Lesson 2 Review Answers

1. Culture is the beliefs, customs, and behaviors of a group. The media are methods of communicating information. Each impacts decisions and behaviors.

2. Technology is used to gather information, control diseases, and detect illness.

3. A positive attitude keeps you safe and encourages others to be healthy.

4. Answers may include physical, mental/emotional, or social health.

5. Habits learned from the family might include eating nutritious foods. Habits learned from peers might include participation in sports.

6. Class discussion should identify ways in which different cultures enrich the community.

FOCUS

Activating Prior Knowledge

What I Know Have volunteers describe examples of skills they have developed in the last year and how those skills have helped them succeed.

Guide to Reading

BUILDING VOCABULARY
- Have students read the vocabulary terms. Ask a volunteer to explain the meaning of the word part *pre* (before). Then discuss with students the meaning of the term *prevention* and how the word means taking action *before* something happens in order to stop it.
- Use Vocabulary PuzzleMaker to reinforce vocabulary terms.

READING STRATEGY
Compare Have students write down the two skills they are comparing. Then have students use complete sentences to describe the similarities and differences between the two skills.

Quick Write

For the health skill chosen, have students include at least three ways in which they already use the skill or could use the skill in their lives.

Building Health Skills

Guide to Reading

● **Building Vocabulary**
Write each term in your notebook. As you read the lesson, add each term's definition.
- prevention (p. 12)
- health skills (p. 12)
- communication (p. 15)
- advocate (p. 15)

● **Focusing on the Main Ideas**
In this lesson, you will learn to
- **identify** skills that can help you say healthy.
- **explain** why health skills are skills for life.
- **demonstrate** how to analyze media influences.

● **Reading Strategy**
Compare Identify similarities and differences between two of the skills mentioned.

Quick Write

Preview the lesson. Choose one health skill. Write about ways you could—or already do—use it in your life.

Skills for a Healthy Life

One of the keys to good health is the prevention of illness and injury. **Prevention** means *practicing health and safety habits to remain free of disease and injury*. You can prevent illness and injury in many ways. Wearing protective gear during certain activities, such as bike riding or playing baseball, can help you prevent injury to your body. You can help prevent common illnesses such as colds by washing your hands often.

These examples demonstrate health skills. **Health skills** are *skills that help you become and stay healthy* (see **Figure 1.3**). Health skills can help you improve your physical, mental/emotional, and social health. Like reading, math, and sports skills, health skills can have a positive effect throughout your life.

◄ Wearing goggles when swimming in a pool is one way of maintaining physical health. **What are some other examples of protective gear you should wear during sports or activities?**

Lesson 3 Resources

📁 **Chapter _Fast File_ Resources**
Guided Reading and Writing 1-3
Concept Mapping Activity 1-3
Health Lab 1-3
Reteaching Activity 1-3
Enrichment Activity 1-3
Lesson Quiz 1-3

Technology
👆 Transparency 1-3
 Audio Summaries
⚙ *ExamView*
Vocabulary PuzzleMaker
⚙ StudentWorks™ Plus

▼ FIGURE 1.3

THE HEALTH SKILLS

These 10 skills affect your physical, mental/emotional, and social health.
Why are these skills important throughout your entire life?

Health Skill	What It Means to You
Accessing Information	You know how to find valid and reliable health information and health-promoting products and services, including medical resources on the Internet.
Practicing Healthful Behaviors	You take action to reduce risks and protect yourself against illness and injury.
Stress Management	You find healthy ways to reduce and manage stress in your life.
Analyzing Influences	You recognize the many factors that influence your health, including culture, media, and technology.
Communication Skills	You express your ideas and feelings and listen when others express theirs.
Refusal Skills	You can say no to risky behaviors.
Conflict Resolution	You work out problems with others in healthful ways.
Decision Making	You think through problems and find healthy solutions.
Goal Setting	You plan for the future and work to see your plans through.
Advocacy	You take a stand to work for the common good and make a difference in your home, school, and community.

Staying Informed

Knowing how to *access*, or get, reliable health information is an important skill. A main source of information is adults you can trust. Parents and guardians, teachers, and your school nurse are reliable sources. They can help you find accurate books, articles, and Web sites on a variety of health topics. Community resources provide other ways to get reliable information. These resources include government health agencies and organizations such as the American Red Cross.

Taking Care of Yourself

Practicing healthy behaviors and managing stress are two skills that all teens should learn. When you eat healthy foods and get enough sleep, you are taking actions that promote good health. Stress management is learning to cope with challenges that put a strain on you mentally or emotionally. Strategies for managing stress can help you deal with stress in a healthy way.

Connect To... Language Arts

An Ounce of Prevention

Benjamin Franklin is known for his collected sayings. Here is one of them: "An ounce of prevention is worth a pound of cure."

Form a small group to discuss the meaning of this saying. As a class, gather your own collection of health sayings. Print out and share your collection.

Lesson 3: Building Health Skills **13**

TEACH

R Reading Strategy

Analyzing a Graphic Have students examine the skills for good health in Figure 1.3. Have each student choose five of the listed skills and identify examples of how they could apply the skills to their everyday lives. Ask for volunteers to share examples with the class. **OL**

Connect To... Language Arts

An Ounce of Prevention

Students should identify that Benjamin Franklin meant that preventing health problems is much easier than curing them. Suggest that students use a variety of sources for collecting health sayings. One useful resource is *Bartlett's Familiar Quotations*, available in the school's media center.

Academic Vocabulary

Resource Students learn that community resources can be a source of health information. Tell students that a *resource* is a source, or supply. Ask for volunteers to relate this to the term *natural resources*.

🏠 Home, School, and Community

Community To help students access reliable health information, assemble a list of reliable community resources. Local hospitals and health agencies are excellent sources of information. The school nurse may also have a list of resources. Students should consult their parents or guardians about any health questions they may have. Remind them that many readily accessible sources of health information are not always reliable. Stress that medical information found on the Internet should always be carefully evaluated.

Caption Answer

Photo Caption, p. 12
Sample answer: Helmets, body pads, and mouth guards are used for football.

Health Skills Activity

Analyzing Influences

Too Good to Be True?

Use the following strategies to help students complete the activity.

- Have students meet in small groups to read the introductory paragraph.
- Provide students with copies of magazine and newspaper advertisements. Have students analyze each ad to determine the source, how it influences health decisions, and the motive.
- Ask groups to share their results.

HS Health Skills Practice

Practicing Healthful Behaviors Have small groups of students write and perform a puppet show that demonstrates the use of one of the health skills in this lesson, such as Analyzing Influences. Have students perform the puppet show without telling the audience which skill they will be demonstrating. After each demonstration, have audience members identify the health skill presented in the puppet show. **OL**

Reading Check

Answer identify the source and think of motive or reason

Health Skills Activity

Analyzing Influences

Too Good to Be True?

Trevor was excited when he first saw an infomercial for a new acne medicine. It promised to make pimples vanish overnight. This health claim sounded too good to be true. He knew the importance of considering

- **the source.** Infomercials are TV ads made to look like programs. There are few rules that control the kinds of claims advertisers can make. Trevor knew infomercials were not reliable health sources.

- **the motive.** When you hear a suspicious health claim, ask yourself, "What am I being encouraged to do?" If the answer is "buy something," beware.

As a Group

Analyze an ad from a magazine, newspaper, or TV. Determine the source and motive behind the ad. Notice the kinds of words the ad uses to try to influence you. Talk about whether the ad is a reliable health source. Share your findings with other groups.

Analyzing Influences

Learning how to analyze health information, products, and services will help you act in ways that protect your health.

The first step in analyzing an influence is to identify its *source*. A TV commercial may tell you a certain food has health benefits. In this case, the source is an advertiser who is trying to get you to buy the food.

Next, you should think about the *motive*, or reason, for the influence. Does the advertiser really take your well-being into consideration, or is the main goal to sell a product?

HS

Health Online

Visit **health.glencoe.com** and complete the Interactive Study Guide for Lesson 3.

Reading Check **Identify** What two steps should you take when analyzing an influence on your health?

What Teens Want to Know

Being Healthy versus Being Cool Teens often experience a feeling that some healthful behaviors conflict with being cool and fitting in. Teens who wear a bicycle helmet, use a safety belt, or select healthy foods may be teased about their choices. Discuss the possible consequences of giving in to teasing. For example, if a student removes his or her bike helmet to avoid teasing, the result could be brain damage or death. After the discussion, have students work in small groups to develop ways to deal with negative peer pressure.

Communicating with Others

Three of the ten health skills involve the way you communicate with other people. **Communication** is *the clear exchange of ideas and information.* Good communication skills include telling others how you feel. They also include listening to others and understanding how *others* feel. You will learn more about communication skills in Chapter 3.

Sometimes you have to say no to others. An example is when you are pressured to do something you believe is wrong. *Refusal skills* help you say no in an effective way. When you have conflicts, or disagreements with others, *conflict-resolution skills* can help you find a solution that is fair to everyone involved.

Advocacy

To advocate something means to support it or speak out in favor of it. When you **advocate** for health, you *encourage other people to live healthy lives.* You influence others to make positive choices. Advocacy also includes keeping others informed. By sharing health information, you enable others to make healthful choices.

▲ Talking through disagreements is a healthful way of dealing with them. **Can you think of another healthful way to handle a disagreement.**

ASSESS

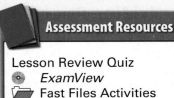

Assessment Resources

Lesson Review Quiz
- *ExamView*
- Fast Files Activities
- Online Quizzes and Activities

Reteaching

- Assign Concept Map 1-3 or Reteaching Activity 1-3 in the Fast Files
- Have students work in groups to brainstorm three ways health skills can help them improve their health and wellness.

Enrichment

- Assign Enrichment Activity 1-3 in the Fast Files.
- Have students write and illustrate a pamphlet about one health skill explained in the lesson and include ways the skill can improve their physical, mental/emotional, or social health.

CLOSE

Ask for volunteers to name one health skill and tell how they can take steps to develop that skill.

Caption Answer

Photo Caption Students may suggest being a good listener.

Lesson 3 Review

 After You Read

Review this lesson for new terms, major headings, and Reading Checks.

What I Learned

1. *Vocabulary* Define *prevention.* Use the word in an original sentence.

2. *Recall* What are two steps you can use to analyze influences?

3. *Explain* Why are health skills important for good health?

Thinking Critically

4. *Apply* Imagine that you overhear two teens talking about a great new CD that everyone "has to have." Analyze the possible sources of this influence.

5. *Hypothesize* Danielle has noticed that many traffic accidents appear at one intersection in her community. How can she use the health skill of advocacy to help correct this problem?

Applying Health Skills

6. *Communication Skills* Practice having a conversation with a classmate. Think about ways of showing you are listening. Why is it important to let the other person know you are listening?

Health Online For more review questions for Lesson 3, go to health.glencoe.com.

Lesson 3: Building Health Skills **15**

Lesson 3 Review Answers

1. Prevention is keeping something from happening. Sentences will vary.
2. Two steps are identifying the source and the motive.
3. Health skills can have a positive effect throughout your life.

4. The source of the influence is a group of peers. The motive of a teen who yields to peer influence and buys the CD might be a desire to fit in.
5. She can make others aware of this hazard or petition the local governing board to add

a stoplight, stop sign, or other measure for making the intersection less hazardous.
6. Student discussions should include various ways of showing that they are listening during a conversation.

FOCUS

Activating Prior Knowledge

What I Know Ask students to name some decisions commonly made by students their age. *Examples might include deciding what to eat for lunch or choosing what to wear.*

Guide to Reading

BUILDING VOCABULARY
- Direct students' attention to the term *cumulative*. Ask for a volunteer to explain the term *(made up of accumulated parts).* Then discuss the definition of *cumulative risk* on this page and why this type of risk is more harmful.
- Use Vocabulary PuzzleMaker to reinforce vocabulary terms.

READING STRATEGY
Sequencing Completed concept maps should include steps in the following order: state the situation, list the options, weigh the possible outcomes, consider values, make a decision and act on it, and evaluate the decision.

Quick Write

Have students write about a problem they recently faced and how they went about solving it. Ask for volunteers to share their paragraphs with the class.

Making Responsible Decisions

Guide to Reading

Building Vocabulary
Find the highlighted terms in the lesson. Write the definition of each in your notebook.
- decisions (p. 16)
- consequences (p. 16)
- risk (p. 16)
- cumulative risk (p. 17)
- values (p. 18)

Focusing on the Main Ideas
In this lesson, you will learn to
- **identify** how to make responsible decisions.
- **explain** why values are important when making decisions.
- **practice** the decision-making process.

Reading Strategy
Sequencing Create a concept map showing the order of the steps in decision-making. Use the diagram to the right as a guide.

> Step 1
> ↓
> Step 2
> ↓
> Step 3

Quick Write

Identify a problem that you faced recently. Write a brief paragraph explaining how you went about solving it.

Your Decisions Count

What are some decisions you made today? **Decisions** are *choices that you make*. Some decisions are small, such as what to eat for breakfast or what to wear. Other decisions are tougher. They can have serious **consequences** or *results*. During your teen years, you will have many important decisions to make. For some decisions, you will want to seek help from your parents, guardians, or other trusted adults.

Risk Factors

Some decisions involve risks. **Risk** is *the chance of harm, or loss*. Any decision that involves a risk to your health is an important one. When making decisions, you should understand the short-term and long-term consequences of safe, risky, and harmful behaviors.

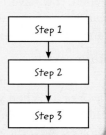

◀ Decisions can sometimes be difficult to make. **What are some decisions that affect your health?**

Lesson 4 Resources

📁 **Chapter *FAST FILE* Resources**
Guided Reading and Writing 1-4
Concept Mapping Activity 1-4
Cross-Curriculum Activity 1-4
Reteaching Activity 1-4
Enrichment Activity 1-4
Lesson Quiz 1-4

Technology
🔥 Transparency 1-4
💿 Audio Summaries
💿 *ExamView*
💿 Vocabulary PuzzleMaker
💿 StudentWorks™ Plus

The Decision-Making Process

Big decisions are a little like math problems. They should be broken down into smaller parts before they can be solved. Using the following six-step process can help you make healthy and responsible decisions.

R Whenever possible, it's a good idea to write down your answers as you work through each step. That way, you won't leave out important details. You can also go back and review the steps.

Step 1: State the Situation

Before you can make a decision, you should understand the situation. Ask yourself the following: What are the facts? Who else is involved?

Step 2: List the Options

Once you have analyzed the situation, think of your options. Try to cover all the possibilities. You may want to ask other people for suggestions. An adult that you trust is a good person to ask for advice when making an important decision.

Step 3: Weigh the Possible Outcomes

Consider your options carefully. Remember the word *HELP* when working through this step:

- **H (Healthful)** What health risks, if any, will this option present?
- **E (Ethical)** Does this choice reflect what you and your family believe to be *ethical*, or right?
- **L (Legal)** Does this option violate any local, state, or federal laws?
- **P (Parent Approval)** Would your parents approve of this choice?

For some decisions, you should think about cumulative risks. **Cumulative** (KYOO·myuh·luh·tiv) **risk** is *the addition of one risk factor to another, increasing the chance of harm or loss.* For example, riding in a car without wearing a seal belt is one risk factor. Riding in a car that is going over the speed limit is another. When combined, the two behaviors increase your risk of harm.

MediaWatch

Decisions, Decisions

In some TV shows, characters face decisions. These shows can be a good way of observing decision making in action. The next time you watch your favorite TV program, be aware of any problems that arise. Notice how characters go about solving these problems. What do they do when solutions don't work?

Describe a problem you saw on TV. How was it solved?

TEACH

MediaWatch

Decisions, Decisions

- Have students work in small groups to read the feature.
- Within their groups, have students discuss for 5 minutes a decision that was made on a television show. Have one of the group members take notes to record the group's discussion.
- Have the groups take turns presenting the results of their discussions.

R Reading Strategy

Sequencing Have students read the information about the six steps of decision making. Have students write each step on the front of a numbered index card. Then have students write a brief description of the step on the back of the card. Have students use the numbered index cards to move through the steps of the decision-making process. **BL**

Academic Vocabulary

Option On this page, students are instructed to list the options they have in a situation. Explain that an *option* is a choice. Have students write a sentence that uses the word *option*.

Dealing with Sensitive Issues

Parent Approval Step three of the decision-making process directs students to consider whether their parents or guardians would approve of their choices. This is challenging for teens seeking independence. Remind students that involving parents does not give them less independence, it simply gives them more information on which to base their decisions. In the case of decisions with negative consequences, remind students that in most states parents are legally responsible for the actions of their minor children.

Health Skills Activity

Decision Making

A Test of Friendship?

Use the following strategies to help students complete the activity on the next page.

- Have students meet in small groups to read the introductory paragraph.
- Ask students to talk through the decision-making steps as a group. Students should state the situation, list the options, weigh the possible outcome of Kris's decision, and consider values. After students have talked through the first four steps, have them state the healthy decision they feel that Kris should make. Then have them evaluate the decision.
- When all groups have completed the activity, have a class discussion. Ask for groups to share their results.

Reading Check

Answer The six steps of decision making are: state the situation, list the options, weigh the possible outcomes, consider values, make a decision and act on it, and evaluate the decision.

Caption Answer

Photo Caption My parents help me make important health decisions such as visiting a doctor.

Step 4: Consider Values

Values are *beliefs you feel strongly about that help guide the way you live*. Values reflect what is important to you and what you have learned is right or wrong. Your values should guide any important decision you make.

Step 5: Make a Decision and Act on It

You've weighed your options. You've mapped out the risks and consequences. Now you're ready for action. Choose the course that seems best and that supports your values. Make sure you are comfortable with your decision. If not, look at other options or ask a trusted adult for help.

Step 6: Evaluate the Decision

After you've acted on your decision, look at the results. Were they positive or negative? Were there any unexpected outcomes? Was there anything you could have done differently? What have you learned from the experience? If the action you took wasn't as successful as you'd hoped, try again. Use the decision-making process to find another way to deal with the situation.

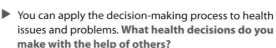

Reading Check

List What are the six steps in the decision-making process?

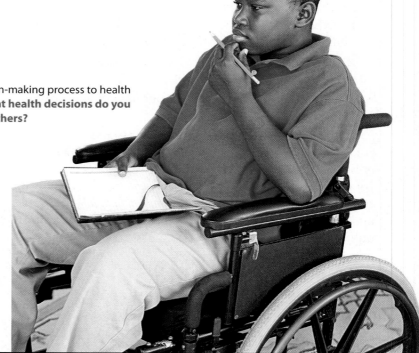

▶ You can apply the decision-making process to health issues and problems. **What health decisions do you make with the help of others?**

Health *Online*

Visit **health.glencoe.com** and complete the Interactive Study Guide for Lesson 4.

Promoting Coordinated School Health

Making Healthful Decisions The decision-making process can be overwhelming for some teens. Remind students that school counselors, teachers, administrators, and staff are all available to discuss major decisions. Be certain to mention parents, guardians, and trusted community members as resources as well. Ask volunteers to name hypothetical situations in which a teen might seek the help of others in making a decision. Explain that seeking the advice of a trusted adult when making a big decision is a sign of maturity, not a sign of weakness.

Health Skills Activity

Decision Making

A Test of Friendship

Kris's family moved to a new town. Almost from the first day, Lisa became her best friend. Lisa showed Kris around the town and introduced her to other teens. At school Lisa asked Kris to help her pass an English test. "All you need to do," Lisa explained, "is move your hand so I can see your paper." Kris was taught to always help out a friend. Yet what Lisa was asking Kris to do was help her cheat. Kris was also taught that cheating is wrong. What should Kris do?

What Would You Do?

Apply the six steps of decision making to Kris's problem. When you've finished, share the decision you would make with the class.

1. State the situation.
2. List the options.
3. Weigh the possible outcome.
4. Consider values.
5. Make a decision, and act on it.
6. Evaluate the decision.

Lesson 4 Review

After You Read

Review this lesson for new terms, major headings, and Reading Checks.

What I Learned

1. ***Vocabulary*** Use the terms *decision* and *consequences* in a sentence.

2. ***Explain*** What are two questions you might ask yourself when stating the situation in the decision-making process?

3. ***Recall*** Why are values important when making a decision?

Thinking Critically

4. ***Analyze*** Choose one of the six steps in the decision-making process, and describe its importance to the process.

5. ***Apply*** Lena is supposed to spend the weekend with a younger cousin from out of town. A friend calls offering an extra ticket to a concert for that Saturday night. How should Lena decide what to do?

Applying Health Skills

6. ***Decision Making*** With a partner, write a skit in which a teen is faced with a tough choice. Show how the teen uses the decision-making skills to arrive at a good solution.

Health *Online* For more review questions for Lesson 4, go to **health.glencoe.com**.

Lesson 4: Making Responsible Decisions **19**

Assessment Resources

Lesson Review Quiz
ExamView
Fast Files Activities
Online Quizzes and Activities

Reteaching

- Assign Concept Map 1-4 or Reteaching Activity 1-4 in the Fast Files.
- Have students work in small groups to think of a health-related decision teens face and have them apply the six steps of decision making.

Enrichment

- Assign Enrichment Activity 1-4 in the Fast Files.
- Have students create a game, book, song, or activity that could be used to teach the six steps of decision making to grade school students.

CLOSE

Go around the room and ask students to give examples of situations when responsible decision making is important.

Lesson 4 Review Answers

1. Sentences will vary but should reflect an understanding of the meaning of and relationship between these terms.
2. These include "What are the facts?" and "Who else is involved?"
3. Your values can guide you toward options that will not compromise your ideals or put you in jeopardy.
4. Answers will vary but should reveal an understanding of the decision-making process.
5. She needs to evaluate her prior commitments to her cousin and weigh these against the personal desire to go to the concert. She could also explore options that include getting a ticket for the cousin.
6. Students' skits should include the steps to decision making found in the lesson.

FOCUS

Activating Prior Knowledge

What I Know Ask students to brainstorm what they think some goals of this health class will be.

Guide to Reading

BUILDING VOCABULARY
- Have students write a sentence that shows a relationship between two of the vocabulary terms.
- Use Vocabulary PuzzleMaker to reinforce vocabulary terms.

READING STRATEGY
Compare and Contrast Have students use complete sentences as they write their answers to the Reading Strategy. Check that students have correctly identified an example of a short-term goal and a long-term goal.

Quick Write

Have each student write a paragraph describing his or her goal. Check to see that students have answered all three parts of the Quick Write question.

Academic Vocabulary

Achieve The focus of Lesson 5 is setting and achieving goals. Students will read the word *achieve*. Explain that *achieve* means "to accomplish." Have students brainstorm a list of synonyms for the term *achieve*.
Samples: *complete, succeed*

20

Setting Health Goals

Guide to Reading

● **Building Vocabulary**
Examine the terms below. Look for relationships between them. As you come across these in the lesson, write them in your notebook.

- goal (p. 20)
- short-term goal (p. 21)
- long-term goal (p. 21)

● **Focusing on the Main Ideas**
In this lesson, you will learn to
- **explain** why having goals is important.
- **describe** how to set goals.
- **develop** a strategy to reach your goals.

● **Reading Strategy**
Comparing and Contrasting What do you think is the difference between a short-term and long-term goal? What is an example of each?

Quick Write

Write about a goal you would like to achieve. Tell why it is important to you, and how you plan to achieve it.

Setting Goals

What do you dream of achieving in your lifetime? What are your ambitions? Your answers to these questions reflect your goals. A **goal** is *something you hope to accomplish*. Some goals are broad, such as wanting to be happy or successful. Other goals are specific, such as getting a good grade on a test. Goal setting is an important skill that will help you achieve and maintain good health.

▶ Achieving your goals requires planning. **What dreams do you hope to achieve? What can you do now to start on the road to achieving them?**

Lesson 5 Resources

📁 **Chapter FAST FILE Resources**
Guided Reading and Writing 1-5
Concept Mapping Activity 1-5
Decision-Making Activity 1-5
Reteaching Activity 1-5
Enrichment Activity 1-5
Lesson Quiz 1-5

Technology
🔦 Transparency 1-5
💿 Audio Summaries
💿 *ExamView*
💿 Vocabulary PuzzleMaker
💿 StudentWorks™ Plus

Types of Goals

Goals may be short-term or long-term. A **short-term goal** is *a goal that you plan to accomplish in a short time*. An example of a short-term goal is getting your homework done in time to watch a certain TV program. A **long-term goal** is *a goal that you hope to achieve within a period of months or years*.

Often, short-term goals lead to long-term goals. Inez's long-term goal is to be a veterinarian, an animal doctor. Her short-term goals include doing well in science and earning money for college. To achieve her short-term goal, Inez walks neighbors' dogs. This also gives her experience running a business and being around animals. Notice that goals such as these form a chain (see **Figure 1.4**). How would you fill in the fourth link of Inez's chain?

By setting clear goals for herself, Inez has taken charge of her life. Have you taken charge of yours?

Reading Check

Identify What are the two types of goals? How are they related?

▶ FIGURE 1.4

THE GOAL CHAIN

R The goal chain illustrates how short-term goals can help you achieve a long-term goal. How will Inez's short-term goals help her become a veterinarian?

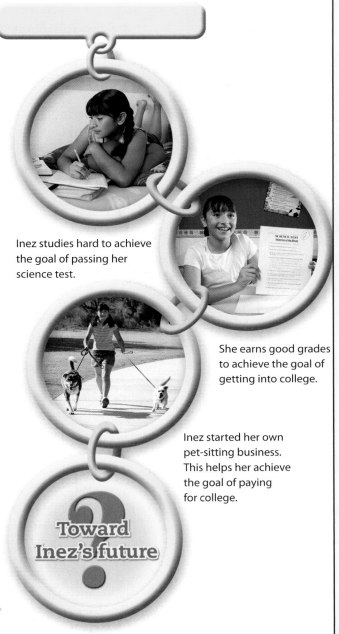

Inez studies hard to achieve the goal of passing her science test.

She earns good grades to achieve the goal of getting into college.

Inez started her own pet-sitting business. This helps her achieve the goal of paying for college.

Toward Inez's future

TEACH

AL Active Learning

Quick Demo Use a stack of textbooks to model the achievement of a long-term goal. Stack five books on a desk. As you place one last book on top of the stack, remind students that the top book could not be in that position without the support of all the other books. In the same way, a long-term goal cannot be achieved without the support of many short-term goals. **BL**

Reading Check

Answer The two types of goals are long-term goals and short-term goals. A long-term goal can often be met by achieving a series of short-term goals.

R Reading Strategy

Analyzing a Graphic Have students examine Figure 1.4. Ask students what short-term goals Inez meets in this figure. *doing well in science, raising money for college* Have students explain how meeting the short-term goals will help Inez reach her long-term goal. **OL**

Caption Answer

Photo Caption, p. 20 Students should state a long-term goal and at least one short-term goal that contribute to the achievement of the long-term goal.

TECHNOLOGY AND HEALTH

Goal-Setting and Technology Software and digital tools may be helpful in organizing steps toward setting and achieving goals. Challenge students to think of ways that computer technology, PDAs, or other digital devices can be put to use in goal-setting. For example, setting priorities and tasks into a calendar, setting reminders, and recording progress can all be accomplished in many e-mail and scheduling programs. Have volunteers demonstrate specific ways they might set short-term and long-term goals using the aid of digital tools.

21

DEVELOPING
Good Character

Setting Goals in a Group
Divide the class into four groups. Give each group the same hypothetical goal on an index card. Do not tell the groups that they all have the same goal. Have each group develop a detailed, written plan for meeting the goal. Then have each group present its plan to the class. Use this activity to launch a discussion of the many ways a goal can be achieved.

C Critical Thinking

Analyzing Concepts Make a T-diagram on the board describing goals, one side labeled "realistic" and the other side labeled "unrealistic." After students have read the information on choosing goals, have students brainstorm entries for each side of the T-diagram. Then lead a class discussion of ways to choose realistic goals. **OL**

Reading Check

Answer A goal must be realistic, it must be in line with my interests, and it should be challenging.

Caption Answer

Photo Caption *Sample answer:* I can achieve a goal of getting all A's and B's next semester.

DEVELOPING
Good Character

Setting Goals in a Group

Setting goals can be challenging, especially when a whole group is involved. Sara's soccer team needed to raise money for new equipment. One team member insisted that a yard sale was the answer. Another argued that they should hold a raffle. A third student suggested doing both, and everyone agreed. By working together, the team reached its goal. **Describe a group goal-setting experience you have been involved in. How did you choose your goal? How did you go about reaching it?**

Choosing Goals

The goals that are right for you depend on your interests, skills, and abilities. Priorities, changing abilities, and responsibilities also influence setting goals. What do you do well? What would you like to improve? Answering questions such as these will help you choose goals you will want to work toward. Being aware of your skills and interests will help you choose goals you can achieve. Here are a few other *do's* and *don'ts* when setting a goal:

C
- *Do a reality check.* Ask yourself whether your goal is realistic. Is it something you can really achieve?
- *Don't sell yourself short.* Select goals that are challenging for you. Don't be afraid to aim high. Believe in yourself, and use all your abilities.

Reading Check **Recognize** Identify three tips for choosing a goal.

Reaching Your Goals

All goals, big and small, have one thing in common. To achieve them, you should have a plan. How do you get from where you are now to where you want to be? Here are some tips:

▶ Following a logical plan can help you achieve many goals. **What realistic goal can you achieve?**

Cultural Perspectives

Media Influence on Career Goals Lead a class discussion of careers that students see portrayed in the media. Examples might include law enforcement and medical professionals. These careers are often portrayed as glamorous and exciting. Lead a discussion of ways in which media portrayal of careers can be misleading. Ask students to develop a list of ways to find reliable, realistic information about careers. *Examples include interviewing adults in a particular profession or reading biographies of those in a profession.*

- **Make your goals specific.** Don't just say, "I want to be a better piano player." Say, "I want to be able to play a certain piece without making any mistakes at my next recital."

- **List the steps to reach your goal.** Break big goals down into smaller tasks. For example, to play piano in the recital, you will need to practice. Set a practice schedule, maybe half an hour each day.

- **Get help from others.** Identify people who can help you achieve your goals. Seek the input of parents, teachers, and other trusted adults. Also, identify sources of information, such as books and magazine articles.

- **Evaluate your progress.** Check periodically to see how well you're progressing toward your goal. In the case of the piano piece, you might record and play back your performances. Your teacher can also give you any necessary feedback. Should you be doing anything differently? Is one part giving you more trouble than others? If necessary, adjust your plan, or seek help.

- **Reward yourself.** Treat yourself in a special way, and celebrate your accomplishments.

Health Online

Visit **health.glencoe.com** and complete the Interactive Study Guide for Lesson 5.

ASSESS

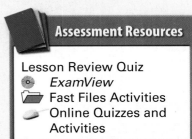

Assessment Resources

Lesson Review Quiz
- *ExamView*
- Fast Files Activities
- Online Quizzes and Activities

Reteaching

- Assign Concept Map 1-5 or Reteaching Activity 1-5 in the Fast Files.
- Have students explain two reasons why having goals is important.

Enrichment

- Assign Enrichment Activity 1-5 in the Fast Files.
- Have students choose a famous person they admire. Then students can research goal-setting by reading a biography of the person and summarizing how goal-setting was important in the person's achievements.

CLOSE

Have students read their comparisons of long-term and short-term goals they prepared for the Guide to Reading activity on page 20. Ask what similarities and differences they can add after reading the lesson.

Lesson 5 Review

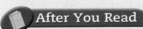 **After You Read**

Review this lesson for new terms, major headings, and Reading Checks.

What I Learned

1. *Vocabulary* Define *short-term goal* and *long-term goal*. Use each term in an original sentence.

2. *Describe* Why is it important to set a realistic goal?

3. *Recall* Describe each step in the goal-setting process.

Thinking Critically

4. *Apply* Seth's long-term goal is to be a professional baseball player.

What short-term goals could Seth set for himself to help him reach this goal?

5. *Hypothesize* Sometimes goals need to be changed. What are some reasons a goal might need to be changed?

Applying Health Skills

6. *Goal Setting* Choose a personal health goal. Discuss strategies and skills needed to attain a personal health goal.

Health Online For more review questions for Lesson 5, go to **health.glencoe.com**.

Lesson 5: Setting Health Goals **23**

Lesson 5 Review Answers

1. A short-term goal can be accomplished in a short time; a long-term goal takes months or years to achieve. Sentence will vary, but should reflect an understanding of the terms.

2. It is important to set realistic goals so that the goals can be achieved.

3. The steps in the goal-setting process are: choose a realistic goal, make your goals specific, list the steps to reach your goal, get help from others, evaluate your progress, and reward yourself when your goal is achieved.

4. *Sample answer:* Seth could set a goal to make the school baseball team.

5. *Sample answer:* A goal might need to be changed if your interests or abilities change.

6. Students should discuss specific behaviors and skills to reach a personal health goal.

Building Health Skills

ANALYZING INFLUENCES

Evaluating Influences on Your Health

SKILL
Analyzing Influences

Activating Prior Knowledge

Ask students to think of factors that influence what they buy. Make a list of students' answers on the board. Ask for volunteers to name the one factor that has the most influence on their purchasing decisions.

- **Objective** After completing the activity, students will be able to analyze the influences that affect their choices.
- **Time** 45 minutes
- **Materials** paper, pencil

Teacher Classroom Resources

📁 Building Health Skills
🖨 Transparency 6-3

Model

- Ask students to compare the factors that influence their decisions to the factors that influenced Darrol's decision. *Sample answer: Darrol and I are both influenced by peers, parents, media, likes/ dislikes, and health.*

Evaluating Influences On Your Health

DIRECTIONS

Analyzing influences involves recognizing the ways in which internal and external factors affect your health choices. This activity will give you the opportunity to develop and master this important health skill. Here's a guide to the different parts of this activity:

❶ In the **Model** section, you will read about a teen who performs the health skill successfully. This "model" scenario will show you how the skill is done.

❷ The **Practice** section will help guide you in practicing the skill.

❸ In the **Apply** section, you will have a chance to perform the skill on your own. You can use the Self-Check to check your work.

To complete this activity, first read the scenario presented in the Model. Then move on to the Practice. Finally, go ahead and try the Apply.

❶ Model

As you know, many factors influence your health. Take the case of Darrol. Darrol went to the mall to buy new sneakers. He planned to buy the same kind of shoes he already owned because they were very comfortable. In the store, the saleswoman showed him a different style. "These just came in, and they're going to be very popular," the saleswoman said. She pointed to a large colorful display. It showed a teen about Darrol's age wearing the new sneakers. Suddenly, Darrol couldn't decide what he wanted.

Darrol told the saleswoman he needed to think about his choice. At home, Darrol thought about the two pairs of shoes. He made a list of what influences were affecting his decision and why. He numbered each influence in the order of its importance to him. Then he went back to the store and bought the shoes he had planned to buy.

Decision: Which shoes should I buy?

Influencing Factors	What I value most right now and why
Likes/dislikes	1—I like the shoes I've owned.
Health	2—I need shoes that are comfortable.
Peers	3—The new sneakers might be popular at school.
Media	4—The poster in the store looked really cool.

Teaching Tips

Learning Through Diversity Group work allows students to share their knowledge and their experiences. It also promotes social interaction between students who may not normally associate with one another. Interaction allows students to learn about different ways of living and thinking. Teachers can encourage diverse group participation by assigning members to a group. Factors to consider include: gender, culture, social associations at school, extra-curricular activities.

② Practice

Darrol has made a new friend, Brock. Brock's friends are different from those Darrol usually hangs out with. Darrol has eaten lunch with Brock several times and has enjoyed getting to know some of the kids in his group. Today, Brock invited Darrol to hang out at his house with a few of the friends from his group. Darrol really wants to go but he has already promised to go to his friend Chris's house.

List the factors that would influence Darrol's decision. Assign a number value to each factor, with number one being the most important influence.

Skill Summary
ANALYZING INFLUENCES

Both internal and external influences affect your choices. These influences may include:

Internal	External
■ knowledge	■ family
■ interests	■ friends
■ likes/dislikes	■ media
■ fears	■ culture
■ curiosity	

③ Apply

Imagine you are choosing which after-school club to join. Think about the different factors that would influence your decision. Make a list like the one Darrol made. Decide which factors are most important to you. Remember to assign a number value to each factor.

Self-Check

■ What influences did I name?
■ Which influence do I value most? Why?

Practice

● Have students list the factors that would influence Darrol's decision and assign a number value to each factor. (Have them use a scale from 1 to 5, with 5 being the highest).
● Ask for volunteers to share their answers. Use the answers to generate class discussion. Point out that the factors and number values will vary from person to person.

Apply/Assess

● Have students review Darrol's options. Then have each student develop a list for the Apply activity.
● Have volunteers share their completed lists.
● You may wish to distribute the Building Health Skills activity in the Fast Files.

ASSESSMENT SCORING

Student work should meet all criteria to achieve the highest score:

Skills Student work identifies:
● Influences that affect the group most.
● Influences that have the least effect.
● Whether internal or external influences are most influential.

Concept Student work provides:
● Accurate information about the connection between influences and health.

Your Personal Health

Time: 20 minutes
Materials: pencil or pen, paper

Introducing Hands-on Health

- Tell students that they are in control of their health triangles. The first step toward improving their overall health is to identify strengths and weaknesses in their health triangles.

Teaching the Activity

- Have students complete the inventory as directed.
- Allow students to keep their answers confidential.
- Have students use their results to identify one area of health in which they could improve their health habits.
- Encourage students to use the information from this activity to set a short-term goal and identify a long-term goal to improve their health triangles.

HANDS-ON HEALTH

Your Personal Health

Do you have a clear picture of your own health triangle? Take this personal health inventory to identify factors that affect your physical, mental/emotional, and social health.

What You Will Need

- Pencil or pen
- Paper

What You Will Do

On your paper, write the numbers 1 to 6 for each health area. Think about each of the following statements and respond with yes or no.

Physical Health

1. I eat at least three well-balanced meals each day and snack on healthful foods such as fruits and vegetables.
2. I get at least 60 minutes of physical activity daily.
3. I sleep at least eight hours a night.
4. I avoid the use of tobacco, alcohol, and other drugs.
5. I have good personal hygiene habits.
6. I follow safety rules.

Mental/Emotional Health

1. I feel good about myself.
2. I can name several things I do well.
3. I generally keep a positive attitude.
4. I ask for help when I need it.
5. I am able to handle stress.
6. I try to improve myself.

Social Health

1. I get along well with my family.
2. I try to work out any differences I have with others.
3. I express my feelings in positive ways.
4. I treat others with respect.
5. I have at least one friend I can talk to.
6. I listen when someone is speaking to me.

Wrapping It Up

Give yourself 1 point for each yes. A score of 5–6 in any area reflects good health. A score of 3–4 indicates you're doing well but can still improve. If you score 0–2 in any area, try to improve that part of your health triangle.

HANDS-ON HEALTH Assessment

Discussion Ask students to name steps to improve physical health. Sample answer: *make healthy food choices, exercise three or more times a week*

Why is it important to maintain all three areas of health? Sample answer: *Overall wellness requires social, mental/ emotional, and physical health.*

What are some actions you could take that would have a positive effect on someone else's health triangle? Sample answer: *Invite a friend to join a club with you; help a friend study for a difficult exam; work with a friend on an athletic skill.*

Reading Review

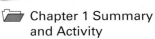

FOLDABLES™ Study Organizer

Foldables™ and Other Study Aids Take out the Foldable™ that you created for Lesson 1 and any graphic organizers that you created for Lessons 1–5. Find a partner, and quiz each other using these study aids.

Lesson 1 | Your Total Health

Key Ideas
- The three parts of the health triangle are physical health, mental/emotional health, and social health.
- Wellness means that all three of the sides of the triangle are healthy and in balance.
- You can balance your physical, mental/emotional, and social health by developing good health habits.

Vocabulary
- health (p. 4)
- wellness (p. 7)
- habit (p. 7)

Lesson 2 | Influences on Your Health

Key Ideas
- Your health is influenced by heredity, environment, family, culture, the media, and technology.
- Maintaining positive attitudes will help you choose health-promoting behaviors.

Vocabulary
- heredity (p. 8)
- environment (p. 9)
- culture (p. 9)
- peers (p. 9)
- media (p. 10)
- technology (p. 10)
- behavior (p. 11)
- attitude (p. 11)

Lesson 3 | Building Health Skills

Key Ideas
- Skills that can help keep you healthy are accessing information, practicing healthful behaviors, stress management, analyzing influences, effective communication, refusal skills, conflict resolution, decision making, goal setting, and advocacy.
- Health skills are skills you will use throughout your life. They can help you prevent or limit illness and injury.

Vocabulary
- prevention (p. 12)
- health skills (p. 12)
- communication (p. 15)
- advocate (p. 15)

Lesson 4 | Making Responsible Decisions

Key Ideas
- You can make good, responsible decisions by learning and practicing the six-step decision-making process.
- You can apply the decision-making process to health issues and problems.

Vocabulary
- decisions (p. 16)
- consequences (p. 16)
- risk (p. 16)
- cumulative risk (p. 17)
- values (p.18)

Lesson 5 | Setting Health Goals

Key Ideas
- Creating goals for yourself teaches you to plan, challenge yourself, and work to achieve those goals.
- You can set goals by following a well-defined series of steps.

Vocabulary
- goal (p. 20)
- short-term goal (p. 21)
- long-term goal (p. 21)

Assessment Resources

- 📁 Chapter 1 Summary and Activity
- 💿 Audio Summaries
- 📁 Reading Tutor
- 📁 Performance Assessment
- 📁 Chapter 1 Test
- 💿 *ExamView*
- 💿 Vocabulary PuzzleMaker
- 💿 Online Learning Center

Reading Review

Study Aids

- **Using the Dinah Zike Foldable™ Study Organizer** Have students use the Foldable™ 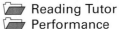 to review the content of Lesson 1. Have students work in pairs to review the three sides of the health triangle. **BL**

Key Ideas

- **Review the Figures** Have students skim the chapter to find graphics that contain a large amount of information. Instruct students to review the art and text portions of each infographic.

Vocabulary Review

- **Vocabulary Flashcards** Have students use index cards to make vocabulary term flashcards. Students can work in pairs to review the terms using their completed flashcards.

Teaching Tips

Independent Previewing Help students become familiar with text material before reading by guiding them through a preview of the chapter. Have students look at the next chapter they are about to read, give them five minutes to preview the chapter, and then have them summarize the chapter either orally or in writing. Students should be able to give a summary that has information from all parts of the chapter, not just the beginning. Students can compare their summaries with other classmates or with a summary provided by the teacher.

Assessment

Reviewing Vocabulary and Main Ideas

1. Wellness
2. Health
3. habit
4. culture
5. media
6. attitudes
7. False, Prevention
8. True
9. False, communication
10. False, consequences
11. True
12. False, parent approval
13. True
14. True

Thinking Critically

15. Plans will vary but should accurately reflect the relationship between an overall task and the steps needed to reach it. A possibility would be a physical goal of doing ten perfect chin-ups, which would start with attention to form and the strength needed to do a single chin-up.

16. *Sample answer:* One example is walking alone, after dark, in an unsafe neighborhood. Adding one risk factor to another increases your risks.

Assessment

📖 **After You Read**

HEALTH INVENTORY

Now that you have read the chapter, look back at your answers to the Health Inventory on the chapter opener. Is there anything that you should do differently?

Reviewing Vocabulary and Main Ideas

On a sheet of paper, write the numbers 1–6. After each number, write the term from the list that best completes each sentence.

- attitudes
- consequences
- culture
- decisions
- habit
- health
- health skills
- media
- prevention
- wellness

Lesson 1 Your Total Health

1. _____ is a state of well-being, or total health.

2. _____ is a combination of physical, mental/emotional, and social well-being.

3. A(n) _____ is a pattern of behavior that you follow almost without thinking.

Lesson 2 Influences on Your Health

4. The sum total of daily habits found within a society is its _____.

5. TV and the Internet are two methods of communicating information grouped together as the _____.

6. Feelings and beliefs, or _____, can play a role in how well you take care of yourself.

*On a sheet of paper, write the numbers 7–14. Write **True** or **False** for each statement below. If the statement is false, change the underlined word or phrase to make it true.*

Lesson 3 Building Health Skills

7. <u>Wellness</u> is keeping something bad from happening to your health.

8. Two parts to the skill of <u>analyzing influences</u> are identifying the source and the motive.

9. Parts of the skill of <u>advocacy</u> are being a good listener and telling others honestly how you feel.

Lesson 4 Making Responsible Decisions

10. Every decision you make has <u>risks</u>, or results.

11. Stating the situation is the <u>first</u> step in the decision-making process.

12. When considering options, remember the word *HELP*, whose letters stand for healthful, ethical, legal, and <u>permission</u>.

Lesson 5 Setting Health Goals

13. It is important to ask yourself whether a goal is <u>realistic</u>, something you can achieve.

14. Breaking down big goals into smaller tasks is a step in <u>goal setting</u>.

Health Online Visit health.glencoe.com and take the Online Quiz for Chapter 1.

Health Online

Have students visit **health.glencoe.com** to take the Chapter 1 Quiz.

HEALTH INVENTORY WRAP-UP

Your Health and Wellness Have students retake the Health Inventory found in the Chapter Opener. Ask for volunteers to share ways in which their answers to the questions have changed as a result of reading the chapter.

Thinking Critically

Using complete sentences, answer the following questions on a sheet of paper.

15. **Synthesize** Write a plan that breaks down the long-term goal of achieving physical fitness into several short-term goals that can be reached one at a time.

16. **Describe** Identify a cumulative risk. How can this affect your health?

Write About It

17. **Analyzing Influences** Write a short story in which a teen becomes a positive role model for a younger child. Show how the teen influences the child by making healthy choices and displaying healthful behaviors.

 Career Corner

Health Teacher Do you like learning about health? Do you think you have a gift for helping others learn? A career as a health teacher might be for you. This career requires excellent communication skills and the ability to motivate others. You'll also need a four-year teaching degree with courses in health education. For more information, visit *Career Corner* at **health.glencoe.com**.

18. **Goal Setting** Write a journal entry describing a goal you have set for yourself. Describe your journey in reaching the goal, including the steps you have taken so far.

Standardized Test Practice

Reading

Read the passage and then answer the questions.

Information on good health habits has been around for a long time. In the 1100s, a physician named Moses Maimonides published a book titled *Rules for Physical Health*.

Rules for Physical Health suggests that people need eight hours of sleep a night to maintain their health. It also encourages its readers to exercise or play sports regularly. It even contains specific suggestions about the kinds of food a person should eat.

The book is not just about what individuals could do to improve their health. It also stresses the importance of breathing clean air. In other words, it recognizes that a healthy environment is an important part of staying healthy.

TEST-TAKING TIP

Read the passage carefully once to find out what information it contains. After you read each question, look back at the passage to find the answer.

1. As described in the passage, *Rules for Physical Health* gives suggestions on all of the following EXCEPT?
   A. healthful eating habits
   B. ways of improving social health
   C. making physical activity a regular habit
   D. getting enough bed rest at night

2. What suggestion in the book relates the environment to personal health?
   A. the importance of sealing garbage bags
   B. the importance of drinking clean water
   C. the importance of recycling
   D. the importance of breathing clean air

Chapter 1 Assessment **29**

Write About It

17. **Narrative Writing** Tell students that narrative writing tells a clear story arranged in a logical order. Remind them to develop interesting characters, describe the setting, and include a plot to describe how their main character makes healthy choices and displays healthful behaviors based on reading from the chapter.

18. **Personal or Descriptive Writing** Tell students to write a journal entry describing a goal they have set for themselves. Remember to respect student privacy. Students should include some of the goal-setting steps, such as make your goal specific, list the steps to reach your goal, get help from others, evaluate your progress, and reward yourself.

Standardized Test Practice

1. B
2. D

 Career Corner

Health Teacher Have students visit the Career Corner at **health.glencoe .com** to gather more information about a career as a health teacher. Have students research the requirements for teacher certification in your state. Relate your experiences as a health teacher to interested students. Explain that health teachers can also work for hospitals and community agencies.

Test-Taking Tips

Timed Tests Tell students that most standardized tests are timed. Students should use a watch or the clock in the testing room to keep track of the time. If students see that time is running out and it is clear that they will not complete the entire test, they should skim for questions that they are sure of and can quickly and easily answer.

CHAPTER 2 pp. 30–59	Standards		Skills and Activities
	National	State/Local	
	National Health Education Standards 4.1, 4.3, 4.4		**IM EXPRESS,** *p. 31* **HANDS-ON-HEALTH** Developing Good Character, *pp. 56* **BUILDING HEALTH SKILLS** Dealing with Feelings, *pp. 54–55*
Lesson 1 **A Healthy Self-Concept** *pp. 32–35*	National Health Education Standards 1.2, 1.4, 1.5, 1.6, 2.2, 2.4, 4.1, 4.3, 4.4, 4.5, 5.2, 6.1, 6.2, 8.2		**HEALTH SKILLS ACTIVITY** *Analyzing Influences* **MEDIA WATCH** How do the Media Influence Your Self-Concept? *p. 34*
Lesson 2 **Your Character Counts** *pp. 36–40*	National Health Education Standards 1.2, 1.4, 2.4, 4.2, 4.3, 4.4, 4.5, 5.1, 5.2, 5.3, 7.1, 7.4, 8.2, 8.4, 8.5		**Connect To... LANGUAGE ARTS** The Idea of Character, *p. 39*
Lesson 3 **Expressing Emotions** *pp. 41–44*	National Health Education Standards 1.1, 1.2, 1.4, 1.8, 2.3, 4.1, 4.2, 4.3, 4.4, 4.5, 4.8, 7.3, 7.4, 7.6, 7.7, 8.2, 8.4		
Lesson 4 **Coping with Stress** *pp. 45–49*	National Health Education Standards 1.2, 1.3, 1.6, 4.1, 7.2, 7.7, 8.2		**HEALTH SKILLS ACTIVITY** *Stress Management* Relaxation Techniques, *p. 48*
Lesson 5 **Emotional Problems** *pp. 50–53*	National Health Education Standards 1.6, 1.8, 3.1, 3.2, 3.6, 5.1, 7.1, 7.4, 8.2, 8.4		**HEALTH SKILLS ACTIVITY** *Decision Making* Helping a Troubled Friend, *p. 52*

PACING THE CHAPTER

Lesson 1	45 min	**Lesson 4**	90 min	**Chapter Review**	45 min
Lesson 2	90 min	**Lesson 5**	45 min	**Hands-on Health**	45 min
Lesson 3	45 min	**Building Health Skills**	45 min		

BLOCK SCHEDULING

For block scheduling, assign students Building Health Skills feature *Dealing with Feelings*, pages 54–55, and Guided Reading and Writing. 📁

Planning Guide

Glencoe Exclusive!
Teacher Works™
All-In-One Planner and Resource Center

Reproducible Resources	Assessment	Media and Technology

Chapter *Fast File* Resources
  Chapter Summaries and Activities `REVIEW`
  Building Health Skills Activity `TEACH`
  Performance Assessment Activity `EXTEND`
  Universal Access Activities `TEACH`
  Parent Letter and Activities
Student Activities Workbook `TEACH`
Reading Tutor `TEACH`
	Building Health Skills Activity, *pp. 54-55*
	Chapter 2 Assessment, *pp. 58–59*
	Chapter *Fast File* Resources
	  Performance Assessment Activity, *p. 4*
	  Chapter 2 Test, *p. 7*
	  ExamView® Test Generator
		Teacher Works™ includes:
		• Interactive Teacher Edition
		• Lesson Planner with Calendar
		• Access to all blackline masters
		• Correlations to standards
		  StudentWorks™ Plus
		  Online Student Edition
		Dinah Zike's Teaching Health with Foldables™

Chapter *Fast File* Resources
  Concept Mapping Activity 2–1 `REVIEW`
  Cross-Curriculum Activity 2–1 `EXTEND`
  Enrichment Activity 2–1 `EXTEND`
  Lesson Plan 2–1
  Guided Reading and Writing 2–1 `TEACH`
  Reteaching Activity 2–1 `REVIEW`
	Lesson 1 Review, *p. 35*
	  Vocabulary PuzzleMaker
	  ExamView® Test Generator
		Vocabulary PuzzleMaker
		ExamView® Test Generator
		StudentWorks™ Plus
		Transparency 2-1
		Health *Online*

Chapter *Fast File* Resources
  Concept Mapping Activity 2–2 `REVIEW`
  Cross-Curriculum Activity 2–2 `TEACH`
  Enrichment Activity 2–2 `EXTEND`
  Lesson Plan 2–2
  Guided Reading and Writing 2–2 `TEACH`
  Reteaching Activity 2–2 `REVIEW`
	Lesson 2 Review, *p. 40*
	  Vocabulary PuzzleMaker
	  ExamView® Test Generator
		Vocabulary PuzzleMaker
		ExamView® Test Generator
		StudentWorks™ Plus
		Transparency 2-2
		Health *Online*

Chapter *Fast File* Resources
  Concept Mapping Activity 2–3 `REVIEW`
  Decision-Making Activity 2–3 `TEACH`
  Enrichment Activity 2–3 `EXTEND`
  Lesson Plan 2–3
  Guided Reading and Writing 2–3 `TEACH`
  Reteaching Activity 2–3 `REVIEW`
	Lesson 3 Review, *p. 44*
	  Vocabulary PuzzleMaker
	  ExamView® Test Generator
		Vocabulary PuzzleMaker
		ExamView® Test Generator
		StudentWorks™ Plus
		Transparency 2-3
		Health *Online*

Chapter *Fast File* Resources
  Concept Mapping Activity 2–4 `REVIEW`
  Enrichment Activity 2–4 `EXTEND`
  Lesson Plan 2–4
  Guided Reading and Writing 2–4 `TEACH`
  Health Lab 2–4 `EXTEND`
  Reteaching Activity 2–4 `REVIEW`
	Lesson 4 Review, *p. 49*
	  Vocabulary PuzzleMaker
	  ExamView® Test Generator
		Vocabulary PuzzleMaker
		ExamView® Test Generator
		StudentWorks™ Plus
		Transparency 2-4
		Health *Online*

Chapter *Fast File* Resources
  Concept Mapping Activity 2–5 `REVIEW`
  Decision-Making Activity 2–5 `TEACH`
  Enrichment Activity 2–5 `EXTEND`
  Lesson Plan 2–5
  Guided Reading and Writing 2–5 `TEACH`
  Reteaching Activity 2–5 `REVIEW`
	Lesson 5 Review, *p. 53*
	  Vocabulary PuzzleMaker
	  ExamView® Test Generator
		Vocabulary PuzzleMaker
		ExamView® Test Generator
		StudentWorks™ Plus
		Transparency 2-5
		Health *Online*

Chapter and Lesson Resources

The *Teen Health* resources are designed for differentiated learning abilities. You may want to use the coded items in this way:

`REVIEW` —activities to review or reinforce content
`TEACH` —activities to teach basic concepts
`EXTEND` —activities to extend or enrich lesson content

 OUT OF TIME?

Use Health Skills Activities *Stress Management*, page 48, and *Helping a Troubled Friend*, page 52.

Stress and the Immune System

The body's response to stress can affect the immune system. Studies have shown that when the body is stressed briefly and undergoes the fight-or-flight response, parts of the immune system are enhanced. Other parts of the immune system slow down. Long-term, chronic stress is associated with a depression of immune function.

The main function of the immune system is to aid the body in protecting against pathogens that cause infection. The slowing down of the immune response, therefore, can lead to an increase in minor infections and major illnesses, along with an increase in symptoms of conditions such as eczema and psoriasis.

Remind students about the importance of balancing all three sides of the health triangle as they study this chapter. The importance of maintaining a healthy immune system is a good example of ways that a person's mental and emotional health can have an effect on the body's physical health. Stress management techniques can be used to reduce the impact of stress on the immune system and helps students in maintaining their overall health.

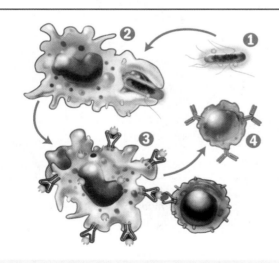

1. Pathogens invade the body.
2. Macrophages engulf the pathogen.
3. Macrophages digest the pathogen and T cells recognize antigens.
4. T cells bind to the antigens.

Stress slows down the process, leading to infection or illness.

Emotions in Times of Crisis

Anyone reading the newspaper or watching television can expect to hear reports of bad news in the media. The messages students are exposed to might be a tragedy that occurred in your community or across the nation. In response to a tragedy, teens may feel many strong emotions, including sadness, anger, fear, and guilt. All of these reactions are normal for any individual. Teens may have a more difficult time knowing how to deal with these strong emotions.

Guide students in dealing with these experiences by sharing the following strategies for handling emotions during stressful times.

- **Maintain your daily routine.** Doing so will help you feel a sense of control.

- **Plan a special activity.** Make a plan each day so that you have something to look forward to.

- **Share your feelings.** Remember that friends and family members are probably experiencing similar emotions. If you're not ready to talk, try writing down your thoughts and feelings in a journal.

- **Turn off the news.** It's easy to become overwhelmed with nonstop media coverage of tragedies.

- **Take a break.** Go for a walk, listen to a favorite CD, or watch a funny movie with friends.

- **Channel your energy.** Choose a worthwhile cause. Volunteer to help raise money for relief efforts, participate in a local memorial service, or create a memory book.

The National Association of School Psychologists provides extensive information at their Web site, including resources and tips for guiding young people through difficult times. Link to the site through the Teacher Center at **health.glencoe.com**.

Support for Teaching Reading

Reading Preview

Activating Background Vocabulary Ask students what comes to mind when they hear the term "self-esteem." Guide students in a discussion to help them recognize the meaning of self-esteem as the measure of how much a person likes and respects him- or herself. Explain that this chapter will help students to develop their positive self-esteem.

FOLDABLES Study Organizer *Dinah Zike's Reading and Study Skills for Teen Health* provides interactive graphic organizers that help students comprehend and retain health concepts as they read. Use the Foldable™ on page 31 or find more Foldables™ activities for the chapter on **Mental and Emotional Wellness** in the separate booklet, available in the TCR.

Lesson 1   A Healthy Self-Concept

Predicting Read aloud the introduction to the lesson on **Self-Concept**. Have students scan the rest of the lesson, paying attention to pictures, lists, and words in bold. Ask them to predict in writing one thing they think they will learn from reading this lesson. After students complete the reading, have them confirm or revise their predictions.

Lesson 2   Your Character Counts

Organizing Information Tell students that each boldface head is a main idea. The text under the head gives details about the main idea. Have students list each boldface head in Lesson 2 on the front of an index card. As students read each section on developing good character, have them write notes on the back of the index card.

Lesson 3   Expressing Emotions

Interactive Reading Have students write three questions on sticky notes regarding emotions. The questions should begin with why, how, where, or when. As they read about types of emotions and expressing emotions, they should use their questions to discuss the content with a partner.

Lesson 4   Coping with Stress

Double-entry Notes Have students fold a sheet of paper in half lengthwise. As they read **Strategies for Managing Stress** (pages 48–49) have them write the bold-faced headings on the left side. On the right side, they should make notes about the important ideas in each section as they read.

Lesson 5   Emotional Problems

Clarifying Text Have students read the section on **Anxiety Disorders, Mood Disorders,** and **Depression** (page 51). Ask: Are any of the concepts unclear? Write student responses on the board. Model ways to clarify the text, such as referring to the illustrations and definitions of terms to find supporting facts. Encourage volunteers who understand the concepts to explain them in their own words to the class.

Post Reading

Technology Based Presentations Have students describe strategies for maintaining mental and emotional wellness. Encourage students to develop a presentation of these concepts for younger students using a variety of media including technology, art, and music. Have them share their presentations with the class.

Key for Using the Teacher Wraparound Edition

Use this key to help you identify the different types of prompts found in the Teacher Wraparound Edition.

R **Reading Strategies** activities help you teach reading skills and vocabulary.

C **Critical Thinking** strategies help students apply and extend what they have learned.

U **Universal Access** activities provide differentiated instruction for students learning to speak English, along with suggestions for teaching various types of learners.

HS **Health Skills Practice** activities reinforce Health Skills concepts and help students apply these skills in their everyday lives.

W **Writing Support** activities provide writing opportunities to help students comprehend the text.

AL **Active Learning** strategies provide a variety of activities for presenting lesson content, including Quick Demos and engaging classroom projects that get students actively involved.

Key to Ability Levels

Teaching Strategies and activities have been coded for ability level and appropriateness

AL Activities for students working above grade level

OL Activities for students working on grade level

BL Activities for students working below grade level

EL Activities for English Learners

Symbols

⚬ Transparencies

⚬ CD-ROM

⚬ health.glencoe.com

⚬ Print Resources

Mental and Emotional Wellness

Chapter at a Glance

Lesson 1 examines self-concept, influences on self-concept, and ways to build positive self-concept.

Lesson 2 identifies the traits of good character, how character develops, and ways of showing good character.

Lesson 3 details various emotions, healthy ways to express feelings, and the importance of abstinence for teens.

Lesson 4 explains stress, the body's response to stress, and ways to manage stress.

Lesson 5 describes emotional problems, the warning signs of suicide, and sources of help for emotional problems.

R Reading Strategy

Interpreting the Photo
Tell students that they can often determine a person's feeling just by looking at the person. Ask students to name emotions displayed by the students in the photo. *Students may say the photo shows compassion, caring, or concern.* Have students explain how they were able to determine the emotions being expressed simply by looking at a picture. **OL**

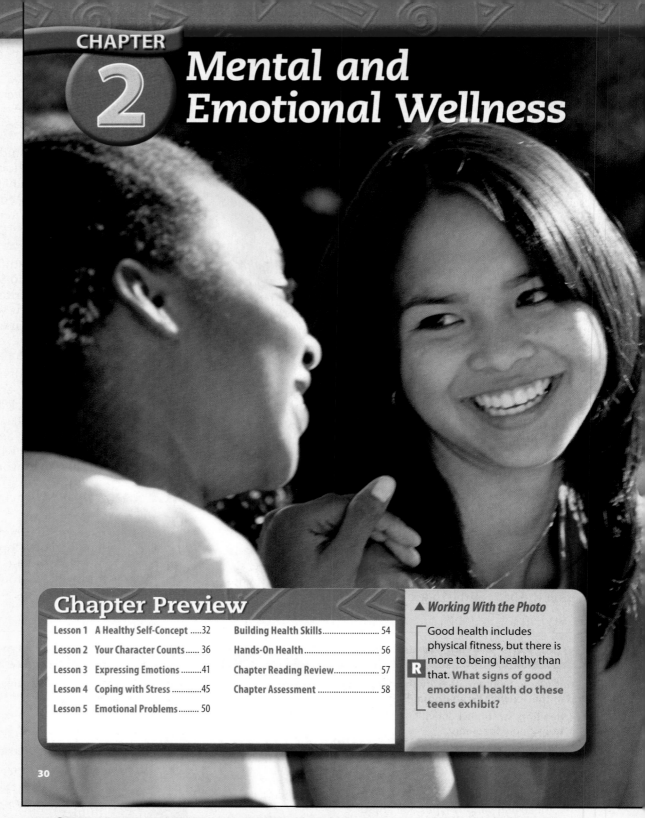

CHAPTER

2 Mental and Emotional Wellness

Chapter Preview

Lesson 1   A Healthy Self-Concept 32

Lesson 2   Your Character Counts 36

Lesson 3   Expressing Emotions 41

Lesson 4   Coping with Stress 45

Lesson 5   Emotional Problems 50

Building Health Skills........................ 54

Hands-On Health 56

Chapter Reading Review.................... 57

Chapter Assessment 58

▲ *Working With the Photo*

Good health includes physical fitness, but there is more to being healthy than that. **What signs of good emotional health do these teens exhibit?**

30

Universal Access

Differentiated Learning Glencoe provides teacher support and student materials for all learners in the health classroom.

- Spanish Glosario and chapter summaries for the English Language Learners.
- *Reading Tutor* and related worksheets supports reluctant readers.

- Universal Access strategies throughout the Teacher Wraparound Edition and Fast Files help you present materials for gifted students, at-risk students, physically impaired students and those with behavior disorders or learning disabilities.

Start-Up Activities

Before You Read Look at the Instant Message below. What would you tell Julie? Keep a record of your answer.

IM *Express*

KatieZ: Hey Jule, how's it going? Miss you! ☺

Julie33: It's OK-Stressed about the new school

FOLDABLES™ Study Organizer

As You Read Make this Foldable™ to record what you learn about positive self-concept in Lesson 1. Begin with a plain sheet of 8½" x 11" paper.

1 Fold the sheet of paper in half along the long axis.

2 Turn the paper and fold it into thirds.

3 Unfold and cut the top layer along both fold lines. This makes three tabs.

4 Draw two overlapping ovals, and label as shown.

Under the appropriate tab, take notes on what you learn about positive self-concept and high self-esteem. Under the middle tab, write down what the two have in common.

Health Online Visit health.glencoe.com and complete the Health Inventory for Chapter 2.

Lesson 1

FOCUS

Activating Prior Knowledge

What I Know Tell students that a person's strengths are things they do well. Have students brainstorm a list of qualities that they would consider to be strengths. *Examples might include being a good student, being a good friend, or having a positive attitude.*

 Guide to Reading

BUILDING VOCABULARY

- Have students use the Glossary/Glosario to find the meanings of the vocabulary terms. Have students write a sentence that shows a relationship between two of the terms.
- Use Vocabulary PuzzleMaker to reinforce vocabulary terms.

READING STRATEGY

 Have students use their Foldables™ as they read Lesson 1.
- **Graphic Organizer** Do a sample concept map on the board with the class to help students get started.

 Quick Write

Have students write a job application letter describing two of their strengths. If students have difficulty thinking of strengths, remind them of those mentioned in the Activating Prior Knowledge activity.

32

Lesson 1

A Healthy Self-Concept

Guide to Reading

Building Vocabulary
Two of the terms below share a common word part. In your notebook, write a definition for each based on what you believe the term means. Revise your definitions as you read the lesson.

- self-concept (p. 32)
- reinforce (p. 33)
- self-esteem (p. 34)
- resilience (p. 34)

Focusing on the Main Ideas
In this lesson, you will learn to
- **explain** what your self-concept is.
- **identify** influences on your self-concept.
- **describe** how you can build a positive self-concept.

Reading Strategy
Analyzing a Graphic Using the diagram to the right as a guide, create a concept map that shows influences on your self-concept.

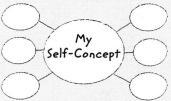

FOLDABLES Study Organizer Use the Foldable™ on p. 31 as you read this lesson.

 Quick Write

Imagine that you are applying for a job. Write a brief letter to the employer describing your strengths.

What Is Self-Concept?

"Is *that* what I sound like?" Theo asked. He was listening to a recording of his voice. Have you ever heard your own voice played back? Other people hear us differently from how we hear ourselves. The same is true of how we see ourselves. Each of us has a different self-concept. Your **self-concept** is *the view you have of yourself.* It may or may not mirror the way other people see you. This much is clear: Having a positive self-concept is an important part of good mental/emotional health.

◀ Also known as self-image, self-concept is your view of your abilities, skills, and talents. **Why is having a positive self-concept important?**

Lesson 1 Resources

📁 **Chapter *FAST FILE* Resources**
Guided Reading and Writing 2-1
Concept Mapping Activity 2-1
Cross-Curriculum Activity 2-1
Reteaching Activity 2-1
Enrichment Activity 2-1
Lesson Quiz 2-1

Technology
- Transparency 2-1
- Audio Summaries
- *ExamView*
- Vocabulary PuzzleMaker
- StudentWorks™ Plus

How Does Self-Concept Develop?

Your self-concept starts forming when you are very young. Parents or guardians are the first and greatest influence. How they speak to you and treat you have a lasting effect. Grandparents, sisters, brothers, and relatives have an effect too.

Your skills and abilities also shape your self-concept. You may see yourself as a good basketball player or a good singer. You may feel you are good at writing stories but average in math. How you view your talents and abilities influences your overall self-concept. Focus on your strengths rather than your weaknesses. When you focus on your weaknesses, you may begin to feel that you are not good at anything. Instead, identify what you do well and what you enjoy doing. This will help you develop a positive self-concept. Seeing yourself in a positive way will help you feel good about yourself.

Family members, friends, and teachers **reinforce,** or *support*, your self-concept through messages. Some of the messages from people around you are spoken or written. Others take the form of looks or gestures. "Way to go!" is an example of a positive word message. Can you think of a look or gesture that carries the same idea?

Positive messages help you develop a positive self-concept. You may think you did well on a school project. Having your parent or teacher tell you that you did a good job reinforces your belief. Keep in mind that sending positive messages is a two-way street. When you support others, they are likely to support you, too.

▶ Messages from others influence your self-concept. These messages may be spoken, written, or communicated through looks or gestures. **What is the message being sent by the gesture pictured here?**

DEVELOPING

Good Character

A Positive Home Environment

A healthy home environment will positively affect your self-concept. You can help create a healthy home environment by being patient with family members and helping them when they need it. **How can you help create a healthy family setting?**

TEACH

DEVELOPING

Good Character

A Positive Home Environment
Discuss attitudes found in a positive home environment, for example cheerfulness and kindness. Have volunteers share their answers to the question in the feature. List their responses on the board. Discuss ways their actions impact their home environment.

R **Reading Strategy**

Finding the Main Idea Ask for a volunteer to define the term *self-concept*. Then ask how a person develops a positive self-concept. **OL**

C **Critical Thinking**

Analyzing Have students brainstorm the kinds of verbal and nonverbal messages they send to each other. Remind students that the messages they send to others can affect the other person's self-concept in positive or negative ways. **AL**

Dealing with Sensitive Issues

Positive Support System The role of parents and guardians in the development of self-esteem and self-concept can be challenging to those students who have a difficult home environment. Be sure to stress that positive self-esteem and self-concept can be nurtured by those outside the home, for example teachers, friends, and community role models. Without singling out individuals, have students brainstorm sources of positive feedback for those who do not receive encouragement or nurturing in their home environment.

Caption Answers

Photo Caption, p. 32 A positive self-concept is an important part of good mental/emotional health.
Photo Caption, p. 33 *Sample Answer:* "Good Job!"

Health Skills Activity

Analyzing Influences

How Do the Media Influence Your Self-Concept?

Use the following to help students complete the activity.

- Provide magazines, video clips, and other media for students. Encourage students to collect other images from home that might influence a teen's self-concept.
- Have each group discuss the messages contained in their examples.
- Each group should select one image to share with the class. After the group members discuss the message in their media example, encourage class discussion.
- After each group has shared, have a class discussion of the following questions: What kinds of messages were present most often in the media examples? Why is it important for teens to be aware of the messages present in media? *So they will understand how the media influences decisions.*

Health Skills Activity

Analyzing Influences

How Do the Media Influence Your Self-Concept?
One factor that affects your self-concept is the media. Think about the images you see on television or in movies. They often show attractive people having fun. Some teens try to look and act like the people they see on-screen. They may feel this will improve their self-concept. It's important to recognize the ways in which media messages influence the way you feel about yourself.

With a Group
Collect pictures, video clips, or descriptions of images from the media. Analyze the message each sends.

Self-Concept and Self-Esteem

Do you like and respect yourself? Do you have confidence to try new things? If you do, you have high self-esteem. Your **self-esteem** is *a measure of how much you like and respect yourself.* Your self-esteem is closely related to your self-concept. Having a positive self-concept will help you build a high level of self-esteem. When you have high self-esteem, you feel good about yourself. You have confidence in what you do and have a positive outlook. You come to new challenges with a "can-do" attitude. When things go wrong, you are resilient. **Resilience** is *the ability to work through and recover from disappointment.* Being resilient helps you cope with failure in a positive way. For example, imagine that you try out for one of the lead parts in the school play. You are disappointed when you find out you didn't get the part. If you are resilient, you won't let this disappointment stop you. Try out for a smaller part or even volunteer to help backstage.

◀ Resiliency is your ability to bounce back from difficulties. **Why is this an important ability? How can a person become more resilient?**

TECHNOLOGY AND HEALTH

Electronic Portfolios Work with students to create electronic portfolios. Electronic portfolios can include Word documents, video clips, scanned images and multimedia projects. Students' collections of media messages in the Health Skills Activity on this page is an excellent project to include. When student work demonstrates mastery of a particular state or school district standard, provide a link to the Web page listing the standard. Guidelines for creating electronic portfolios are available online.

Developing a Positive Self-Concept

Developing a positive self-concept is an important part of emotional health. To develop a positive view of yourself, list your strengths and weaknesses. Focus on what you do well. This gives you the confidence you need to try new things. Here are some other suggestions:

- Have confidence in yourself and your abilities.
- Accept encouragement; use it to recognize your strengths.
- Set a goal and work to reach it. This will give you a sense of accomplishment.
- Develop realistic expectations. Remember that no one is perfect.
- Find friends that support and encourage you.
- Avoid worrying about hurtful remarks or looks. Put them behind you and move on.

 **Reading Check** **Explain** Give three suggestions for improving your self-concept.

Health Online

Visit **health.glencoe.com** and complete the Interactive Study Guide for Lesson 1.

Lesson 1 Review

 After You Read

Review this lesson for new terms, major headings, and Reading Checks.

What I Learned

1. *Vocabulary* Define the terms *self-concept* and *self-esteem.* Write a sentence that includes both terms.

2. *Identify* What is resilience?

3. *Give Examples* Name three ways to improve your self-concept.

Thinking Critically

4. *Analyze* How might having a high level of self-esteem help you set goals for the future?

5. *Apply* Yolanda didn't make the soccer team. She was disappointed, but decided to try out again next season. Does Yolanda have a positive self-concept? Why or why not?

Applying Health Skills

6. *Goal Setting* List three things you do well. Set a goal to improve one of these strengths during the next week. Follow your plan carefully. Then write a paragraph describing the results.

Health Online For more review questions for Lesson 1, go to **health.glencoe.com**.

Lesson 1: A Healthy Self-Concept **35**

FOCUS

Activating Prior Knowledge

What I Know Ask students to describe two qualities of a person with good character. Tell students that in this lesson they will learn why character is important.

Guide to Reading

BUILDING VOCABULARY

- Have students skim the lesson for the definition of each vocabulary term. Have students write each term on the front of an index card and the definition on the back of the card.
- Use Vocabulary PuzzleMaker to reinforce vocabulary terms.

READING STRATEGY

Predicting Each student should generate a question after reading the heads in the lesson. After completing the lesson, check to be sure students have answered their questions.

uick Write

Have students write a paragraph describing two good deeds they did this month. Remind students that they can describe good deeds they carried out at home, at school, or in the community.

Your Character Counts

Guide to Reading

● **Building Vocabulary**
List each term below in your notebook. As you come across it in your reading, write the definition.

- character (p. 36)
- advocacy (p. 38)
- role model (p. 39)

● **Focusing on the Main Ideas**
In this lesson, you will learn to

- **identify** the traits of good character.
- **explain** how character develops.
- **list** ways of showing good character.

● **Reading Strategy**
Predicting Look over the headings in this lesson. Write a question that you think the lesson will answer. After reading, check to see if your question was answered.

uick Write

Make a list of the good deeds you did this month. Then describe two of them in a paragraph.

What Is Character?

Do you help out with chores at home? Are you honest? Do you help others when you can?

If you truthfully answered yes to these questions, you probably have good character. **Character** is *the way you think, feel, and act.* Your character is reflected in your attitudes, views, and words. Do you recall reading about values in Chapter 1? Your character is an outward expression of your inner values. It's an important part of your relationships and the choices you make.

◄ Keeping an open mind helps you grow as a person. It gives you a chance to see the world through someone else's eyes. **How can being open-minded positively affect your health?**

Lesson 2 Resources

📁 **Chapter FAST FILE Resources**
Guided Reading and Writing 2-2
Concept Mapping Activity 2-2
Cross-Curriculum Activity 2-2
Reteaching Activity 2-2
Enrichment Activity 2-2
Lesson Quiz 2-2

Technology
🔌 Transparency 2-2
💿 Audio Summaries
💿 *ExamView*
💿 Vocabulary PuzzleMaker
💿 StudentWorks™ Plus

People with good character are loyal to their friends. They respect others and their property. They try to keep an open mind to ideas and views different from their own. People with good character do not cheat or lie. They do not take credit for someone else's work.

Your character affects your physical, mental/emotional, and social health. Taking care of your body shows that you have respect for your physical health. When you act responsibly and follow safety rules, you are protecting your physical health. When you are kind to others you feel good about yourself. This strengthens your mental/emotional health. Good character also improves your social health. Being fair and honest helps you get along well with others. You can build strong relationships by treating others with respect and understanding.

▲ Caring for younger brothers or sisters is a sign of good character. **What are some other ways to demonstrate good character?**

 **Explain** What is character?

Traits of Good Character

There are six main character traits. They are *trustworthiness, respect, responsibility, fairness, caring,* and *citizenship.* Developing these character traits will help you communicate care, consideration, and acceptance of self and others.

Trustworthiness

HS People who are trustworthy are reliable—they keep the promises they make. For example, if a teen promises his parents to be home on time, he keeps his word. People who are trustworthy are also honest.

Respect

U Demonstrating respect means showing regard for other people, for property, and for authority. This involves treating others the way you'd like them to treat you.

TEACH

Reading Check

Answer Character is the way you think, feel, and act.

HS Health Skills Practice

Communication Skills Have students work in small groups to write and perform a short role-play that demonstrates the character trait of trustworthiness. Use the role-plays to generate class discussion about the importance of trustworthiness. **AL**

U Universal Access

Different Learning Styles Explain that showing respect and accepting responsibility for one's actions is an important part of having good character. Have students discuss the following scenario: While playing hockey, Nate accidentally breaks his friend's hockey stick. Ask students to describe how Nate could demonstrate respect for his friend's property and take responsibility for his mistake. *Students may say he should tell his friend right away.* **AL**

What Teens Want to Know

How can I earn my parents' trust? Teens can use communication skills to strengthen their relationship with parents. The six traits of good character can be used to help a student earn or maintain their parents' trust. Offer the following suggestions to students struggling with this issue: Respect your parents—they are trying to keep you safe and healthy; show responsibility for your actions; be trustworthy and reliable; show fairness and caring toward others.

Caption Answers

Photo Caption, p. 36 It can help improve relationships.
Photo Caption, p. 37 by keeping your word

AL Active Learning

Quick Demo Announce a (fictional) surprise quiz. State that students sitting on the left half of the room will be allowed to use their textbooks during the quiz, while students on the right half of the room cannot use their textbooks. Students will immediately point out that this is not fair. Use this demo to highlight one of the traits of good character—treating people fairly. **OL**

C Critical Thinking

Applying Concepts Ask students to brainstorm ways that teens can practice advocacy in their school and in their community. Have students think of examples of teens they have read about who have served as advocates, for example, a student who participated in a fun-run to raise money for a healthy cause. **OL**

Reading Check

Answer Trustworthiness, Respect, Responsibility, Fairness, Caring, Citizenship

Caption Answer

Photo Caption obeying laws; following rules

▲ Helping to keep your community clean is an example of good citizenship. **What are some other examples of good citizenship?**

Responsibility

Accepting responsibility means being willing to take on duties or tasks. It also means being willing to accept blame for mistakes you have made. A responsible person accepts the consequences of his or her actions and decisions.

Fairness

When you were young, you were taught to take turns and share your toys. You were taught fairness. Being fair means treating everyone equally and honestly. A fair person judges a contest on the basis of talent. She or he doesn't just award first prize to a friend in the contest.

Fairness also includes being a good sport. It means knowing how to accept defeat when you lose and not showing off when you win.

Caring

Caring means treating others with understanding. Caring people are kind and consider the feelings of others. They try to help others when they can. Show that you care about others. Make an effort to welcome new students to your school. Listen to a friend when he or she needs you.

Citizenship

Being a good citizen means following rules and obeying laws. Good citizens also take action to make their community better. This is called advocacy. **Advocacy** is *taking a stand to make a difference.*

Reading Check **Recall** Name and define three traits of good character.

How Does Character Develop?

Your character is shaped by your family and others around you. It is also influenced by your experiences in life and your values.

Family members are often the first teachers of character. Through their words and actions, they help you develop your

---

🏠 Home, School, and Community

In the Community Explain to students that good citizenship requires people to take actions to make their school or community a better or safer place. Point out the figure on this page that shows students picking up litter. Ask students to brainstorm other problems in their school or community.

Have students write a letter to the principal, the student council, or the editor of the local newspaper explaining the problem in their community and a plan to address the problem. Post students' letters on a display or bulletin board.

own values. For example, your family may volunteer to help others in need. This teaches you to be a good citizen. You also learn responsibility at home. Doing chores or helping younger siblings with homework teaches responsibility. Being kind and helpful are ways that family members show they care about each other.

 As you grow older, you learn from experience. Sports and games teach the importance of fairness and of following rules. At school you learn responsibility. You are responsible for getting your work done and in on time. School also teaches respect for authority.

Reading Check Explain Who are the first teachers of character?

Role Models

 One of the most important ways in which you learn character and values is by watching and listening to others. You learn by their examples. Some of these people may become positive role models for you. A **role model** is *a person whose success or behavior serves as a good example for others*. Parents or guardians are among the most important role models for their children.

Connect To...
Language Arts

The Idea of Character

The word character comes from a Greek word meaning "mark or engrave." Look up the word character in a dictionary.

What other meanings do you find? How are they related?

Connect To...
Language Arts

The Idea of Character
Many of the definitions students find will relate to distinctive qualities—those that that define a person as an individual. Discuss some of the different meanings that students identify.

Reading Check

Answer Family members are the first teachers of character.

▼ Team players demonstrate character through good sportsmanship. **What are some ways that team sports help build character?**

Lesson 2: Your Character Counts **39**

HS Health Skills Practice

Analyzing Influences Have students name activities and experiences that shape their characters. List their responses on the board. Then have them list the attributes of character that are developed by each item. **OL**

R Reading Strategy

Word Meaning Discuss with students the definition of *role model*. Ask for a volunteer to explain the term *model*. *An example to be followed or imitated.* **BL**

Cultural Perspectives

Competition and Character Participation in sports has been a cultural phenomenon in societies around the world. Sports are an excellent way to build character. However, the nature of youth sports has changed dramatically over the past decades.

Competition is often emphasized over cooperation, even in sports for preteens. Competitive sports are also a source of stress for many students. Have students brainstorm positive and negative effects of trends in competitive sports for youth.

Caption Answer

Photo Caption Team sports teach the importance of fairness and following the rules.

TV Character

After identifying TV role models, allow students to discuss the positive traits these characters possess.

ASSESS

Assessment Resources

Lesson Review Quiz
* *ExamView*
* Fast Files Activities
* Online Quizzes and Activities

Reteaching

* Assign Concept Map 2-2 or Reteaching Activity 2-2 in the Fast Files. 📁
* Have students work in pairs to review the traits of good character, found on page 37.

Enrichment

* Assign Enrichment Activity 2-2 in the Fast Files. 📁
* Have students write and illustrate a book appropriate for students in grades 1 and 2 that tells about one character trait.

CLOSE

Ask volunteers to describe examples of individuals who demonstrate qualities of good character.

MediaWatch

TV Character

Many TV programs feature teens who show positive character traits. These teens can be considered good role models.

Name three examples of positive teen role models from your favorite TV shows.

Health *Online*

Visit **health.glencoe.com** and complete the Interactive Study Guide for Lesson 2.

Character in Action

Good character is not something you feel or show once in a while. It is part of who you are. It is a way of living. By having good character, you promote your own health and the health of others. You feel good about yourself and are able to make responsible decisions. At the same time, you set a good example for others to follow.

At home, you can demonstrate good character by showing respect for your parents and other family members. Be honest with them. Listen when they talk to you. Show responsibility by getting up on time for school and by doing your chores. Let your family members know that you care about them. Work out your differences calmly and peacefully.

At school or during other activities, you can show you have good character by being a good citizen. Work together with others to advocate for healthy individuals, families, and communities. Follow school or other rules. Help to keep your school and community clean. Show respect for teachers, other adults, and students. Be honest—don't cheat on your schoolwork. In sports, play fair and responsibly.

Lesson 2 Review

After You Read

Review this lesson for new terms, major headings, and Reading Checks.

What I Learned

1. *Vocabulary* Define *character*. What are the six character traits?

2. *Recall* What is advocacy?

3. *Explain* Tell how role models can shape a person's character.

Thinking Critically

4. *Evaluate* Give an example of how good character might influence your health.

5. *Analyze* How is making responsible decisions related to good character?

6. *Synthesize* Give two examples of how life experiences might have a positive influence on character.

Applying Health Skills

7. *Communication Skills* Write a short story about a teen faced with a difficult choice. Tell how he or she demonstrates good character in making a decision.

Health *Online* For more review questions for Lesson 2, go to **health.glencoe.com**.

Lesson 2 Review Answers

1. Character is the way you think, feel, and act. Trustworthiness, respect, responsibility, fairness, caring, and citizenship.
2. Advocacy is taking a stand to make a difference.

3. Role models shape a person's character by setting a good example.
4. If you have good character, you will show self-respect by making healthy choices in food and physical activity, for example.
5. A person with good character takes responsibility for his or her decisions.

6. Examples may include parents demonstrating good manners; having a good friend.
7. Students' stories should describe a teen making a difficult choice, for example, whether to quit the track team.

Expressing Emotions

Guide to Reading

● **Building Vocabulary**
Read each of the words. If the word is familiar, write down what you think its meaning is. If it's not, guess at its meaning using word clues. These include word parts, such as *ab-*, meaning "from."

- emotions (p. 41)
- hormones (p. 41)
- abstinence (p. 44)

● **Focusing on the Main Ideas**
In this lesson, you will learn to

- **explain** what causes the emotions we experience.
- **express** strong feelings healthfully.
- **discuss** why abstinence is important for teens.

● **Reading Strategy**
Identifying Cause and Effect As you read, think about examples of each emotion described. Identify a possible cause of this emotion in your daily life.

Your Emotions

What are you feeling right now? Maybe you are feeling happy about some good news that you got today. Maybe you are feeling down. You may even be having several different emotions at once. **Emotions** are *feelings such as joy, love, or fear.* Your emotions affect all sides of your health triangle.

What Causes Emotions?

Emotions are often triggered by daily events. You are passed over for a part in the class play and feel sad. Your friend returns a borrowed jacket with a rip and you feel angry.

During your teen years, another emotional trigger is at work. It is deep inside you and beyond your control. Have you had days lately where you feel "up" one minute, "down" the next? These mood shifts are related to your body's release of hormones (HOR·mohnz). **Hormones** are *powerful chemicals, produced by glands, which regulate many body functions.* These hormones are preparing your body for adulthood. The emotional swings hormones cause can be confusing or even scary. If you've had these feelings, relax. Mood swings are part of growing up.

Reading Check
Explain What are hormones? How do they affect emotions during the teen years?

Quick Write

List five ways you show you're happy. Now list five ways you show you're angry. Which feeling do you find easier to express? What does this tell you?

Lesson 3: Expressing Emotions **41**

FOCUS

Activating Prior Knowledge

What I Know Ask "How do you know when another person is happy or angry?" In this lesson students will learn more about emotions.

Guide to Reading

BUILDING VOCABULARY
- Have students find the definition and write a sentence using each of the terms.
- Use Vocabulary PuzzleMaker to reinforce vocabulary terms.

READING STRATEGY
Cause and Effect Have students list each emotion described in the lesson. Then have them list a cause of that emotion. Allow students to keep these lists private.

Quick Write

Have students list five ways to show happiness and five ways to show anger. Ask for volunteers to share their lists.

Reading Check

Answer Hormones are chemicals that regulate many body functions. Hormones can cause emotional mood swings.

Academic Vocabulary

Release On this page, students learn that mood shifts are caused by the body's release of hormones. The word *release* means to let go or discharge.

Lesson 3 Resources

Chapter *Fast File* **Resources**
Guided Reading and Writing 2-3
Concept-Mapping Activity 2-3
Decision-Making Activity 2-3
Reteaching Activity 2-3
Enrichment Activity 2-3
Lesson Quiz 2-3

Technology
- Transparency 2-3
- Audio Summaries
- *ExamView*
- Vocabulary PuzzleMaker
- StudentWorks™ Plus

TEACH

AL Active Learning

Collage Have students work in small groups to create a collage of emotions. Provide students with magazines, markers, poster board, and glue. First have groups decide which emotion(s) they will display. Then have them brainstorm a list of creative ways the emotion can be demonstrated—either through images of facial expressions or other ways that might include words, pictures, colors, for example. Display collages in the classroom and allow time to discuss the emotions shown. **OL**

HS Health Skills Practice

Practicing Healthful Behaviors Have small groups of students write and perform a role play that shows healthful ways of expressing strong emotions. Instruct students to use the strategies mentioned in the lesson: Stop and think about what you are feeling and why; engage in physical activity; talk with people you trust; create something; listen to music. **OL**

▶ Mood swings can feel as if you are riding an emotional roller coaster. **What is the cause of mood swings during the teen years?**

Types of Emotions

AL Some emotions, such as happiness, are pleasant to experience. Other feelings, while less enjoyable, are still normal. Every person feels angry or afraid at one time or another. These emotions aren't good or bad—they just *are*. An important part of good mental/emotional health is learning how to handle your emotions in healthy ways.

Understanding Your Emotions

HS The first step in responding healthfully to a strong or difficult emotion is understanding what you're feeling. Sometimes, you know exactly what you are feeling and why. Other times, it's easy to confuse one emotion with another. This is especially true of anger. Strong words like "I hate you!" often mean "I'm angry with you." When you feel a strong emotion, take a moment to stop and think about what you are feeling and why. Try to focus on what is bothering you or making you angry. Ask yourself: What am I really reacting to? Am I angry because I feel hurt or disappointed? Once you understand your feelings, you can learn to manage them in healthy ways.

Caption Answer

Photo Caption Mood swings during the teen years are caused by hormones.

HEALTH LITERACY

Emotions, Hormones, and Steroids When discussing the dramatic effect of hormones on the teen body in this lesson, tie in the dangers of anabolic steroid use. Teens may not realize that anabolic steroids are hormones. Those used to improve athletic performance are artificially synthesized forms of testosterone, a hormone that occurs naturally in both males and females. Hormones, including anabolic steroids, have effects on the entire body. Anabolic steroids have dangerous side-effects, including aggressive behavior, acne, liver cancer, and baldness.

Expressing Your Emotions

Expressing your emotions healthfully is an important strategy for dealing with strong feelings. It is also important to effectively express feelings and opinions on health issues. Holding emotions inside can harm all sides of your health triangle. It can lead to stomachaches and headaches. It can make it hard to focus on what you are doing. Keeping your feelings inside can also have a negative effect on your relationships. It is better to let emotions out, especially strong ones. For instance, suppose you are angry or upset with someone. Pause for a moment and take a deep breath. Think of words that will express your true feelings without being hurtful. Then calmly tell the other person how you feel. For example, Cara was angry when her friend Jen called to cancel their plans. Cara took a moment to breathe slowly and deeply. She realized that she felt hurt because she and Jen hadn't been spending much time together lately. She called Jen back and they talked calmly about the situation. Cara felt much better afterward.

There are many other healthful strategies for dealing with strong or difficult feelings. These include the following:

- Engage in physical activity. This can help relieve tension.
- Talk with family members or friends. They can provide help and support.
- Create something, such as a drawing or poem.
- Listen to music. This can help you relax.

Reading Check

Explain Is keeping feelings inside a good idea? Why or why not?

▶ Listening to music is one good way to manage strong feelings. **Name two other ways to express emotions healthfully.**

Health *Online*

Topic: Managing Strong Emotions

Visit health.glencoe.com for Student Web Activities on identifying and expressing your emotions.

Activity: Using the information provided at the link above, write down four healthful ways you can manage strong emotions.

Health *Online*

Have students create fact sheets using the online resources provided at **health.glencoe.com**. Encourage students to work in pairs to review the health information and develop fact sheets on positive ways to manage strong emotions. **EL**

AL Active Learning

Survey Students While students perform their role-plays in the Health Skills Practice, keep the other students actively involved. Prepare in advance a short survey to encourage audience participation. Possible questions for the survey include: What emotion is being expressed? How does the character deal with this emotion in a healthful manner?

W Writing Support

Creating Poems Have students generate a poem that describes an emotion. Remind them that not all poetry has to rhyme. Have students carefully choose words to express the emotion they have chosen. **AL**

Reading Check

Answer No. Holding your emotions inside can be harmful to your health.

Caption Answer

Photo Caption engaging in physical activity or creating a poem

⟨ Promoting Coordinated School Health

Sources of Help for Teens Develop a list of types of resources available for teens who feel troubled or confused by their emotions. School nurses, counselors, trusted teachers, administrators, and staff can all serve as resources for students. Parent and community involvement is an essential component of a coordinated school health program. Be certain to include parents, guardians, and trusted community members as possible types of resources. Post the list in a location that is accessible to all students.

Reading Check

Answer Practicing abstinence requires good decisions to avoid health-risk behaviors.

ASSESS

Assessment Resources

Lesson Review Quiz
- *ExamView*
- Fast Files Activities
- Online Quizzes and Activities

Reteaching

- Assign Concept Map 2-3 or Reteaching Activity 2-3 in the Fast Files.
- Have students work in pairs to review the main ideas for Lesson 3, page 41.

Enrichment

- Assign Enrichment Activity 2-3 in the Fast Files.
- Have students create a comic strip that shows a character expressing emotions in a healthy way.

CLOSE

Ask students what they have learned about emotions and their effects on health-risk behaviors.

Practicing Abstinence

Everyone has basic emotional needs. These include the need to be loved and accepted. Some teens try to fill their emotional needs by participating in risky behavior. They may join gangs. Some may use tobacco, alcohol, or illegal drugs. Others become sexually active. These behaviors do not really meet emotional needs. Dealing with emotions in healthy ways includes saying no to high-risk behaviors like these.

Abstinence (AB·stuh·nuhns) is *not participating in high-risk behaviors*. Abstinence is a strategy for avoiding harmful situations. It protects your health and the health of others. Being abstinent tells others you refuse to take part in unsafe behaviors. It also shows you have self-control. You will learn more about the value of abstinence in Chapter 3 and Chapter 8.

Health Online

Visit health.glencoe.com and complete the Interactive Study Guide for Lesson 3.

 Reading Check **Discuss** How is abstinence related to making good decisions?

Lesson 3 Review

 After You Read

Review this lesson for new terms, major headings, and Reading Checks.

What I Learned

1. *Vocabulary* Define the word *emotion*, and use it in a sentence.

2. *Explain* Why are mood swings common during the teen years?

3. *Identify* What are two strategies for expressing emotions healthfully?

Thinking Critically

4. *Analyze* How might expressing emotions affect your social health?

5. *Apply* You are angry because your brother or sister has borrowed your headphones without asking. Explain how you will deal with your emotions.

6. *Summarize* What might you say to someone who tried to fill his or her emotional needs by participating in high-risk behaviors?

Applying Health Skills

7. *Practicing Healthful Behaviors* Describe how abstinence can help you avoid harmful situations.

Health Online For more review questions for Lesson 3, go to **health.glencoe.com**.

Lesson 3 Review Answers

1. An emotion is a feeling, such as joy, love, or fear. *Sample sentence:* The emotion I felt was fear.
2. Mood swings in the teen years are caused by changing hormones.
3. Any two: Stop and think about what you are feeling and why; engage in physical activity, talk to people you trust, create something, listen to music.
4. *Sample answer:* Expressing your emotions can allow you to resolve conflicts peacefully.
5. Take time to think about why you are angry and talk to your sibling calmly.
6. *Sample answer:* Protect your health by making choices that keep you safe.
7. *Sample answer:* Abstinence is the practice of avoiding high-risk behaviors.

Lesson 4

Coping with Stress

Guide to Reading

● Building Vocabulary
As you read this lesson, write each new highlighted term and its definition in your notebook.

■ stress (p. 45)
■ anxiety (p. 46)
■ adrenaline (p. 47)

● Focusing on the Main Ideas
In this lesson, you will learn to

■ **explain** what stress is.
■ **describe** how your body responds to stress.
■ **list** ways to manage stress.

● Reading Strategy
Finding the Main Idea Copy each main heading in the lesson. For each, write one sentence that states the main idea.

What Is Stress?

Sonya has to give an oral report in class. Her mouth feels dry, and her palms are sweaty. Her stomach feels like butterflies are fluttering around inside it. Alex is on the soccer team. The championship game is coming up, so he's been at practice every night this week. He also has a big test to study for and a major project due. Lately Alex has been having trouble sleeping. He's been lying awake thinking about all the things he has to do. Whenever he worries about how he's going to get everything done, his heart starts to race. Sonya and Alex are feeling stress. **Stress** is *your body's response to changes around you*. Everyone feels stress from time to time—it's a normal part of life. Stress can give you energy and help you get things done. However, stress that continues over a long period of time can harm your physical, mental/emotional, and social health. While you can't always avoid stress, you can learn strategies for managing stress. This is an important part of staying healthy.

Quick Write

Write about a stressful situation you have been in and how you dealt with the stress.

▶ Stress is a part of life. **What are some examples of stressful events?**

Lesson 4 Resources

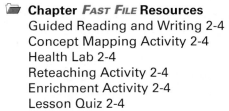

📁 **Chapter *FAST FILE* Resources**
Guided Reading and Writing 2-4
Concept Mapping Activity 2-4
Health Lab 2-4
Reteaching Activity 2-4
Enrichment Activity 2-4
Lesson Quiz 2-4

Technology
🔦 Transparency 2-4
💿 Audio Summaries
💿 *ExamView*
💿 Vocabulary PuzzleMaker
💿 StudentWorks™ Plus

Lesson 4

FOCUS

Activating Prior Knowledge

What I Know Ask students to describe the first thing that comes to their mind when they hear the term *stressful situation*. Explain that in this lesson students will learn ways to manage stress.

Guide to Reading

BUILDING VOCABULARY
■ Have students use the Glossary/Glosario to find the definition of each vocabulary term. Then, have students write a definition for each term using their own words. Ask for volunteers to share their definitions with the class.
■ Use Vocabulary PuzzleMaker to reinforce vocabulary terms. 🖱

READING STRATEGY
Main Idea Check that students have copied each main heading in the lesson. Have students brainstorm ways to find the main idea of a section. After students have completed the lesson, ask for volunteers to share the main idea of each section.

Quick Write

Have students write about a stressful situation a teen might experience. How might he or she deal with the stress. Ask for volunteers to share what they have written with the class.

TEACH

U Universal Access

Learning Disabled Organize the lesson in an outline format. Use the major headings in the lesson as the main ideas (Sources of Stress, Types of Stress). Use one or two bullet points under each heading. Model outlining for students:

1. Sources of Stress
   a. small events
      • forgetting something
   b. major events
      • moving
      • starting new school
   c. anxiety
      • worrying BL

HS Health Skills Practice

Goal Setting Tell students that positive stress can help them to reach their goals. Have students identify one health-related goal, such as improving performance in their favorite sport. Have them fold a piece of paper into three horizontal sections. In the top section, have students write their goal. In the middle section, have students list steps to reach their goals, for example, by increasing their practice time. In the bottom section, have students record ways in which positive stress might help them achieve their goals. OL

Caption Answer

Photo Caption Use the extra energy to accomplish a goal.

▶ Positive stress gives athletes the motivation they need to perform. **How can you use positive stress to your own benefit?**

Sources of Stress

U Many different things can cause stress. It can result from small events, like forgetting your locker combination. Stress can also come from major events. These include life-changing situations—for example, moving to a new city or starting a new school. People sometimes respond to stressful events with anxiety. **Anxiety** is *feelings of uncertainty or worry over what may happen.*

People may view different events as stressful. You may feel stress when trying out for a part in the school play. Your friend may find this situation exciting rather than stressful. What has happened to you in the past may affect your views on what is stressful. For example, maybe you forgot some of your lines when performing in the school play. This might make you more anxious in similar situations. Your beliefs, attitudes, and values also influence what you think of as stressful.

Types of Stress

HS Stress can be positive or negative. For example, Jay was really excited about the race. When the signal to start sounded, he felt a burst of energy and took the lead. Jay was experiencing what is known as *positive stress.* Positive stress has many benefits. It can help you reach goals and accomplish tasks. It also provides needed energy to help you escape danger.

TECHNOLOGY AND HEALTH

Digital Tools to Ease Stress Students can feel stress when busy schedules do not allow time for studying, family activities, or relaxation. Today's teens may not recognize how much more efficient many tasks have become with recent advances in technology. People use these tools to make better use of their time, such as cell phones and e-mail to keep in touch with family and friends, PDAs for keeping assignments and reminders, and the Internet for quick research. Ask students to add examples of ways technology can be used to relieve stress.

Negative stress gets in your way and holds you back. Sources of negative stress are often out of your control. They may include problems at home or school. Too much negative stress can be unhealthy.

 **Reading Check** **Analyze** Compare and contrast positive and negative stress. Give an example of each.

The Stress Response

The stress response is how nature prepares the body to deal with threats of harm. This is also known as the *fight-or-flight response*. Your body is preparing to *fight* the threat or take *flight* from it. During the stress response, your body undergoes a series of physical changes, which are summarized in **Figure 2.1.**

 **Reading Check** **Recall** Name two physical changes that occur during the fight-or-flight response.

▼ FIGURE 2.1

THE FIGHT-OR-FLIGHT RESPONSE

This illustration shows some of the physical changes stress can cause.

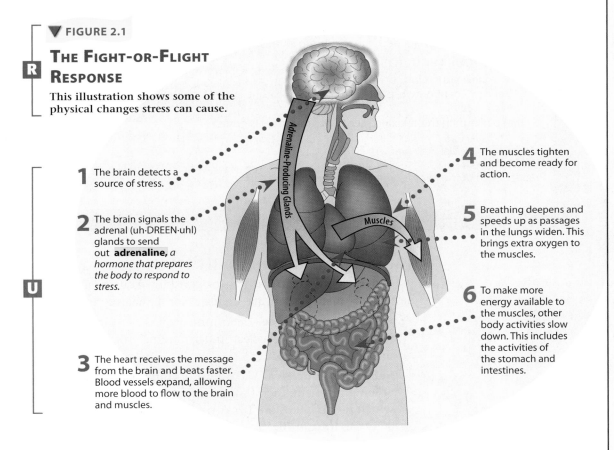

1 The brain detects a source of stress.

2 The brain signals the adrenal (uh·DREEN·uhl) glands to send out **adrenaline,** *a hormone that prepares the body to respond to stress.*

3 The heart receives the message from the brain and beats faster. Blood vessels expand, allowing more blood to flow to the brain and muscles.

4 The muscles tighten and become ready for action.

5 Breathing deepens and speeds up as passages in the lungs widen. This brings extra oxygen to the muscles.

6 To make more energy available to the muscles, other body activities slow down. This includes the activities of the stomach and intestines.

Lesson 4: Coping with Stress **47**

HEALTH LITERACY

Alcohol and Other Drugs Remind students that using alcohol or other drugs is not a healthy way to cope with stress. Encourage student discussion by asking: What additional short- and long-term problems will drug or alcohol use create? List student responses on the board. Then ask: Do these seem like problems that will reduce or increase an individual's overall level of stress? Conclude the discussion by asking volunteers for ways to communicate the dangers of substance abuse to mental and emotional health.

U Universal Access

Gifted After students have read this section, have them write and illustrate a pamphlet of strategies for managing stress. The pamphlet can highlight one or more of the strategies in the text. Have students do additional research on stress management and include the results of their research in their pamphlet. **AL**

Health Skills Activity

Stress Management

Relaxation Exercises
Use the following suggestions to help students complete the activity.

- Allow time for students to practice each of the relaxation strategies listed.
- Remind students that the relaxation techniques take practice to be used effectively.
- Have students write a response to the On Your Own question in the activity.

Reading Check

Answer, p. 49 Students should name any two of the following: set your priorities, budget your time, redirect your energy, talk to someone, put things in perspective, and increase physical activity.

Health Skills Activity

Stress Management

Relaxation Exercises
When you're feeling stress, your whole body is affected. You may feel stiffness in your shoulders or neck. Your mind may be cluttered with troubling thoughts. One strategy for dealing with stress is to use relaxation exercises.

There are three main types of relaxation exercises:

DEEP BREATHING
1. Close your eyes and inhale deeply.
2. Hold the breath for a moment, then slowly exhale.
3. Repeat these steps several times.

MUSCULAR RELAXATION
1. Picture the muscles in your body.
2. Working one at a time, tighten a muscle group.
3. Hold the position for a moment, then relax.
4. Repeat these steps for each muscle group in the body.

DIRECTING YOUR THOUGHTS
1. Try to clear your mind.
2. After a moment or two, picture someplace pleasant, such as a sunny beach or park.
3. Keep picturing this relaxing scene until the stress is gone.

On Your Own
Practice each of the relaxation techniques described. Which one works best for you?

Strategies for Managing Stress

When stress levels are high or constant, your health can suffer. Fortunately, there are strategies for managing stress.

- **Identify the source.** Determine what is causing you to feel stressed. Having a clear understanding will help you manage the stress better.
- **Set your priorities.** Make a list of things you want to accomplish. Rank each task in order of importance. Decide which task to focus on. Don't try to include too many activities in your life.

48 Chapter 2: Mental and Emotional Wellness

HEALTH LITERACY

Positive Thinking Ask whether students are familiar with the expression, "Look on the bright side." Having a positive outlook protects and promotes health on all three sides of the health triangle. Laughter, in particular, can influence positive physiological changes as well as improve mental outlook or mood. One scientific study demonstrated that stress-related hormones decreased during laughter. Humor and a positive outlook can help a person cope with pressures such as taking tests and maintaining friendships.

- **Budget your time.** Set aside regular times for homework and chores. That way you won't have to rush to get them done at the last minute.
- **Redirect your energy.** Stress increases your energy. Use that energy for something positive. Learn a hobby. Offer to help a family member with a project.
- **Talk to someone.** Talking about stress can reduce it. A parent, friend, or school counselor may give you some useful advice.
- **Put things in perspective.** Remember that you are not alone. Everyone has stress and other problems. Don't make your problems bigger than they are.
- **Increase physical activity.** Becoming more active releases built-up energy from stress. Vigorous physical activity naturally relaxes the body.

 **Reading Check** **Identify** What are two strategies for managing stress?

Health Online

Visit **health.glencoe.com** and complete the Interactive Study Guide for Lesson 4.

Lesson 4 Review

 **After You Read**

Review this lesson for new terms, major headings, and Reading Checks.

What I Learned

1. *Vocabulary* Define the term *stress*.
2. *Describe* What does adrenaline do during the stress response?
3. *Give Examples* Name a major event and minor event that might cause stress.
4. *Identify* List two strategies for managing stress.

Thinking Critically

5. *Hypothesize* Do you think it's possible to have too much positive stress? Explain why or why not.

6. *Synthesize* Identify two stresses family members might experience.
7. *Apply* How can setting priorities help a teen manage stress?

Applying Health Skills

8. *Stress Management* Jamal is anxious about starting a new school. What are some ways that Jamal could manage his stress?

Health Online For more review questions for Lesson 4, go to **health.glencoe.com**.   Lesson 4: Coping with Stress   **49**

ASSESS

Assessment Resources

- Lesson Review Quiz
- *ExamView*
- Fast Files Activities
- Online Quizzes and Activities

Reteaching
- Assign Concept Map 2-4 or Reteaching Activity 2-4 in the Fast Files.
- Have students work in small groups to discuss strategies for managing stress, found on pages 48–49.

Enrichment
- Assign Enrichment Activity 2-4 in the Fast Files.
- Have students design a board game based on the positive and negative stresses in a typical teen's life. Stress management techniques should be a component of the game.

CLOSE

Ask students to name one technique they could use to relieve stress before a big test.

Lesson 4 Review Answers

1. Stress is your body's response to changes around you.
2. Adrenaline prepares the body to respond to a stressor.
3. *Sample answer:* A minor event that might cause stress is a pop quiz. A family move is a major event that causes stress.
4. Answers should include two strategies from pages 48–49.
5. *Sample answer:* Yes, if you have too much positive stress, you might have difficulty sleeping.
6. *Sample answer:* Two examples are job loss and moving to a new home.
7. Prioritizing tasks helps you make choices about what's important.
8. Answers should include at least one of the strategies for managing stress, found on pages 48–49.

FOCUS

Activating Prior Knowledge

What I Know Ask for volunteers to share a situation in which they experienced sadness. Tell students this lesson will discuss dealing with strong emotions.

 Guide to Reading

BUILDING VOCABULARY
- Have students make flash cards for the vocabulary terms in the section. Have students review their flashcards with a partner.
- Use Vocabulary PuzzleMaker to reinforce vocabulary terms.

READING STRATEGY
Graphic Organizer As students read the lesson, have them add to their graphic organizer describing mental health problems. Have them name the following problems and list symptoms of each: anxiety disorders, mood disorders, depression, and phobias.

uick Write

Have students write a paragraph describing the action they would take in response to a friend who has been sad for weeks.

Caption Answer

Photo Caption by being a good listener and showing that you care

---

Emotional Problems

Guide to Reading

Building Vocabulary
Two of the terms below contain the word *disorder.* Look up this word in a dictionary. See if you can guess the meaning of the two terms.
- anxiety disorder (p. 51)
- mood disorder (p. 51)
- depression (p. 51)
- suicide (p. 51)

Focusing on the Main Ideas
In this lesson, you will learn to
- **describe** types of emotional problems.
- **recognize** the warning signs of suicide.
- **identify** sources of help for emotional problems.

Reading Strategy
Analyzing a Graphic Using the diagram below as a guide, create a chart that lists and describes different types of emotional disorders.

Mental Health Problems	
Name of Problem	Symptoms

uick Write

Imagine a friend writes you to say she or he has been feeling sad for weeks. Write a paragraph describing what positive action you could take.

▶ When sadness or other emotions last for weeks or months, action is needed. **How might you show your concern for someone who is dealing with an emotional problem?**

What Are Emotional Problems?

Cindy's friend Jon seemed sad, but she figured he would soon bounce back from whatever was bothering him. Then a month went by and Jon still rarely smiled or spoke to anyone. Cindy began to worry that something was really wrong.

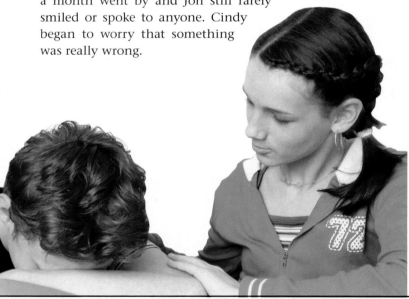

50

Lesson 5 Resources

📁 **Chapter *FAST FILE* Resources**
Guided Reading and Writing 2-5
Concept Mapping Activity 2-5
Decision-Making Activity 2-5
Reteaching Activity 2-5
Enrichment Activity 2-5
Lesson Quiz 2-5

Technology
- Transparency 2-5
- Audio Summaries
- *ExamView*
- Vocabulary PuzzleMaker
- StudentWorks™ Plus

It's normal to feel sad or afraid from time to time. However, when such feelings last for weeks, it can be a sign of an emotional problem. Help is needed to reduce risks related to emotional problems of adolescents. Some common emotional problems are described below.

Anxiety Disorders

An **anxiety disorder** is *a serious emotional problem that keeps a person from functioning normally.* An anxiety disorder is not the same thing as anxiety, or worry, mentioned in Lesson 4. Anxiety disorders prevent people from leading normal lives.

One type of anxiety disorder is *phobia* (FOH·bee·uh). Phobias are unreasonable fears of objects or ideas. Some people, for example, have a phobia about being in high places. Others have an unreasonable fear of spiders. Another anxiety disorder is *obsessive-compulsive disorder* (OCD). People with OCD can't keep certain thoughts or images out of their minds. They may repeat behaviors, such as washing their hands, over and over. In the person's mind, this helps relieve anxiety.

▲ Some people have an intense fear of spiders. **What type of anxiety disorder would such a person have?**

 **Recall** Name and describe two anxiety disorders.

Mood Disorders

Another type of emotional problem is mood disorders. A **mood disorder** is *a serious emotional problem where a person's mood goes from one extreme to another.* These changes are far more extreme than the mood swings typical in teens. A person may "cycle" between feelings of deep sadness and extreme happiness. In some people, both moods happen at once. In others, the happiness is replaced by rage.

Depression

Sometimes when they're feeling down, people will say they "feel depressed." **Depression** is *an emotional problem marked by long periods of hopelessness and despair.* It is different from ordinary sadness. Depression can make it hard for a person to function.

Suicide

Sometimes, the effects of emotional problems are so severe the person considers suicide. **Suicide** is *the deliberate act of taking one's own life.* Suicide is the third leading cause of death in people ages 10 to 14. Most of the time, these young people don't want to die. They just want their problems to go away.

Lesson 5: Emotional Problems **51**

TEACH

R Reading Strategy

Comparing and Contrasting
Ask students to name ways in which sadness and depression are different. Then have students name ways that depression and sadness are alike. OL

HS Health Skills Practice

Communication Help students review their communication skills and then develop an action plan they can follow to help a friend that has mentioned suicide. Tell students that having a plan in place will allow them to act swiftly to help a friend. Students' plans should include contact information for several sources of adult help. OL

 Reading Check

Answer Descriptions should include phobias and obsessive-compulsive disorder.

Academic Vocabulary

Source Sources of help for emotional problems are discussed on page 52. Tell students that one definition of source is "a person who supplies information." Have students identify one other meaning.

What Teens Want to Know

How do I know if I'm depressed or just sad? Teens often experience sadness due to school issues, family issues, and mood swings. A teen experiencing normal short-term sadness may question whether he or she is experiencing depression. Remind students that depression is a long-term feeling of sadness. A person suffering from depression experiences hopelessness and despair and finds it hard to carry out everyday activities. Encourage students to discuss persistent sadness with parents or guardians, school counselor, or a medical professional.

Caption Answer
Photo Caption phobia

51

Health Skills Activity

Decision Making

Helping a Troubled Friend

Use the following strategies to help students complete the activity.

- Have students meet in small groups to read the introduction.
- Ask students to talk through the decision-making steps as a group.
- When all groups have completed the activity, have a class discussion. Ask for groups to share their results.

▲ Caring adults can provide comfort when the going is rough. **How would you comfort a close friend with a problem?**

Health Online

Visit **health.glencoe.com** and complete the Interactive Study Guide for Lesson 5.

Suicide is not the answer. If someone you know is talking about suicide, go for help immediately. Urge the person to talk to a concerned adult. Tell an adult about the situation yourself. Never promise to keep the person's plan a secret. Suicide is one secret no friend should keep.

Warning Signs of Suicide

Sometimes, a person planning suicide doesn't use the word suicide, but there are other signs that a person may be thinking about it. If you notice any of the following behaviors, remember to tell a trusted adult right away.

- Avoiding activities that involve family or friends
- Taking greater risks than usual
- Losing interest in hobbies, sports, or school
- Giving away prized possessions

W

Reading Check

Explain What should you do if someone you know talks about suicide?

Help for Emotional Problems

Emotional problems have many causes. Some come from chemical changes in a person's brain. Others may be passed on through heredity.

It's important to know that emotional problems can be treated. Some are treated with medication, others with counseling, still others with both. Having an emotional problem is no different from having any other illness. Being able to ask for help shows you are taking responsibility for your health.

Sources of Help

There are many sources of help and support for emotional problems. Some are in your home or at school. You might talk to a parent or other family member. A teacher or a school counselor is another good person to turn to. Some people find it helpful to talk to a religious leader.

Often, people with emotional problems see a mental health professional. These are people specially trained to deal with emotional problems. They can give the person the specialized care he or she needs.

Reading Check

Recall Name two sources of help for people with emotional problems.

🏠 Home, School, and Community

At School Invite a qualified speaker to discuss teen suicide with the class. Possible speakers include mental health professionals, school counselors, suicide hotline volunteers, or medical professionals. Have students read the text to prepare for the speaker. Allow students to submit anonymous written questions that the speaker can answer. Encourage the speaker to discuss the importance of seeking immediate help when someone mentions suicide, even if that person seems to be joking.

Health Skills Activity

Decision Making

Helping a Troubled Friend

Caitlin's best friend Torry has been acting moody lately. When Caitlin asked her about it, Torry shrugged. "There's nothing to talk about," she said. Caitlin is worried that her friend may have a serious emotional problem. She wishes she could get Torry to open up. She knows from experience, however, that Torry doesn't like to be pressured. What should Caitlin do?

What Would You Do?

Put yourself in Caitlin's position. Use the decision-making process to decide what you would do.

1. State the situation.
2. List the options.
3. Weigh the possible outcomes.
4. Consider values.
5. Make a decision and act on it.
6. Evaluate the decision.

Lesson 5 Review

After You Read

Review this lesson for new terms, major headings, and Reading Checks.

What I Learned

1. *Vocabulary* Define the term *depression*.

2. *Give Examples* What is an example of a phobia?

3. *List* Name three warning signs of suicide.

Thinking Critically

4. *Analyze* Imagine overhearing someone saying he or she planned to commit suicide. What would you do?

5. *Synthesize* A friend says, "I've been depressed lately." What positive health behaviors could you take to help your friend?

Applying Health Skills

6. *Advocacy* Write an article for the school paper about emotional problems. Identify what students should do if they are feeling very stressed or unhappy. Tell how they can help a friend with those feelings.

Health Online For more review questions for Lesson 5, go to **health.glencoe.com**.

Lesson 5: Emotional Problems **53**

Assessment Resources

Lesson Review Quiz
- *ExamView*
- Fast Files Activities
- Online Quizzes and Activities

Reteaching

- Assign Concept Map 2-5 or Reteaching Activity 2-5 in the Fast Files.
- Have students reread the headings in the lesson. For each heading, have students state the main idea of the section.

Enrichment

- Assign Enrichment Activity 2-5 in the Fast Files.
- Have students research the use of medication and counseling to treat emotional problems. Students should write a report of their findings.

CLOSE

Have students review their concept maps and discuss in small groups the symptoms of mental health problems.

Lesson 5 Review Answers

1. Depression is an emotional problem marked by long periods of hopelessness and despair.
2. *Sample answer:* One example of a phobia is fear of heights.
3. Any three of the following: avoiding activities with families and friends; taking greater risks than normal; losing interest in hobbies, sports, or school; giving away prized possessions
4. I would immediately ask a trusted adult for help.
5. Help the friend understand his or her feelings; be a good listener; get help from a trusted adult.
6. Students' articles should name one or more of the emotional problems listed in the lesson, a plan for students that includes ideas discussed in the Health Skills Activity on this page.

Building Health Skills
PRACTICING HEALTHFUL BEHAVIORS

Dealing with Feelings

SKILL
Practicing Healthful Behaviors

Activating Prior Knowledge

Ask students to recall a time they felt a strong emotion, such as anger or sadness. Have a volunteer describe a situation in which he or she healthfully managed a strong emotion.

- **Objective** After completing the activity, students will be able to respond in a healthy way to strong emotions.
- **Time** 45 minutes
- **Materials** poster board, crayons or markers

Teacher Classroom Resources
📁 Building Health Skills
🖈 Transparency 2-3

Model

- Have students identify the steps Aiden used to manage his feelings. *He identified his feelings, he evaluated the cause of the feelings, he asked for help in dealing with the feelings, he developed a healthy response to his feelings.*

Dealing with Feelings

DIRECTIONS

Practicing Healthful Behaviors involves taking specific actions to stay healthy and avoid risky behaviors. This activity will give you the opportunity to develop and master this important health skill. Here's a guide to the different parts of this activity:

❶ In the **Model** section, you will read about a teen who performs the health skill successfully. This "model" scenario will show you how the skill is done.

❷ The **Practice** section will help guide you in practicing the skill.

❸ In the **Apply** section, you will have a chance to perform the skill on your own. You can use the Self-Check to check your work.

To complete this activity, first read the scenario presented in the Model. Then move on to the Practice. Finally, go ahead and try the Apply.

❶ **Model**

Part of growing up is learning to cope with feelings healthfully. Aiden wanted to lash out when his cousin Rob called him a baby. Instead, he followed the steps for handling strong emotions:

1. First, he determined what he was feeling (*angry and hurt*).
2. Then he evaluated the cause (*my cousin made fun of me*).
3. He asked his older brother for help in coping with his feelings.
4. Aiden decided to respond to Rob by calmly explaining why the comment upset him.

National Health Standards Addressed
- - - - - - - - - - - -
4.1, 4.3, 4.4

▶ **Teaching Tips**

Teaching Health Skills Health skills must be specifically taught. The *Teen Health* program provides the modeling and practice necessary for students to apply these skills. With this approach you will see improvements in student performance and behaviors.

Building Self-Esteem Emphasize that if a student were unsuccessful the first time he or she attempted to accomplish a goal, this does not mean that he or she failed. Stress how important it is to learn from each experience and how to use that experience to be successful next time.

② Practice

Aiden had a difficult day. First, he forgot his math homework. Then, he found out he did poorly on a test. To top it off, his bike had a flat tire, and he had to walk it all the way home from school.

1. What emotion is Aiden experiencing?
2. What caused his emotion?
3. Where could Aiden get help for dealing with his emotion?
4. What would be a healthy response to this emotion?

③ Apply

Think of a situation that created a strong emotion in you. Then draw the steps for handling emotions.

Divide a piece of poster board into four sections.

1. In the first section, draw a picture of how you felt.
2. In the second section, list the causes.
3. In the third section, list people who could help you handle your emotions.
4. Draw a healthy response to the emotion in the last section.

Explain your drawing to the class, and tell why your response is healthy.

Skill Summary
PRACTICING HEALTHFUL BEHAVIORS

You can deal with strong emotions by following these steps:
- Determine the emotion.
- Evaluate the cause.
- Ask for help if needed.
- Learn to respond in a way that does not hurt anyone.

Self-Check

- Did I illustrate an emotion?
- Did I include examples of sources of help?
- Did I show a healthy response?
- Can I explain why my response is healthy?

Practice

- Challenge students to write answers to each of the four questions in the Practice section.
- Ask for volunteers to provide an answer to each question. Use the answers to generate class discussion. Remind students that there is more than one correct answer to these questions.

Apply/Assess

- If students are having difficulty with their posters, have them review the Model and Practice sections, which explain the four steps of dealing with feelings.
- Allow adequate time for each student to share his or her poster.
- You may wish to distribute the Building Health Skills Activity in the Fast Files.

ASSESSMENT SCORING

Student work should meet all criteria to achieve the highest score:

Skills Student work identifies:
- An example and illustration of an emotion.
- Sources of help to handle the emotion.

Concept Student work explains:
- The cause of the emotion.
- Examples of healthy responses.

Developing Good Character

Time: 45 minutes
Materials: poster board, crayons or markers

Introducing Hands-on Health

- Have students read and discuss the introductory paragraph. If needed, students can review Lesson 2 for more information on developing good character.

Teaching the Activity

- Divide the class into groups and have them complete the poster.
- Allow time for each group to present its poster.
- Use the questions presented in the *Wrapping it Up* section to generate class discussion.

R Reading Strategy

Organizing Information Have students review Lesson 2 to find information on their assigned character trait. Working in groups, have them develop a word web by writing the trait in the center of a sheet of paper and then adding words associated with that character trait on lines radiating out from the word in the center. **OL**

HANDS-ON HEALTH

Developing Good Character

Character is formed every day by your thoughts and actions. Developing good character is important to your health. It will help you develop positive relationships and behaviors. A person of good character is trustworthy, treats people with respect, is responsible, fair, caring, and a good citizen. In this activity you will create a poster with examples of how to develop one of the six traits of character.

What You Will Need

- Poster board
- Markers or crayons

What You Will Do

1 Your teacher will divide the class into six small groups and assign each group one of the six traits of character: trustworthiness, respect, responsibility, fairness, caring, or citizenship.

2 In your group, brainstorm and list examples of how teens can develop the assigned character trait. For example, if your group was assigned trustworthiness, you might list telling the truth and keeping promises.

3 Now, create a colorful poster featuring the examples you listed in Step 2. Use your group's character trait as the title for your poster. As a group, explain to the class how your examples can help a teen develop good character.

Wrapping It Up

After all the groups have presented their posters, discuss these questions as a class: How can teens help other teens develop good character? How can good character affect your physical, mental/ emotional, and social health?

Display your posters where your classmates can see them. This will help other students learn about the six traits of good character.

56 Chapter 2: Mental and Emotional Wellness

HANDS-ON HEALTH Assessment

Discussion Ask students: What are two positive effects of having good character? Sample answer: *Good character leads to better physical health, helps to build friendships, leads to high self-esteem.*

How could you help another person develop a trait of good character?

Sample answer: *I could set an example; I could be a positive role model.*

How do your actions reflect your character? Sample answer: *A person with good character will act with consideration for others.*

Reading Review

 Assessment Resources

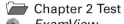

📁 Chapter 2 Summary and Activity
🎧 Audio Summaries
📁 Reading Tutor
📁 Performance Assessment
📁 Chapter 2 Test
⊙ *ExamView*
🎧 Vocabulary PuzzleMaker
🎧 Online Learning Center

FOLDABLES™ Study Organizer

Foldables™ and Other Study Aids Take out the Foldable™ that you created for Lesson 1 and any graphic organizers that you created for Lessons 1–5. Find a partner and quiz each other using these study aids.

Lesson 1 A Healthy Self-Concept

Key Ideas
- Your self-concept is the view you have of yourself.
- Your self-concept is influenced by parents, guardians, and those around you.
- You can build a positive self-concept by thinking positive thoughts, accepting encouragement, and finding friends that support you.

Vocabulary
- self-concept (p. 32)
- reinforce (p. 33)
- self-esteem (p. 34)
- resilience (p. 34)

Lesson 2 Your Character Counts

Key Ideas
- Traits of good character are trustworthiness, respect, responsibility, fairness, caring, and citizenship.
- You develop character by learning from parents, guardians, other role models, your environment, and your understanding of right and wrong.
- You can show good character by making responsible decisions and setting an example for others.

Vocabulary
- character (p. 36)
- advocacy (p. 38)
- role model (p. 39)

Lesson 3 Expressing Emotions

Key Ideas
- Emotions and mood swings are caused by events around you and by hormones in your body.
- You can learn to express your feelings in healthful ways.
- Choosing abstinence from high-risk behaviors protects your health and the health of others.

Vocabulary
- emotions (p. 41)
- hormones (p. 41)
- abstinence (p. 44)

Lesson 4 Coping with Stress

Key Ideas
- Your body responds to stress through a series of physical changes known as the fight-or-flight response.
- You can manage stress by setting priorities, budgeting your time, redirecting your energy, keeping perspective, and increasing physical activity.

Vocabulary
- stress (p. 45)
- anxiety (p. 46)
- adrenaline (p. 47)

Lesson 5 Emotional Problems

Key Ideas
- Emotional problems include anxiety disorders, mood disorders, and depression.
- Warning signs of suicide are avoiding activities, taking risks, losing interest in hobbies or school, and giving away prized possessions.

Vocabulary
- anxiety disorder (p. 51)
- suicide (p. 51)
- depression (p. 51)
- mood disorder (p. 51)

Reading Review

Study Aids

- **Using the Dinah Zike Foldable™ Study Organizer** Have students use the Foldable™ to review and explain to a partner the relationship between self-concept and self-esteem.

FOLDABLES™ Study Organizer

Key Ideas

- **Using Chapter Headings** Have students skim the chapter to find the bold-face headings. As students locate each heading, have them silently review any key ideas contained in the section.

Vocabulary Review

- **Vocabulary Game Show** Use a game-show format to review the definitions of the vocabulary terms in the chapter.

Teaching Tips

SQ3R Method SQ3R provides students with a systematic way to learn from reading. It is made up of five steps. 1) Survey: Read the chapter title, headings, and review questions. 2) Question: Read the first bold-face topic in the chapter and restate it in the form of a question.

3) Read: Read the material following the first subtopic to find the answer to the question posed in Step 2. 4) Recite: Pause and reflect on the answer. 5) Review: Spend five minutes reviewing notes and recall the main points. Reread headings and recall content.

Reviewing Vocabulary and Main Ideas

1. self-concept
2. confidence
3. encouragement
4. character
5. advocacy
6. role model
7. Hormones
8. abstinence
9. True
10. False, uncertainty or worry
11. False, prepares the body to respond
12. b
13. c

Thinking Critically

14. *Sample answer:*
Influences from parents, guardians, and other relatives influence your self-concept when you are young. Spoken words, gestures, or written messages, including the media, can have a positive effect on your self-concept.

15. Answers will vary but should include examples of positive and negative stress and should demonstrate an understanding of types of stress.

 Health **Online**

Have students visit **health.glencoe.com** to take the Chapter 2 Quiz.

CHAPTER

2

Assessment

📖 **After You Read**

IM *Express*

Now that you have read the chapter, review your answer to the I.M. Express on the chapter opener. Have your ideas changed? What would your answer be now?

Reviewing Vocabulary and Main Ideas

On a sheet of paper, write the numbers 1–8. After each number, write the term from the list that best completes each statement.

- abstinence
- advocacy
- character
- confidence
- emotions
- encouragement
- hormones
- role model
- self-concept

Lesson 1) A Healthy Self-Concept

1. The view you have of yourself is known as your _____.
2. When you have high self-esteem, you have _____ in what you do.
3. Accepting _____ is one way to develop a positive self-concept.

Lesson 2) Your Character Counts

4. The way you think, feel, and act is known as your _____.
5. Taking a stand to make a difference is known as _____.
6. A person whose success or behavior serves as an example for others is a _____.

Lesson 3) Expressing Emotions

7. _____ are powerful chemicals that regulate many body functions.
8. Refusing to participate in high-risk behaviors is called _____.

Lesson 4) Coping with Stress

*On a sheet of paper, write the numbers 10–12. Write **True** or **False** for each statement below. If the statement is false, change the underlined word or phrase to make it true.*

9. Your body's response to changes around you is known as <u>stress</u>.
10. Anxiety refers to feelings of <u>happiness</u> over what may happen.
11. Adrenaline is a hormone that <u>stops the body from responding</u> to stress.

Lesson 5) Emotional Problems

On a sheet of paper, write the numbers 12 and 13. After each number, write the letter of the answer that best completes each statement.

12. A disorder in which a person has an unreasonable fear of an object or idea is known as
    a. depression.
    b. phobia.
    c. obsessive-compulsive disorder.
13. Signs that a person might be thinking about suicide include
    a. avoiding activities with friends.
    b. taking greater risks than usual.
    c. both of the above.

Health Online Visit **health.glencoe.com** and take the Online Quiz for Chapter 2.

IM *Express Wrap-Up*

Stress Management Have students review the list of stressful events they made in the chapter opening activity. Ask if the stress rating they assigned to any event has changed after reading this chapter. Then ask if the stress management techniques introduced in this chapter could be helpful in dealing with the events rated as very stressful. Have volunteers share ways in which they could apply stress management techniques to an event on their lists.

Thinking Critically

Using complete sentences, answer the following questions on a sheet of paper.

14. **Interpret** How do messages from those around you affect your self-concept?

15. **Analyze** Identify three events that have caused stress in your life.

Write About It

16. **Analyzing Influences** Imagine you are writing an article on self-esteem for the school newspaper. In your article, explain what factors might affect a teen's self-esteem.

17. **Stress Management** Write a short story about a teen who is having a stressful day.

 Career Corner

School Counselor You may enjoy helping young people discover their talents and plan for their future. If so, consider a career as a school counselor. These professionals work in a school setting to help students solve problems and set career goals. School counselors need a four-year college degree and two years of graduate training. Read more about this and other health careers by visiting *Career Corner* at **health.glencoe.com**.

Identify what is causing the teen stress. Show how the teen handles the stress in a healthy way.

Standardized Test Practice

Math

Use the table to answer the questions.

Percentage of Schools Teaching Suicide Prevention, by Topic		
Topic	Middle School	High School
How to handle stress in healthy ways	90.0	96.5
Recognizing types of stress and signs of depression that might be associated with suicide	64.8	86.5
What to do if someone is thinking about suicide	60.3	82.1

TEST-TAKING TIP

When questions use tables, read the title of the table. This will help you figure out its subject. Read each column heading and the label of each row.

1. What percentage of middle school students learn what to do if someone is thinking about suicide?
   - **A.** 60.3
   - **B.** 64.8
   - **C.** 90.0
   - **D.** 96.5

2. Which statement is *true*?
   - **A.** More middle school students learn healthful ways of handling stress than high school students.
   - **B.** Over 90 percent of high school students learn what to do if someone is thinking about suicide.
   - **C.** Nearly 65 percent of middle school students learn to recognize the types of stress associated with suicide.
   - **D.** Less than 60 percent of middle school students learn what to do if someone is thinking about suicide.

Chapter 2 Assessment **59**

CHAPTER

 2

Write About It

16. **Expository Writing** Prior to assigning the article, explain that expository writing shares knowledge to help others understand. Articles will vary, but should include a description of self-esteem, confidence to try new things, or how good you feel about yourself.

17. **Narrative Writing** Tell students that narrative writing tells a clear story arranged in a logical order. Remind students to develop interesting characters, describe the setting, and include a plot. Stories will vary, but should show how the teen handles stress in healthful ways.

Standardized Test Practice

1. A
2. C

 Career Corner

School Counselor Have students visit the Career Corner at **health.glencoe.com** for more about this career. Invite the school counselor to your class. Encourage students to ask about high school classes that could help them prepare for a career in school counseling.

Test-Taking Tips

Reading Directions Remind students to take the time to read the direction lines on the test. Tell students that some tests have several sections, each with different instructions. Encourage students to underline important parts of the instructions, for example, "write your answer in complete sentences" or "show your work."

CHAPTER 3 pp. 60–91	Standards		Skills and Activities
	National	**State/Local**	**HEALTH QUIZ**, *p. 61*
	National Health Education Standards 4.1, 4.3, 4.7, 4.8		TIME HEALTH NEWS Schoolroom Torment, *p. 88* **BUILDING HEALTH SKILLS** *Conflict Resolution* Working Things Out, *pp. 86-87*
Lesson 1 Communication Skills pp. 62–66	National Health Education Standards 1.4, 2.3, 4.1, 4.3, 4.4, 4.5, 7.4, 8.1, 8.3		**MEDIA WATCH** Commercial Count, *p. 63* **HEALTH SKILLS ACTIVITY** *Practicing Healthful Behaviors* Safety Online, *p. 64*
Lesson 2 Your Family pp. 67–72	National Health Education Standards 1.4, 1.5, 1.6, 1.8, 3.1, 3.2, 3.4, 4.2, 4.3, 4.4, 4.5, 7.4, 7.6, 8.2, 8.4		**DEVELOPING GOOD CHARACTER** *Teaching Character, p. 68* **HEALTH SKILLS ACTIVITY** *Communication Skills* Family Meetings, *p. 70*
Lesson 3 Your Friends and Peers pp. 73–77	National Health Education Standards 1.4, 1.5, 2.4, 4.2, 4.3, 4.4, 4.6, 4.7, 7.4, 8.2		
Lesson 4 Refusal Skills pp. 78–80	National Health Education Standards 1.1, 1.6, 1.8, 2.4, 3.2, 4.3, 4.4, 4.5, 4.6, 5.2, 5.3, 7.1, 7.3, 7.4		**HEALTH SKILLS ACTIVITY** *Refusal Skills* Saying No, *p. 79*
Lesson 5 Resolving Conflicts pp. 81–85	National Health Education Standards 1.5, 3.2, 4.1, 4.2, 4.7, 4.8, 7.5, 7.6, 8.1, 8.2, 8.5		**DEVELOPING GOOD CHARACTER** *The Myth of Positive Prejudice, p. 82*

PACING THE CHAPTER

Lesson 1	90 min	Lesson 4	45 min	Chapter Review	45 min
Lesson 2	90 min	Lesson 5	90 min	TIME Health News	20 min
Lesson 3	45 min	Building Health Skills	45 min		

BLOCK SCHEDULING

For block scheduling, assign students Building Health Skills feature *Working Things Out*, pages 86–87, and Guided Reading and Writing in the *Fast Files*. 📁

Planning Guide

 StudentWorks *Plus*

 Glencoe Exclusive! TeacherWorks™
All-In-One Planner and Resource Center

Reproducible Resources	Assessment	Media and Technology
Chapter *FAST FILE* **Resources** Chapter Summaries and Activities `REVIEW` Building Health Skills Activity `TEACH` Performance Assessment Activity `EXTEND` Universal Access Activities `TEACH` Parent Letter and Activities **Student Activities Workbook** `TEACH` **Reading Tutor** `TEACH`	Building Health Skills Activity, *pp. 86–87* Chapter 3 Assessment, *pp. 90–91* **Chapter** *FAST FILE* **Resources** Performance Assessment Activity, *p. 4* Chapter 3 Test, *p. 7* ⊙ *ExamView® Test Generator*	**TeacherWorks™** includes: • Interactive Teacher Edition • Lesson Planner with Calendar • Access to all blackline masters • Correlations to standards ⊙ StudentWorks™ Plus ⊙ Online Student Edition Dinah Zike's Teaching Health with Foldables™
Chapter *FAST FILE* **Resources** Concept Mapping Activity 3-1 `REVIEW` Enrichment Activity 3-1 `EXTEND` Guided Reading and Writing 3-1 `TEACH` Health Lab 3-1 `EXTEND` Lesson Plan 3-1 Reteaching Activity 3-1 `REVIEW`	Lesson 1 Review, *p. 66* ⊙ Vocabulary PuzzleMaker ⊙ *ExamView® Test Generator*	⊙ Vocabulary PuzzleMaker ⊙ *ExamView® Test Generator* ⊙ StudentWorks™ Plus ⊙ Transparency 3-1 ⊙ **Health Online**
Chapter *FAST FILE* **Resources** Concept Mapping Activity 3-2 `REVIEW` Decision-Making Activity 3-2 `EXTEND` Enrichment Activity 3-2 `EXTEND` Guided Reading and Writing 3-2 `TEACH` Lesson Plan 3-2 Reteaching Activity 3-2 `REVIEW`	Lesson 2 Review, *p. 72* ⊙ Vocabulary PuzzleMaker ⊙ *ExamView® Test Generator*	⊙ Vocabulary PuzzleMaker ⊙ *ExamView® Test Generator* ⊙ StudentWorks™ Plus ⊙ Transparency 3-2 ⊙ **Health Online**
Chapter *FAST FILE* **Resources** Concept Mapping Activity 3-3 `REVIEW` Decision-Making Activity 3-3 `EXTEND` Enrichment Activity 3-3 `EXTEND` Guided Reading and Writing 3-3 `TEACH` Lesson Plan 3-3 Reteaching Activity 3-3 `REVIEW`	Lesson 3 Review, *p. 77* ⊙ Vocabulary PuzzleMaker ⊙ *ExamView® Test Generator*	⊙ Vocabulary PuzzleMaker ⊙ *ExamView® Test Generator* ⊙ StudentWorks™ Plus ⊙ Transparency 3-3 ⊙ **Health Online**
Chapter *FAST FILE* **Resources** Concept Mapping Activity 3-4 `REVIEW` Cross-Curriculum Activity 3-4 `EXTEND` Enrichment Activity 3-4 `EXTEND` Guided Reading and Writing 3-4 `TEACH` Lesson Plan 3-4 Reteaching Activity 3-4 `REVIEW`	Lesson 4 Review, *p. 80* ⊙ Vocabulary PuzzleMaker ⊙ *ExamView® Test Generator*	⊙ Vocabulary PuzzleMaker ⊙ *ExamView® Test Generator* ⊙ StudentWorks™ Plus ⊙ Transparency 3-4 ⊙ **Health Online**
Chapter *FAST FILE* **Resources** Concept Mapping Activity 3-5 `REVIEW` Cross-Curriculum Activity 3-5 `TEACH` Enrichment Activity 3-4 `EXTEND` Guided Reading and Writing 3-5 `TEACH` Lesson Plan 3-5 Reteaching Activity 3-5 `REVIEW`	Lesson 5 Review, *p. 85* ⊙ Vocabulary PuzzleMaker ⊙ *ExamView® Test Generator*	⊙ Vocabulary PuzzleMaker ⊙ *ExamView® Test Generator* ⊙ StudentWorks™ Plus ⊙ Transparency 3-5 ⊙ **Health Online**

Chapter and Lesson Resources

The *Teen Health* resources are designed for differentiated learning abilities. You may want to use the coded items in this way:

`REVIEW` —activities to review or reinforce content

`TEACH` —activities to teach basic concepts

`EXTEND` —activities to extend or enrich lesson content

 OUT OF TIME?

Use Health Skills Activities *Safety Online,* page 64 and *Saying No,* page 79 or Developing Good Character, page 68.

Teen Bullies

Bullying is a common problem among teens. Bullying can take many forms, and is practiced by both boys and girls.

Emotional and verbal bullying take the form of mockery, teasing, and exclusion from activities. These forms of bullying are more commonly practiced by girls. Physical bullying includes hitting, tripping, and pushing, and is more commonly practiced by boys. Sexual comments and inappropriate touching are sexual bullying. Online, or electronic, bullying is carried out with emails, instant messages, and by placing damaging content on Web pages and in blogs.

Symptoms of those being bullied usually include low self-esteem, depression, sleep problems, and avoiding school. Some victims of bullies resort to violence in an attempt to solve the problem. Parents may note these symptoms but may be unable to identify a cause, because bullied students often do not confide in adults.

Teachers who note students being bullied or carrying out bullying should take action. Consult the school guidance counselor, nurse, or principal for support.

Facilitating Communication for Special Needs Students

Students with special communication needs include hearing impaired students, students with speech impairments, and students with developmental delays. Students with autism and behavior disorders might also have special communications needs. Use the following ideas to engage students with special communication needs in the health classroom.

- **Be a Model** Model good communication skills by speaking clearly and slowly. Use complete sentences to express your ideas.

- **Face the Class** Speak only when you are facing the class. Avoid speaking while writing on the board or handing out papers.

- **Provide Written Outlines** Before beginning each chapter, prepare printed outlines of your lessons to distribute to students with special communication needs.

- **Allow Tape Recording** Allow students to use tape recorders or other devices to record your lessons.

- **Use the Buddy System** Have peers assist students with communication disorders as needed.

- **Allow Extra Time** Allow students with speech impairments extra time to form and express their answers. Be inclusive when choosing students for role-plays and skits.

- **Speak to the Student** If a student uses an interpreter in the class room, address your questions and comments to the student, not to the interpreter.

Support for Teaching Reading

 Reading Support   **Health Online**   **Academic Integration** For additional academic integration strategies, visit the Teacher Center at **health.glencoe.com**.

Reading Preview

Vocabulary Builders Many of the terms in this chapter are related to interpersonal relationships. To introduce the topic of friendships, encourage students to share their ideas of what it means to be *reliable* and *loyal*. Ask them how they would define *cooperation*. Then discuss how these terms come into play in a *relationship*.

FOLDABLES™ Study Organizer *Dinah Zike's Reading and Study Skills for Teen Health* provides interactive graphic organizers that help students comprehend and retain health concepts as they read. Use the Foldable™ on page 61 or find more Foldables™ activities for the chapter on **Healthy Relationships** in the separate booklet, available in the TCR.

Lesson 1   Communication Skills

Summarizing Students will be asked to organize information in this lesson by writing summary sentences. Work with the class to provide introductory phrases to guide them in what makes a good summary sentence. For example, "Communication is…" Some different ways to communicate include…"

Lesson 2   Your Family

Finding the Main Idea Guide students to look at the Guide to Reading on page 67 and read the section called "Focusing on the Main Ideas." Ask students to keep this in mind as they read each paragraph. Then have them prepare index cards with a description of each of the four main ideas listed.

Lesson 3   Your Friends and Peers

Drawing Conclusions To get students thinking about the qualities and traits of a good friend, have them preview the photos and read the captions in this lesson. Brainstorm answers to the caption questions and record their answers. Then after they have read the lesson, review their answers as a class.

Lesson 4   Refusal Skills

Sequencing Have students illustrate the events in the first paragraph of the lesson on a time line. They should begin with Lance's situation, how he can use refusal skills, and how he avoids a situation that might otherwise have negative consequences. As students read, they can add details from the lesson, for example, including getting help from adults

Lesson 5   Resolving Conflicts

Identifying Cause and Effect This lesson deals with how to effectively resolve conflicts. Have students divide a paper in half and head one side *cause* and the other side *effect*. As they read through the lesson, have them note causes of conflict and the effect that can be reached by applying one of the conflict resolution skills they read about in the lesson.

Post Reading

Applying Concepts Have students choose a story or play that they have read in which the characters demonstrated healthy relationship skills. Have students write a brief summary describing how the characters used communication skills, refusal skills, or peacefully resolved a conflict, based on the lesson content.

Key for Using the Teacher Wraparound Edition

Use this key to help you identify the different types of prompts found in the Teacher Wraparound Edition.

R   **Reading Strategies** activities help you teach reading skills and vocabulary.

C   **Critical Thinking** strategies help students apply and extend what they have learned.

U   **Universal Access** activities provide differentiated instruction for students learning to speak English, along with suggestions for teaching various types of learners.

HS   **Health Skills Practice** activities reinforce Health Skills concepts and help students apply these skills in their everyday lives.

W   **Writing Support** activities provide writing opportunities to help students comprehend the text.

AL   **Active Learning** strategies provide a variety of activities for presenting lesson content, including Quick Demos and engaging classroom projects that get students actively involved.

Key to Ability Levels

Teaching Strategies and activities have been coded for ability level and appropriateness

AL   Activities for students working above grade level

OL   Activities for students working on grade level

BL   Activities for students working below grade level

EL   Activities for English Learners

Symbols

⚓   Transparencies

💿   CD-ROM

🖱   health.glencoe.com

📁   Print Resources

Chapter at a Glance

Lesson 1 explains different ways people communicate, describes how to be a better speaker and listener, and identifies three styles of communication.

Lesson 2 describes different types of families, identifies roles within families, describes how family members care for each other, and explains ways of handling problems in families.

Lesson 3 identifies qualities of a good friend, recognizes character traits found in friends, and identifies two kinds of peer pressure.

Lesson 4 identifies how to use refusal skills to resist peer pressure and explains the importance of abstinence from unhealthful and risky behaviors.

Lesson 5 tells why conflicts occur, explains what students can do if they are not getting along with someone, and describes ways to protect against violence.

R Reading Strategy

Interpreting the Photo
Have students look at the photo of two friends. Point out that friends are important in life. Ask students to think about other people who are important in their lives, for example, family members and teachers. Have volunteers share their ideas with the class. **OL**

60

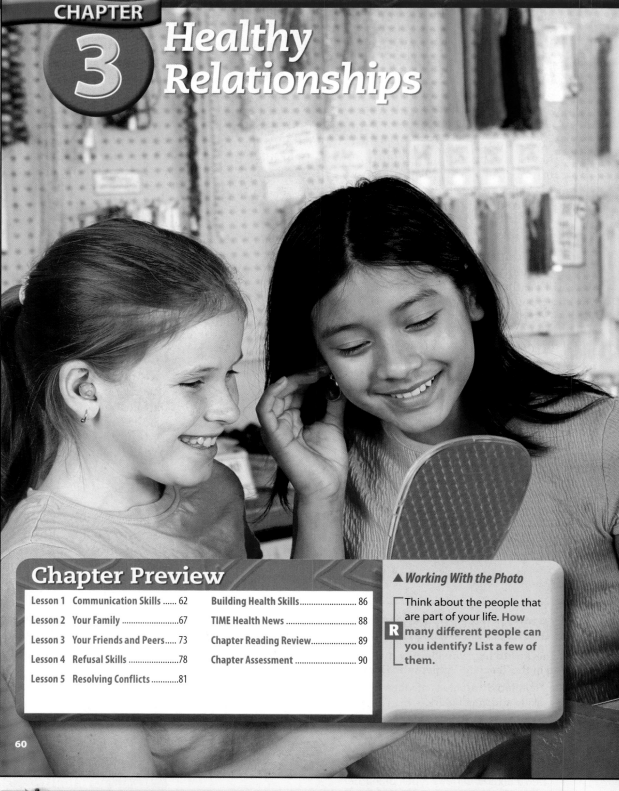

CHAPTER

3

Healthy Relationships

Chapter Preview

Lesson 1 Communication Skills 62

Lesson 2 Your Family 67

Lesson 3 Your Friends and Peers..... 73

Lesson 4 Refusal Skills 78

Lesson 5 Resolving Conflicts 81

Building Health Skills.......................... 86

TIME Health News 88

Chapter Reading Review..................... 89

Chapter Assessment 90

▲ *Working With the Photo*

R Think about the people that are part of your life. **How many different people can you identify? List a few of them.**

60

Universal Access

Differentiated Learning Glencoe provides teacher support and student materials for all learners in the health classroom.

● Spanish Glosario and chapter summaries for the English Language Learners.

● *Reading Tutor* and related worksheets support reluctant readers.

● Universal Access strategies throughout the Teacher Wraparound Edition and Fast Files help you present materials for gifted students, at-risk students, physically impaired students, and those with behavior disorders or learning disabilities.

Start-Up Activities

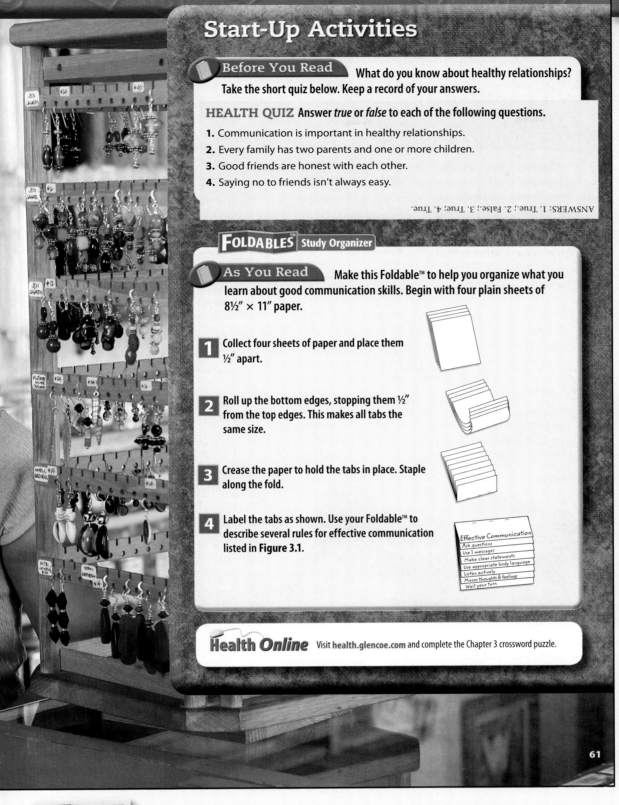

Before You Read
What do you know about healthy relationships? Take the short quiz below. Keep a record of your answers.

HEALTH QUIZ Answer *true* or *false* to each of the following questions.

1. Communication is important in healthy relationships.
2. Every family has two parents and one or more children.
3. Good friends are honest with each other.
4. Saying no to friends isn't always easy.

ANSWERS: 1. True; 2. False; 3. True; 4. True.

FOLDABLES Study Organizer

As You Read
Make this Foldable™ to help you organize what you learn about good communication skills. Begin with four plain sheets of 8½" × 11" paper.

1 Collect four sheets of paper and place them ½" apart.

2 Roll up the bottom edges, stopping them ½" from the top edges. This makes all tabs the same size.

3 Crease the paper to hold the tabs in place. Staple along the fold.

4 Label the tabs as shown. Use your Foldable™ to describe several rules for effective communication listed in **Figure 3.1**.

> Effective Communication
> Ask questions
> Use I messages
> Make clear statements
> Use appropriate body language
> Listen actively
> Mirror thoughts & feelings
> Wait your turn

Health Online Visit **health.glencoe.com** and complete the Chapter 3 crossword puzzle.

FOCUS

Activating Prior Knowledge

What I Know Ask students to describe what makes a person fun to talk to. Record ideas in "word balloons" on the board. *Students may indicate listening, asking questions, or being interested.*

Guide to Reading

BUILDING VOCABULARY

- Explain that the term *communication* is a noun. Ask: What is the verb form of this term? *communicate*
- Use Vocabulary PuzzleMaker to reinforce vocabulary terms.

READING STRATEGY

FOLDABLES Study Organizer Guide students in identifying communication styles and skills using their Foldable™ as they read Lesson 1.

- **Organizing Information** Allow time for students to preview the lesson.

Quick Write

Students' paragraphs should explain why they enjoy talking with a particular person. They may call upon ideas from the Activating Prior Knowledge discussion.

Caption Answer

Photo Caption, p. 62
e-mail, telephone, instant messaging

Communication Skills

Guide to Reading

Building Vocabulary
Copy the terms below into your notebook. Guess the meaning of each. As you read, see how many terms you got right.

- communication (p. 62)
- relationship (p. 62)
- body language (p. 63)

Focusing on the Main Ideas
In this lesson, you will learn to

- **explain** different ways people communicate.
- **describe** how you can be a better speaker and listener.
- **identify** the three styles of communication.
- **develop** skills to communicate safely online.

Reading Strategy
Organizing Information Copy the major and minor headings from the lesson onto a sheet of paper. Leave space beneath each. Write a sentence beneath each heading that summarizes the ideas under that heading.

FOLDABLES Study Organizer Use the Foldable™ on p. 61 as you read this lesson.

Quick Write

Think of someone you like talking with. In a short paragraph, explain why you enjoy talking with this person.

What Is Communication?

Each day you communicate with people. **Communication** is *the clear exchange of ideas and information*. When you communicate, you send or receive a message. Successful communication is at the root of healthy relationships. A **relationship** is *a connection you have with another person or group*. Good communication helps people understand each other and get along.

◄ Talking is the main way people communicate. **What are some other forms of communication?**

62

 **Chapter** *FAST FILE* **Resources**
Guided Reading and Writing 3-1
Concept Mapping Activity 3-1
Health Lab 3-1
Reteaching Activity 3-1
Enrichment Activity 3-1
Lesson Quiz 3-1

Technology
Transparency 3-1
Audio Summaries
ExamView
Vocabulary PuzzleMaker
StudentWorks™ Plus

◀ Body language can be a powerful communication device. **What message is being sent by the teen leaning in?**

Good communication requires special skills. Both the sender of the message and the receiver should have them. In this chapter, you will learn about these skills and how to use them.

Reading Check Define What is *communication?*

Different Ways to Communicate

The main way people communicate is through language. On one end of the communication, there is a speaker or writer. On the other end, there is a listener or reader.

Communication, however, runs much deeper than just words. One way to demonstrate attentive communication is through body language. **Body language** refers to *facial expressions, eye contact, gestures, and posture.* Shrugging your shoulders at a question you can't answer is an example of body language. So is leaning in toward someone who's speaking about something you find interesting. People are often unaware of their body language. Sometimes, without knowing it, they send *mixed messages.* Their words don't match what their body is saying. For example, a friend might say, "That is a good idea," but roll her eyes. Mixed messages are confusing for listeners.

You can communicate with others in several different ways. You can speak face-to-face or by telephone. You can send written messages using e-mail, text messaging, or mail services. You can also give someone a written note or letter in person. For people with hearing loss, sign language is an effective way to communicate face-to-face.

Commercial Count

How many commercials do you think you see each day? According to one industry source, over 1,500 commercials can be seen on TV daily. Many commercials are repeated again and again. At first, you may not be aware of the messages they're communicating. Eventually though, they will sink in.

Make a list of health products or services advertised on TV within one hour. Notice if any of the ads are repeated and what messages they contain.

TEACH

R **Reading Strategy**

Organizing Information Make a T-diagram on the board describing body language. Label one side "Attentive" and the other side "Not Paying Attention." Ask two or three volunteers to demonstrate examples of body language, for example, eye rolling, leaning forward, and making eye contact. Have the class identify and categorize each example. Then have students brainstorm other examples of body language. Add their ideas to the T-diagram. **OL**

Reading Check

Answer Communication is the sharing of thoughts and feelings.

Commercial Count

Have students categorize the advertisements they recorded by product type. Then have students make bar graphs or circle graphs to show the number or percentage of ads in each of the categories.

Cultural Perspectives

Cultural Differences in Nonverbal Communication Many nonverbal communication cues are specific to a particular culture. Point out to students that different cultures have different practices regarding the appropriate amount of space between the speaker and the listener, the amount of eye contact, and the role of body contact in conversation. What is considered proper in one culture can be considered rude in another. Remind students to respect and appreciate the differences of other cultures. Have interested students research nonverbal communication in different cultures.

Caption Answer

Photo Caption Leaning in indicates the teen is interested in the conversation.

63

Health Skills Activity

Practicing Healthful Behaviors

Safety Online

- Have students work in groups to discuss the list of tips presented in the activity. As a group, have students spend 10 minutes generating reasons that the tips are important. Ask a member from each group to share the group's responses.
- Ask volunteers to add any other safety tips they can think of.
- Provide index cards, paper, or other materials for students to use when making a copy of the tips.

AL Active Learning

Creative Project Ask students to identify advertising slogans with which they are familiar. Then have students work in small groups to create slogans for safe Internet use and e-mail communication. **OL**

> **Reading Check**
>
> facial expressions, eye contact, gestures, and posture

Academic Vocabulary

Visual On this page, students learn about *visual* clues as a part of communication. Help students recognize that related words can help identify a word's meaning. For example, explain that the words *vision* and *visible* can help identify the meaning of the word *visual* (mental images).

Health Skills Activity

Practicing Healthful Behaviors

Safety Online

Instant messaging (IM) is a great example of how technology improves communication in our lives. So is e-mail. When using these technologies, it is important to play it safe. Here are some tips:

- Make sure that a parent or guardian gives you permission to communicate with others online.
- Never give out any information about yourself or your family. That includes your address, phone number, age, passwords, or the names of your family members.
- Stay out of unsupervised chat rooms.
- Never agree to meet anyone in person you have met online, without asking a parent or guardian.
- If an online conversation makes you feel uncomfortable, exit and tell a parent or other adult right away.

On Your Own

These are good rules for all members of the family. Make a copy and post it near your home computer.

AL There are advantages and disadvantages to different kinds of communication. Talking on the phone, for example, allows you to communicate your feelings, exchange ideas and information, and get an immediate response. However, when you speak on the telephone, visual clues such as facial expressions are absent. Communicating by e-mail gives you a chance to think and make corrections before you hit the send button. E-mail also gives you the ability to communicate information that needs to be remembered. You might e-mail directions to a birthday party or a list of supplies you should bring to school. Sometimes it is easier to express feelings or difficult emotions in writing than face-to-face or on the phone. In written messages, your reader can't see your facial expressions or hear the tone of your voice. All forms of communication allow you to communicate successfully.

> **Reading Check** **Give Examples** Give two examples of body language.

TECHNOLOGY AND HEALTH

Internet Communication Instant messaging is a popular way to communicate with friends. Instant messaging uses its own spellings, abbreviations, and etiquette. Discuss communicating by instant messaging as compared to other forms of communication. Point out the differences of IM communication and formal written communication. Have students list situations in which "IM language" is appropriate, for example, in notes to friends. Then have students name places where "IM language" is not appropriate, for example, in written school assignments. **OL**

Using Good Communication Skills

Figure 3.1 summarizes effective verbal and nonverbal communication skills for both sending and receiving messages. Whether you are speaking or listening, it is important to use good communication skills.

Communication Styles

In addition to the variety of ways we can communicate, there are also different *communication styles*. Tom is aggressive in his communication. When he wants something, he will say, "Give me that!" in a threatening tone. His sister Abby is the opposite. If she wants something, she'll ask for it in a low, timid voice. Her meek and shy style of communication is *passive*.

▼ FIGURE 3.1 **COMMUNICATION SKILLS**

Giving and getting messages each have their own "skill set." How do these skills relate to each other? What rules could you add for communication that is not face-to-face?

Outbound ("Sending")	Inbound ("Receiving")
■ **Think, then speak.** Don't just blurt out the first words that come into your mind. Plan what you're going to say. Think it through.	■ **Listen actively.** Recognize the difference between hearing and listening. Hearing is just being aware of sound. Listening is paying attention to it. Use your mind as well as your ears.
■ **Use "I" messages.** Express your concerns in terms of yourself. You'll be less likely to make others angry or feel defensive.	■ Ask questions. This is another way to show you are listening. It also helps clear up anything you don't understand. It prevents misunderstandings, which are a roadblock to successful communication.
■ **Make clear, simple statements.** Be specific and accurate. Stick to the subject. Give the other person a chance to do the same.	■ Mirror thoughts and feelings. Pay attention to what is being said. Repeat what someone says to show that you understand.
■ **Be honest with thoughts and feelings.** Say what you really think and feel, but be polite. Respect the feelings of your listener.	■ Use appropriate body language. Even if you disagree, listen to what the other person has to say. Make eye contact, and don't turn away.
■ **Use appropriate body language.** Make eye contact. Show that you are involved as a speaker. Avoid mixed messages. Beware of gestures, especially when speaking with people of different cultural backgrounds. Some gestures, such as pointing, are considered rude in certain cultures.	■ Wait **your turn.** Don't interrupt. Let the person finish speaking. You'll expect the same courtesy when it's your turn.

C Critical Thinking

Contrast To help students practice making everyday requests in an assertive style, develop a list of common situations (for example, someone cuts in front of them in line at lunch). Have students practice assertive responses. To contrast the different styles of communication, have students restate their requests in a passive style and an aggressive style. Then have students explain why assertive requests are more likely to result in the desired response. **OL**

R Reading Strategy

Analyzing a Graphic Have students examine Figure 3.1. Divide the class into small groups. Have each group write and perform a skit using at least two of the skills from each side of the chart. As students perform their skits, have the other class members identify the skills being demonstrated. **OL**

Caption Answer

Figure Caption These skills are both important to conversation. For conversations that are not face-to-face, using a pleasant tone of voice is especially important.

HEALTH LITERACY

Interpersonal Communication Good communication is a vital key to success in today's world. Employers seek out individuals with strong communication skills to create a positive work environment. Developing a strong foundation in communicating with others will provide many benefits for students. Discuss with students ways that effective communication skills can enhance student-teacher relationships. Ask students to identify communication skills that they feel they are good at and where they might improve.

Reading Check

Answer The three styles of communication are passive, aggressive, and assertive.

ASSESS

Assessment Resources

Lesson Review Quiz
- *ExamView*
- Fast Files Activities
- Online Quizzes and Activities

Reteaching

- Assign Concept Map 3-1 or Reteaching Activity 3-1 in the Fast Files.
- Ask students to name and describe three examples of ways people demonstrate good communication skills.

Enrichment

- Assign Enrichment Activity 3-1 in the Fast Files.
- Have students prepare videos that teach effective communication skills. Encourage students to incorporate the lesson content in creative or humorous ways.

CLOSE

Ask students to describe the benefits of good communication skills.

Neither Tom's nor Abby's approach to communication is very effective. Speaking aggressively can cause arguments or hurt feelings. People who communicate in a passive tone may not clearly express their needs to others. They risk not being heard or taken seriously. To communicate effectively, you must learn to use an *assertive* style. Assertive communication means you aren't shy or hesitant about expressing yourself. It is making your wants or needs known in a positive, active manner. A positive approach means the tone and feeling of your words are calm and pleasant. Suppose someone sitting near you at the movies is talking. An aggressive person might say something rude. A shy person might say nothing at all. But an assertive communicator would politely but firmly ask the person to stop talking.

Health *Online*

Visit **health.glencoe.com** and complete the Interactive Study Guide for Lesson 1.

Reading Check **Identify** What are three styles of communication?

Lesson 1 Review

After You Read

Review this lesson for new terms, major headings, and Reading Checks.

What I Learned

1. *Vocabulary* Define *body language*.

2. *Identify* List four speaking skills a good communicator uses.

3. *Recall* What is assertive communication?

Thinking Critically

4. *Evaluate* Max was wrapped up in a TV show. His mother said something to him and got no response. When she scolded him for not listening, he replied, "I heard every word you said." What communication skills could Max have used to show his mother he was listening?

5. *Apply* "I'd love to come," Karen said when her friend called to invite her to a party. Karen's voice sounded uncomfortable. Did Karen's words match her voice? What kind of message was she giving her friend?

Applying Health Skills

6. *Communication Skills* You and two classmates are having a conversation. Demonstrate attentive communication skills. Make eye contact and use appropriate hand and body gestures.

Health *Online* For more review questions for Lesson 1, go to **health.glencoe.com**.

Lesson 1 Review Answers

1. It is a term referring to facial expressions, gestures, posture, and eye contact.
2. Answers, which will vary, may include any four of the items listed in Figure 3.1 on page 65.

3. Making your wants or needs known in a positive, active manner
4. Max should use eye contact. He should respond to what his mother says to let her know he is listening.

5. Karen was not sending a clear message. Her tone and words sent mixed messages.
6. Students' conversations should demonstrate understanding of good communication skills.

Lesson 2

Your Family

Guide to Reading

● Building Vocabulary
As you read this lesson, write each new highlighted term and its definition in your notebook.

- family (p. 67)
- nurture (p. 69)
- abuse (p. 71)
- physical abuse (p. 71)
- sexual abuse (p. 71)
- neglect (p. 71)

● Focusing on the Main Ideas
In this lesson, you will learn to

- **recognize** different types of family units.
- **identify** your role within your family.
- **explain** how family members care for each other.
- **develop** effective communication skills for family meetings.

● Reading Strategy
Organizing Information Make two lists. One list should contain types of family units. The other should list roles people play within a family.

Family Relationships

Think of the different relationships you have in your life. You have relationships with family, friends, classmates, teachers, and others in the community. Relationships are an important part of your social health. Good relationships make you feel loved, wanted, safe and secure.

Family relationships are some of the most important. The **family** is *the basic unit of society.* A family includes two or more people brought together by blood, marriage, adoption, or a desire for mutual support.

There are many different kinds of families. Some families have two parents, others one. Trevor lives with his father, stepmother, and half-sister. Trevor's is a *blended family.* Can you guess what an *extended* family might be? Extend means to reach out or make bigger. What kinds of people might be in an extended family? **Figure 3.2** shows several different family types. Which type is your family?

▶ Extended families include members from more than one generation. This family, for example, is made up of a mother, child, and grandfather. **What are some other types of family units?**

Quick Write

List some activities you do regularly with your family. Choose one activity and explain how it brings your family closer together.

Lesson 2: Your Family **67**

Lesson 2 Resources

Chapter FAST FILE Resources
Guided Reading and Writing 3-2
Concept Mapping Activity 3-2
Decision-Making Activity 3-2
Reteaching Activity 3-2
Enrichment Activity 3-2
Lesson Quiz 3-2

Technology
Transparency 3-2
Audio Summaries
ExamView
Vocabulary PuzzleMaker
StudentWorks™ Plus

FOCUS

Activating Prior Knowledge

What I Know Ask students to name ways that family members can help one another. Students may mention household chores, lending support, caring for siblings.

Guide to Reading

BUILDING VOCABULARY
- Have students write a sentence that shows a relationship between two of the vocabulary terms.
- Use Vocabulary PuzzleMaker to reinforce vocabulary terms.

READING STRATEGY
Organizing Information Have each student fold a piece of paper in half lengthwise. At the top of the page, have students write "Family Units" and "Roles." Instruct students to add to their lists as they read the lesson.

Quick Write

Refer students to the list of family activities generated in the Activating Prior Knowledge activity. Each student should prepare a brief written explanation of the way an activity brings his or her family closer together.

Caption Answer

Photo Caption nuclear, blended, couples, or single-parent families

TEACH

Analyzing a Graphic Have students examine the different types of families in Figure 3.2. Ask students to name ways in which all of the family types are similar (for example, they consist of individuals who care for one another). Point out that many people are members of two families. **OL**

DEVELOPING Good Character

Teaching Character
Have students list the traits of good character. Write their traits on the board. Then have students identify ways that they could model each trait for a younger child. After students have completed the suggested activity, have them present their results to the class.

Academic Vocabulary

Role Students are introduced to the various roles of family members. Ask students to describe other terms that use the word *role*. Samples: *role-play, role model*

Reading Check

Answer Students should name and describe any three family types shown in the table. For example, a nuclear family consists of two parents and one or more children.

▶ **FIGURE 3.2**

FAMILY TYPES

R There are many different types of family units. **Are there examples of each type of family in your community?**

Family Type	Makeup
Couple	A husband and a wife who do not have children
Nuclear family	Two parents and one or more children
Extended family	A nuclear family plus other relatives such as grandparents
Single-parent family	One parent and one or more children
Blended family	Two people, one or both with children from previous marriages
Foster family	Adults caring for one or more children born to different parents
Adoptive family	A couple plus one or more adopted children
Joint-custody family	Two parents living apart, sharing custody of their children
Single-custody family	Two parents living apart and one or more children living with only one parent

DEVELOPING Good Character

Teaching Character
One of the biggest responsibilities parents have is to help their children develop good character. They do this through both their words and actions. For example, Nikki's father talks to her about the importance of honesty. He also demonstrates honesty in his own life, giving her a good example to follow. Which character trait do you think would be hardest to teach? Try teaching it to a younger sibling or friend.

Roles and Responsibilities in the Family

Every family member has a role to play. Parents and other adults are responsible for making sure the basic needs of the family are met. Their jobs also include teaching and practicing good health habits. They have a responsibility to model good communication and other health skills. They also should encourage young people in the family to practice these skills.

Not all responsibilities in the family fall on parents and other adults. Children have special jobs, too. In many families, for example, children share the household chores. Helping around the house is one way to demonstrate that you are responsible. Another way to contribute to the health and happiness of your family is by showing appreciation. To appreciate means to value someone or something. Saying "thank you" to the person who cooked dinner, for example, is a good way to show appreciation. You could also help with the dishes, volunteer to carry groceries, or do other tasks. As a teen, your role may also include helping other family members. You may be asked to spend time with a grandparent who has trouble getting around, or help a brother or sister with homework, However you choose to help, it's important to realize that your support helps make your family healthier.

 **List** Name and describe three types of families.

Dealing with Sensitive Issues

Is Everyone's Family Picture-Perfect? Teens can feel self-conscious or embarrassed by their families, particularly if their families are a different type than most families in their community or peer group. As you teach the lesson, be certain to give equal time to the positive aspects of all family types. Stress the similarities of all families, rather than differences between family types. Have students make a poster showing many types of families using magazine pictures, photos, drawings, or written words. They can include aspects and characteristics associated with all types of families.

Building Strong Families

HS

The main job of any family is to meet the needs of its members. A strong family nurtures its members. To **nurture** is *to fulfill physical, mental/emotional, and social needs.* Nurturing families meet each other's needs on all three sides of the health triangle.

Some of the physical needs your family should provide include a place to live, food, and clothing. Healthy families go beyond these basics. They look after each other during difficult times. They show concern for one another's safety and well-being.

U

Emotional support from the family includes love, but it's more than that. Strong families provide an atmosphere of warmth and security. Members make each other feel welcome and accepted. They celebrate one another's successes and help each other deal with disappointments and challenges.

Socially, strong families understand the importance of sharing. Members willingly pitch in with tasks or chores. Strong families spend time together. They may watch television, attend school functions, or participate in physical activities together.

Reading Check **List** What are three kinds of support that strong families provide?

Coping with Family Changes

Just as individuals go through changes, so do families. Some changes, such as a job promotion or graduation, are positive. Other changes can be difficult, for example, when a family member becomes ill or loses a job. These events can be stressful for the whole family.

Two especially difficult changes are separation and divorce. A split in the family can bring on feelings of anger, sadness, or guilt. It can make you feel uncertain about the future. Children are never the cause of divorce or separation. It is an adult problem. If your family is going through a separation or divorce, share your feelings with your parents or another trusted adult. They can help you understand how these changes will affect you and other

Health Online

Showing Appreciation

Visit **health.glencoe.com** for Student Web Activities that will give you more information on how to show appreciation.

Activity: Using the information from the link above, make plans to show three people in your life how much you appreciate them.

▼ Spending time together helps build strong family relationships. **What are some qualities of a strong, healthy family?**

Health Online

Allow time in the computer lab or suggest as a homework assignment that students explore the Student Web Activities at **health.glencoe.com**. Ask students to share their plans and explain how they could be implemented.

HS Health Skills Practice

Practicing Healthful Behaviors After students have read about strong families, have them list ways a student their age could contribute to a family. For example, a teen who does chores helps make his or her family stronger. Have students silently select one behavior that they could use in their own families. **OL**

Reading Check

Answer Strong families support the physical, mental/emotional, and social needs of its members.

U Universal Access

Learning Disabled Provide students with magazine pictures showing a wide range of family types. After a class discussion of various types of families, have students prepare a family collage to show the support a family can provide. **BL**

Caption Answer

Photo Caption an atmosphere of warmth, love, and acceptance

🏠 Home, School, and Community

At Home Have each student prepare a written plan for an activity that will include all or part of his or her family. Students' plans should take into consideration the cost of the activity, the time required for the activity, and the likes and dislikes of family members. Activities might be a physical activity, such as a family bike ride. A family game or a trip to the library are activities that do not require extra money or a long time commitment. Have students carry out their activities with their families. Ask volunteers to share their results with the class. **OL**

Health Skills Activity

Communication Skills

Family Meetings

Respect student and family privacy throughout this activity. Do not require an actual family meeting as a part of this activity.

- Have students meet in small groups to read the introductory paragraph.
- Ask students to discuss possible rules for family meetings and include communication strategies they have learned.
- When all groups have completed their discussions, have students prepare family contracts.
- Have each group share its contract with the class.

AL Active Learning

Creative Project Have students write stories about a fictional family that is dealing with a family change. Have students use words and illustrations to convey the emotions of the members of the fictional family. **OL**

Reading Check

Answer May include job loss, illness, or a death as changes that can affect the health of a family.

Caption Answer

Photo Caption *Sample answer:* A school counselor is a source of help for teens experiencing family difficulties.

Health Skills Activity

Communication Skills

Family Meetings

The behavior of family members and peers affects interpersonal communication. One way of improving communication between family members is through *family meetings*. In family meetings, all members meet to discuss problems and find solutions. Each family member should be encouraged to share opinions and offer suggestions.

It is important during family meetings to speak respectfully to one another. Each family member should have a chance to speak. It is also important for each member to listen carefully while others are speaking.

With a Group

Discuss how you think a family meeting should be run. Make a list of rules and guidelines to follow during a family meeting. When should people speak? Should all members vote on decisions to be made?

AL family members. Remember that parents, whether together or apart, love and care about their children.

Among the hardest changes to cope with is the death of a family member. Strong emotions are common and include sadness, grief, fear, and even anger. Expressing these feelings is an effective communication strategy for managing grief caused by disappointment, separation, or loss. Share your thoughts and feelings with people you can trust. Comforting others may also help you deal with your own feelings. It takes a long time to manage all the feelings caused by loss. Don't hesitate to ask for help. You might want to talk to a counselor who specializes in helping people manage grief.

▼ Dealing with family changes can be difficult. **Who are some people a teen could go to for help?**

Reading Check **Give Examples**
What are some changes that can affect the health of a family?

🏠 Home, School, and Community

In the Community As students read this lesson, emphasize to the class that communities and states have put laws into place to protect abused children. By law, a child or teen can be removed from an abusive home environment until the situation is corrected. First, however, the abuse must be reported. All states require doctors and health professionals to report suspected child abuse, and many states require anyone who suspects child abuse to report it. Remind students that the laws in your state are incorporated into your school's policies. **OL**

Serious Family Problems

We all have our ups and downs, good days and bad. The same is true of families. A healthy family manages to get over the bumps. Sometimes, however, the situation is more serious. It is beyond the family's ability to handle. One such problem is abuse (uh·BYOOS). **Abuse** is *a pattern of mistreatment of another person.* An adult or a child can be the target of abuse. Abuse is a serious problem that can have long-lasting effects on all family members. A family with an abuse problem needs to get help immediately.

Abuse can take several different forms. **Physical abuse** *involves the use of physical force.* A physically abused person often shows signs such as bruises, burns, or broken bones.

Emotional abuse is harder to spot. It often involves yelling and putting a family member down. Although there may be no physical harm, emotional abuse is just as serious. An emotionally abused person often feels worthless and angry.

Sexual abuse is *any mistreatment of a child or adult involving sexual activity.* Sexual abuse includes any type of unwanted or forced sexual activity. This can include touching one's private body parts or being forced to touch someone else. Displaying sexual material to a child is another act of sexual abuse. It is often difficult to see that a person is being sexually abused.

Parents are responsible for taking care of their children. When parents fail to do so, they are neglecting their children. **Neglect** is *the failure of parents to provide their children with basic physical and emotional care and protection.* Physical neglect involves not providing enough food, clothing, shelter, or medical care. Emotional neglect involves not giving love, respect, and other forms of emotional support.

Another serious problem for a family is when a family member is addicted to alcohol or drugs. You will learn strategies for coping with addiction in Chapter 10.

▲ Some victims of abuse are afraid to talk to someone. Talking to a trusted adult, however, is the first step in getting help. **What are some sources of help for families with problems of abuse or neglect?**

HS Health Skills Practice

Advocacy Reinforce with students the importance of getting help for families with problems concerning abuse. Provide students with a list of community resources for families dealing with abuse. Have students use the information to create pamphlets to inform teens about these resources. Obtain permission for students to display their pamphlets on a bulletin board, in a hallway or other area at school. **OL**

U Universal Access

At-Risk Students Many at-risk students cope with difficult family situations. Be sensitive to students with ongoing family difficulties as you discuss the material in this lesson. Be certain that family privacy is respected. Discussing hypothetical families and situations rather than asking students to volunteer their own experiences. As you discuss resources for students in difficult family situations, be certain that the lists of resources are accessible to all students. Without singling out individual students, use the material in this lesson to address ways to cope with difficult family situations. **OL**

Promoting Coordinated School Health

Resources for Teens Develop a list of resources available for teens who are dealing with separation, divorce, or a death in the family. School nurses, counselors, trusted teachers, administrators, and staff can all serve as resources for students. With the school counselor, develop a list of books and reliable online resources dealing with these issues. Post the list in a location that is accessible to all students. Be certain that students know how to access the school counselor. Ask students to suggest additional sources of help for teens struggling with family issues. **OL**

Caption Answer

Photo Caption A medical professional, school counselor, or trusted teacher is a good source of help for these problems.

Reading Check

Answer Emotional abuse is yelling and putting down another family member; physical abuse involves the use of physical force.

ASSESS

Assessment Resources

Lesson Review Quiz
- *ExamView*
- Fast Files Activities
- Online Quizzes and Activities

Reteaching
- Assign Concept Map 3-2 or Reteaching Activity 3-2 in the Fast Files. 📁
- Have students work with partners to list the types of families and roles people play within a family.

Enrichment
- Assign Enrichment Activity 3-2 in the Fast Files. 📁
- Have students read a story about a family going through change and write a summary book report.

CLOSE

Ask students to describe the benefits of good communication skills.

Help for Troubled Families

If you ever feel you are in danger from a family member, you must be brave enough to get help right away. Families where there is abuse need help. Start by speaking with an adult you feel you can trust. This might be a teacher or school counselor. The abuser needs help, too. He or she must understand the reasons behind the behavior and why it must change. If the danger is immediate, the police should be called. Abusing others is never acceptable.

Situations involving abuse or neglect often require professional health services. Social workers are professionals trained to help families with problems. Religious leaders and crisis centers can also offer help. You can call hotlines listed under "crisis intervention" in your telephone book. Still other resources to turn to are school counselors and doctors. They can suggest support and self-help groups. Some support groups are for those who are abused. Others are for the abusers. Both types try to help all the people involved.

 Health *Online*

Visit **health.glencoe.com** and complete the Interactive Study Guide for Lesson 2.

 Reading Check   **List** Name and describe two forms of abuse.

Lesson 2 Review

 After You Read

Review this lesson for new terms, major headings, and Reading Checks.

What I Learned
1. *Give Examples* Name two roles a person can have in a family.
2. *Vocabulary* Define *nurture*, and use it in a sentence.
3. *List* What are two forms of neglect?

Thinking Critically
4. *Apply* Al lives in an extended family that includes a grandparent and a younger cousin. What are some ways in which Al could show he cares about the members of his family?

5. *Synthesize* Kelly just found out her parents are getting divorced. How would you suggest that Kelly get help dealing with her concerns and fears?

Applying Health Skills
6. *Accessing Information* Use the phone book to access the names of community agencies that advocate healthy individuals, families, and communities. Make a list of these agencies.

72   Chapter 3: Healthy Relationships

Health *Online* For more review questions for Lesson 2, go to **health.glencoe.com**.

Lesson 2 Review Answers

1. Answers, which will vary, may include son or daughter, brother or sister, niece or nephew.
2. Nurture means to provide physical, mental/emotional, and social needs. Sentences will vary.

3. Neglect may be either physical or emotional.
4. Answers, which will vary, might include helping his cousin with homework or providing guidance, or helping his grandparent with chores.

5. She can share her feelings with a trusted adult, including a family member, someone at school, or a religious leader.
6. Provide phone books for students to use in the activity. Help students identify appropriate organizations to include in their lists.

Your Friends and Peers

Guide to Reading

Building Vocabulary
How are the terms below related? Are there words that have similar or related meanings? Define each term as best you can.

- friendship (p. 73)
- reliable (p. 74)
- loyal (p. 74)
- empathy (p. 74)
- cooperation (p. 75)
- peers (p. 76)
- peer pressure (p. 76)

Focusing on the Main Ideas
In this lesson, you will learn to

- **identify** the qualities of a good friend.
- **recognize** character traits found in friends.
- **understand** the two kinds of peer pressure.

Reading Strategy
Organizing Information As you read the lesson, make two lists. One should contain a list of the positive character traits of good friends. The second should list the ways peers can be negative influences.

Who Are Your Friends?

A friendship is an important relationship. A **friendship** is *a special type of relationship between people who enjoy being together.* There are many reasons people become friends. When you are young, location is a factor. Most of your current friends are probably from the same neighborhood or school. Another reason for choosing friends is shared interests, such as hobbies or activities. Personality traits, such as a sense of humor, may also lead people to each other so they that become friends.

Sometimes making new friends can be tough, especially when you move to a new school or city. Here are some tips to help you build friendships.

Quick Write

Write a poem or short story about an imaginary friend you want to meet. Include the qualities you would look for.

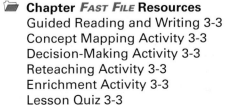

▶ Participating in activities helps you make friends with similar interests. **What are some activities and hobbies you enjoy?**

Lesson 3: Your Friends and Peers   **73**

Lesson 3 Resources

📁 **Chapter *FAST FILE* Resources**
Guided Reading and Writing 3-3
Concept Mapping Activity 3-3
Decision-Making Activity 3-3
Reteaching Activity 3-3
Enrichment Activity 3-3
Lesson Quiz 3-3

Technology
🔌 Transparency 3-3
🔊 Audio Summaries
💿 *ExamView*
💿 Vocabulary PuzzleMaker
🔊 StudentWorks™ Plus

FOCUS

Activating Prior Knowledge

What I Know Have students name examples of positive and negative peer pressure. Explain that in this lesson students will learn how peer pressure influences health.

Guide to Reading

BUILDING VOCABULARY

- Have students use the Glossary/Glosario to find the definitions of the vocabulary terms. Then have students make a matching game using index cards to practice the terms.
- Use Vocabulary PuzzleMaker to reinforce vocabulary terms.

READING STRATEGY
Organizing Information
Ask students to brainstorm positive aspects of having friends. Have them prepare a sheet of paper with two headings. As they read the lesson, they can complete their lists.

Quick Write

As students create their poems or stories they may want to use some of the words and phrases from the Activating Prior Knowledge activity. Ask for volunteers to share their completed writings.

Caption Answer

Photo Caption Joining a club or musical group is a way to make friends.

TEACH

HS Health Skills Practice

Making Friends Have each student work individually to complete the list of his or her interests, talents, and positive qualities under *Getting to Know Yourself.* Then have students work in small groups to write and perform a role-play of a student "breaking the ice" with someone he or she does not know. After all the groups have performed their role-plays, launch a class discussion on making friends. Ask students to name the most difficult part of making a new friend. Point out that different students will have different answers to the question—there is not one correct answer. Explain that role-plays are an excellent way to practice breaking the ice with someone you do not know. **OL**

C Critical Thinking

Analyze Have students work in small groups for 10 minutes to discuss the importance of shared values to friendships. Have each group rate the importance of having shared values with friends from 1 (not important) to 5 (very important). Then have each group share its results with the class. **OL**

Caption Answer

Photo Caption *Sample answer:* I enjoy swimming, and several students in my grade are in the swim club. We depend on each other for support.

HS

- *Get to know yourself.* Make a list of your own interests and talents. What are your positive qualities? What would make you a good friend to others?
- *Break the ice.* Start a conversation with a classmate you think you'd like to know better. Ask a question, or give a compliment. Talk about sports, movies, or whatever else interests you. If the other person shares the same interests, a friendship may develop.
- *Join a club, sports team, or community group that interests you.* You will be able to meet people with shared interests.
- *Offer a helping hand.* Help a classmate or neighbor with homework or other projects. When you reach out, you let others know you're a good friend to have.

Character Traits of Good Friends

It is important to choose friends who have positive values and attitudes. Good friends often have the same views of what is right and wrong. They may share common character traits such as trustworthiness and caring.

C

Do you have friends you can share your thoughts and feelings with? People who fit this description are trustworthy. Good friends should also be **reliable,** or *dependable.* They keep their promises. If they say they'll meet you at 4:00 o'clock, they show up at 4:00. They don't arrive thirty minutes late. Good friends are also **loyal,** or *faithful.* A loyal friend will not allow others to say untrue or mean things about you.

Good friends care about each other and support each other, through good and difficult times. They display **empathy,** *the ability to identify and share another person's feelings.* When you're feeling sad or disappointed, a good friend shares your pain. He or she will listen carefully when you talk about your problems.

▶ Friendships are relationships that you actively seek out. **What are qualities you and your friends share in common?**

74   Chapter 3: Healthy Relationships

What Teens Want to Know

Are cliques good or bad? Cliques, the tight-knit groups of friends that form in the preteen and teen years, can be a positive or a negative experience. Teens in cliques often lose the opportunities to interact with other peer groups. Cliques can influence a teen to do something that is against his or her values. Often, a clique will be exclusive and encourage its members to belittle students who are not a part of their group. Have students discuss ways to avoid the negative aspects of cliques. Suggest that students become active in several activities and develop variety in their friendships. **OL**

◀ Friends often help each other improve their skills. **How does this benefit both of you?**

Does being friends with someone mean the two of you will always agree? Of course not. It is only natural for the two of you to have occasional disagreements. Accepting views and opinions that are different from your own is a sign of respect. It is also a measure of maturity, a sign that you're growing up.

 **Reading Check** **Give Examples** Give one example each of reliability and empathy.

Building Strong Friendships

Building and maintaining positive friendships is important. You can build stronger friendships through cooperation. **Cooperation** means *working together for the common good.* Eduardo and Ben help each other prepare when one of them has a test. Ben will ask Eduardo questions, and vice versa. As members of the same little league team, the two also practice fielding together. As friends, Eduardo and Ben help each other reach goals.

Another way of making friendships stronger is through mutual respect and support. This means that friends listen and respect each other's opinions. Talking together about problems or concerns is a form of support. Supporting each other will help you and your friend make more healthful decisions. This includes saying no to negative peer pressure.

Practicing Healthful Behaviors Point out that cooperation is an important skill for building strong friendships. Tell students that, like all skills, cooperation takes practice. Have the class brainstorm a list of common school-related activities that require the cooperation of two or more students. Have students work in teams to write and perform short skits that demonstrate two or more people cooperating in one of the activities from the list. After all groups have performed their skits, have students describe ways in which their small groups cooperated during the writing and preparation of the skits. **OL**

 Reading Check

Answer An example of reliability is arriving at your friend's house at the time that was arranged. An example of empathy is showing understanding when a friend is sad.

Dealing with Sensitive Issues

Behavioral Disorders Empathy—the ability to identify and share another person's feelings—is a difficult skill for many students with behavior disorders. With a small group, or as a whole-class exercise, display various magazine pictures of people. Ask students to use clues from a picture to identify the person's feelings. Then ask volunteers to describe an appropriate response. For example, if a picture shows someone crying, an appropriate response is asking if they need help. **BL**

Caption Answer

Photo Caption When friends help each other, both people benefit because each person has a chance to learn from the other's strengths.

75

▶ When your peers see you doing good work, they may feel motivated themselves. **What are some other examples of positive peer pressure?**

Peer Pressure

Peers, as noted in Chapter 1, are *friends and other people in your age group.* During the teen years, your expanding abilities, independence, and responsibilities can influence personal behavior. Peers can give you support and confidence during this *transition,* or move, toward adulthood.

During this time, peer pressure can influence healthful choices. **Peer pressure** is *the influence that people your age may have on you.* Peer pressure can be something you feel indirectly. You see classmates wearing a certain type of clothing. Without a word from anyone else, you go out and buy the same item or something similar. At other times, peer pressure is direct. A peer may tell you what you should do to blend in or be accepted. Sometimes, this may come in the form of a demand or threat. Because it influences your decisions, peer pressure can affect your health in many ways.

Positive Peer Pressure

Peer pressure can be either positive or negative. Positive peer pressure can inspire you to improve yourself or do something worthwhile. For example, you may be encouraged to study for a test by studying together with friends or other peers. They are having a positive influence on you.

Inspiring you to improve your health and appearance, or to perform well on a team, are other ways to be positive influences. Maggie joined the yearbook staff partly because of encouragement from her friends. In what ways do your friends positively influence your behavior?

What Teens Want to Know

How can peer pressure affect my health? Most teens can easily identify how peer pressure can affect their choices in clothing and music. However, teens might have a more difficult time identifying how peer pressure affects their health. Ask students to list the choices they make each day that directly affect their health (for example, their choice of food at lunch, their choice to exercise or not, or the decision to take part in risky behaviors such as smoking and drinking alcohol). Then have students identify the ways in which peers could influence those choices. **OL**

Negative Peer Pressure

"I dare you!" When Shauna heard these words, she knew it was time to walk away. Daring someone to behave in dangerous or illegal ways is an example of negative peer pressure. The same is true of challenges that go against your beliefs and values. Here are some examples:

- Urging a peer to use tobacco, alcohol, or other drugs
- Talking a peer into being unkind to someone who is different
- Persuading a peer to do something illegal such as shoplifting
- Encouraging a peer to be disrespectful to parents or other adults
- Urging a peer to fight or get involved in gangs

Standing up to negative peer pressure can be difficult. It is, nevertheless, an important skill to learn. In the next lesson, you'll learn ways to say no to negative peer pressure.

 Reading Check **Explain** What is the difference between negative and positive peer pressure?

Health Online

Visit **health.glencoe.com** and complete the Interactive Study Guide for Lesson 3.

Health Online For more review questions for Lesson 3, go to **health.glencoe.com**.

Lesson 3 Review

 **After You Read**

Review this lesson for new terms, major headings, and Reading Checks.

What I Learned

1. *Vocabulary* Define *friendship*.
2. *Identify* What are two characteristics of a good friend?
3. *List* Give two examples of negative peer pressure.

Thinking Critically

4. *Apply* How do you show empathy to a friend who has just lost a pet?

5. *Analyze* Ted has been told that "all the cool kids are smoking." What kind of peer pressure is Ted experiencing?

Applying Health Skills

6. *Decision Making* Write a story in which a teen chooses to volunteer time because of positive peer pressure. In your story, show how the teen uses the six decision-making steps.

CHAPTER 3
Lesson 3

ASSESS

Assessment Resources

Lesson Review Quiz
- *ExamView*
- Fast Files Activities
- Online Quizzes and Activities

Reteaching
- Assign Concept Map 3-3 or Reteaching Activity 3-3 in the Fast Files.
- Have students skim the headings in the lesson. For each heading, have students write a sentence that tells the main idea of the section.

Enrichment
- Assign Enrichment Activity 3-3 in the Fast Files.
- Have each student develop and conduct a survey of adults and teens to find the qualities each group values most in friends. Have students present their findings to the class.

CLOSE

Ask students to name qualities they would look for in friendships after having read the lesson.

Lesson 3 Review Answers

1. Friendship is a relationship between people who enjoy being together.
2. Answers may include any two of the following traits: reliable, dependable, trustworthy, caring, loyal, faithful, empathetic, willing to cooperate.
3. Students should list two examples from the bulleted list on this page.
4. Answers might include listening to the person and trying to be a source of comfort.
5. It is negative peer pressure. Ted is being encouraged to take part in a behavior that carries health risks.
6. Students' stories should describe peer pressure influencing a student's decision to volunteer. Check that each story includes the six steps of decision making (state the situation, list the options, weigh the possible outcomes, consider values, make a decision and act on it, evaluate the decision).

77

FOCUS

Activating Prior Knowledge

What I Know Ask students to identify ways to say no to negative peer pressure. List their answers on the board. *Students may use refusal skills as examples.*

Guide to Reading

BUILDING VOCABULARY

■ Have students skim the lesson to find the definition of each vocabulary term. Then have students write the definition of the term in their own words.

■ Use Vocabulary PuzzleMaker to reinforce vocabulary terms.

READING STRATEGY

Identifying Problems and Solutions Have students work in pairs to complete the Reading Strategy. Have them create lists from the lesson and write examples of ways to say no. Model the activity by naming a common example of peer pressure and describing a way to say no to that pressure.

*Q*uick Write

After students have created their lists of ways to say no to dangerous or unhealthful choices, develop a class list. Announce the number of ways the class has identified to say no. As students read the lesson, challenge them to add to the list.

Refusal Skills

Guide to Reading

● **Building Vocabulary**
Write the terms below in your notebook. Define each term as you read about it in the lesson.

■ refusal skills (p. 78)
■ abstinence (p. 80)

● **Focusing on the Main Ideas**
In this lesson, you will learn to

■ **identify** how to use refusal skills to resist peer pressure.

■ **demonstrate** refusal skills to resist negative peer pressure.

■ **explain** the importance of abstinence during the teen years.

● **Reading Strategy**
Identifying Problems and Solutions After reading this lesson, give examples of peer pressure. Tell how you might say no in each situation.

*Q*uick Write

List as many ways as you can of saying no when someone pressures you to do something dangerous or unhealthy.

◀ When pressure builds, something has to give.
What is a method for resisting pressure without having a situation get out of control?

What Are Refusal Skills?

Lance worked in the school store. Stan, another student, asked Lance to let him have a notebook without paying. "Come on, no one will notice," Stan said. Lance knew he was being asked to do something wrong. He could get into trouble. Even if he didn't get into trouble, his conscience would bother him.

When you are pressured to do something wrong, tension can build. You may worry what will happen if you don't go along with the group. Will your friends still like you? Will you still be a part of the group? It is at these times that refusal skills can help. **Refusal skills** are *ways of saying no.* They are communication strategies for avoiding potentially harmful situations.

Using Refusal Skills

You may find yourself in a situation in which you feel pressure to participate in unsafe behaviors. One way of refusing effectively is to use the S.T.O.P. strategy. Each of the letters stands for a different step:

78 Chapter 3: Healthy Relationships

Lesson 4 Resources

📁 **Chapter** *FAST FILE* **Resources**
Guided Reading and Writing 3-4
Concept Mapping Activity 3-4
Cross-Curriculum Activity 3-4
Reteaching Activity 3-4
Enrichment Activity 3-4
Lesson Quiz 3-4

Technology
🔦 Transparency 3-4
⊛ Audio Summaries
⊛ *ExamView*
 Vocabulary PuzzleMaker
⊛ StudentWorks™ Plus

Health Skills Activity

Refusal Skills

Saying No

Apply the S.T.O.P. strategy to Lance's problem in the lesson opener. Role-play the story with two classmates. One of you is to take the role of Lance. The other two are to be the classmates pressuring Lance. Prepare a script for your story. Show how Lance uses the four steps to say no to his friends.

With a Group

Be prepared to perform your role-play for classmates. *What is another situation in which you could you use the S.T.O.P. strategy to avoid negative peer pressure?*

- **Say no in a firm voice.** Sometimes, saying no is enough. Friends who respect you will take no for an answer. People are more likely to believe you if you speak firmly. Show self-confidence without being insulting to others.

- **Tell why not.** Explain your reasons for saying no. Let your peers know that you value your health and safety. It's also a chance to show your good character traits.

- **Offer other ideas.** Change the subject by coming up with something else to do instead.

- **Promptly leave.** If people continue to put pressure on you, walk away. If certain people always put pressure on you whenever you see them, avoid them.

Remember that you are not alone when you face a difficult situation. You can always get help from a trusted adult. A parent, older brother or sister, or counselor will listen to your problem. They can help you decide the best course of action to take. They might even suggest some options you hadn't thought about.

 **Reading Check**

Explain How do refusal skills protect your health and safety?

▼ Saying no to risky behaviors can be tough. **What are some ways to say no to risky behaviors?**

TEACH

Health Skills Activity

Refusal Skills

Saying No

- Have students prepare the scripts for their role-plays and rehearse their skits.
- Have each group perform its role-play for the class.
- Have volunteers supply answers to the question at the end of the feature. Make a list of situations on the board. Then have the class choose one and brainstorm how the S.T.O.P. strategy could be applied to this situation.

Reading Check

Answer Refusal skills can protect your health by helping you to say no to high-risk behaviors.

Academic Vocabulary

Participate On page 80, students learn that abstinence is the active choice not to participate in health-risk behaviors. Explain that *participate* means "to take part in." Ask students to list school activities in which they participate.

Home, School, and Community

In School Invite a school counselor to speak to students about peer pressure and high-risk behaviors. Ask the counselor to discuss the characteristics of teens who are able to resist negative peer pressure. Also have the speaker discuss the consequences he or she has observed for students who give in to negative peer pressure. Before the speaker is scheduled to talk, have a class discussion about possible questions for the guest speaker. Give students the opportunity to submit written questions to the speaker. **OL**

Caption Answers

Photo Caption, p. 78
S.T.O.P.

Photo Caption, p. 79
Refusal skills are a way to resist pressure.

ASSESS

Assessment Resources

Lesson Review Quiz
- *ExamView*
- Fast Files
- Online Quizzes and Activities

Reteaching

- Assign Concept Map 3-4 or Reteaching Activity 3-4 in the Fast Files.
- Have students write out the four steps of the S.T.O.P. strategy.

Enrichment

- Assign Enrichment Activity 3-4 in the Fast Files.
- Have students prepare a lesson to teach the S.T.O.P. strategy to younger students. Arrange for students to visit a class and teach their lessons.

CLOSE

Challenge students to give examples of peer pressure and refusal strategies.

What Is Abstinence?

Some of the negative pressures you face as a teen are relatively minor. Others can be major. Among these are pressures to take part in high-risk behaviors such as using tobacco, alcohol, or illegal drugs. Becoming sexually active is another high-risk behavior. When you say no to high-risk behaviors, you are practicing abstinence (AB·stuh·nuhns). **Abstinence** is *not participating in high-risk behaviors*. Abstinence protects your health and that of others. It shows you have self-control.

Choosing Abstinence

When you choose abstinence, you protect the three sides of your health triangle. Abstaining from tobacco, for example, protects your lungs and heart. Abstaining from alcohol and illegal drugs protects your body and mind. Abstaining from sexual activity protects you against pregnancy and sexually transmitted diseases. Teens who abstain from high-risk behaviors understand the importance of practicing positive health behaviors.

Health *Online*

Visit **health.glencoe.com** and complete the Interactive Study Guide for Lesson 4.

Reading Check **List** Name three benefits of choosing abstinence.

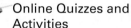

Lesson 4 Review

After You Read

Review this lesson for new terms, major headings, and Reading Checks.

What I Learned

1. *Vocabulary* What are *refusal skills?*

2. *Identify* Describe the relationship between peer pressure and refusal skills.

3. *Recall* Why is abstinence important during the teen years?

Thinking Critically

4. *Explain* Tell how positive peer pressure can make a friendship stronger.

5. *Analyze* Hannah told her friend that smoking harms a person's lungs and heart. Her friend continues to urge Hannah to smoke a cigarette. What must Hannah do next? Explain.

Applying Health Skills

6. *Advocacy* Create a poster that colorfully explains the S.T.O.P. strategy. With permission from school administrators, place your poster on a hallway wall.

80   Chapter 3: Healthy Relationships

Health Online For more review questions for Lesson 4, go to **health.glencoe.com**.

Lesson 4 Review Answers

1. They are methods for saying no.
2. Answers might include the idea that when peer pressure to engage in high-risk behaviors is intense, refusal skills can allow you to say no without worrying about what your peers might think of you.

3. Abstinence from high-risk behaviors protects all three sides of the health triangle.
4. Answers, which will vary, might include the idea that friends encourage and inspire each other to do their best.

5. Hannah needs to offer other ideas. Having told her friend why not, she is now at the "O" step of the S.T.O.P. strategy.
6. Students' posters should include all four steps of the S.T.O.P. strategy.

Resolving Conflicts

Guide to Reading

● **Building Vocabulary**
Arrange the terms below in two columns: problems and solutions. Match each problem with a solution.

- conflicts (p. 81)
- prejudice (p. 82)
- tolerance (p. 82)
- compromise (p. 83)
- negotiation (p. 83)
- peer mediation (p. 83)
- violence (p. 84)
- gang (p. 84)

● **Focusing on the Main Ideas**
In this lesson, you will be able to

- **explain** why conflicts occur.
- **describe** ways of protecting yourself from violence.
- **identify** a strategy to resolve conflicts through negotiation.

● **Reading Strategy**
Sequencing Create a flow chart to show the steps that lead up to violence. Then add steps that show how to prevent conflicts from turning violent.

What Are Conflicts?

"Give that back to me! It's mine." The twins Jenny was babysitting were at it again. It seemed they couldn't go more than a few minutes without arguing. Luckily, Jenny had learned about conflicts in health class. **Conflicts** are *disagreements in ideas, beliefs, or interests*. The first step in preventing conflicts is understanding what causes them.

Quick Write

Do you think schools with violence problems should install video cameras? Why or why not? Explain in a brief paragraph.

◀ When conflict arises, it is no game. **What are some healthy ways to resolve conflicts?**

Lesson 5: Resolving Conflicts **81**

Lesson 5 Resources

📁 **Chapter *FAST FILE* Resources**
Guided Reading and Writing 3-5
Concept Mapping Activity 3-5
Cross-Curriculum Activity 3-5
Reteaching Activity 3-5
Enrichment Activity 3-5
Lesson Quiz 3-5

Technology
🔦 Transparency 3-5
💿 Audio Summaries
💿 *ExamView*
 Vocabulary PuzzleMaker
💿 StudentWorks™ Plus

FOCUS

Activating Prior Knowledge

What I Know Ask volunteers to define the terms *violence* and *conflict*. Explain that in this lesson students will learn techniques to resolve conflicts and avoid violence.

Guide to Reading

BUILDING VOCABULARY
- Have students make flash cards for the vocabulary terms in the section. Have students review their flashcards with a partner.
- Use Vocabulary PuzzleMaker to reinforce vocabulary terms. ✎

READING STRATEGY
Sequencing A completed flow chart might contain the following steps that lead to violence: a conflict develops, a conflict escalates, violence results. Steps to avoid violence include: a conflict develops, a compromise is reached through negotiation, the conflict is resolved peacefully.

Quick Write

Have students write a paragraph stating their opinions of whether schools should install video cameras. Remind students to proofread and revise their rough drafts.

> **Caption Answer**
> **Photo Caption** use communication skills, be tolerant

TEACH

DEVELOPING

Good Character

The Myth of Positive Prejudice
Have students work in small groups to discuss positive prejudice. Ask students to discuss with their groups any examples of positive prejudice with which they are familiar. Then have each group work together to write a response to one of its examples. Ask student groups to share their responses and explain how their responses would correct a prejudiced belief without causing a conflict.

Reading Strategy

Identifying Cause and Effect After students have read about causes of conflict in the text, have them make a list of causes of conflict. For each cause, have students identify a possible effect. For example, the cause of a conflict might be one student insulting another. The effect might be a verbal argument. Then have students identify ways that causes of conflict can be prevented. **OL**

Reading Check

Answer Causes of conflict include differences of opinions and emotions such as jealousy or competition.

DEVELOPING

Good Character

The Myth of Positive Prejudice

Some kinds of prejudice can seem positive. For example, saying all French people are good cooks may sound like a compliment. However, it is really a form of prejudice. Prejudices assume things about people based on their race, culture, or the groups they belong to. Don't assume anything about a person until you get to know him or her. Imagine hearing a prejudiced remark at school. **What would you say to correct the prejudice without creating conflict?**

Causes of Conflict

When you understand the possible causes of conflict, you can develop positive communication strategies for preventing conflict. Most conflicts can be traced back to an act or event. A difference of opinion, or jealousy, can create a conflict. For example, a group of students working on a school project might disagree over the jobs each person should do.

Sometimes conflicts are started *because of* prejudice (PREH·juh·dis). **Prejudice** is *an opinion or fear formed without having facts or firsthand knowledge.* Disliking a person because of their skin color or culture is an example of prejudice. Prejudice can cause both emotional and social health risks within a community.

 **Identify** Name some common causes of conflict.

Preventing Conflicts

The first step in preventing conflict is using good communication skills. When you disagree with someone, state your case clearly and calmly. Use "I" statements that do not accuse or blame. An example of an "I" statement is "I feel like I am being left out of the group." Compare this with the more aggressive "You are ignoring me!"

Another valuable tool in preventing conflicts is tolerance. **Tolerance** is *the ability to accept other people as they are.* Accepting people who are different from you can help you build and maintain positive interpersonal relationships.

Resolving Conflicts

When a conflict occurs, conflict resolution skills can help you resolve it in a positive way. One skill is knowing when to walk away. Sometimes the right response to a possible conflict is no response. Often, the disagreement will end quickly if you walk away.

No matter what the disagreement, refuse to fight. If a conflict appears to be turning physical, just walk away. This does not make you a coward or chicken. It makes you wiser and more mature than the other person.

If a conflict is brewing between two other people, don't get in the middle or take sides. If a fight breaks out, don't get between the fighters. Instead, go get help from an adult right away.

Dealing with Sensitive Issues

The Roots of Prejudice When discussing prejudice, explain how and why prejudiced beliefs form. Prejudiced beliefs often have their roots in a negative experience. When a person has had a negative interaction with one member of a different culture or race, negative feelings are sometimes applied to the entire race or culture. Point out that an entire group should not be judged by the actions of an individual. Remind students that lack of prejudice does not mean ignoring differences between cultures. Differences between cultures should be celebrated and appreciated.

Reaching a Compromise

One important conflict-resolution skill is compromise. **Compromise** is *a skill in which each side gives up something in order to reach an agreeable solution.* Suppose that you and your friends go to the schoolyard to play soccer. Unfortunately, you arrive at the exact same time as a girl from your class and you both try to grab the only ball left. Instead of fighting over the ball however, you reach a compromise. You all join in a game together. Compromise is a great way to resolve conflicts, as long as it does not go against your values.

▲ A peer mediator can help students resolve conflict. **What are some other ways to resolve conflict?**

HS Reaching a compromise sometimes requires negotiation (neh·GOH·shee·AY·shuhn). **Negotiation** is *the process of talking about a conflict and deciding how to reach a compromise.* The T.A.L.K. strategy is an effective way of resolving conflict through negotiation. The steps are as follows:

- **Take a time-out.** Wait at least 30 minutes before you talk over the situation. This will give both of you a chance to calm down and think more clearly.

- **Allow each person to tell his or her side.** Each person should have the chance to explain his or her feelings without interruption. Choose a time and place to talk where you won't be interrupted or distracted. Always listen carefully, and show respect for the other person.

- **Let each person ask questions.** Each person should have the chance to question the other. Stay calm and respectful. Also, stay focused on one problem. Don't bring up other problems at this time.

- **Keep brainstorming.** Try to see the situation from the other person's point of view. Work to find a solution that will satisfy you both.

U When all else fails, get help from a school counselor, parent, or other adult. An option in some schools is peer mediation (mee·dee·AY·shuhn). **Peer mediation** is *a process in which a specially trained student listens to both sides of an argument to help the people reach a solution.* Your teacher or school counselor can tell you if your school has peer mediators.

 **Reading Check** **List** Identify two steps in the T.A.L.K. strategy. Tell what happens in each.

HS Health Skills Practice

Conflict Resolution Have students practice using the T.A.L.K. strategy for conflict resolution. Make a list of scenarios of conflict between two students (for example, one student pushes another student in the hallway). For each scenario, have two volunteers act out conflict resolution through the T.A.L.K strategy. After they have talked through the conflict, ask the class for suggestions and comments. **OL**

U Universal Access

Gifted Students Have students who need an extra challenge research the use of peer mediation for conflict resolution at school. Have students research the qualifications and training required for peer mediators and prepare a written plan for implementing a peer mediation program. **AL**

Reading Check

Answer May include take a time-out—each person calms down before speaking. Allow each person to tell his or her side without interruption. Let each person ask questions—stay calm and respectful. Try to understand the other person's point of view.

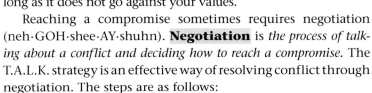

Home, School, and Community

In School Have students make a list of resources in the school for students involved in conflicts. With students, develop a step-by-step action plan they can follow to deal with conflicts that arise during the school day. Students may wish to consult the school guidance counselor or the vice principal as they develop their plans. Then have students make posters that describe their action plans. Obtain permission for students to display their posters in hallways or the cafeteria. **OL**

Caption Answer

Photo Caption Use the T.A.L.K. strategy.

Health *Online*

Visit health.glencoe.com and complete the Interactive Study Guide for Lesson 5.

When Conflicts Get Out of Hand

When conflicts are not dealt with, they can get out of hand. This in turn can lead to violence. **Violence** is *the use of physical force to harm someone or something.* Violence is a growing problem in the United States. It can lead to injury and even death.

In some communities, there is gang violence. A **gang** is *a group whose members often uses violence or takes part in criminal activity.* Some teens join gangs because of peer pressure. Many teens who join gangs come from troubled families. They seek a sense of belonging that is missing in their lives. Gang membership is never an answer to life's problems. Belonging to a gang only makes problems worse. Teens in gangs have a higher school drop-out rate than nonmembers. They are arrested more often, too. Because gangs often use weapons, these teens have a higher risk of getting seriously injured or of dying.

Avoiding Violence

There may be times when conflict or violence finds you. For example, someone may try to bully you or pull you into a fight. Fortunately, there are techniques for avoiding threatening situations.

For starters, learn and practice self-control. Do not fight or threaten others. Don't wear any clothing that could be mistaken for gang clothing. If you use a purse, carry it with the strap across your chest. Whenever you can, steer clear of harmful situations. If you know a party might include alcohol or drugs, don't go. If you know or suspect someone has a weapon, report it immediately to a parent or another trusted adult.

Avoid violence by becoming an advocate for peace. Let others know you are a nonviolent person. Serve as a positive example. Use good communication skills. Being polite and showing respect for others are also good ways to avoid violence.

Protecting Yourself from Violence

Observing safety rules is another way of protecting yourself from violence. If you're home alone, do not open the door to anyone you don't know. Keep doors and windows locked. Never tell visitors or callers you are alone. Instead, say your parents are busy or can't come to the phone.

▼ This teen is wearing her handbag in a way that lessens her risk of becoming a victim of violence. **What are some other injury-prevention strategies for personal and family health?**

84 Chapter 3: Healthy Relationships

What Teens Want to Know

How do I avoid gangs? Most students are aware of the negative aspects of gangs. Help students develop a list of tips for avoiding gangs. Suggest: avoid being alone—gangs often seek out teens who are alone; avoid being seen wearing gang colors or clothing; don't use drugs—drug dealers are often gang members; avoid gang territory or gang hang-outs; end friendships with students who join gangs. Then have students make a list of positive activities and values that can help them avoid gangs. For example: join a sport, a club, or a musical group. **OL**

If you are going out, tell your family where you are going and how you will get there. Make sure they also know when you expect to return. When walking home, try to walk in pairs or with a group. Stay in familiar neighborhoods; avoid deserted streets and dangerous shortcuts.

Avoid strangers. Never get into or go near a stranger's car or hitchhike. Do not enter a building with a stranger. Don't agree to run errands or do other tasks for strangers. Finally, if someone tries to grab you, scream and run away. Go to the nearest place with people. Ask them to call 911, or your parents.

▲ Remember that there is safety in numbers. Bullies are less likely to pick on a group. **What are some other ways of protecting yourself against violence?**

 **Reading Check**

Identify What are some ways of avoiding violence?

 Reading Check

Answer You can avoid violence by avoiding strangers and staying in familiar neighborhoods.

ASSESS

Assessment Resources

Lesson Review Quiz
- *ExamView*
- Fast Files Activities
- Online Quizzes and Activities

Reteaching

- Assign Concept Map 3-5 or Reteaching Activity 3-5 in the Fast Files. 📁
- Ask volunteers to name and describe the four steps of the T.A.L.K. strategy.

Enrichment

- Assign Enrichment Activity 3-5 in the Fast Files. 📁
- Have students research the effectiveness and cost of various violence prevention methods used by schools. Have students present their findings to the class.

CLOSE

Challenge students to name effective ways to prevent conflicts from turning violent.

Lesson 5 Review

After You Read

Review this lesson for new terms, major headings, and Reading Checks.

What I Learned

1. ***Vocabulary*** Use *prejudice* and *tolerance* in a sentence.

2. ***List*** Name two ways in which you can help prevent conflicts from occurring.

3. ***Recall*** When should you not be willing to compromise?

Thinking Critically

4. ***Evaluate*** When Seth walks away from a fight, he hears his opponent call him "chicken." What should Seth do? Explain.

5. ***Analyze*** Darla notices it is dark when she leaves her friend's house. Suggest some things Darla should do to avoid becoming a victim of violence.

Applying Health Skills

6. ***Communication Skills*** With a partner, practice changing "you" sentences into "I" sentences. How does the use of "I" sentences help prevent conflict?

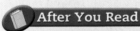 **Health Online** For more review questions for Lesson 5, go to **health.glencoe.com**.

Lesson 5: Resolving Conflicts **85**

Lesson 5 Review Answers

1. Sentences should reflect correct definitions of the two terms on page 82.
2. Possible answers include using good communication skills, knowing when to walk away, not taking sides, learning and practicing tolerance, and recognizing that fighting is not a solution.

3. Never compromise if your values are involved.
4. Seth should keep walking because fighting is never a solution. Walking away is the wise decision, not the cowardly one.
5. *Sample answers:* Actions she should take include walking down well-lighted streets and

avoiding risky shortcuts. Let parents know when she will be home and the route she is taking. Actions she should not take include any dealings with strangers.
6. *Sample answer:* "You ignored me at lunch." could be changed to "I feel disappointed when we don't sit together at lunch."

Building Health Skills
CONFLICT RESOLUTION

Working Things Out

Working Things Out

SKILL
Conflict Resolution

Activating Prior Knowledge

Ask students to recall a situation involving a conflict. Tell students that conflicts are a part of all relationships.

- **Objective** After completing the activity, students will be able to resolve conflicts in a healthy way.
- **Time** 45 minutes
- **Materials** paper, pencil

Teacher Classroom Resources

- Building Health Skills
- Transparency 3-5

Model

- Have students identify the steps Samantha and Kari used to resolve their conflict. *take a time out, let each person ask questions, allow each person to tell his or her side uninterrupted, keep brainstorming to find a good solution*

DIRECTIONS

Conflict resolution involves finding a positive solution to a disagreement or preventing it from becoming a larger conflict. This activity will give you the opportunity to develop and master this important health skill. Here's a guide to the different parts of this activity:

❶ In the **Model** section, you will read about a teen who performs the health skill successfully. This "model" scenario will show you how the skill is done.

❷ The **Practice** section will help guide you in practicing the skill.

❸ In the **Apply** section, you will have a chance to perform the skill on your own. You can use the Self-Check to check your work.

To complete this activity, first read the scenario presented in the Model. Then move on to the Practice. Finally, go ahead and try the Apply.

❶ Model

Conflicts are common in relationships. A healthy way to resolve these conflicts is to discuss the problem. Read about how two teen sisters, Kari and Samantha, resolve a conflict.

Kari: Sam, I'd like to talk to you about something that is bothering me.
T—Take a time-out.

Samantha: Sure, what's going on, Sis?

Kari: I get upset when you borrow my clothes without asking. I didn't get a chance to wear that sweater yet. I wish you had asked me before putting it on.
A—Allow each person to tell his or her side uninterrupted.

Samantha: Sorry, Kari. I didn't think you would mind if I borrowed it. Do you want it back right now?
L—Let each person ask questions.

Kari: No, it's okay if you wear it, but can we make an agreement? What if from now on we ask before borrowing each other's stuff?
K—Keep brainstorming to find a good solution.

Samantha: It's a deal.

National Health Standards Addressed
- - - - - - - - - - - - - - - - - -
4.1, 4.3, 4.7, 4.8

Teaching Tips

Conflict Resolution Role-Play Some students may need a model before they are able to complete an assignment. Ask for volunteers who understand the conflict-resolution process clearly to demonstrate a scene. Follow these guidelines:
- Have students role-play without words.

- Make sure all students understand the conflict and what happened.
- Role-play again without words to show the conflict being resolved.
- Make sure all students understand how the conflict was resolved.

② Practice

To practice what you have learned about resolving conflict, read the following conversation between Kari and Anne. Can you identify the T.A.L.K. steps the girls took to resolve their conflict? Write the conversation on your own paper, and label each step with a T., A., L., or K. Complete the conversation by writing an ending where Kari and Anne agree on a solution.

Kari: Anne, can you please pay for the CD you lost?

Anne: It was an accident so I don't think I should have to pay for it.

Kari: I know it was an accident, but it's my favorite CD. I would really like to buy a new one.

Anne: So what should we do?

Skill Summary
CONFLICT RESOLUTION

T Take a time-out.

A Allow each person to tell his or her side uninterrupted.

L Let each person ask questions.

K Keep brainstorming to find a good solution.

③ Apply

Conflict-resolution skills promote healthy relationships. On your paper, list several situations that lead to conflict for teens. Choose one of these situations, and write a script showing how the conflict can be resolved. Remember to use the T.A.L.K. steps for conflict resolution.

Self-Check

- Did my script show how to use the T.A.L.K. steps for conflict resolution?
- Did my script show both sides of the conflict?
- Did my script show a positive solution?

Practice

- Have students copy the conversation and label the steps of conflict resolution. Then have students write an ending for the conversation.
- Ask for volunteers to share their endings. After several volunteers have shared their endings, ask students to decide if there is more than one "right" way to peacefully resolve a conflict.

Apply/Assess

- If students are having difficulty with their scripts, have them review the steps shown in the Model and Practice activities.
- Have students work in small groups to prepare role-plays using their scripts. As students perform their role-plays, have audience members take note of the steps of the T.A.L.K. strategy demonstrated in each script.
- You may wish to distribute the Building Health Skills Activity in the Fast Files.

ASSESSMENT SCORING

Student work should meet all criteria to achieve the highest score:

Skills Student work demonstrates:
- A time-out from the situation.
- Both persons' points of view.
- Questions to clarify the conflict.
- Brainstorming to find a solution.

Concept Student work provides:
- Accurate information about causes of conflict and how to resolve conflict.

Schoolroom Torment

Objectives

Students will be able to
- identify misconceptions about bullies
- describe the characteristics of a bully
- name ways to avoid being bullied

Motivator

Ask students to name some of the forms that bullying can take. Sample answers: *name-calling, teasing, or hitting*

Teaching The Feature

- After reading the feature, ask students to identify some of the reasons bullying occurs. Then have students generate a list of solutions to the problem of bullying. Challenge students to think beyond the suggestions given in the text to generate some of their own solutions. **OL**

- Have students discuss appropriate actions to take if they witness another student being bullied. Suggest that small actions, such as speaking kindly to the victim, can make a big difference in the life of a bullied student. Remind students that those witnessing bullying should seek help from an adult rather than intervening on their own if a situation seems to be turning violent. **AL**

TIME *health news*

Schoolroom
TORMENT

Do you have the wrong idea about bullies?

Many people think that bullies don't have any friends and are lonely. If you know a bully, you probably know that isn't always true. According to psychologist Dorothy Espelage, the typical bully is not a loner at all. Instead, bullies are popular and athletic. Bullies know how to get their way with adults while bullying their schoolmates at the same time.

Here's how Dr. Espelage answered some of our questions about bullies.

Q: How do you define "bully"?

A: A bully is a kid who teases and intimidates other students. Bullies spread rumors about other kids. Bullies form social groups that keep many kids out.

Q: What's behind bullying behavior?

A: First of all, with some teens, you can fit in and be cool if you bully others. Second, bullies don't feel that great about themselves, and bullying can block some of those feelings. Lastly, some teens don't always have the skills to tolerate differences in other kids. So when bullies see people who are different, they lash out and make fun of them.

Q: Are bullies usually from single-parent homes?

A: We find bullying just as often where there is a mom and a dad at home. It's all about parental supervision. If kids are unsupervised, they're more likely to become bullies.

Q: What can young people do about bullies and bullying?

A: Kids shouldn't be easy targets for bullies. Look the bully in the eye and walk away confidently. Bullies want to hurt your feelings. Even if they're being really mean, act as if they're not succeeding and don't get into a fight.

Also, tell a parent or a teacher. They want to know what is happening and how you feel about it. If the bullying happened at school, have a parent talk it over with your teacher. Parents shouldn't call the parents of the bully.

Activity — Media, Technology, and Culture

Culture Have each student design and create a pamphlet about bullying in today's culture. Instruct students to fold sheets of paper into thirds. Students should describe popular misconceptions about bullies on one side and characteristics of bullies on the second part. On the third section, students should offer suggestions for avoiding being bullied. Have students use a computer to add clip art or use original illustrations to make their pamphlets attractive. Make the pamphlets available to other students in the school through the school counselor's office.

Reading Review

FOLDABLES | Study Organizer

Foldables™ and Other Study Aids Take out the Foldable™ that you created for Lesson 1 and any graphic organizers that you created for Lessons 1-5. Find a partner, and quiz each other using these study aids.

Lesson 1 | Communication Skills

Key Ideas

- Good communication skills include both verbal and nonverbal forms of communication.
- The three styles of communication are assertive, passive, and aggressive.

Vocabulary

- communication (p. 62)
- relationship (p. 62)
- body language (p. 63)

Lesson 2 | Your Family

Key Ideas

- Different types of family units include nuclear, blended, extended, and single-parent families.
- A teen's role within the family includes helping other family members in need.
- Family members care for each other by providing physical, mental/emotional, and social support.

Vocabulary

- family (p. 67)
- nurture (p. 69)
- abuse (p. 71)
- physical abuse (p. 71)
- sexual abuse (p. 71)
- neglect (p. 71)

Lesson 3 | Your Friends and Peers

Key Ideas

- People may become good friends because of shared interests.
- Character traits found in friends include reliability, loyalty, and a willingness to show empathy.
- The two kinds of peer pressure are positive and negative.

Vocabulary

- friendship (p. 73)
- reliable (p. 74)
- loyal (p. 74)
- empathy (p. 74)
- cooperation (p. 75)
- peers (p. 76)
- peer pressure (p. 76)

Lesson 4 | Refusal Skills

Key Ideas

- You can resist negative peer pressure by using the S.T.O.P. strategy of refusal.
- Practicing abstinence is important in order to avoid high-risk behaviors.

Vocabulary

- refusal skills (p. 78)
- abstinence (p. 80)

Lesson 5 | Resolving Conflicts

Key Ideas

- Conflicts occur for a number of reasons, including jealousy and competition.
- Conflict-resolution skills include compromise and negotiation.
- You can protect yourself from violence by avoiding dangerous situations.

Vocabulary

- conflicts (p. 81)
- prejudice (p. 82)
- tolerance (p. 82)
- compromise (p. 83)
- negotiation (p. 83)
- peer mediation (p. 83)
- violence (p. 84)
- gang (p. 84)

Chapter 3 Reading Review **89**

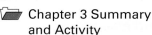

Assessment Resources

- 📁 Chapter 3 Summary and Activity
- 💿 Audio Summaries
- 📁 Reading Tutor
- 📁 Performance Assessment
- 📁 Chapter 3 Test
- 💿 *ExamView*
- 💿 Vocabulary PuzzleMaker
- 💿 Online Learning Center

Reading Review

Study Aids

- **Using the Dinah Zike Foldable™ Study Organizer** Have students use the Foldable™ to review the content of Lesson 1. Have students write a sentence describing the benefits of good communication skills.

FOLDABLES | Study Organizer

Key Ideas

- **Using Lesson Reviews** Have students reread the Lesson Review questions found at the end of each lesson. Students should review the text to find any answers they have forgotten.

Vocabulary Review

- **Vocabulary Sentences** Have students work in pairs. Students should take turns correctly using chapter vocabulary terms in sentences.

▶ **Teaching Tips**

Using Graphic Organizers Graphic organizers are a visual representation of knowledge. They can be used for prereading, postreading, writing, reasoning, and discussion exercises. Organizing and illustrating ideas and information helps students to comprehend and learn. Some common types of graphic organizers include K-W-L charts, word webs, concept maps, T-charts, Venn diagrams, time lines, pyramids, and many more. The positive effects of graphic organizers are greatest when students are trained in their use and then create their own graphic organizers.

Assessment

Reviewing Vocabulary and Main Ideas

1. Body language
2. Communication
3. nurture
4. abuse
5. Neglect
6. True
7. False, Peer pressure
8. False, S.T.O.P.
9. True
10. False, prejudice
11. False, negotiation

Thinking Critically

12. He is using good communication skills, specifically listening skills.
13. Examples will vary, but should include peer pressure that encourages a teen to engage in healthful behaviors such as physical activity or advocacy.

90

Assessment

After You Read

HEALTH QUIZ

Now that you have read the chapter, look back at your answers to the Health Quiz in the chapter opener. Would you change any of them? What would your answers be now?

Reviewing Vocabulary and Main Ideas

On a sheet of paper, write the numbers 1–6. After each number, write the term from the list that best completes each statement.

- abuse
- body language
- communication
- empathy
- loyal
- neglect
- nurture
- relationship

Lesson 1 Communication Skills

1. _____ includes facial expressions, eye contact, gestures, and posture.

2. _____ is the sharing of thoughts and feelings between two or more people.

Lesson 2 Your Family

3. Healthy families _____ their members, or provide physical, mental/emotional, and social needs.

4. A pattern of mistreatment of another person is known as _____.

5. _____ is the failure of parents to provide their children with basic physical and emotional care and protection.

*On a sheet of paper, write the number 6–11. Write **True** or **False** for each statement. If the statement is false, change the underlined word to make it true.*

Lesson 3 Your Friends and Peers

6. When you can depend on a person to keep promises, that person is <u>reliable</u>.

7. <u>Cooperation</u> is the influence to take on behaviors and/or beliefs of your peers.

Lesson 4 Refusal Skills

8. The <u>T.A.L.K.</u> strategy can help you say no when you face a high-pressure situation.

9. The active choice not to participate in high-risk behaviors is <u>abstinence</u>.

Lesson 5 Resolving Conflicts

10. An opinion or fear formed without having facts or firsthand knowledge is known as <u>tolerance</u>.

11. The process of talking about a conflict and deciding how to reach a compromise is called <u>peer mediation</u>.

Thinking Critically

Using complete sentences, answer the following questions on a sheet of paper.

12. **Recognize** Mike and his sister Meg are having a dispute. Mike waits patiently for Meg to finish speaking before he speaks. What type of skill is Mike demonstrating?

Health Online Visit **health.glencoe.com** and take the Online Quiz for Chapter 3.

HEALTH QUIZ Wrap-Up

Healthy Relationships Have students retake the Chapter Opener Health Quiz. Some students may find that their answers have changed after reading the chapter. Have those students write a short paragraph explaining how their answers have changed. Students who did not change any of their answers should write a short paragraph describing one new concept they learned while reading the chapter.

13. **Give Examples** Give an example of peer pressure that can positively affect your health.

Write About It

14. **Communication Skills** Write a letter of appreciation to someone in your family. In your letter, identify what they did, and tell how it made you feel.

15. **Analyzing Influences** Write a paragraph describing the positive character traits of a good friend. How can a good friend influence you in positive ways? Use specific examples in your paragraph.

 **Career Corner**

Family Counselor A family that is having problems can find help from a family counselor. These professionals teach family members how to listen to one another. They help families work together to find solutions. A family counselor needs a four-year college degree plus two years of graduate work in counseling. To learn more, click on *Career Corner* at **health.glencoe.com**.

Write About It

14. **Personal or Descriptive Writing** Tell students that personal writing should include words of appreciation to a family member. Student letters will vary but should explain how they feel. Be sure to respect student privacy.

15. **Descriptive Writing** Inform students that their paragraphs should be written in the descriptive form. This type of writing presents a clear picture, attracts the reader, and presents broad views or focuses on details. Student descriptions will vary but should include specific examples of how a friend demonstrates good character traits.

Standardized Test Practice

1. A
2. C

 Career Corner

Family Counselor Have students visit the Career Corner at **health.glencoe .com** to gather more information about a career in family counseling. Explain that a family counselor must have excellent communication skills and an understanding of the many different types of families. If possible, invite a family counselor to the classroom to share more information about this career.

Standardized Test Practice

Reading

Read the passage and then answer the questions.

Every culture of the world uses body language. In many cultures, people are not aware of their body's "messages." In some, however, people go to great lengths to "speak" through their bodies. In one culture, for example, people at work never smile. To outsiders, they may look angry. Actually, smiling on the job means you are not serious about your work.

Sometimes misunderstandings arise over gestures and posture. Americans, for example, like to put space between themselves and those they're speaking with. In the Middle East, this posture is interpreted differently. It means you are not interested in what the speaker is saying.

Facial expressions can also have different interpretations. In the United States it is rude to stare. In Greece, people feel ignored if they are not stared at in public. Europeans usually change their facial expression to show happiness, anger, boredom, and sadness. In Asia, facial expressions change less frequently.

TEST-TAKING TIP

Read the passage carefully once to find out what information it contains. After you read each question, look back at the passage to find the answer.

1. Which best sums up the author's purpose?
   A. To show that body language differs among cultures
   B. To show that Americans are viewed as rude worldwide
   C. To show that body language is meaningless
   D. To show that facial expression is less important than posture

2. If you stare at someone in Greece, he or she is likely to
   A. become angry
   B. feel ignored
   C. feel as though you are paying attention to him or her
   D. feel as though you are being rude

Chapter 3 Assessment **91**

Test-Taking Tips

Multiple Choice Tell students to use the following strategy on multiple-choice questions: After carefully reading a question, cross out any answers that are obviously wrong. This will reduce the number of possible answers. After the obviously wrong answers are eliminated, focus on choosing between the remaining answers.

CHAPTER 4 pp. 92–117	Standards		Skills and Activities
	National	State/Local	
	National Health Education Standards 5.1, 5.2, 5.3		**HEALTH INVENTORY**, *p. 93* **HANDS-ON HEALTH** Keeping a Food Diary, *p. 114* **BUILDING HEALTH SKILLS** *Decision Making* Choosing Health-Promoting Foods, *pp. 112-113*
Lesson 1 **Your Body's Nutrient Needs** pp. 94–97	National Health Education Standards 1.1, 3.1, 4.3, 7.1, 8.2		
Lesson 2 **Following a Healthful Eating Plan** pp. 98–101	National Health Education Standards 1.1, 2.2, 3.1, 4.3, 7.1, 7.4, 8.2		
Lesson 3 **Making Healthful Food Choices** pp. 102–107	National Health Education Standards 1.1, 2.2, 3.1, 5.1, 5.2, 5.3, 6.1, 7.1, 7.4, 8.2		**HEALTH SKILLS ACTIVITY** *Accessing Information* Mastering Nutrition Facts, *p. 104*
Lesson 4 **Managing Your Weight** pp. 108–111	National Health Education Standards 1.2, 1.6, 1.7, 1.8, 2.2, 3.2, 3.3, 3.6, 4.2, 4.3, 4.4, 4.5, 5.1, 6.2, 7.1, 7.6, 8.2, 8.4		**DEVELOPING GOOD CHARACTER** *Respect for Others' Bodies and Feelings, p. 109* **HEALTH SKILLS ACTIVITY** *Decision Making* Help for a Friend with an Eating Disorder, *p. 111*

PACING THE CHAPTER

Lesson 1	45 min	Lesson 4	90 min	Chapter Review	45 min
Lesson 2	45 min	Hands-on Health	20 min		
Lesson 3	90 min	Building Health Skills	90 min		

BLOCK SCHEDULING

For block scheduling, assign students Building Health Skills feature *Choosing Health-Promoting Foods*, pages 112–113, and Guided Reading and Writing in the *Fast Files*.

Planning Guide

Glencoe Exclusive!
TeacherWorks™
All-In-One Planner and Resource Center

Reproducible Resources	Assessment	Media and Technology

Chapter FAST FILE Resources
  Chapter Summaries and Activities REVIEW
  Building Health Skills Activity TEACH
  Performance Assessment Activity EXTEND
  Universal Access Activities TEACH
  Parent Letter and Activities
Student Activities Workbook TEACH
Reading Tutor TEACH
	Building Health Skills Activity, *pp. 112–113*
	Chapter 4 Assessment, *pp. 116–117*
	Chapter FAST FILE Resources
	  Performance Assessment Activity, *p. 4*
	  Chapter 4 Test, *p. 7*
	⊙ *ExamView® Test Generator*
		TeacherWorks™ includes:
		• Interactive Teacher Edition
		• Lesson Planner with Calendar
		• Access to all blackline masters
		• Correlations to standards
		⊙ StudentWorks™ Plus
		⬭ Online Student Edition
		Dinah Zike's Teaching Health with Foldables™

Chapter FAST FILE Resources
  Concept Mapping Activity 4-1 REVIEW
  Cross-Curriculum Activity 4-1 EXTEND
  Enrichment Activity 4-1 EXTEND
  Guided Reading and Writing 4-1 TEACH
  Lesson Plan 4-1
  Reteaching Activity 4-1 REVIEW
	Lesson 1 Review, *p. 97*
	⬭ Vocabulary PuzzleMaker
	⊙ *ExamView® Test Generator*
		⬭ Vocabulary PuzzleMaker
		⊙ *ExamView® Test Generator*
		⊙ StudentWorks™ Plus
		⚓ Transparency 4-1
		⬭ **Health Online**

Chapter FAST FILE Resources
  Concept Mapping Activity 4-2 REVIEW
  Enrichment Activity 4-2 EXTEND
  Guided Reading and Writing 4-2 TEACH
  Health Lab 4-2 EXTEND
  Lesson Plan 4-2
  Reteaching Activity 4-2 REVIEW
	Lesson 2 Review, *p. 101*
	⬭ Vocabulary PuzzleMaker
	⊙ *ExamView® Test Generator*
		⬭ Vocabulary PuzzleMaker
		⊙ *ExamView® Test Generator*
		⊙ StudentWorks™ Plus
		⚓ Transparency 4-2
		⬭ **Health Online**

Chapter FAST FILE Resources
  Concept Mapping Activity 4-3 REVIEW
  Cross-Curriculum Activity 4-3 EXTEND
  Enrichment Activity 4-3 EXTEND
  Guided Reading and Writing 4-3 TEACH
  Lesson Plan 4-3
  Reteaching Activity 4-3 REVIEW
	Lesson 3 Review, *p. 107*
	⬭ Vocabulary PuzzleMaker
	⊙ *ExamView® Test Generator*
		⬭ Vocabulary PuzzleMaker
		⊙ *ExamView® Test Generator*
		⊙ StudentWorks™ Plus
		⚓ Transparency 4-3
		⬭ **Health Online**

Chapter FAST FILE Resources
  Concept Mapping Activity 4-4 REVIEW
  Decision-Making Activity 4-4 EXTEND
  Enrichment Activity 4-4 EXTEND
  Guided Reading and Writing 4-4 TEACH
  Lesson Plan 4-4
  Reteaching Activity 4-4 REVIEW
	Lesson 4 Review, *p. 111*
	⬭ Vocabulary PuzzleMaker
	⊙ *ExamView® Test Generator*
		⬭ Vocabulary PuzzleMaker
		⊙ *ExamView® Test Generator*
		⊙ StudentWorks™ Plus
		⚓ Transparency 4-4
		⬭ **Health Online**

Chapter and Lesson Resources

The *Teen Health* resources are designed for differentiated learning abilities. You may want to use the coded items in this way:

REVIEW —activities to review or reinforce content

TEACH —activities to teach basic concepts

EXTEND —activities to extend or enrich lesson content

OUT OF TIME?

Use Health Skills Activities *Mastering Nutrition Facts*, page 104 and *Help for a Friend with an Eating Disorder*, page 111.

Teens and Diet Trends

Many teens diet to control their weight. For the majority of these teens, the decision to diet is motivated by appearance concerns rather than health concerns. During discussions with the class, stress the influence of nutrition on health, rather than the influence of nutrition on appearance.

As students read the chapter and examine the USDA Food Guidance System, they may have questions about how popular diet plans fit into these guidelines. For example, a popular low-carbohydrate diet plan restricts carbohydrate consumption, making it difficult to meet the guidelines for food groups such as whole grains.

If a student asks about a particular diet plan, the student should be referred to his or her family physician or the school nurse for advice. Remind students that dieting has health consequences, particularly among teens. Teens should always discuss any plans for dieting with their parent or guardian.

Emphasize that growing bodies require good nutrition to maintain health, and some diet plans do not include all of the essential vitamins and minerals. Be certain to incorporate information about dangerous fad diets during discussions of the chapter content.

Cultural Sensitivity

It is important to be sensitive to cultural differences when teaching about nutrition. Students from different cultural, religious, and ethnic backgrounds may have diets that are very different from what is considered a typical American diet.

When presenting ideas about healthy eating plans, be certain to include healthful food representing many cultures. Spend time discussing a healthful vegetarian diet. Whenever you use pictures or visual aids to illustrate a point about nutrition, include pictures of foods from many cultures.

If time permits, allow students to explore differences in the diets of various cultures. Try some of the following project ideas:

- Have students investigate the relationship between the diets of various cultures and the incidence of certain diseases. For example, women who eat a typical Asian diet have a much lower incidence of breast cancer than women who eat a typical American diet.

- Have students collect recipes of healthful foods from various cultures. Then, have students create a cookbook incorporating the recipes.

- Provide students with food labels from foods that are not typically a part of their diets. Have students use the food labels to identify the nutrients found in each of the foods.

- Work with the family and consumer sciences teacher to give students an opportunity to prepare a food from another culture. Have students work together to choose a recipe that is healthful.

- Have students make posters that show healthy food choices from many cultures. Obtain permission for students to display their posters in the school hallways or cafeteria.

Support for Teaching Reading

 Reading Support   **Health Online**   **Academic Integration** For additional academic integration strategies, visit the Teacher Center at **health.glencoe.com**.

Reading Preview

Previewing Ask volunteers to describe meanings for the saying, "A picture is worth a thousand words." After discussing the meaning of the expression, have volunteers predict definition of "MyPyramid Food Guidance System," without looking ahead in the text. Ask students to predict what information they imagine the MyPyramid will present.

FOLDABLES Study Organizer *Dinah Zike's Reading and Study Skills for Teen Health* provides interactive graphic organizers that help students comprehend and retain health concepts as they read. Use the Foldable™ on page 93 or find more Foldables™ activities for the chapter on **Nutrition** in the separate booklet, available in the TCR.

Lesson 1   Your Body's Nutrient Needs

Clarifying Text Have students choose one of the key terms they will learn about in this lesson and write it in the middle of their papers. Ask them to write ideas down around the term as they read that are related to the term they chose. For example, students might write the term *vitamins* and note what the term means, examples of different vitamins, and food sources.

Lesson 2   Following a Healthful Eating Plan

Discussion As students read this chapter, have them note reasons they feel that the United States Department of Agriculture (USDA) has provided a nutrition guidance system for Americans to follow. Have them note ways that this system can have an effect on the health of individuals. Encourage discussion that examines ideas that students have noted.

Lesson 3   Making Healthful Food Choices

Predicting Ask a volunteer to read aloud the first paragraph of this lesson. Have students scan the headings in the rest of the lesson, noting figures, photos, and headings. Ask students to predict in writing one thing they think they will learn from reading the lesson.

Lesson 4   Managing Your Weight

Summarizing Have students each choose a heading from this lesson. Ask students to reread their section and write two sentences that summarize the content. Allow students to share their summaries with a partner.

Post Reading

Extension Have interested students note questions they may have about making healthful food choices after studying this chapter. Encourage these students to conduct more research, using online sources, journals, and the school's media center to find answers to these questions. Have students share their results.

Key for Using the Teacher Wraparound Edition

Use this key to help you identify the different types of prompts found in the Teacher Wraparound Edition.

R   **Reading Strategies** activities help you teach reading skills and vocabulary.

C   **Critical Thinking** strategies help students apply and extend what they have learned.

U   **Universal Access** activities provide differentiated instruction for students learning to speak English, along with suggestions for teaching various types of learners.

HS   **Health Skills Practice** activities reinforce Health Skills concepts and help students apply these skills in their everyday lives.

W   **Writing Support** activities provide writing opportunities to help students comprehend the text.

AL   **Active Learning** strategies provide a variety of activities for presenting lesson content, including Quick Demos and engaging classroom projects that get students actively involved.

Key to Ability Levels

Teaching Strategies and activities have been coded for ability level and appropriateness

AL   Activities for students working above grade level

OL   Activities for students working on grade level

BL   Activities for students working below grade level

EL   Activities for English Learners

Symbols

 Transparencies

 CD-ROM

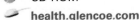 health.glencoe.com

 Print Resources

Nutrition

Chapter at a Glance

Lesson 1 identifies the six main classes of nutrients, describes what foods can be eaten to obtain certain nutrients, and analyzes the key nutrients found in a recipe.

Lesson 2 discusses how to use the USDA food guidance system, lists the names of the five food groups, and demonstrates how to plan a balanced meal using MyPyramid.

Lesson 3 identifies influences on food choices, explains guidelines for making healthy food choices, and analyzes the key nutrients in a food product.

Lesson 4 explains how to maintain a healthy weight, identifies problem eating behaviors, and demonstrates how to use decision-making skills.

R Reading Strategy

Interpreting the Photo Have students look at the photo of the students eating their lunches. Ask students to describe some foods they enjoy eating for lunch. Point out that although different people enjoy different foods, good nutrition is important for everyone. **OL**

CHAPTER

4 **Nutrition**

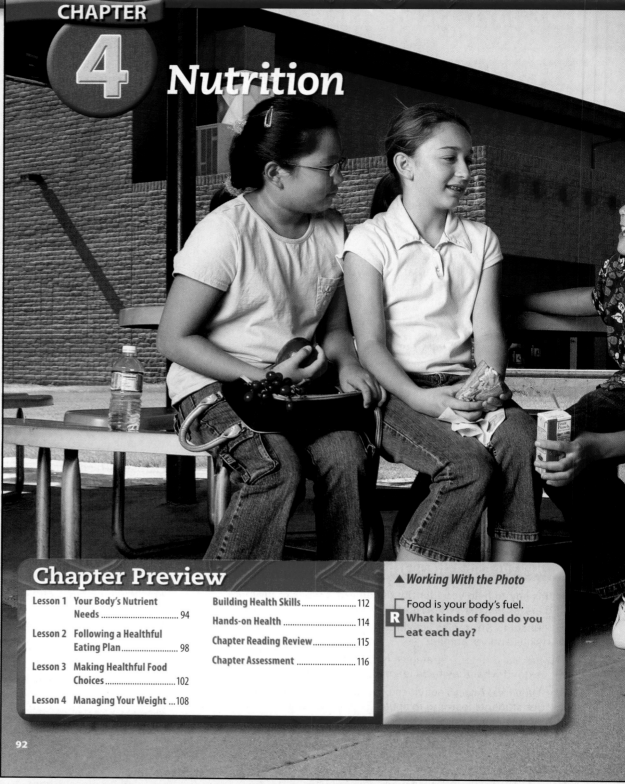

Chapter Preview

Lesson 1 Your Body's Nutrient Needs 94

Lesson 2 Following a Healthful Eating Plan 98

Lesson 3 Making Healthful Food Choices 102

Lesson 4 Managing Your Weight ...108

Building Health Skills 112

Hands-on Health 114

Chapter Reading Review 115

Chapter Assessment 116

 Working With the Photo

R Food is your body's fuel. What kinds of food do you eat each day?

92

Universal Access

Differentiated Learning Glencoe provides teacher support and student materials for all learners in the health classroom.

- Spanish Glosario and chapter summaries for the English Language Learners.
- *Reading Tutor* and related worksheets support reluctant readers.

- Universal Access strategies throughout the Teacher Wraparound Edition and Fast Files help you present materials for gifted students, at-risk students, physically impaired students and those with behavior disorders or learning disabilities.

Start-Up Activities

Before You Read Do you make healthy food choices? To find out, take the health inventory below. Keep a record of your answers.

HEALTH INVENTORY

1. I drink water every day.
(a) always   (b) sometimes   (c) never

2. I make sure to eat breakfast.
(a) always   (b) sometimes   (c) never

3. I try to limit the amount of fat I eat.
(a) always   (b) sometimes   (c) never

4. I try to maintain a weight that is healthy for me.
(a) always   (b) sometimes   (c) never

FOLDABLES™ Study Organizer

As You Read Make this Foldable™ to help you organize the material in Lesson 1 on nutrients. Begin with a plain sheet of 8½″ × 11″ paper, or one sheet of notebook paper.

1 Fold a sheet of paper along the long axis, leaving a ½″ tab along the side.

2 Turn the paper, and fold into thirds.

3 Cut the top layer along both folds. Then cut each tab in half to make six tabs.

4 Turn the paper vertically, and label the tabs as shown. Under the appropriate tab, write down major concepts, definitions, and food sources of each type of nutrient.

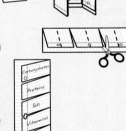

Health Online Visit **health.glencoe.com** and use the e-flashcards to preview Chapter 4 vocabulary terms.

93

FOCUS

Activating Prior Knowledge

What I Know Have students name foods they have eaten in the past 24 hours. List their responses on the board. Tell students they will learn about the nutritional value of foods.

Guide to Reading

BUILDING VOCABULARY

- Have students use the Glossary/Glosario to find the meanings of the vocabulary terms. Then have them write a sentence that shows a relationship between two terms.
- Use Vocabulary PuzzleMaker to reinforce vocabulary terms.

READING STRATEGY

FOLDABLES Study Organizer Have students use their Foldables™ as they read Lesson 1.

- **Classifying** Begin a sample concept map and ask how many sections to plan for main classes of nutrients. *six*

Quick Write

Have students generate a list of the foods they frequently eat. Have volunteers share their influences. Influences might include the media, family, or friends.

Your Body's Nutrient Needs

Guide to Reading

● Building Vocabulary
You may already know the meaning of some words in the list below. Write each word and what you think it means.

- nutrients (p. 94)
- nutrition (p. 94)
- carbohydrates (p. 95)
- fiber (p. 95)
- proteins (p. 95)
- fats (p. 95)
- vitamins (p. 96)
- minerals (p. 96)

● Focusing on the Main Ideas
In this lesson, you will be able to

- **identify** the six main classes of nutrients.
- **determine** what foods you can eat to obtain the nutrients you need.
- **analyze** the key nutrients found in a recipe.

● Reading Strategy
Classifying Using the diagram to the right as a guide, create a concept map that identifies the main nutrient classes.

FOLDABLES | Study Organizer Use the Foldable™ on p. 93 as you read this lesson.

Quick Write

Make a list of the foods you eat often. What do you think influences your food choices?

Nutrients and Nutrition

How is your body like a car? It needs fuel in order to run. The fuel your body uses comes from food, or more specifically from nutrients (NOO·tree·ents). **Nutrients** are *substances in food that your body needs to carry out its normal functions.*

Which nutrients does your body need? The answer to that question is the subject of nutrition (noo·TRIH·shun). **Nutrition** is *the process of taking in food and using it for energy, growth, and good health.* There are more than forty kinds of

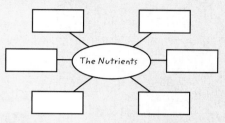

▶ The nutrients in the foods you choose give you energy. **What is another important role of these nutrients?**

Lesson 1 Resources

📁 **Chapter FAST FILE Resources**
Guided Reading and Writing 4-1
Concept Mapping Activity 4-1
Cross-Curriculum Activity 4-1
Reteaching Activity 4-1
Enrichment Activity 4-1
Lesson Quiz 4-1

Technology
🔌 Transparency 4-1
💿 Audio Summaries
💿 *ExamView*
💿 Vocabulary PuzzleMaker
💿 StudentWorks™ Plus

nutrients. Some give you energy for work and play. Others provide the building blocks your body needs to grow and to repair itself. Since different foods contain different nutrients, you should eat a variety of foods each day.

All nutrients are grouped into one of six categories: *carbohydrates, fats, proteins, vitamins, minerals*, and *water*.

Carbohydrates

The fuel your body gets the best mileage from is carbohydrates (kar·boh·HY·drayts). **Carbohydrates** are *sugars and starches contained in foods.* Carbohydrates are your body's primary energy source.

There are two main types of carbohydrate. *Simple carbohydrates*, or sugars, are found in fruits, milk, and table sugar. *Complex carbohydrates*, or starches, are found in bread, rice, pasta, beans, and other vegetables. Your body cannot use these nutrients directly. First, it must break them down through the process of *digestion*. You'll learn more about digestion in Chapter 7.

Another type of complex carbohydrate, fiber, cannot be digested. **Fiber** is the *tough, stringy part of raw fruits, raw vegetables, whole wheat, and other whole grains.* Fiber helps carry wastes out of your body.

Proteins

Proteins (PROH·teens) are *nutrients that provide the building blocks your body needs for growth.* Proteins promote healing and aid in the repair of tissues. Protein sources include fish, chicken, beef, eggs, milk, and other dairy products. You can also get protein from beans, nuts, and most soy-based products.

Fats

This may surprise you, but did you know your body needs some fat? **Fats** are *a nutrient found in fatty animal tissue and plant oils.* Fats carry certain vitamins in your bloodstream and help keep your skin healthy. They also help you feel full after a meal. Fats are also a source of energy for your body.

Although fats are important, you only need small amounts in your diet. Eating too many foods that are high in fat can contribute to health problems, such as heart disease and obesity. These conditions usually appear later in life. Yet, they can often be traced to unhealthy habits developed earlier in life. Salad dressings, doughnuts, and fried foods are often high in fat. You should only eat small amounts of these foods.

▼ Eating a variety of different nutrients is important to good health. **Which of these foods do you enjoy eating?**

Lesson 1: Your Body's Nutrient Needs **95**

R **Reading Strategy**

Analyzing a Table Direct students' attention to Figure 4.1 on vitamins and minerals needed by teens. Ask: What food listed in the table is a good source of both calcium and vitamin E? *fortified ready-to-eat cereal* OL

HS **Health Skills Practice**

Practicing Healthful Behaviors As students read about the importance of vitamins and minerals, ask them to examine the table in Figure 4.1 that shows vitamins and minerals needed by teens. Challenge students to develop a menu plan for one meal that incorporates at least three of the foods mentioned in the table. OL

R **Reading Strategy**

Analyzing a Graphic After students have examined Figure 4.2 on page 97. Ask students to discuss the main message of the graphic. Have volunteers explain how consuming these foods is important to a healthy eating plan. OL

Caption Answers

Figure Caption *Sample answer:* Cereal, milk, and oranges are a part of my regular diet.
Photo Caption, p. 97 Lettuce contains vitamin A; watermelon contains vitamin C and potassium; yogurt is rich in calcium.

Health Online

Visit **health.glencoe.com** and complete the Interactive Study Guide for Lesson 1.

▼ **FIGURE 4.1**

R **Most teens don't get enough of the nutrients shown. Which foods in the chart are part of your regular eating plan?**

Vitamins

Vitamins (VY·tuh·muhns) are *nutrients that help regulate body functions*. Your body needs only tiny amounts of these nutrients. Vitamins help your body use other nutrients and fight disease.

Many foods are naturally rich in vitamins. This includes many fruits and vegetables, such as oranges, carrots, and broccoli. Whole-grain breads and some meats are also excellent sources of some vitamins.

Some vitamins, such as vitamin C and the B-complex vitamins, need to be replaced daily. Other vitamins—including vitamins A, D, E, and K—are stored in your body. Vitamin A is important for good vision. Vitamin D promotes strong bones and teeth.

HS **Minerals**

Minerals (MIN·uh·ruhls) are *elements in foods that help your body work properly*. Like vitamins, minerals are needed only in small amounts. Calcium is a mineral that helps build strong bones and teeth. Calcium is important during the teen years but also throughout your life. So is the iron found in red meats, beans, and other foods. Iron contributes to healthy blood, which in turn helps you fight many diseases.

Some people take supplements to get extra vitamins and minerals. However, food sources are best. Eating a variety of foods will help you get the nutrients you need. Always check with a parent or guardian before taking any vitamin or mineral supplements. **Figure 4.1** provides additional information on vitamins and minerals important to teens.

	Vitamins	Minerals	Food Sources
✓	Vitamin A		Dark green leafy vegetables (such as spinach), milk and other dairy products, carrots, apricots, eggs, liver
✓	Vitamin B12		Eggs, meat, poultry, fish, dairy products, some soy products
✓	Vitamin C		Oranges, grapefruits, cantaloupe, strawberries, mangoes, cabbage, broccoli
✓	Vitamin E		Fortified ready-to-eat cereals, peanut butter, almonds
✓		Calcium	Milk, fortified ready-to-eat cereals, oatmeal, canned salmon
✓		Potassium	Baked potato, peaches, bananas
✓		Magnesium	Pumpkin seeds, cashews, almonds

HEALTH LITERACY

Teens, Calcium, and Osteoporosis Teens' food choices can impact their health later in life. For example, consumption of adequate calcium by teen girls can help prevent osteoporosis. Explain that bones store calcium during the teen years that is used to maintain bone health later in life. The Centers for Disease Control has launched an education campaign, "Powerful Bones. Powerful Girls™," to provide information about bone health to teenage girls and their parents. It recommends that teen girls consume 1,300 mg of calcium each day. OL

Water

Did you know that about two-thirds of your body is water? Water is essential to life. It carries other nutrients around your body. It helps with digestion, removes waste, and cools you off. You need at least eight cups of water every day. Even more is needed in hot weather and when you exercise. Let thirst be your guide. Drink when you are thirsty and with meals to help your body get enough water. You can also get water from many foods and from beverages such as milk. See **Figure 4.2** for some examples of foods with a high water content.

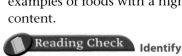 **Reading Check** **Identify**
What are two types of carbohydrates?

 ▼ **FIGURE 4.2**

WATER, WATER EVERYWHERE
Most of the weight of the foods shown is from water. What other nutrients do you think these foods contain?

95% Water

92% Water

73% Water

Health *Online* For more review questions for Lesson 1, go to **health.glencoe.com**.

Lesson 1: Your Body's Nutrient Needs **97**

Lesson 1 Review

 **After You Read**

Review this lesson for new terms, major headings, and Reading Checks.

What I Learned

1. *Vocabulary* Define the term *nutrition*. Use it in an original sentence.

2. *Identify* Name the six categories of nutrients.

3. *Recall* Why is calcium important to your body?

Thinking Critically

4. *Hypothesize* How might your knowledge of nutrients influence your snack food choices?

5. *Analyze* Record what you eat for one day. Remember to count the cups of water you drink. What nutrients have you eaten? What improvements, if any, can you make?

Applying Health Skills

6. *Accessing Information* Analyze the key nutrients in a recipe from a magazine or newspaper. What other foods could be served at the same meal to provide an even greater variety of nutrients.

 Reading Check

Answer simple carbohydrates and complex carbohydrates

ASSESS

 Assessment Resources

Lesson Review Quiz
- *ExamView*
- Fast Files Activities
- Online Quizzes and Activities

Reteaching
- Assign Concept Map 4-1 or Reteaching Activity 4-1 in the Fast Files.
- Ask students to list the six main classes of nutrients on a sheet of paper. Then have them write a food source for each class of nutrient.

Enrichment
- Assign Enrichment Activity 4-1 in the Fast Files.
- Have students research the positive and negative aspects of the use of vitamin and mineral supplements. Ask students to report their findings to the class.

CLOSE

Ask students to create public service announcements that encourage teens to think about nutrients when they make food choices.

Lesson 1 Review Answers

1. Nutrition is the science that studies the substances in food and how the body uses them. Sentences will vary.

2. The six categories of nutrients are carbohydrates, fats, proteins, vitamins, minerals, and water.

3. Calcium builds strong bones and teeth.

4. Knowing which foods provide needed nutrients may direct the individual to make snack choices that fill a gap in the person's daily nutrient intake.

5. Answers will vary. Check that students have recorded their food and water intake for a day and have determined the categories of nutrients consumed.

6. Provide recipes from magazines and newspapers for students to use to answer question 6.

97

Lesson 2

FOCUS

Activating Prior Knowledge

What I Know Ask volunteers to name one of the food groups. Challenge the class to list all five food groups. Students will learn about these food groups and healthful eating in this lesson.

Guide to Reading

BUILDING VOCABULARY
- Have students skim the lesson for the definition of each vocabulary term. Then have students work in pairs to review the meaning of each term.
- Use Vocabulary PuzzleMaker to reinforce vocabulary terms. 🖱

READING STRATEGY
Identifying Problems and Solutions Have students use prior knowledge to start their lists. As they read the lesson, students should add to their lists.

Quick Write

To introduce the Quick Write, have students imagine what it would be like to eat the same foods at every meal.

Caption Answer

Photo Caption *Sample answer:* I can tell which foods will meet my health needs by reading the ingredients lists and food labels.

Following a Healthful Eating Plan

Guide to Reading

🔵 **Building Vocabulary**
As you read this lesson, write the following terms and their definitions in your notebook.
- MyPyramid food guidance system (p. 98)
- calorie (p. 100)

🔵 **Focusing on the Main Ideas**
In this lesson, you will be able to
- **discuss** how to use the MyPyramid food guidance system.
- **list** the names of the five food groups.
- **demonstrate** how to plan a nutrient-rich meal using MyPyramid.

🔵 **Reading Strategy**
Identifying Problems and Solutions Many teens and other people make unhealthy food choices. What solutions to this problem can you suggest?

Quick Write

In a paragraph, explain why you think it is important to eat a variety of foods.

The MyPyramid Food Guidance System

Have you ever been inside a mega-supermarket? These giant food warehouses have thousands of foods and food products to choose from. How do you know which foods give your body the nutrients it needs?

The United States Department of Agriculture (USDA) publishes information to help you decide what foods are best for your health. One source of information appears in **Figure 4.3** on page 99. This is the **MyPyramid food guidance system,** *a system designed to help Americans make healthful food choices.*

◀ Food supermarkets offer many choices. **How can you tell which foods will help your body meet its nutrient needs?**

Lesson 2 Resources

📁 **Chapter** *FAST FILE* **Resources**
Guided Reading and Writing 4-2
Concept Mapping Activity 4-2
Health Lab 4-2
Reteaching Activity 4-2
Enrichment Activity 4-2
Lesson Quiz 4-2

Technology
⚡ Transparency 4-2
🔊 Audio Summaries
💿 *ExamView*
🖱 Vocabulary PuzzleMaker
💿 StudentWorks™ Plus

The colorful graphic, named "MyPyramid," is meant to provide healthful reminders. One is that you should eat a variety of foods. Notice that a different food group appears for each color band. Another reminder appears in the form of the figure going up the stairs. This is to remind you to make regular physical activity part of your lifestyle. Both of these topics will be explored in more depth in the next lesson.

 **Reading Check** **Identify** What does the MyPyramid graphic remind people to do?

▼ **FIGURE 4.3**

R **MYPYRAMID FOOD GUIDANCE SYSTEM**

The MyPyramid food guidance system can help you make healthful food choices. Why do you think some color bands are larger than others?

MyPyramid
STEPS TO A HEALTHIER YOU

GRAINS	VEGETABLES	FRUITS	MILK	MEAT & BEANS
Make half your grains whole	Vary your veggies	Focus on fruits	Get your calcium-rich foods	Go lean with protein

Lesson 2: Following a Healthful Eating Plan **99**

CHAPTER 4
Lesson 2

TEACH

R Reading Strategy

Analyzing a Graphic Have students examine the USDA MyPyramid food guidance system in Figure 4.3. Explain that the color bands show the role of each food group in a balanced eating plan. Ask: Which group of foods is represented by the widest band on the pyramid? *the grains group* Ask: What are some examples of foods in that group? *breads, cereals, rice, pasta* **OL**

AL Active Learning

Lessons for Younger Students Have students choose one of the following: create a song, board game, or piece of art work that could be used to teach younger students about the USDA MyPyramid food guidance system. Have each student share his or her work with the class. Have students explain how their own understanding of the material improved as they planned ways to teach younger students. Then have students brainstorm a list of additional ways that this information could be taught to younger students. **OL**

Reading Check

Answer The MyPyramid food guidance system reminds people to eat a variety of foods and get regular physical activity.

TECHNOLOGY AND HEALTH

Accessing MyPyramid Arrange a time for your class to have computer access. Guide students to **health.glencoe.com** to access the MyPyramid food guidance system at the United States Department of Agriculture Web site. Explain that at the Web site, they can generate individualized food guidelines based on their age, gender, and usual amount of physical activity. The Web site also contains resources and tips to promote healthy eating and physical activity. **OL**

HS Health Skills Practice

Decision Making Ask: How can the information on these two pages about how to use My Pyramid be used to make healthful food decisions?

Sample answer: *I can keep track of the foods from each group I've had in a day and select the foods from the groups from which I still need to choose.* **OL**

C Critical Thinking

Evaluating Have students design a menu for one day, including drinks and snacks. Have students label each food on the menu with the color of the MyPyramid band to which it corresponds. Ask students to evaluate whether their menus meet the guidelines shown in MyPyramid. **OL**

W Writing Support

Expository Writing Have students imagine they are just about to dig into a meal from their favorite fast-food restaurant. They have to pass through a "nutrition scanner" that evaluates the nutritional value of their food choices. Have them write a paragraph describing what the readout from the "nutrition scanner" would say. Remind them that the goal of expository writing is to inform others. **OL**

Academic Vocabulary

Gender On this page, *gender* is mentioned as one factor that determines the number of calories required daily. Tell students that *gender* means male or female.

100

Health Online

Topic: MyPyramid

Visit **health.glencoe.com** for Student Web Activities that will help you develop a personal eating plan using MyPyramid.

Activity: Using the information from the link above, create a personal eating plan based on your age, gender, and activity level.

A Closer Look at MyPyramid

The idea behind MyPyramid is not to avoid certain foods. Rather, it is designed to help each person develop a personal eating plan based on how many calories he or she needs. A **calorie** is *a unit of heat that measures the energy available in* **HS** *foods*. Your body converts the calories it receives from the foods you eat into energy. The amount of calories your body needs is based on your age, gender, and how physically active you are.

If you are physically active on most days, your body needs more calories than someone who is not physically active. MyPyramid estimates that females between the ages of 9 and thirteen need 1,600 to 2,200 calories per day, based on activity level. Males in the same age group need 1,800 to 2,600 calories per day.

Your main source of calories should come from nutrient-rich foods. MyPyramid lets you know how much of which foods to eat in order to stay healthy. The diagonal color bands on the pyramid represent the different food groups that you should be eating. These foods are shown by the broad color bands: orange, green, blue, red, and purple. Figure 4.3 shows food possibilities for each color group. These represent just a few of the many ways of meeting your daily food group recommendations.

The following is an example of what a moderately active teen should eat. If you are very active most days, you may need to eat a little more. Likewise, if you are less active or not at all active, you may need to eat less.

- **Grains—the Orange Group:** Girls should have five to seven 1-ounce equivalents of grain products each day. Boys should have six to nine 1-ounce equivalents. In general, 1 slice of bread, 1 cup cold cereal, or ½ cup cooked rice, pasta, or cooked cereal is the equal to 1 ounce from the grains group. Half of these choices should come from whole-grain foods such as whole-wheat bread.

- **Vegetables—the Green Group:** Most boys need 2½ to 3½ cups of vegetables a day, girls 2 to 3 cups. When eating leafy greens such as lettuce, 2 cups equals 1 cup of vegetables.

- **Fruits—the Red Group:** Most girls and boys should both have 1½ to 2 cups from this group daily. When eating dried fruit such as raisins, ½ cup is equal to 1 cup from the fruit group.

Promoting Coordinated School Health

Food Choices in the Cafeteria For many teens, food consumed in the school cafeteria represents a major portion of their total food intake. Obtain a menu or food list from the school cafeteria. Have students examine the menu to find healthy food choices. Ask students to identify the nutrients contained in the listed foods. Have students consider the calories, nutritional content, and cost of various food choices. Then have students make pamphlets showing how to use foods available in the school cafeteria as a part of a healthy eating plan. **OL**

- **Milk—the Blue Group:** Boys and girls should both have 3 cups of milk or other foods made from milk. In general, 1 cup of yogurt, 1½ ounces natural cheese, or 2 ounces of processed cheese is equal to 1 cup from the milk group.

- **Meats and Beans—the Purple Group:** Most girls should have 5 to 6 ounces from the meat or beans group every day. Most boys should have 5–6½ ounces. In general, 1 egg, 1 tablespoon peanut butter, ¼ cup cooked beans, or ½ ounce of nuts is equal to 1 ounce from the meat and beans group.

Notice that the narrow yellow color band in MyPyramid has not been mentioned. This group represents fats and other foods you should eat in only very small amounts. Examples include sweets and many salty snacks, such as potato chips. In the next lesson, you will learn how to include these foods in a healthy eating plan.

 **Reading Check** **List** Identify the names of the five food groups in MyPyramid.

> **Health Online**
>
> Visit **health.glencoe.com** and complete the Interactive Study Guide for Lesson 2.

Lesson 2 Review

 **After You Read**

Review this lesson for new terms, major headings, and Reading Checks.

What I Learned

1. *Vocabulary* What is the *MyPyramid food guidance system?*

2. *Explain* Why does your level of activity affect how many calories your body needs?

3. *Recall* How many cups of fruit should a moderately active 12-year-old eat per day? How many cups of vegetables?

Thinking Critically

4. *Synthesize* Describe a healthful meal that includes three different food groups.

5. *Analyze* Stacy had a cup of milk at breakfast and a cup of yogurt after school. How many more cups from the milk group does she need to meet her daily recommendation?

Applying Health Skills

6. *Analyzing Influences* As you watch television, describe an advertisement you see about food. What does the advertisement tell you about the food? Does it make you want to try the food? Use your findings to discuss how television influences eating habits.

Health Online For more review questions for Lesson 2, go to **health.glencoe.com**.

Lesson 2: Following a Healthful Eating Plan **101**

> **Reading Check**
>
> **Answer** grains, vegetables, fruits, milk, meats and beans, and fats and sweets

ASSESS

Assessment Resources

Lesson Review Quiz
- *ExamView*
- Fast Files Activities
- Online Quizzes and Activities

Reteaching

- Assign Concept Map 4-2 or Reteaching Activity 4-2 in the Fast Files.
- Have partners review the information in Figure 4.3 on page 99 and outline the important facts.

Enrichment

- Assign Enrichment Activity 4-2 in the Fast Files.
- Have students create five quiz questions based on the lesson content. Then allow students to quiz their classmates.

CLOSE

Develop a class list of suggestions for making healthy food choices. Have students use one of the suggestions to make a poster that can be displayed in the school hallways or cafeteria.

Lesson 2 Review Answers

1. It is a visual aid designed to help Americans make healthful food choices.
2. The more active you are, the more energy your body needs.
3. Both boys and girls should eat 1½ to 2 cups of fruit each day. Boys need 2½ to 3½ cups of vegetables, girls need 2 to 3 cups.
4. Answers, which will vary, should include three of the five food groups. One example is a turkey sandwich with a glass of milk.
5. Stacy needs one more cup of milk.
6. Answers will vary. As students discuss the advertisements they saw, have them also reflect on the food choices offered in the ads.

FOCUS

Activating Prior Knowledge

What I Know Ask students to describe a time when they made a healthy food choice.

Guide to Reading

BUILDING VOCABULARY

- Have the students use the Glossary/Glosario to find the definitions of the vocabulary terms.
- Use Vocabulary PuzzleMaker to reinforce vocabulary terms.

READING STRATEGY

Cause and Effect As students read the lesson, have them underline any cause on the lists they prepared that are mentioned in the lesson.

uick Write

Have students discuss ways that snacks can be a part of a healthy eating plan.

Academic Vocabulary

Affect Students will learn that the foods they chose can *affect* their health. Tell students that *affect* is a verb that means "to influence." Have students find the definition of the word *effect* and compare the usage of these often-confused words

---

Making Healthful Food Choices

Guide to Reading

Building Vocabulary
How are the terms below related? As you read the lesson, write the definitions in your notebook.

- saturated fat (p. 106)
- cholesterol (p. 106)
- trans fats (p. 106)
- sodium (p. 106)

Focusing on the Main Ideas
In this lesson, you will be able to

- **recognize** influences on your food choices.
- **identify** guidelines to make healthy food choices.
- **analyze** key nutrients in a food product.

Reading Strategy
Identifying Cause-and-Effect Identify three factors that you think cause people to be overweight. As you read, notice which of these factors is or is not mentioned.

uick Write

Write about your current eating habits. What kind of foods do you eat most often? What kind of snacks do you usually eat?

Your Food Choices and You

What does the statement "You are what you eat" mean to you? The foods you choose to eat affect your health. Eating too much of certain foods can lead to health problems. As a teen, you need a variety of foods that give your body nutrients to grow and be healthy. Eating a variety of foods helps you feel better and gives you energy for school and other activities.

Your Eating Habits and Influences

As a teen, your body is growing rapidly. Your nutrient needs right now are great. To make sure you're meeting those needs, you should look closely at your eating habits. This includes being aware of what you eat and when. When you are hungry, do you reach for a piece of fruit or a bag of potato chips? Do you snack, for example, while watching TV?

Have you ever thought about why you eat the foods you do? There are several factors that influence your food choices, including the taste, texture, and appearance of food. Your appetite also influences the foods you choose. *Appetite* is an emotional desire for certain foods or tastes.

Lesson 3 Resources

📁 **Chapter *FAST FILE* Resources**
Guided Reading and Writing 4-3
Concept Mapping Activity 4-3
Cross-Curriculum Activity 4-3
Reteaching Activity 4-3
Enrichment Activity 4-3
Lesson Quiz 4-3

Technology
🔦 Transparency 4-3
💿 Audio Summaries
💿 *ExamView*
💿 Vocabulary PuzzleMaker
💿 StudentWorks™ Plus

Other influences include your friends, family, culture, and convenience. You might get a snack from a vending machine because it is handy. One big influence on many people's food choices is the media. Think about the food advertisements you see each day. How do you think advertisers persuade you to buy their foods?

Reading Check **List** Name four factors that influence a person's eating habits.

Guidelines for Healthy Teens

How can you make sure you're getting the nutrients you need? One way that you've already read about is the MyPyramid food guidance system. MyPyramid reflects the scientific advice in the *Dietary Guidelines for Americans*. These guidelines encourage people of all ages to develop a healthy lifestyle. The *Dietary Guidelines* give the following advice on choosing healthy foods and staying active.

Eat a Variety of Foods

Imagine eating the same food at every single meal of every day. Eventually you'd get tired of it. Adding variety to your eating plan is one way to make eating more fun. It can also help you get the nutrients your body needs. Use your imagination to create some meals that include a variety of healthful foods. Ask a parent or guardian for help.

Control the Amount You Eat

Pay attention to the portion sizes and calories that you are eating. Remember that one slice of bread is equal to one ounce. If you eat a sandwich with two slices of bread, you are eating two ounces and double the calories. Only consume as many calories as your body needs. Healthy teens will normally gain weight as they grow and develop. However, if you take in more calories than your body needs, you could gain more weight than is healthy for your body.

▶ Your likes and dislikes influence what you choose to eat. **What other influences affect your food choices?**

Reading Check

Answer Friends, family, culture, and convenience influence what a person eats.

TEACH

HS Health Skills Practice

Analyzing Influences Have students discuss food advertisements they have seen on television. Ask: What methods do advertisers use to make you want to buy the foods in the advertisements? *Students may note that commercials show happy-looking people enjoying the food.* Have students record the number of commercials and print advertisements for food they see in three days. Ask students to analyze which of the advertised foods could be a healthful addition to their diets. Have volunteers share their results with the class. **OL**

U Universal Access

Learning Disabled Help students make a mural showing one of the tips from the *Dietary Guidelines* discussed in this section. (Eat more complex carbohydrates. Know your fats. Limit added sugar. Limit salt.) Provide each student with poster board, construction paper, markers or crayons, and pictures cut from magazines. Have students work with a peer if needed. **BL**

Caption Answer

Photo Caption *Sample answer:* I eat fast food because it is convenient.

◆ Promoting Coordinated School Health

Physical Education Discuss the role of physical activity in maintaining a healthy weight. Ask students to keep track of the amount of time they exercise each day for one week. Allow students to keep their results confidential. Have students use their results to set a health goal concerning physical activity. Have students periodically record their progress toward meeting their goals. Tell students that they will learn more about the role of physical activity in maintaining health in Chapter 5. **OL**

Health Skills Activity

Accessing Information

Mastering Nutrition Facts

Prepare in advance nutrition labels from a variety of foods that can be used with this activity. Use the following strategies to help students complete the activity:

- Divide the class into small groups. Have a volunteer read the introductory paragraph aloud.
- Have students work in their groups to follow the bulleted information and analyze the nutrition information for this food.
- Then distribute one nutrition label to each group. Have the students in each group analyze the nutrition facts on the label.
- Ask students in each group to give a short presentation describing the nutritional value of the food they analyzed. **OL**

Health Skills Activity

Accessing Information

Mastering Nutrition Facts

How can you tell how many calories a packaged food has? The answer is to look at the Nutrition Facts panel on the product's label. This will tell you how many calories are in a serving, which nutrients, and how much of those nutrients the product contains.

- **Serving Size** is the amount of food in one serving. How many cups are in one serving of this product?

- **Servings per Container** is the number of servings the package contains. How many servings are in this product?

- **Calories** shown on the label reflect the number of calories in one serving. If the product contains two servings and you ate the whole product, you would consume twice the number of calories.

- **Daily Values** is the amount of a nutrient a person needs in one day. The label shows a percentage of the Daily Value for each nutrient in a serving of food. What percent of the Daily Value of Vitamin A does this product contain, based on a 2000 calorie diet?

Nutrition Facts	
Serving Size 1 cup (226 g)	
Servings Per Container 2	
Amount Per Serving	
Calories 250	Calories from Fat 110
	% Daily Value*
Total Fat 12g	18%
Saturated Fat 3g	15%
Trans Fat 3g	
Cholesterol 30g	10%
Sodium 470mg	20%
Potassium 700mg	20%
Total Carbohydrate 31mg	10%
Dietary Fiber 0g	0%
Sugar 10g	
Protein 5g	
Vitamin A 4%	Vitamin C 2%
Calcium 2%	Iron 4%

*Percent Daily Values are based on a 2,000 calorie diet. Your Daily Values may be higer or lower depending on your calorie needs

	Calories	2,000	2,500
Total Fat	Less than	65g	80g
Sat Fat	Less than	20g	25g
Cholesterol	Less than	300mg	300mg
Sodium	Less than	2,400mg	2,400mg
Total Carbohydrate		300g	375g
Dietary Fiber		25g	30g

With a Group

Analyze the Nutrition Facts panel shown above. Which nutrients does this product contain? If you ate this entire food product, how many calories would you consume? How much of each nutrient would you consume, based on a 2000 calorie per-day diet?

Cultural Perspectives

Low-Fat Foods in the American Diet
Nutrition Facts panels are an excellent tool for students to use to monitor their fat intake. Remind students that most Americans eat far more fat than is essential for good health. Have students discuss ways to keep their fat intake at healthy levels. Use these tips to start the discussion:

- Use the nutrition facts offered by fast-food restaurants to make lower-fat choices.
- Eat food that is baked, steamed, or grilled rather than fried.
- Avoid adding fats such as butter to foods.

Be Physically Active

To maintain a healthy weight, you should balance the food you eat with physical activity. Teens should be physically active for at least one hour on most days. Physical activity helps you burn off some of the calories you consume. It also builds strength and helps you feel good about yourself. What are some ways you can add physical activity into your day?

Keep Foods Safe to Eat

"Wait, you better use another cutting board!" Gail warned Philip. Her brother was about to cut up vegetables on a board he had just used for cutting raw meat.

Gail was right. Using the same cutting board or even the same knife, without washing them first, can spread germs. This is one rule of food safety. Here are some others:

- Wash your hands before handling food. Wash them again if you are about to handle a different kind of food.
- Separate raw, cooked, and ready-to-eat foods while shopping, preparing, or storing them.
- Cook meat, chicken, turkey, and fish to safe internal temperatures. Refrigerate cooked leftovers right away after meals. Both these actions will help stop the spread of germs. See **Figure 4.4** for safe food temperatures.

Choose Foods Wisely

The *Dietary Guidelines for Americans* contains additional tips for making wise food choices. Some of these tips are explored in the following sections.

Eat More Fruits, Vegetables, and Whole Grains. Try "coloring" your plate with green, orange, red, and yellow vegetables at mealtimes. As for grains, here is a tip to remember: Make half your grains whole. In other words, choose as many whole grain as other grain products. These include whole-wheat breads, crackers, and brown rice.

▼ **FIGURE 4.4**

FOOD TEMPERATURES

Remember to keep hot foods hot and cold foods cold. How does this help keep foods safe to eat?

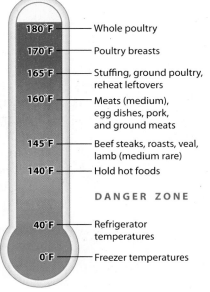

180°F	Whole poultry
170°F	Poultry breasts
165°F	Stuffing, ground poultry, reheat leftovers
160°F	Meats (medium), egg dishes, pork, and ground meats
145°F	Beef steaks, roasts, veal, lamb (medium rare)
140°F	Hold hot foods
	DANGER ZONE
40°F	Refrigerator temperatures
0°F	Freezer temperatures

R Reading Strategy

Analyzing a Graphic Have students use the information in the photo and caption in Figure 4.4 to draw a conclusion about the way to keep foods at proper temperatures. Ask: If a restaurant wants to maintain hot foods for a buffet at a safe temperature, how hot should the food be kept? *140°F* BL

AL Active Learning

Role-Play Divide the class into small groups. Have students write a short role-play that incorporates some of the tips for keeping food safe. Have each group perform its role-play for the class. OL

W Writing Support

Expository Writing Have students write an expository paragraph that gives tips on how to follow the *Dietary Guidelines*. Remind students that expository writing shares knowledge to help others understand. Students should proofread and revise their work before turning in a final copy. OL

TECHNOLOGY AND HEALTH

Using Database Technology Create a project for each chapter that will require each student to gather data and enter his or her information in a class database. For example, students were assigned to record the number of advertisements for food they viewed in one day for the Health Skills Practice on page 103. Their results could be entered into a class database. The database could then be used to generate graphs and charts showing the class results. OL

Caption Answer

Figure Caption When foods are kept at proper temperature, bacteria and germs will be less likely to grow and spread disease.

▶ Some of the calories you take in are burned off during physical activity. If you take in more calories than you burn, you gain weight. **What happens if you take in fewer calories?**

Know Your Fats. Did you know that some fats are more healthful than others? A fatty oil found in salmon and other fish may actually promote heart health; so does olive oil when used in reasonable amounts. These fats are mostly unsaturated. Saturated (SAT·chur·a·tuhd) fats, on the other hand, should be limited. **Saturated fats** are *fats found in many animal products such as butter, meat, and cheese.* Eating too much saturated fat may increase your body's level of cholesterol (kuh·LES·tuh·rawl). **Cholesterol** is *a waxy chemical our bodies produce and need in small amounts.* Too much, however, can lead to heart disease and stroke. Another fat to limit is trans fats. **Trans fats** *start off as oils and are made solid through processing.* Like saturated fats, trans fats are linked to heart problems.

Limit Added Sugars. Some food products have sugars added. Cakes, candy, and soft drinks fall into this category. So, surprisingly, do many nondessert items. Did you know many salad dressings and breads such as donuts or sweet rolls have added sugars? Like complex carbohydrates, foods high in added sugar provide food energy. However, they may be low in other nutrients. Eat only small amounts of these foods.

Limit Salt. Watch your intake of salt. Salt contains **sodium,** *a mineral that helps control the amount of fluid in your body.* Too much sodium can promote high blood pressure in some

HEALTH LITERACY

people. You can find out how much sodium is in a given amount of food by reading the label.

 Reading Check **Identify** Give two pieces of advice from the *Dietary Guidelines for Americans*.

Tips on Snacks

Snacks are an important part of eating for teens on the go. Just try to keep them healthy. Peanuts or other nuts provide protein. They can give you more nutrients than a candy bar. Tuck a small box of dried fruits, such as raisins, into your backpack. Healthy snacks will provide some of the nutrients your body needs.

 Reading Check **Give Examples** What is one example of a healthy snack?

 Health Online

Visit **health.glencoe.com** and complete the Interactive Study Guide for Lesson 3.

Lesson 3 Review

 **After You Read**

Review this lesson for new terms, major headings, and Reading Checks.

What I Learned

1. **List** Name two foods that contain saturated fat.

2. **Recall** Why is limiting salt and fat important?

3. **Identify** What are three guidelines to follow when choosing what to eat?

Thinking Critically

4. **Analyze** Think about the influences on your eating habits. Which factor do you think influences you most? Is this a positive or negative influence?

5. **Hypothesize** Todd, who is active in sports, burns 2,500 calories a day. He eats 2,000 calories a day. What will happen to Todd's weight over time if he keeps up this routine?

Applying Health Skills

6. **Goal Setting** Choose a goal that will help you follow a more healthful eating plan. Describe the steps you need to take to reach your goal.

 Health Online For more review questions for Lesson 3, go to **health.glencoe.com**.

Lesson 3: Healthful Food Choices **107**

Reading Check

Answer Eat more complex carbohydrates and limit added sugar.

ASSESS

Assessment Resources

Lesson Review Quiz
ExamView
Fast Files Activities
Online Quizzes and Activities

Reteaching

● Assign Concept Map 4-3 or Reteaching Activity 4-3 in the Fast Files.
● Have students work in small groups to describe three main influences on their food choices.

Enrichment

● Assign Enrichment Activity 4-3 in the Fast Files.
● Have each student create a script for a short radio commercial promoting healthful food choices by teens.

CLOSE

Have students look back at their written description of their current eating habits. Ask students to use the lesson content to think of one way in which their eating habits could be improved.

Lesson 3 Review Answers

1. Saturated fats are contained in animal products such as butter, meat, and cheese.
2. Excess salt and fat are linked to health problems, such as high blood pressure.
3. Answers should include eating a variety of foods, controlling the amount you eat, knowing your fats, and limiting added sugar and salt.
4. Answers, which will vary, should show an understanding of the lesson content and an ability to apply the content to the student's own habits.
5. Todd will lose weight.
6. Students' goals will vary, but should reflect an understanding of lesson content about healthful eating.

FOCUS

Activating Prior Knowledge

What I Know Ask students to describe characteristics of a healthy body. Introduce the lesson by discussing why being thin does not always indicate being healthy.

Guide to Reading

BUILDING VOCABULARY
- Have students preview the lesson to find the vocabulary terms and their meanings.
- Use Vocabulary PuzzleMaker to reinforce vocabulary terms.

READING STRATEGY
Predicting Have students write one question related to each heading. Ask volunteers to share examples of questions with the class.

Quick Write

After students have made their lists, ask how weight affects all three sides of the health triangle.

Reading Check

Answer Growth pattern is the rate a person gains weight and height.

Academic Vocabulary

Professional Ask students to name uses of the word *professional* with which they are familiar (for example, professional sports).

Managing Your Weight

Guide to Reading

Building Vocabulary
List each term below in your notebook. As you come across it in your reading, write the definition.
- body image (p. 109)
- eating disorder (p. 110)

Focusing on the Main Ideas
In this lesson, you will be able to
- **explain** how to maintain a healthy weight.
- **identify** problem eating behaviors
- **demonstrate** decision-making skills to help a friend.

Reading Strategy
Predicting Look over the headings in this lesson. Write a question that you think the lesson will answer. After reading, check to see if your question was answered.

Quick Write

In a few sentences tell what you think the benefits are of maintaining a healthful weight.

Achieving a Healthful Weight

Knowing the weight that is right for you is tricky during the teen years. That's because your body is growing so fast. The only way to tell for sure is to see a health professional. This person will be able to judge whether your growth pattern is normal. Growth pattern is the rate at which you gain weight and grow in height.

If your weight is right for your height, try and keep it that way. Try to get enough physical activity to burn off some of the calories you take in. If you are concerned about your weight, talk to your doctor. He or she can help you create a healthful eating plan.

Reading Check

Explain What is growth pattern?

Weight Problems and Teens

The number of overweight young people has risen dramatically in the past twenty years. Being overweight can slow down your performance in school and other activities. Your self-esteem can be negatively affected too. Some children and teens are becoming *obese* (oh·BEES), which means they are significantly overweight. People who are obese have a very high

---

Lesson 4 Resources

📁 **Chapter *FAST FILE* Resources**
Guided Reading and Writing 4-4
Concept Mapping Activity 4-4
Decision-Making Activity 4-4
Reteaching Activity 4-4
Enrichment Activity 4-4
Lesson Quiz 4-4

Technology
⚓ Transparency 4-5
🔊 Audio Summaries
💿 *ExamView*
🔊 Vocabulary PuzzleMaker
💿 StudentWorks™ Plus

amount of body fat. This puts them at risk for developing other diseases such as diabetes and heart disease. You will learn more about these diseases in Chapter 11.

Treatment for Obese Teens

Obesity is a serious health problem. Teens who are obese should be under a doctor's care. The extra weight they carry around puts them at risk for developing other health problems. These teens should reach a healthy weight slowly. Sometimes the best approach is to keep from gaining more weight as your body grows.

 **Reading Check** **List** Name two health problems that can occur in obese people.

Body Image and the Teen Years

Do you see yourself as overweight? Underweight? Just right? Maybe you feel some parts of you are too wide or too narrow. Feelings like these are tied to your body image. **Body image** is *how you view your body*. Like your self-concept, your body image may differ from how others see you. You may feel you are too thin or not thin enough. You might compare yourself to people in the media. Making this comparison leads some teens to develop a negative body image. It is important to know that most people do not look like those you see on television or in magazines. Instead of comparing yourself to others, try to be realistic about your body. Remember that bodies come in all shapes and sizes. Take care of your body by eating healthfully and staying active. These habits will help you look and feel better.

Reading Check **Define** What is body image?

► Weight problems in teens can lead to other health problems. **What are some health problems that can develop from being overweight?**

Lesson 4: Managing Your Weight **109**

DEVELOPING
Good Character

Respect for Others' Bodies and Feelings

Some teens tease peers who are overweight or underweight. They may make hurtful comments or use impolite nicknames. This type of behavior shows a lack of respect. It is a form of bias, acting cruelly to those who look different. A person who does this is not demonstrating good character. What advice would you give a person who was behaving this way?

CHAPTER 4
Lesson 4

TEACH

DEVELOPING
Good Character

Respect for Others' Bodies and Feelings
Have students work in small groups to develop and present role-plays demonstrating ways to discourage teasing about physical appearance and weight. As each group performs, have the other students in the class each write one positive comment about the role-play.

C Critical Thinking

Analyzing Lead a class discussion on the influences on body image. Ask: Other than the media, what factors influence how teens feel about their bodies? Sample answers: *friends, family* Ask: Name one way that these can be a positive influence. Sample answer: *a parent telling a teen that he or she looks nice* Ask: Name one way that these can be a negative influence. Sample answer: *a friend encouraging excessive dieting* **OL**

Reading Check

Answer low self-esteem, heart disease, and diabetes
Answer Body image is how you view your body.

Caption Answer

Photo Caption Overweight teens may develop negative body image and other health problems.

What Teens Want to Know

What is a safe way to lose weight? Discuss some basic guidelines for choosing a healthy weight-loss plan. First, tell students that they should discuss any weight-loss plan with their parents or guardian and family doctor. Then discuss the following: Choose a weight-loss plan that includes a wide variety of foods, an increase in physical activity, encourages slow weight loss and long-term maintenance. Avoid plans that include pills or medications, unless approved by your family doctor or that promise extremely rapid weight loss. **OL**

Health Skills Activity

Decision Making

Help for a Friend with an Eating Disorder

Use the following strategies to help students complete the activity on page 111:

● Have students work in pairs. Give each pair of students a set of six index cards. On the front of each index card, have students write one of the six steps of decision making. On the back of the index cards, have students write down what they think Rachel should do at each step.

● Discuss the life-threatening nature of eating disorders. Tell students that, while it is not wrong for Rachel to talk to Kara about her concerns, a trusted adult such as a parent, teacher, or school nurse should always be informed about a student who might have an eating disorder. OL

Reading Check

Answer These are both serious eating disorders; they are different in the way in which the person seeks to achieve weight loss.

Caption Answer

Photo Caption by understanding that the media are not a helpful influence on body image

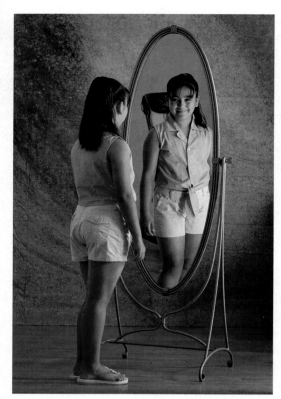

▲ Having a healthy body image is important to good mental/emotional health. **What are some ways you can develop a healthy body image?**

Eating Disorders

Some teens, and even some adults, become overly concerned with their body weight. They may have a negative body image. They may feel they need to lose weight, even when they don't. These people are at risk for developing an eating disorder. An **eating disorder** is an *extreme eating behavior that can seriously damage the body*. Eating disorders are most common among teen girls and young women. However, males can develop them as well. Two of the most common eating disorders are *anorexia nervosa* (an·uh·REK·see·uh ner·VOH·suh) and *bulimia* (boo·LEE·mee·uh) *nervosa*.

People with anorexia are overly concerned with weight gain. They may starve themselves. They eat far fewer calories than they need to stay healthy. They may exercise excessively. Even after they have become dangerously thin, they still see themselves as overweight.

People with bulimia eat large amounts of food, then "purge" themselves. They rid their body of food by vomiting or taking *laxatives*. These are medicines meant for people who have trouble moving their bowels. Victims of bulimia also may exercise excessively to burn off the calories from the foods they eat.

Treatment for Eating Disorders

Eating disorders are a mental health problem. They are often associated with a negative body image. Eating disorders can affect normal growth and development. They can lead to serious health problems, including death. If you are concerned that you or someone you know may have an eating disorder, talk to a trusted adult. A person with an eating disorder should get help right away. The sooner a person gets treatment, the better his or her chances of recovering.

Reading Check

Compare How are anorexia nervosa and bulimia nervosa similar? How are they different?

Health Online

Visit **health.glencoe.com** and complete the Interactive Study Guide for Lesson 4.

🏠 **Home, School, and Community**

At School Invite a school nurse or counselor to speak to students about eating disorders. Have each student write a question about eating disorders that the speaker could address. Review questions in advance with the speaker. Ask the speaker to stress the serious, life-threatening nature of these disorders. Have the speaker provide a list of local resources for students who struggle with eating disorders or who are concerned about a friend. If a guest speaker is not available, work with students to brainstorm a list of local resources. OL

Health Skills Activity

Decision Making

Help for a Friend with an Eating Disorder

Kara and Rachel have been friends since kindergarten. Lately, Rachel has begun to notice some changes in Kara. During lunch, Kara hardly eats anything. She claims she is not hungry. She also seems to be getting very thin. Rachel is beginning to worry that Kara may have an eating disorder. Rachel isn't sure whether she should talk to Kara about her concerns or tell someone else.

What Would You Do?

Apply the six steps of decision making to Rachel's problem. Tell what decision you would make if you were her, and why.

1. State the situation.
2. List the options.
3. Weigh the possible outcome.
4. Consider values.
5. Make a decision and act on it.
6. Evaluate the decision.

Lesson 4 Review

 After You Read

Review this lesson for new terms, major headings, and Reading Checks.

What I Learned

1. *Vocabulary* What is the difference between being *obese* and just being overweight?

2. *Recall* Name two eating disorders.

3. *Explain* Why is it important to develop a realistic body image?

Thinking Critically

4. *Analyze* Why do you think more teens are overweight today than in the past?

5. *Apply* Ryan has created an exercise plan to help him achieve a healthy weight. Why is it important for Ryan to start exercising slowly?

Applying Health Skills

6. *Analyze Influences* Explain how images in the media might play a role in a teen's body image.

Health Online For more review questions for Lesson 4, go to health.glencoe.com.

Assessment Resources

Lesson Review Quiz
ExamView
Fast Files Activities
Online Quizzes and Activities

Reteaching

- Assign Concept Map 4-4 or Reteaching Activity 4-4 in the Fast Files.
- Ask students to describe ways to help a friend who might have an eating disorder.

Enrichment

- Assign Enrichment Activity 4-4 in the Fast Files.
- Have students research and compare the incidence of obesity and eating disorders in teens in the United States and other countries. Have students present their findings to the class.

CLOSE

Have students identify three reasons for maintaining a healthy weight.

Lesson 4 Review Answers

1. Being overweight means being over a weight that is right for people of the same age and height. Being obese means weighing twenty percent or more than is healthful for height.

2. These include anorexia nervosa and bulimia nervosa.

3. A teen with a realistic image is more likely to eat healthfully and exercise rather than worrying about his or her body.

4. Teens are more sedentary than in the past.

5. Ryan should gradually increase physical activity to build muscle and avoid injury.

6. Images in the media present an unrealistic view and can lead to a distorted body image for teens.

111

Building Health Skills

DECISION MAKING

Choosing Health-Promoting Foods

SKILL
Decision making

Activating Prior Knowledge

Have students name three of the factors that affect their food choices.

- **Objective** After completing the activity, students will be able to apply the six steps of decision making to food choices.

- **Time** 90 minutes

- **Materials** paper, pencil

Teacher Classroom Resources

📁 Building Health Skills
🖨 Transparency 1-4

Model

- Have students discuss Teri's options. *Teri can stand in line to get a salad, but she might be late for the movie. She could get a slice of pizza, but she will be eating pizza with her family later.*

Choosing Health-Promoting Foods

DIRECTIONS

Decision making involves taking steps to make healthy and responsible choices. This activity will give you the opportunity to develop and master this important health skill. Here's a guide to the different parts of this activity:

❶ In the **Model** section, you will read about a teen who performs the health skill successfully. This "model" scenario will show you how the skill is done.

❷ The **Practice** section will help guide you in practicing the skill.

❸ In the **Apply** section, you will have a chance to perform the skill on your own. You can use the Self-Check to check your work.

To complete this activity, first read the scenario presented in the Model. Then move on to the Practice. Finally, go ahead and try the Apply.

112 Chapter 4: Nutrition

❶ Model

Teri was having lunch at the mall with friends. Teri wanted a salad, but the line was long. "Just get a burger," Corey said. "You need to hurry so we can get to our movie on time." Teri felt pressured. She decided to use the decision-making process to help her choose. In her mind, she went through the six steps:

Step 1. State the Situation.

I want a salad, but the line is long. My friends are bugging me to get a burger.

Step 2. List the Options.

I could tell Corey and Sheila I prefer to wait and meet them at the movie theater. I could just have a burger and do something more healthful tomorrow.

Step 3. Weigh the Possible Outcomes.

I'm having pizza for dinner with my family. I want something for lunch that has fewer calories and less fat.

Step 4. Consider Your Values.

Eating right is important to me.

Step 5. Make a Decision and Act.

I will wait in the salad line and ask my friends to save me a seat at the movie theater.

Step 6. Evaluate the Decision.

I made the right choice. I ate my salad and still made it to the movie.

Teaching Tips

Internet Resources Direct students to preselected Internet sites to access information on nutritional value of foods. Students may wish to search for their favorite fast-food restaurants to get detailed information about the nutrient content of foods offered by the restaurants.

❷ Practice

Later that week, Teri faced a similar problem. She had to be at soccer practice by 4:00 o'clock. It was now 3:45 p.m. Teri wanted something that would give her a quick energy boost. She studied the choices in the school vending machine. She knew the snack cake was a source of energy but had added sugar and could also be high in fat. The other choices included peanut butter crackers, potato chips, and candy bars. Write out the decision-making steps to help Teri choose a snack.

Skill Summary
DECISION MAKING

1. State the situation.
2. List the options.
3. Weigh the possible outcomes.
4. Consider values.
5. Make a decision and act.
6. Evaluate the decision.

❸ Apply

Think of a situation in which you need to decide what to eat. One possibility might be choosing what to eat for breakfast. Think about the type of food you generally choose in this situation. Is your usual choice healthy? Are their healthier foods you could choose? Think through your decision using the six-step model.

Self-Check

- Did I list several food choices?
- Did I consider my values when making my decision?
- Did I use each step in the decision-making process?

Building Health Skills **113**

Practice

- Have students apply the six steps of decision making to help Teri choose a snack from the school vending machine.
- Ask volunteers to share their answers. Have students explain how they used the six steps of decision making to arrive at their answers.

Apply/Assess

- Have students apply the six steps of decision making to another food-choice situation. Ask students to write a paragraph explaining their choice and summarizing how the six steps of decision making helped them make that choice.
- You may wish to distribute the Building Health Skills Activity in the Fast Files.

Keeping a Food Diary

Time: 20 minutes over several days
Materials: pencil or pen, paper

Introducing Hands-on Health

- Tell students that a food diary is an excellent tool to use to evaluate their food choices. Explain that a food diary is only useful if it accurately reflects what was eaten. Encourage students to record foods as they are eaten, rather than trying to remember several days' worth of food choices at once.

Teaching the Activity

- Have students complete the food diary as directed.
- Allow students to keep their answers confidential.
- Have students use their results to identify how they could improve their food choices.

Food Diary

Foods Eaten	Amount	Food Group
Monday		
Pancakes	2 cups	Grains
Orange juice	1/2 cup	Fruits
Turkey sandwich	2 ounces turkey	Meat and beans
on wheat bread	2 slices of bread	Grains
Baby carrots	1/2 cup	Vegetables
Carton of milk	1 cup	Milk

Keeping a Food Diary

In this chapter, you learned about making healthful food choices using MyPyramid. You can begin to make more healthful food choices by taking a look at what foods you typically eat each day. In this activity, you will make a food diary. This will help you compare your food choices to the recommendations provided by MyPyramid for a teen your age. That way you can see what changes, if any, you need to make.

What You Will Need

- pencil or pen
- ruler
- paper

What You Will Do

1. Make three vertical columns on your paper.
2. In the first column, list all the foods you ate in the past few days. Be sure to include any snacks you had. Draw a horizontal line to show the end of each day. Use extra pages for your food diary as needed.
3. In the second column, write down the amount of each food eaten. Record the amount as a weight (such as ounces) or volume (such as cups).
4. In the third column, write down the name of the food group each food eaten belongs to. For example, a peanut butter sandwich would belong to the grains group, and the meat and beans group.
5. For each day, total up the amount eaten in each food group.

Wrapping It Up

1. How well does your list for each day match the recommendations from MyPyramid?
2. Did you eat foods from each food group? If not, which group is missing?
3. Was there too much from any food group? If so, which group?
4. How could you improve your food choices?

HANDS-ON HEALTH Assessment

Discussion Ask students:
- Why is it important to record both the type of food eaten and the amount of each food eaten? Sample answer: *Both the amount and type of food eaten can affect health.*

- What are some actions you could take to make your food choices match the USDA Food Guidance System? Sample answer: *I would need to reduce the amount of candy I eat and increase the amount of fruit I eat.*

Reading Review

FOLDABLES Study Organizer

Foldables™ and Other Study Aids Take out the Foldable™ that you created for Lesson 1 and any graphic organizers that you created for Lessons 1–4. Find a partner, and quiz each other using these study aids.

Lesson 1 Your Body's Nutrient Needs

Key Ideas

- The six main classes of nutrients are carbohydrates, fats, proteins, vitamins, minerals, and water.
- Complex carbohydrates are found in bread, rice, pasta, beans, and other vegetables. Another type of complex carbohydrate, fiber, is the tough, stringy part of raw fruits, raw vegetables, whole wheat, and other whole grains.
- Protein sources include fish, chicken, beef, eggs, milk and other dairy products, beans, nuts, and most soy-based products.
- Salad dressings, doughnuts, and fried foods are often high in fat.
- Vitamins and minerals are found in a wide variety of foods.

Vocabulary
- nutrients (p. 94)
- nutrition (p. 94)
- carbohydrates (p. 95)
- fiber (p. 95)
- proteins (p. 95)
- fats (p. 95)
- vitamins (p. 96)
- minerals (p. 96)

Lesson 2 Following a Healthful Eating Plan

Key Ideas

- MyPyramid shows you how to balance your daily nutrient needs by eating a variety of nutrient-rich foods. It also encourages you to stay within your calorie needs based on age, gender, and activity level.
- The five most important food groups are the grain group, the meat and beans group, the milk group, the vegetable group, and the fruit group.

Vocabulary
- MyPyramid food guidance system (p. 98)
- calorie (p. 100)

Lesson 3 Making Healthful Food Choices

Key Ideas

- Influences on your food choices include the taste, texture, and appearance of food, your appetite, your friends, family, culture, and convenience.
- You can make healthful food choices by eating more fruits, vegetables, and whole grains, knowing your fats, and limiting added sugars and salt.

Vocabulary
- saturated fat (p. 106)
- cholesterol (p. 106)
- trans fats (p. 106)
- sodium (p. 106)

Lesson 4 Managing Your Weight

Key Ideas

- You can maintain a healthy weight by controlling the amount you eat and by getting enough physical activity.
- People who are obese are at risk of developing other serious health problems.
- Two common eating disorders are anorexia nervosa and bulimia nervosa.

Vocabulary
- body image (p. 109)
- eating disorder (p. 110)

Chapter 4 Reading Review **115**

Assessment Resources

- Chapter 4 Summary and Activity
- Audio Summaries
- Reading Tutor
- Performance Assessment
- Chapter 4 Test
- *ExamView*
- Vocabulary PuzzleMaker
- Online Learning Center

Reading Review

Study Aids

- **Using the Dinah Zike Foldable™ Study Organizer** Have students use the Foldable™ to review the content of Lesson 1. Have students use their Foldables™ to describe the six main classes of nutrients.

FOLDABLES Study Organizer

Key Ideas

- **Use the Reading Checks** Have students review each of the Reading Checks throughout the chapter. If a student has difficulty answering any of the reading checks, have him or her review the material in that section.

Vocabulary Review

- **Vocabulary Matching** Prepare two stacks of index cards, one stack with a chapter vocabulary term and the other stack with the definition of a vocabulary term. Have students work in teams to match the cards from the two stacks.

Teaching Tips

Guided Reading Guided reading helps students recall information they have read silently. First prepare students by using a strategy such as the survey technique. Have students read silently and then turn the text over. Ask what they remember and record the information on the board. Add or correct any incorrect information. Ask students to sequence main ideas in the order they were presented, and create an outline. Ask questions such as: Do you see how this relates to what we have already learned?

Assessment

Reviewing Vocabulary and Main Ideas

1. proteins
2. Minerals
3. nutrients
4. calorie
5. MyPyramid
6. d
7. c
8. a
9. b

Thinking Critically

10. These facts can guide a consumer to make more healthful choices whenever shopping for food products.
11. The person might be cautioned to pay close attention to the nutrient content of the foods he or she ate to ensure that his or her nutritional needs are met.

CHAPTER

4

Assessment

After You Read

HEALTH INVENTORY

Now that you have read the chapter, look back at your answers to the Health Inventory on the chapter opener. Is there anything you should do differently?

Reviewing Vocabulary and Main Ideas

On a sheet of paper, write the numbers 1–5. After each number, write the term from the list that best completes each sentence.

- body image
- calorie
- eating disorder
- minerals
- MyPyramid
- nutrients
- proteins
- saturated fats

Lesson 1 Your Body's Nutrient Needs

1. Nutrients that provide the building blocks your body needs for growth are called _____.
2. _____ are elements in foods that help your body work properly.
3. Substances in food that your body needs to carry out its normal functions are called _____.

Lesson 2 Following a Healthful Eating Plan

4. A _____ is a unit of heat that measures the energy available in foods.
5. _____ is a system designed to help Americans make healthful food choices.

On a sheet of paper, write the numbers 6–9. After each number, write the letter of the answer that best completes each statement

Lesson 3 Making Healthful Food Choices

6. According to MyPyramid, nutrients provided by the grain group include the following:
   a. complex carbohydrates
   b. vitamins
   c. fiber
   d. all of the above
7. How many cups per day from the milk group is recommended for most teens?
   a. 2 cups
   b. 2½ cups
   c. 3 cups
   d. 4½ cups

Lesson 4 Managing Your Weight

8. Which of the following is true about obesity?
   a. It can slow down your performance in school and other activities.
   b. It is a health problem that can be corrected quickly.
   c. The number of obese teens has been dropping steadily.
9. Which of the following is true both of people with anorexia and people with bulimia?
   a. They "purge" after eating large amounts of food.
   b. They are overly concerned with weight gain.
   c. They eat far fewer calories than their body needs.

Health Online Visit **health.glencoe.com** and take the Online Quiz for Chapter 4.

Health Online

Have students visit **health.glencoe.com** to take the Chapter 4 Quiz.

HEALTH INVENTORY WRAP-UP

Nutrition and Your Health Have students review their responses to the Health Inventory. Ask volunteers to name a goal for healthy eating they could develop based on their responses to the Health Inventory and the content of this chapter.

Thinking Critically

Using complete sentences, answer the following questions on a sheet of paper.

10. **Identify** Why is it important to use a product's Nutrition Facts panel to guide your eating habits?

11. **Synthesize** What might you tell a friend who said he was planning to eat only vegetables from now on?

Write About It

12. **Analyzing Influences.** Write a paragraph describing how influences can affect your food choices.

13. **Advocacy.** Write a story about a teen who is concerned about his or her body image? What advice might you give this teen?

Write About It

12. **Descriptive Writing** Family and cultural traditions can influence the types of foods a teen is exposed to and therefore develops a taste for. Teens often want to fit in with their peers. Therefore, they may choose to eat the same foods as their peers are eating. An advertisement for a new food may influence your decision to try the food. Other answers may include personal likes/dislikes, appetite, and convenience.

13. **Narrative Writing** Answers might include the idea that as a teen, the person's body image was changing and that, moreover, it is important to learn to accept the body one was given.

Standardized Test Practice

1. B
2. D

Standardized Test Practice

Math

The graph below helps you determine which foods give you the most fiber without adding excess calories. Use the graph to answer the questions.

1. How many calories are there in the food with the second highest amount of fiber?

   A. 32   **C.** 178

   B. 154   **D.** None of the above

2. To get the ratio of fiber to calories, you would divide the number of calories by grams of fiber. For example, ½ a cup of cooked broccoli has 26 calories and 2.8 grams of fiber. 26 ÷ 2.8 = 9.3, or a ratio of 1 to 9.3. What is the ratio of fiber to calories for ½ cup of raspberries?

   A. 1 to 17   **C.** 1 to 60

   B. 1 to 25   **D.** 1 to 8

TEST-TAKING TIP

Questions about graphs sometimes rely on outside knowledge. If an answer is not stated directly, try eliminating choices that are clearly wrong.

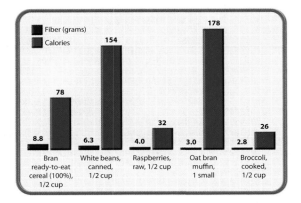

Test-Taking Tips

Test Practice Tell students to use practice tests whenever they are available. Many previously administered standardized tests are available for use as practice tests.

Remind students that tests often change from year to year, but that practice tests can be used to practice test-taking strategies and to review content.

CHAPTER 5 pp. 118–141	Standards		Skills and Activities
	National	**State/Local**	
	National Health Education Standards 6.1, 6.2, 6.3		**HEALTH QUIZ**, *p. 119* TIME HEALTH NEWS How to Stay Fit for Life, *p. 138* **BUILDING HEALTH SKILLS** *Goal Setting* Developing a Personal Fitness Plan, *p. 136*
Lesson 1 **Physical Activity and Your Health** pp. 120–125	National Health Education Standards 1.1, 1.2, 1.4, 1.6, 1.8, 4.3, 7.4, 8.2, 8.4		**HEALTH SKILLS ACTIVITY** *Practicing Healthful Behaviors* Fun for the Family, *p. 122*
Lesson 2 **Creating a Personal Fitness Plan** pp. 126–131	National Health Education Standards 3.6, 4.3, 6.1, 6.2, 6.3, 7.4, 8.2		**Connect To... MATH** Hitting the Target, *p. 130* **HEALTH SKILLS ACTIVITY** *Practicing Healthful Behaviors* Exercise with "Eye Appeal," *p. 130*
Lesson 3 **Safety in Sports and Physical Activities** pp. 132–135	National Health Education Standards 1.1, 1.6, 3.1, 3.3, 5.3, 7.4, 7.5, 8.2, 8.4, 8.5		**MEDIA WATCH** If the Shoe Fits, *p. 134*

PACING THE CHAPTER

Lesson 1	45 min	Chapter Review	45 min
Lesson 2	90 min	TIME Health News	20 min
Lesson 3	45 min	Building Health Skills	45 min

BLOCK SCHEDULING

For block scheduling, assign students Building Health Skills Feature *Developing a Personal Fitness Plan*, pages 136–137, and Guided Reading and Writing in the *Fast Files*. 📁

Planning Guide

Glencoe Exclusive!
TeacherWorks™
All-In-One Planner and Resource Center

Reproducible Resources	Assessment	Media and Technology
Chapter FAST FILE Resources Chapter Summaries and Activities REVIEW Building Health Skills Activity TEACH Performance Assessment Activity EXTEND Universal Access Activities TEACH Parent Letter and Activities **Student Activities Workbook** TEACH **Reading Tutor** TEACH	Building Health Skills Activity, *pp. 136–137* Chapter 5 Assessment, *pp. 140–141* **Chapter FAST FILE Resources** Performance Assessment Activity, *p. 4* Chapter 5 Test, *p. 7* ⊙ *ExamView® Test Generator*	**TeacherWorks™** includes: • Interactive Teacher Edition • Lesson Planner with Calendar • Access to all blackline masters • Correlations to standards ⊙ StudentWorks™ Plus ◠ Online Student Edition Dinah Zike's Teaching Health with Foldables™
Chapter FAST FILE Resources Concept Mapping Activity 5-1 REVIEW Cross-Curriculum Activity 5-1 EXTEND Enrichment Activity 5-1 EXTEND Guided Reading and Writing 5-1 TEACH Lesson Plan 5-1 Reteaching Activity 5-1 REVIEW	Lesson 1 Review, *p. 125* ◠ Vocabulary PuzzleMaker ⊙ *ExamView® Test Generator*	◠ Vocabulary PuzzleMaker ⊙ *ExamView® Test Generator* ⊙ StudentWorks™ Plus ⎚ Transparency 5-1 ◠ **Health Online**
Chapter FAST FILE Resources Concept Mapping Activity 5-2 REVIEW Enrichment Activity 5-2 EXTEND Guided Reading and Writing 5-2 TEACH Health Lab 5-2 EXTEND Lesson Plan 5-2 Reteaching Activity 5-2 REVIEW	Lesson 2 Review, *p. 131* ◠ Vocabulary PuzzleMaker ⊙ *ExamView® Test Generator*	◠ Vocabulary PuzzleMaker ⊙ *ExamView® Test Generator* ⊙ StudentWorks™ Plus ⎚ Transparency 5-2 ◠ **Health Online**
Chapter FAST FILE Resources Concept Mapping Activity 5-3 REVIEW Decision-Making Activity 5-3 EXTEND Enrichment Activity 5-3 EXTEND Guided Reading and Writing 5-3 TEACH Lesson Plan 5-3 Reteaching Activity 5-3 REVIEW	Lesson 3 Review, *p. 135* ◠ Vocabulary PuzzleMaker ⊙ *ExamView® Test Generator*	◠ Vocabulary PuzzleMaker ⊙ *ExamView® Test Generator* ⊙ StudentWorks™ Plus ⎚ Transparency 5-3 ◠ **Health Online**

Chapter and Lesson Resources

The *Teen Health* resources are designed for differentiated learning abilities. You may want to use the coded items in this way:

REVIEW —activities to review or reinforce content

TEACH —activities to teach basic concepts

EXTEND —activities to extend or enrich lesson content

 OUT OF TIME?

Use Health Skills Activities *Fun for the Family,* page 122 and *Exercise with "Eye Appeal,"* page 130 or TIME Health News, page 138.

Diabetes, Obesity, and Physical Activity

According to a study conducted by the Centers for Disease Control and Prevention, the rates of obesity and diabetes in young people in the United States are increasing rapidly. Type 2 diabetes, which was previously known as adult-onset diabetes, is becoming more and more common in young people. In this type of diabetes, insulin is produced by the body, but the body cannot use it properly. Until about 20 years ago 3 to 5 percent of the cases of diabetes in children were type 2 diabetes. Between 25 and 30 percent of cases of childhood diabetes are now type 2 diabetes.

Type 2 diabetes can have few or no symptoms in young people. Many children have type 2 diabetes for a long period of time before the disease is recognized. Diabetes is diagnosed using a blood test. If students recognize the risk factors for diabetes, they can discuss diabetes with their parents or guardians and health-care providers. They can also take steps to maintain a healthy lifestyle that can help prevent diabetes.

Type 2 diabetes is strongly associated with obesity. The rise in rates of type 2 diabetes among young people is associated with the increase in rates of childhood obesity. Maintaining a healthy weight is one of the most important steps in preventing type 2 diabetes.

Lack of physical activity is another risk factor for type 2 diabetes. Studies in adults have shown that starting a program of physical activity can help prevent the onset of diabetes in adults.

When students are studying the positive effects of regular physical activity, emphasize the importance of physical activity in the prevention of diabetes.

Another risk factor for type 2 diabetes includes having one or more family members with type 2 diabetes. Encourage students to ask their parents or guardians about a family history of diabetes.

Fitness Assessment Strategies

In Lesson 2, students learn about ways to assess their current fitness levels. By assessing fitness levels, students are able to make realistic health goals and evaluate their progress toward those goals.

Informal fitness assessments can be used by students to measure progress toward increased overall fitness. For example, the ease with which a student climbs a flight of stairs can be used as an informal gauge of his or her fitness level.

Formal fitness assessments include jumping jacks, zipper stretch, and push-ups. Jumping jacks can be used to assess cardiovascular fitness. The pulse rate following 30 seconds of exercise is used for assessment.

Fitness Rating: Jumping Jacks

Beats per Minute	Rating
Under 60 beats	Pass
Over 60 beats	Needs Work

Push-ups can be used to evaluate muscular strength in the arms and chest. The number of completed push-ups is used to measure fitness.

Fitness Rating: Push-Ups

Number of Push-Ups	Rating
Males: 5 or more	Pass
Less than 5	Needs Work
Females: 3 or more	Pass
Less than 3	Needs Work

Fitness Rating: Zipper Stretch

Ability to Touch	Rating
Touch or overlap	Pass
Inability to touch	Needs Work

Reading Support   **Health Online**   Academic Integration For additional academic integration strategies, visit the Teacher Center at **health.glencoe.com**.

Reading Preview

Activating Background Vocabulary Ask students what comes to mind when they hear the words *physical activity*. Record appropriate responses on the board. Then, ask students what they know about physical fitness. Guide students in a discussion of how physical activity can help people become physically fit.

FOLDABLES Study Organizer *Dinah Zike's Reading and Study Skills for Teen Health* provides interactive graphic organizers that help students comprehend and retain health concepts as they read. Use the Foldable™ on page 119 or find more Foldables™ activities for the chapter on **Physical Activity** in the separate booklet, available in the TCR.

Lesson 1   Physical Activity and Your Health

Question-Answer Relationship (QAR) Help students identify the four task demands of questioning: "Right there" questions are text explicit, such as, "What is physical activity?" "Think and search" questions are text implicit, such as, "What are the differences between strength, endurance, and flexibility?" "Author and you" questions require reading the text, such as, "Does the author think physical activity should be a part of your daily routine?" "On my own" questions can be answered without reading, such as, "Do you think exercise is important?"

Lesson 2   Setting Fitness Goals

SQ3R Guide students to: 1) Survey—scan the title and headings of the lesson. 2) Question— restate each heading in the form of a question. Reword **"Creating a Personal Fitness Plan"** to become "How do you create a personal fitness plan?" 3) Read—find out how to create a plan by asking: what, when, where, who, and how. 4) Recite—record information about setting fitness goals in a notebook. 5) Review—go over notes and summarize each section.

Lesson 3   Safety in Sports and Physical Activities

List-Describe-Example While they read, have students create a list of the main ideas in the chapter. Have student pairs define each term, record it on a simple chart, then give an example of each. To illustrate: main idea=appropriate sports gear; definition=sports clothing and safety equipment; example=helmets and proper shoes.

Post Reading

Twin Text Reports To supplement the text, provide students with both fictional and informational reading material on physical fitness topics. After reading, have students express their ideas in a written report, incorporating the factual information from the text in a response to the fictional material.

Key for Using the Teacher Wraparound Edition

Use this key to help you identify the different types of prompts found in the Teacher Wraparound Edition.

R **Reading Strategies** activities help you teach reading skills and vocabulary.

C **Critical Thinking** strategies help students apply and extend what they have learned.

U **Universal Access** activities provide differentiated instruction for students learning to speak English, along with suggestions for teaching various types of learners.

HS **Health Skills Practice** activities reinforce Health Skills concepts and help students apply these skills in their everyday lives.

W **Writing Support** activities provide writing opportunities to help students comprehend the text.

AL **Active Learning** strategies provide a variety of activities for presenting lesson content, including Quick Demos and engaging classroom projects that get students actively involved.

Key to Ability Levels

Teaching Strategies and activities have been coded for ability level and appropriateness

AL Activities for students working above grade level

OL Activities for students working on grade level

BL Activities for students working below grade level

EL Activities for English Learners

Symbols

Transparencies

CD-ROM

health.glencoe.com

Print Resources

Physical Activity

Chapter at a Glance

Lesson 1 explains the benefits of regular physical activity, identifies measures of physical fitness, and identifies benefits of different exercises.

Lesson 2 identifies the parts of a fitness plan and describes warm-ups and cool-downs.

Lesson 3 identifies types of proper sports gear, describes treatment for sports-related injuries, and explains how to avoid weather-related injuries.

R Reading Strategy

Interpreting the Photo
Have students name lifestyle activities other than walking that can contribute to physical fitness. Record their responses on the board. If possible, leave the list on the board and have students add other physical activities as they read the chapter. **OL**

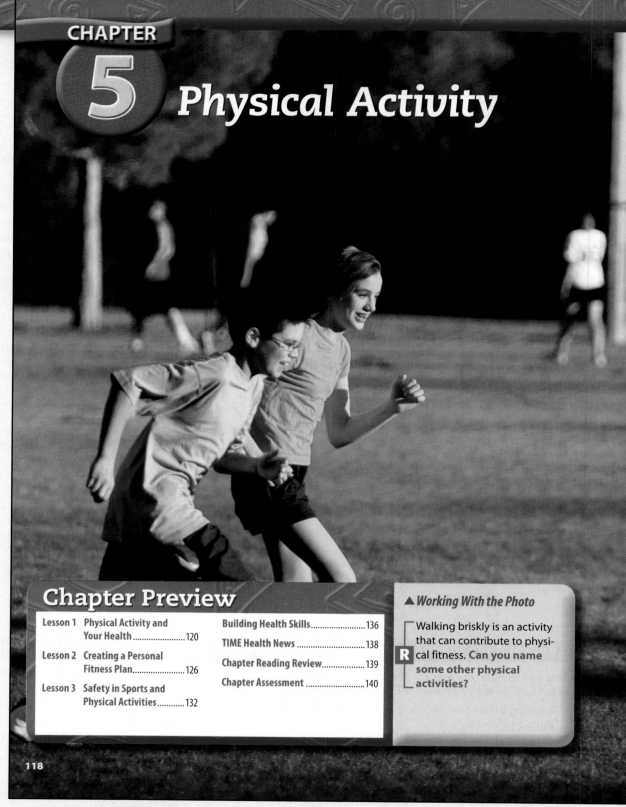

CHAPTER 5 Physical Activity

Chapter Preview

Lesson 1 Physical Activity and
Your Health 120

Lesson 2 Creating a Personal
Fitness Plan......................126

Lesson 3 Safety in Sports and
Physical Activities............132

Building Health Skills.......................136

TIME Health News 138

Chapter Reading Review...................139

Chapter Assessment 140

▲ *Working With the Photo*

Walking briskly is an activity that can contribute to physical fitness. **Can you name some other physical activities?**

118

👥 Universal Access

Differentiated Learning Glencoe provides teacher support and student materials for all learners in the health classroom.
- Spanish Glosario and chapter summaries for the English Language Learner.
- *Reading Tutor* and related worksheets support reluctant readers.

- Universal Access strategies throughout this Teacher Wraparound Edition and Fast Files help you present materials for gifted students, at-risk students, physically impaired students and those with behavior disorders or learning disabilities.

Start-Up Activities

What do you know about the health benefits of physical activity? To find out, take this short quiz. Keep a record of your answers.

HEALTH QUIZ Answer *true* or *false* to each of the following questions.

1. The only way to become physically fit is by doing exercise.

2. Physical activity is important only to physical health.

3. Physical activity reduces your risk of developing certain diseases.

ANSWERS: 1. false; 2. false; 3. true

FOLDABLES Study Organizer

As You Read Make this Foldable™ to record what you learn in Lesson 1 about the importance of physical activity. Begin with a plain sheet of 8½" × 11" notebook paper.

1 Fold a sheet of notebook paper from bottom to top leaving the heading uncovered.

2 Fold into thirds from side to side.

3 Unfold the paper once and cut along the two lines on the top, short layer of paper. This makes three tabs.

4 Label the tabs as shown.

Record information about strength, endurance, and flexibility under the appropriate tabs. Give examples of ways to build each type of physical activity.

Health Online Visit health.glencoe.com and complete the Chapter 5 crossword puzzle.

119

HEALTH QUIZ

Physical Activity Have students complete the Health Quiz. Ask volunteers to share their answers. Allow for class discussion of each question. Tell students that they will take the quiz again after they have read the chapter to see if their answers have changed. After discussing the Health Quiz, have students generate a list of topics that they anticipate the chapter will address.

No Child Left Behind

Classroom Management Throughout the year, gather health-related information from the news to share with students. If possible, make a dedicated bulletin board in the classroom for magazine and newspaper articles related to health. Ask students to contribute articles for the bulletin board. The articles allow students to make a connection between the topics in the text and real life. It also gives students the chance to preview topics that have not yet been taught and to review those topics that have already been discussed.

FOLDABLES Study Organizer **Dinah Zike Foldables™**

Formulating Questions Have students record questions as they read the first lesson of this chapter. Guide them to record notes about the importance of strength, endurance, and flexibility in physical activity. Encourage them to write questions about each of these areas before they read each section. Then as they work through the lesson, have them write the answers to their questions under each tab. Self-questioning is a strategy that helps students stay focused during reading and writing. **BL**

Health Online

Have students visit **health.glencoe.com** and complete the Health Inventory for Chapter 5.

FOCUS

Activating Prior Knowledge

What I Know Ask students to describe ways that physical activity can positively affect their health triangle.

Guide to Reading

BUILDING VOCABULARY

- Ask students to define the word *lifestyle* in the term *lifestyle activity*.
  Sample answer: *something that is a part of day-to-day life*
- Use Vocabulary PuzzleMaker to reinforce vocabulary terms.

READING STRATEGY

 Have students use their Foldables™ as they read Lesson 1. **BL**

- **Organizing Information** Allow time for students to review the lesson and write headings on their concept maps.

Quick Write

Introduce the Quick Write activity by having volunteers describe sports or activities they would enjoy learning. Ask volunteers to read their paragraphs aloud to the class.

Lesson 1

Physical Activity and Your Health

Guide to Reading

Building Vocabulary
Some terms below are related or have similar meanings. Can you tell which ones?

- physical activity (p. 120)
- lifestyle activities (p. 121)
- physical fitness (p. 121)
- strength (p. 123)
- endurance (p. 123)
- stamina (p. 123)
- flexibility (p. 124)
- exercise (p. 125)

Focusing on the Main Ideas
In this lesson, you will learn to

- **explain** the benefits of regular physical activity.
- **identify** measures of physical fitness.
- **recognize** the two main types of exercise.
- **practice** healthful behaviors with your family.

Reading Strategy
Organizing Information Create a concept map that captures the main ideas in the lesson. Use the diagram below as a guide.

Physical Activity	
Type of Activity	Builds Strength, Endurance, or Flexibility
1. running	1. endurance
2.	2.
3.	3.

FOLDABLES Study Organizer Use the Foldable™ on p. 119 as you read this lesson.

Quick Write

Write a paragraph about a sport or other activity you like playing or would enjoy learning.

What Is Physical Activity?

Shannon swims at the community pool every chance she gets. Matt is really into rock climbing. Kate and her friends have started an inline skating club. What do all these teens have in common? They all make physical activity a part of their lives. **Physical activity** is *any kind of movement that causes your body to use energy.*

How about you? Do you participate in regular physical activity? If not, it is never too late to start. Health experts recommend that teens get 60 minutes of physical activity most days. This hour can be done all at once or in moderate to vigorous 10- to 15-minute bursts. What are some ways you could fit 60 minutes of physical activity into your daily routine?

Lesson 1 Resources

📁 **Chapter *Fast File* Resources**
Guided Reading and Writing 5-1
Concept Mapping Activity 5-1
Cross-Curriculum Activity 5-1
Reteaching Activity 5-1
Enrichment Activity 5-1
Lesson Quiz 5-1

Technology
 Transparency 5-1
Audio Summaries
ExamView
Vocabulary PuzzleMaker
StudentWorks™ Plus

Lifestyle Activities

Do you have daily chores you do at home, such as raking leaves or shoveling snow? Do you enjoy outdoor activities, such as hiking or skateboarding? These are examples of lifestyle activities. **Lifestyle activities** are *physical activities that are part of your day-to-day routine or recreation.* They can become part of a lifelong commitment to fitness.

The Benefits of Physical Activity

Physical activity helps you use, or burn, calories from the foods you eat. See **Figure 5.1** for examples of how many calories are burned during a variety of activities. Burning calories means your body won't store extra calories as fat. This will help you maintain a healthy weight. Physical activity also contributes to physical fitness. **Physical fitness** is *the ability to handle everyday physical work and play without becoming tired.* Being physically fit can reduce your risk of developing certain diseases like diabetes, obesity, and heart disease.

▼ **FIGURE 5.1**

CALORIES BURNED DURING VARIOUS ACTIVITIES

The graph shows how many calories a 100-pound person burns during 60 minutes of different activities. Which activity burns the most calories? Which activity burns the fewest?

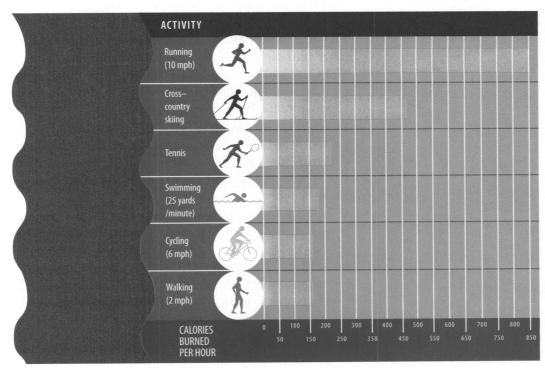

ACTIVITY

Running (10 mph)

Cross–country skiing

Tennis

Swimming (25 yards /minute)

Cycling (6 mph)

Walking (2 mph)

CALORIES BURNED PER HOUR

0   100   200   300   400   500   600   700   800
  50   150   250   350   450   550   650   750   850

Lesson 1: Physical Activity and Your Health   **121**

TEACH

R Reading Strategy

Analyzing a Graph Have students examine the graph in Figure 5.1. Sample answer: *running for an hour burns the most, walking burns the least in the same amount of time.* Ask: Would a 100-pound person burn more or fewer than 150 calories if he or she walked at a pace of 3 miles per hour? *more* Ask: How do you know? *The graph shows that more vigorous activity burns more calories.* **OL**

C Critical Thinking

Analyzing Information Ask: Why are lifestyle activities an important part of physical fitness? Sample answer: *They are important because they are activities that are likely to be kept up over many years.* **OL**

AL Active Learning

Creative Project Have students make comic strips that include information about the benefits of physical fitness. Have them include the recommended amount of physical activity for teens (60 minutes per day on most days). Display the completed comic strips in the classroom. Evaluate the comic strips based on creativity, neatness, and inclusion of the required information. **OL**

Academic Vocabulary

Commitment On this page students learn about a lifelong *commitment* to fitness. Explain that a commitment is a promise. Have students use the term in a sentence.

TECHNOLOGY AND HEALTH

Pedometers for Fitness Pedometers are a type of technology that can help students measure their physical activity. Pedometers measure the number of steps taken by the wearer. A pedometer is particularly valuable for students who want to use walking as a part of their fitness plans. The President's Council on Physical Fitness and Sports recommends that teens and adults walk 10,000 steps a day. Remind students to gradually increase the number of steps they take each day, rather than aiming for 10,000 steps immediately. If possible, bring a pedometer to class for students to try. **OL**

Health Skills Activity

Practicing Healthful Behaviors

Fun for the Family

Use the following suggestions to help students complete the activity:

- As a class, have students generate a list of family activities that involve physical activity. Record their responses on the board.
- Have each student choose two of the activities from the list that his or her family could take part in. Each student should write a paragraph explaining how his or her family would benefit from the two chosen activities.

Universal Access

Physically Impaired Students Students with physical limitations may not be able to participate in the sports and activities mentioned in this lesson. Point out that many people with physical limitations are accomplished athletes. When discussing physical activities, include wheelchair sports, such as racing and basketball. Have students research competitions for physically challenged athletes, for example the Paralympics and the Transplant Games. **OL**

Reading Check

Answer Benefits are strengthened muscles and improved concentration.

Health Skills Activity

Practicing Healthful Behaviors

Fun for the Family

Kiara's family skis every winter. Louis and his family go camping whenever they can. These kinds of outings give family members a chance to spend time together and be physically active. Take camping, for example. Carrying a backpack, finding and carrying wood, and setting up tents all work the body's muscles.

Of course not all family activities need to take place away from home. Tossing a Frisbee in the backyard, weeding the garden, or taking a walk are all excellent ways to combine physical activity with family time.

On Your Own

Think of an activity you could get your family involved in.

Your physical, mental/emotional, and social health all benefit when you are physically active and fit.

- **Physical benefits.** Physical activity strengthens and tones your muscles. It also strengthens your heart and lungs and builds strong bones. You will have more energy for school and other activities. Physical activity also helps you maintain a healthy weight.

- **Mental/Emotional benefits.** When you are physically fit, you sleep better. You can concentrate longer in school, deal with stress more easily, and get along better with others. In addition, developing new skills and interests can help you build your self-esteem.

- **Social benefits.** Physical activities that involve partners or teams are a great way to make friends. They also help you work together as a group and learn about other cultures. Max, for example, learned the rules of Canadian football from a classmate from Alberta. Thanks to Jorge, Greg was able to learn about the Latin sport of *pelota*. This sport is played similarly to tennis.

Reading Check **Identify** Name two health benefits of physical activity.

 What Teens Want to Know

Are sports drinks helpful? Sports drinks are often advertised as a way to enhance athletic performance. Sports drinks contain carbohydrates, which may be valuable to athletes who have worked out for more than 60 minutes. The taste of sports drinks may make it more appealing for a student to consume an adequate amount of liquid. However, sports drinks have been shown to cause damage to teeth, due to the high sugar content and low pH of the drinks. Have students research the effectiveness of sports drinks and water for hydration and present their results to the class. **OL**

▲ Sports such as swimming can promote fitness. So can activities at home such as raking leaves. **What other activities can you do at home to promote fitness?**

Measures of Fitness

To find out how physically fit you are, you would measure three things: *strength, endurance,* and *flexibility.*

Strength is *the ability of your muscles to exert a force.* Muscles help support your bones and make your joints stronger. You build muscle strength by pushing or pulling against a force such as gravity. Pull-ups, for instance, build muscle strength in your arms. Do you know some ways to increase the strength of your leg muscles?

Endurance (en·DER·uhns) is *the ability to keep up a physical activity without becoming overly tired.* There are two kinds of endurance. *Muscular endurance* is how long your muscles can perform a task without tiring. *Heart and lung endurance* is how well these organs can provide your body with oxygen. This type of endurance is important in many physical activities, including biking, swimming, and playing ball. Both kinds of endurance help build stamina (STA·mih·nuh). **Stamina** is *your ability to stick with a task or activity for a long period of time.* Building stamina will help you be active for longer periods of time without getting tired or out of breath.

Health Online

Topic: Get Moving

Visit **health.glencoe.com** for Student Web Activities that will help you choose an exercise or other physical activity.

Activity: Using the information provided at the link above, choose an exercise to do for one month. Keep a journal, recording how you feel on the days you exercise and the days you don't. For example, do you feel more energetic on the days you exercise?

R Reading Strategy

Organizing Information
Direct students to page 125. Make a T-diagram on the board. Label one side "Aerobic Physical Activities" and the other side "Anaerobic Physical Activities." Challenge students to suggest entries for both sides of the T-diagram. **BL**

AL Active Learning

Calendar Provide students with copies of a blank one-month calendar. Have students write a suggestion for incorporating physical activity into everyday life onto each day's square. To get students started, provide some examples of everyday physical activities such as using the stairs instead of the elevator, raking leaves, taking a walk, and riding a bicycle. **OL**

Reading Check

Answer Strength is the ability of a muscle to exert a force. Endurance is the ability to keep up a physical activity without becoming overly tired. Flexibility is the ability to move joints through a full range of motion.

▲ Yoga is an activity that improves flexibility. **Why is flexibility important to your health?**

Visit health.glencoe.com and complete the Interactive Study Guide for Lesson 1.

Activities that build muscular endurance include dancing, jumping rope, and biking. Activities that build heart and lung endurance include walking or running, swimming, and many team sports. It's important to recognize that many activities build *both* kinds of endurance. Playing tennis for long periods is one example. Running after the ball builds up your heart and lungs; hitting the ball works the muscles.

Flexibility is *the ability to move body joints through a full range of motion.* For the joints to be able to move easily, the muscles, tendons, and ligaments around them can't be too tight. Flexibility helps you with everything from stopping and turning to throwing a ball. Being flexible also helps prevent injuries. You build flexibility by stretching your muscles and joints. Activities that promote flexibility include yoga, swimming, karate, and gymnastics.

Reading Check

List Name and explain two measures of fitness.

Fitness for Life

Fitness is a result of regular, ongoing activity. It is an important goal for a healthy life. If you are currently physically active, stay active. If you are not, now is the time to get started. Make physical activity part of your daily routine. Walk or ride your bike to school if it's not too far. Take a walk with your family or with a friend. Even cleaning your room is a way to get your body moving.

When it comes to activities and sports, think *variety*. In the same way mixing up your diet makes eating more fun, varying activities adds enjoyment. Set fitness goals for yourself, and explore a variety of ways to achieve them so you don't get bored. Try different sports. Sign up for a dance class or karate. Shoot baskets, or skateboard in your neighborhood. Choose activities that interest you. You're more likely to stick with something you like doing.

Exercise

In the last section, we talked about the important role physical activity plays in your overall health and well-being. One of the best ways to ensure that you get enough physical activity is

Caption Answers

Photo Caption Flexibility allows you to move easily and prevents injury.
Photo Caption, p. 125 Push-ups are anaerobic exercise.

✖ Promoting Coordinated School Health

Physical Activity Prepare a list of opportunities for physical activity that are available through the school. In addition to physical education class, add to the list clubs or other after-school activities that promote physical activity. Also include sports teams or intramural sports clubs.

After the list is complete, suggest additional ways to include physical activity in the school day. When students are considering ways to add physical activity to their lives, provide the list you have generated as a resource.

to exercise. **Exercise** is *planned, structured, repetitive physical activity that improves or maintains physical fitness.*

There are two main types of exercise, *aerobic* (ayr·OH·bik) and *anaerobic*. Aerobic exercise is nonstop, moderate to vigorous activity. It strengthens the heart and lungs, allowing you to breathe in more oxygen. Strengthening your heart and lungs can lower your risk of heart disease and diabetes. Aerobic exercise should be done at least five times a week. Swimming, bike riding, running, and walking are great aerobic exercises. You should do them for at least 20 to 30 minutes at a time to get their full aerobic benefits.

Anaerobic exercises build muscle strength and endurance. Examples include push-ups and pull-ups. Weight lifting, gymnastics, and hiking build muscle strength, too. Anaerobic exercises should be done two to three times per week.

 Push-ups build muscle strength in the upper arms and shoulders. **Which type of exercise are push-ups, aerobic or anaerobic?**

 **Reading Check**

Compare Explain the difference between aerobic and anaerobic exercise.

Lesson 1 Review

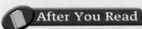 **After You Read**

Review this lesson for new terms, major headings, and Reading Checks.

What I Learned

1. *Vocabulary* What are *strength, endurance,* and *flexibility*?

2. *Identify* Name an activity that builds muscular strength. Name an activity that builds heart and lung endurance.

3. *Recall* What are the benefits of aerobic exercise*?*

Thinking Critically

4. *Apply* Why should endurance be a goal even for a weight lifter?

5. *Evaluate* What aerobic activities might you recommend for a teen who doesn't have access to a bicycle?

Applying Health Skills

6. *Advocacy* Create a pamphlet that explains the importance of physical fitness to teens. With your teacher's permission, distribute these around the school or post them on a bulletin board.

Health Online For more review questions for Lesson 1, go to health.glencoe.com. Lesson 1: Physical Activity and Your Health **125**

 Reading Check

Answer Aerobic strengthens the heart and lungs. Anaerobic increases muscle endurance.

ASSESS

Assessment Resources

Lesson Review Quiz
⚙ *ExamView*
📁 Fast Files Activities
✐ Online Quizzes and Activities

Reteaching

● Assign Concept Map 5-1 or Reteaching Activity 5-1 in the Fast Files. 📁
● Ask students to define *strength, endurance, stamina,* and *flexibility*. Ask several students to share one of their definitions.

Enrichment

● Assign Enrichment Activity 5-1 in the Fast Files. 📁
● Have students create a board game that incorporates the lesson content and addresses the Main Ideas on page 120.

CLOSE

Ask students to name one physical activity that could improve their strength, endurance, or flexibility.

Lesson 1 Review Answers

1. Strength is the ability of your muscles to exert a force. Endurance is the ability to keep up a physical activity without becoming overly tired. Flexibility is the ability to move body joints through a full range of motion.
2. Activities that build muscular strength include weight-lifting, push-ups and pull-ups.

Activities that build heart and lung endurance include swimming and running.
3. Aerobic exercise strengthens your heart and lungs.
4. Building endurance leads to greater stamina. This could prove useful to a weight lifter in the late stages of a competition.

5. Possibilities might include swimming, running, walking, or any other activity that builds heart and lung endurance.
6. Pamphlets should include examples of the benefits of physical activity such as increased energy and reduced risk of some diseases.

FOCUS

Activating Prior Knowledge

What I Know Have each student write a sentence describing a fitness goal. Point out that a fitness goal is an important part of a fitness plan.

Guide to Reading

BUILDING VOCABULARY
- Have students skim the lesson to find the definition of each vocabulary term, then define each term using their own words.
- Use Vocabulary PuzzleMaker to reinforce vocabulary terms.

READING STRATEGY
Organizing Information Model the Reading Strategy activity for students by copying the first head from the lesson onto the board. Then write a sentence next to the head summing up the main point of that section.

Quick Write
Remind students that plans do not need to be formal. For example, students might have planned what they will do over the weekend.

Academic Vocabulary

Eventually Explain that *eventually,* used on this page, means "at an unspecified later time." Have students write a short paragraph that correctly uses the word *eventually.*

Creating a Personal Fitness Plan

Guide to Reading

Building Vocabulary
Find each term below in the lesson. Write its definition in your notebook.
- FITT principle (p. 128)
- resting heart rate (p. 129)
- target heart rate (p. 130)
- recovery heart rate (p. 130)
- warm-up (p. 130)
- cool-down (p. 131)

Focusing on the Main Ideas
In this lesson, you will learn to
- **identify** the parts of a fitness plan.
- **develop** fitness goals.
- **describe** the benefits of warm-ups and cool-downs.
- **create** a schedule to achieve fitness goals

Reading Strategy
Organizing Information Copy the major and minor heads from the lesson onto a sheet of paper. As you read, write one sentence or phrase next to each that capture the main point.

uick Write

Think about an activity in your life that required developing a plan. Write a brief description of how you got started.

Setting Fitness Goals

You wouldn't build a house without a blueprint, or plan. The same goes for starting a physical fitness program. Before you begin, you need a plan. Like any good plan, yours should start with a statement of your goals. What do you eventually hope to accomplish? Would you like to find a new aerobic exercise or improve flexibility? Maybe you want to become stronger or to have more stamina. If you're not sure, talk to your physical education teacher or coach. Students with weight problems should check with their doctors before starting a new fitness plan.

▶ Pickup games are a great way to stay active and meet people. **Do you know of any parks or other locations in your community where pickup games are played?**

Lesson 2 Resources

📁 **Chapter *Fast File* Resources**
Guided Reading and Writing 5-2
Concept Mapping Activity 5-2
Health Lab 5-2
Reteaching Activity 5-2
Enrichment Activity 5-2
Lesson Quiz 5-2

Technology
🔦 Transparency 5-2
💿 Audio Summaries
⊙ *ExamView*
💿 Vocabulary PuzzleMaker
⊙ StudentWorks™ Plus

Healthy Fitness Zones for Ages 11 and 12			
Test	Sex	Age 11	Age 12
Curl-ups	Boys	15–28	18–36
	Girls	15–29	18–32
1-mile run (in minutes and seconds)	Boys	11:00–8:30	10:30–8:00
	Girls	12:00–9:00	12:00–9:00
Pull-ups	Boys	1–3	1–3
	Girls	1–2	1–3
Sit and Reach	Boys	8	8
	Girls	10	10

◀ FIGURE 5.2

HEALTHY FITNESS ZONES FOR AGES 11 AND 12

R

Some fitness assessments, such as the 1-mile run, are formal. Others, such as walking a flight of stairs, are informal. Can you think of other informal assessments to test your fitness levels?

CHAPTER 5

Lesson 2

TEACH

R Reading Strategy

Analyzing a Chart Have students examine the chart in Figure 5.2 showing fitness assessments. Ask: Which of these tests measures flexibility? *sit and reach* Which test measures strength? *pull-ups or curl-ups* OL

U Universal Access

Learning Disabled Provide students with magazine pictures showing a wide range of physical activities. Have students discuss the activities. Use some of the questions about activities provided in the text to extend the discussion of each activity. Have students choose several of the pictures to use in a physical activity collage. BL

AL Active Learning

Small-Group Interviews Divide the class into small groups. Have students read the bulleted questions in the text under the heading "Choose Activities." Have each group use an interview format to present information to the class about one physical activity. Interviewers should use the questions from the text. OL

Measuring Your Fitness Level

Once you've identified your goals, you will need to test your current fitness level. **Figure 5.2** shows several tests, called fitness assessments, commonly used to determine fitness. The chart shows typical results for teens your age. The assessments shown in the chart are formal assessments, but you can use informal assessments to measure your fitness level, too. For example, can you walk up a flight of stairs without feeling short of breath? If you've already begun a fitness program, you can use the results of these fitness assessments as guides for making changes to your program.

Choose Activities

U

Now that you know your fitness level and have set some goals, it's time to choose activities that will help you meet those goals. Start by making a list of the activities you like or would consider doing. The list can include anything from team sports and exercise classes to activities you can do at home such as sit-ups and push-ups. Here are some questions to think about when choosing an activity:

AL

- Will I need a partner or teammates?
- Are there special skills I'll need to learn?
- Will I need special equipment?
- Where will I practice?
- How much time is required?
- If it's a team sport, is there a team nearby that I can join?
- How much, if anything, will it cost?

Lesson 2: Creating a Personal Fitness Plan **127**

Dealing with Sensitive Issues

Costs of Physical Activities The expense of a physical activity is one of the points to consider when choosing a physical activity. Costs include participation, uniforms, and/or equipment. Many public schools have instituted a pay-to-play policy for sports as well. For some students, the costs of these activities can be prohibitive. When discussing physical activities with the class, be certain to mention low- or no-cost choices, such as running or walking. Ask students to work as a class to generate a list of low- or no-cost physical activities. OL

Caption Answer

Photo Caption, p. 126 *Sample answer:* People meet to play ball in the schoolyard.

R Reading Strategy

Analyzing a Graph Have students examine the graph in Figure 5.3. Ask: Name an activity that promotes flexibility more than it promotes heart and lung endurance. *gymnastics, softball* Ask: Which two activities in the table would be best for promoting heart and lung endurance? *running, swimming*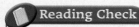

Reading Check

Answer Where will I practice? How much time is required?

HS Health Skills Practice

Practicing Healthful Behaviors After students have read about the FITT principle, have them write a paragraph explaining how they could use the FITT principle when planning to increase the amount of physical activity they get. Have each student include at least one specific way that he or she will benefit from the increase in exercise. Have students review their paragraphs to be sure they included all four aspects of the FITT principle. Ask volunteers to share their paragraphs with the class. OL

Caption Answer

Figure Caption *Sample answer:* My goal is to increase heart and lung endurance. I would choose running to help achieve this goal.

▶ **FIGURE 5.3**

R FITNESS RATINGS FOR DIFFERENT ACTIVITIES

Different activities promote different areas of fitness. What are your fitness goals? Which activities can best help you achieve those goals?

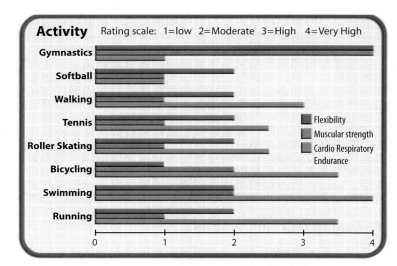

The chart in **Figure 5.3** lists some other common activities. It also shows the fitness rating of each.

Reading Check

Identify What are two questions you should ask when choosing a fitness activity?

Achieving Your Goals

Whatever activity you choose, start small. If you've never run before, you're probably not ready to run a five-kilometer race. Begin by running short distances. For example, you might run one block and walk two. Increase your distance slowly.

As you increase the amount of activity in your life, keep the FITT principle in mind. The **FITT principle** is *a method for safely increasing aspects of your workout without injuring yourself.*

The **F** in FITT stands for "frequency." This is how often you work muscles of the body.

HS **I** stands for "intensity." This is how hard you work different muscle groups.

The first **T** stands for "time," meaning the length of time you spend exercising.

The last **T** stands for "type," the type of activity you choose to do.

As a teen just beginning to exercise, pay close attention to the FITT aspects of your fitness plan. If you're not sure how to determine the FITT level that is best for you, ask a coach or physical education teacher for help. This is especially important before you increase your intensity level. Overdoing it can be harmful.

🏔 Home, School, and Community

At Home Have each student prepare a fitness log like the one shown in Figure 5.4 to use at home for one week. At the end of the week, have students evaluate the balance of activities they took part in. Ask students to write a brief response to the following questions: Were all three areas of fitness addressed by the activities you took part in? If not, what area of fitness should you work on more? What activities could you use to address this area of fitness? OL

Fitness Log Week 1		
Aerobic Activity	**Day**	**Minutes**
Running	Monday	30
Basketball	Tuesday	60
Strength Training		
Push-ups	Monday	10
Sit-ups	Tuesday	10
Weight Training	Wednesday	20
Flexibility		
Stretching	Monday	15
Karate	Friday	60

◀ **FIGURE 5.4**

SAMPLE FITNESS LOG R

A fitness log will show your progress in the different areas of fitness. *How does a fitness log help you achieve your fitness goals?*

Creating a Schedule

Before beginning your program, you will need to make a fitness log. A fitness log is a record of your physical activities that lets you keep track of your progress. **Figure 5.4** shows a sample log. A complete fitness program should include a balance of aerobic, strength training, and flexibility activities. Your goal should be to spend 60 minutes a day, four to five days a week, on physical activity. If you have been inactive, you may need to work up to this goal. For aerobic workouts, it is best to spend at least 20 to 30 minutes at a time. On days in which time is limited, try working in 10- to 15-minute bursts of moderate to vigorous activity.

Checking Your Heart Rate

One way of measuring fitness is to check your *heart rate*. This is the number of times your heart beats per minute. **Figure 5.5** gives information on how to measure your heart rate. There are three heart rate readings you need to take when doing vigorous physical activity. The first is your resting heart rate. **Resting heart rate** is

▼ **FIGURE 5.5**

MEASURING YOUR HEART RATE R

Measure your resting heart rate. *What number did you arrive at?*

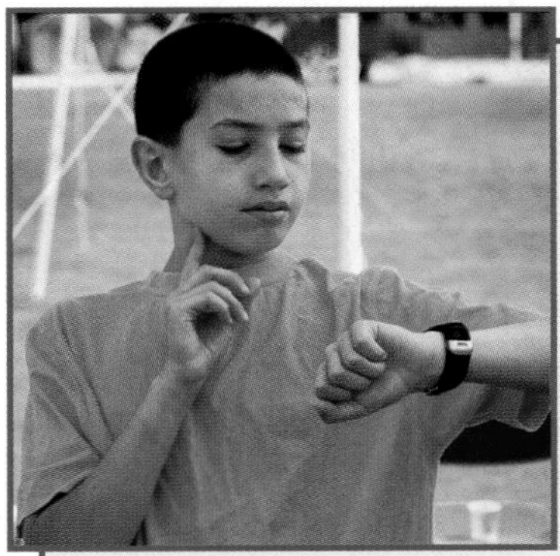

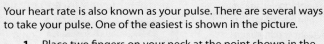

Your heart rate is also known as your pulse. There are several ways to take your pulse. One of the easiest is shown in the picture.

1. Place two fingers on your neck at the point shown in the picture. Find the throb in your neck. This is your pulse. Your heart is pumping blood through an artery in your neck. <u>NOTE:</u> Do not use your thumb for this activity.

2. Use a watch or clock with a second hand. Time the number of throbs, or pulses, that take place in 10 seconds.

3. Multiply the number you get by 6. This gives you your pulse.

Measure your resting pulse. What number did you arrive at?

R Reading Strategy

Analyzing a Graphic Let students examine the sample fitness log in Figure 5.4. Point out that workouts should last 20–30 minutes. Then have each student follow the steps shown in Figure 5.5 below, to find his or her resting pulse rate. Help students complete this activity by announcing the starting time and the ending time. Ask: Why do you need to multiply by 6 to find your resting pulse rate? *Sample answer: We counted our pulse for only 10 seconds, but pulse rate is measured by the minute. By multiplying by six, we find the number of pulses in one minute.* **OL**

C Critical Thinking

Synthesizing After students read about the importance of creating a schedule and keeping a fitness log, have them consider ways to record their heart rate measurements. Ask: Why is it important to measure your pulse during a workout? *to be sure you're getting the benefits of physical activity* When should you measure your heart rate? *twice during a workout* Have volunteers suggest ways to record their heart rates in their fitness logs. **OL**

TECHNOLOGY AND HEALTH

Heart Rate Monitors Explain that heart rate monitors designed for use during exercise can make it easier to monitor progress toward a health goal. If possible, borrow a heart rate monitor from the physical education teacher to use with this lesson. Explain that the monitor is strapped on before exercise and provides a constant read-out of the wearer's heart rate. Some monitors also store data that can be downloaded to a computer. Have students research heart rate monitors using print resources. Ask students to write a one paragraph summary of their findings. **OL**

Caption Answer

Figure Caption Student pulse rates will vary.

Health Skills Activity

Practicing Healthful Behaviors

Exercise with "Eye Appeal"

- As a class, have students discuss various sports and physical activities that are a pleasure to watch.
- Have students complete the On Your Own activity by selecting two activities they enjoy watching. Extend the activity by having volunteers demonstrate or describe one of the activities they have discussed.

Math

Hitting the Target

Lead students through the steps of the sample calculation shown in the feature. Explain each step as you write. Students may need to review the algorithm for finding a percent of a number. To find 70% of 208

- First, change 70% to an equivalent decimal by dividing 70 by 100. The result is 0.70.
- Multiply 0.70 by 208 to find 70% of 208.

Reading Check

Answer Resting heart rate is measured before working out, and target heart rate is the rate you should achieve during exercise. Both resting and target heart rates measure how many times your heart beats in a minute.

Health Skills Activity

Practicing Healthful Behaviors

Exercise with "Eye Appeal"
There's a lot more to physical activity than setting goals and working up a sweat. It's also a lot of fun to develop and test your skills, not to mention express your creativity. Just think of the satisfaction an ice skater gets when she lands a double axel. What about the thrill of sinking a basket during a close game. Many physical activities such as dance, gymnastics, and cheerleading are also a pleasure to watch.

On Your Own
Think of two other activities that are fun to watch as well as play. What are some activities that allow you to express your creativity?

Math

Hitting the Target

To find your target heart rate, first, you need to find your *maximum heart rate*. To do this, subtract your age from 220. Then determine 60 to 90 percent of that number to get your *target heart rate*. For example, using a factor of 70%, the target rate of a 12 year-old would be figured like this: 220 − 12 = 208. 70% of 208 is 145.6, so you should shoot for a target heart rate of 146.

the number of times your heart beats per minute when you are relaxing. You should take this measurement before you begin working out.

Once you have worked out for a while, you should take your target heart rate. **Target heart rate** is *the level at which your heart and lungs receive the most benefit from a workout.* A 12-year-old's target heart rate is 125 to 167 beats per minute. To gain aerobic benefits from an exercise or activity, you need to maintain your target heart rate for 20 to 30 minutes. You should measure your target heart rate twice during a standard workout.

The third heart measurement is your recovery heart rate. **Recovery heart rate** is *how quickly your heart rate returns to normal right after exercise is stopped.* The higher your fitness level, the faster the drop in heart rate. An aerobic fitness goal should be to achieve a lower resting heart.

Reading Check **Compare** Explain the differences between your resting heart rate and target heart rate.

Warm-Up and Cool-Down

Before beginning any workout or exercise session, you need to warm up. A **warm-up** is *gentle activity that prepares your body for exercise or sport.* The warm-up prevents injuries to muscles, joints, and connective tissue. A good warm-up usually includes an easy exercise to get your heart pumping a little faster and

Home, School, and Community

At Home Have each student make a written plan for a physical activity he or she could do with family members. Brainstorm with the class a list of low-cost physical activities from which students can choose, for example a family walk. Have students ask their families to participate. Remind students that they do not need to include their entire families if that is not possible. Tell students that any family members with medical problems should participate only with a doctor's okay. **OL**

blood flowing into the muscles. Walking or jogging in place for five to ten minutes are good examples of warm-up activities. Warm-up can also include practicing skills for the activity you will be doing. For example, you might warm up before playing basketball by shooting baskets, passing the ball, or dribbling.

After you have warmed up your body, you can do some basic stretches. Stretching gives your muscles, tendons, ligaments, and joints a chance to loosen and prepare for more activity. Only stretch muscles that have been warmed up. Stretching muscles that have not been warmed up could cause injury.

At the end of your workout, you need to cool down. A **cool-down** consists of *gentle activity to slow down after exercise*. The idea of the cool-down is to gradually return your body to its resting state. Stretching is an important part of a cool-down. Stretching builds flexibility and helps ease your muscles back into their resting state.

In addition, many activities and sports have their own *training techniques*. These include exercises you should do off the playing field. They help prepare your body for the next event or competition. Talk to your coach or physical education teacher about the kinds of techniques you'll need.

 Health *Online*

Visit **health.glencoe.com** and complete the Interactive Study Guide for Lesson 2.

 Reading Check **Define** What is a *cool-down*?

Lesson 2 Review

 After You Read

Review this lesson for new terms, major headings, and Reading Checks.

What I Learned

1. *Vocabulary* Define *target heart rate*.

2. *List* What are the parts of a fitness plan?

3. *Describe* Describe what you need to do in order to warm up before physical activity.

Thinking Critically

4. *Analyze* Calvin would like to bowl as a fitness activity. How can he determine whether this activity will provide fitness benefits?

5. *Apply* Dana plans to swim to achieve fitness. She claims that because you stretch during swimming, there is no need to cool down. How would you respond?

Applying Health Skills

6. *Goal Setting* Choose a fitness goal. Think of two activities you can do at home that will help you meet your fitness goal. Create a schedule for yourself that shows when, how often, and for how long you'll perform these activities.

Health *Online* For more review questions for Lesson 2, go to **health.glencoe.com**.

Lesson 2: Creating a Personal Fitness Plan **131**

 Reading Check

Answer A cool-down is a gentle activity used to slow down after exercising.

ASSESS

Assessment Resources

Lesson Review Quiz
- *ExamView*
- Fast Files Activities
- Online Quizzes and Activities

Reteaching
- Assign Concept Map 5-2 or Reteaching Activity 5-2 in the Fast Files.
- Have students work with partners to review the FITT principle. Ask how the principles of FITT improve fitness.

Enrichment
- Assign Enrichment Activity 5-2 in the Fast Files.
- Have students research the training techniques for a specific sport and present their findings to the class or the coach.

CLOSE

Have students review the outlines they prepared as they read the lesson. For each head, have a volunteer share the main ideas.

Lesson 2 Review Answers

1. It is the level at which your heart and lungs receive the most benefit from a workout.
2. A fitness plan includes setting fitness goals, measuring fitness level, choosing activities, and creating a schedule.
3. A warm-up should begin with a brief period of gentle activity such as walking or jogging in place for 5 to 10 minutes, followed by basic stretches for flexibility.
4. Calvin needs to know which part of his fitness goal bowling will help him meet. Bowling will increase his strength, flexibility, and eye-hand coordination.
5. Answers might include advising her that cooling down is important because it returns your muscles to their resting state.
6. After three weeks, ask students to turn in a copy of their schedules and progress logs.

FOCUS

Activating Prior Knowledge

What I Know Have students describe ways that professional athletes keep themselves safe when participating in their sport.

Guide to Reading

BUILDING VOCABULARY

- Point out the word part *de-* in the term *dehydration*. Tell students that *de-* means "the opposite of" or "remove." Ask students to use this information to determine the meaning of the word part *hydration* (having adequate water).
- Use Vocabulary PuzzleMaker to reinforce vocabulary terms.

READING STRATEGY

Identifying Problems and Solutions Have students make a vertical line down the center of a piece of paper. Have them list Problems on one side and Solutions on the other.

*Q*uick Write

Ask volunteers to share a strategy for feeling better when they became overheated or tired. Compile a list of their responses on the board. As students read the lesson, have them add strategies to the list.

Lesson 3

Safety in Sports and Physical Activities

Guide to Reading

● **Building Vocabulary**
Some of the terms below may seem familiar. Write down what you think they mean. Then check your answers as you come across them in the text.

- sports gear (p. 132)
- PRICE (p. 134)
- dehydration (p. 134)
- heat exhaustion (p. 134)
- frostbite (p. 135)

● **Focusing on the Main Ideas**
In this lesson, you will learn to

- **identify** types of proper sports gear.
- **describe** treatment for sports-related injuries.
- **apply** the skill of advocacy to inform other teens about exercise.

● **Reading Strategy**
Identifying Problems and Solutions As you read the lesson, list health problems or injuries that are described. Next to each, identify a solution.

*Q*uick Write

Write about a time when you became overly hot or tired while playing. Explain what you did to feel better.

Playing It Safe

Physical activity, as you have seen, can be fun. It should also be free of injury. You have already learned two ways to make your workouts safe: warming up and cooling down. In this lesson, you'll learn techniques for making them safer still. You'll also learn how to treat some sports injuries when they occur.

The Right Stuff

A first step to injury-free exercise is proper sports gear. **Sports gear** includes *sports clothing and safety equipment*. Depending on the sport or activity, safety equipment can include helmets, protective pads, and goggles. **Figure 5.7** shows several activities and the types of gear needed.

Note that some activities call for "approved" helmets. Be aware that different activities have different helmet requirements. For example, bicycle helmets should be certified by the Snell Memorial Foundation. Make sure you know which type is right for your activity.

Lesson 3 Resources

 Chapter *Fast File* Resources
Guided Reading and Writing 5-3
Concept Mapping Activity 5-3
Decision-Making Activity 5-3
Reteaching Activity 5-3
Enrichment Activity 5-3
Lesson Quiz 5-3

Technology
 Transparency 5-3
Audio Summaries
ExamView
Vocabulary PuzzleMaker
StudentWorks™ Plus

▼ FIGURE 5.7

R SAFETY GEAR BY SPORT OR ACTIVITY

The chart below lists some of the safety gear needed for different activities. Is there a sport or activity you play that is not listed? Where could you get additional information on safety gear you might need?

Sport or Activity	Safety Gear
Skating, skateboarding, and scooter riding	Helmet, wrist pads, knee pads, elbow pads
Bicycling	Bike helmet
Contact sports, including wrestling and volleyball	Mouth guard, knee pads
Racquetball, snowboarding, street hockey	Goggles, helmet for snowboarding, eyeguards for racquetball
Hockey, football, baseball	Pads, helmet, mouth guard

Choose athletic clothing that is comfortable. It should not be so loose that it can snag or get caught on objects. Yet it should be loose enough to allow free movement. As you grow older, your body, hands, and feet will grow. It is important to update your sports gear to meet these changes.

Drink Water

AL During moderate to vigorous activity, your body can lose a lot of water through *perspiration*, or sweat. It is important to replace this lost fluid. The solution is to drink plenty of water. Before beginning your activity, give your body a head start. Drink at least 8 ounces of water. Take small sips from time to time during a workout or game. You should drink about 8 ounces of water for every 30 minutes of heavy exercise. This is true even in cold weather. If there is no source of drinking water at the field or park, bring some from home.

▼ Getting plenty of fluid during vigorous activity is important. **Explain why this is so.**

Lesson 3: Safety in Sports and Physical Activities **133**

TEACH

R Reading Strategy

Analyzing a Graphic Let students examine Figure 5.7. Have them use one of the tips for safety during physical activity to develop public service announcements. Have volunteers share their public service announcements with the class. OL

AL Active Learning

Lessons for Younger Students Discuss ways to share information with younger students, for example, in a book, as a skit, or in a puppet show. Divide the class into small groups. Have each group develop a plan for teaching younger students about the importance of drinking water and prevention of weather-related injuries. Have each group share its results with the class. If possible, arrange for students to visit another classroom to share their lessons with younger students. OL

Academic Vocabulary

Techniques On page 132, students learn about safety *techniques*. Explain that another word for *technique* is *method*. Ask students to generate a list of other synonyms for the word *technique* (procedure, process).

Caption Answer

Photo Caption During physical activity, perspiration can cause excessive fluid loss, resulting in dehydration.

HEALTH LITERACY

Hyponatremia Students should be aware that in certain circumstances, athletes can become severely ill from consuming too much water. Hyponatremia is caused by a depletion of sodium in the body, which leads to symptoms that are similar to the symptoms of dehydration. According to the *New England Journal of Medicine*, marathon runners who consumed more than 3 liters of water while running a marathon were particularly at risk. Hyponatremia is a particular danger for marathon runners and endurance athletes.

MediaWatch

If the Shoe Fits

- Remind students of the tactics used by advertisers to make a product seem attractive, for example, using celebrity endorsements. Have students work in small groups to discuss advertisements for athletic shoes.
- Have each small group rewrite one advertisement or slogan to emphasize the fit or performance of an athletic shoe. Each group should share its advertisement with the class.

U Universal Access

Reluctant Readers and Writers Divide the class into groups of five students. Direct students' attention to the bullet points that describe the PRICE strategy for treating injuries. Have the students in each group divide the bulleted statements, one per group member. Direct each student to silently read his or her assigned bullet point. Then have students explain the information they read to the rest of their group. **BL**

Caption Answers

Photo Caption The letters in PRICE stand for *protect, rest, ice, compress,* and *elevate.*
Photo Caption, p. 135 Frostbite is a danger of cold-weather activities.

MediaWatch

If the Shoe Fits

Athletic shoes are frequently advertised in the media. Although it's tempting to purchase shoes based on how they look in an ad, remember that fit and performance are more important than anything else. Many sports require special footwear. Make sure the shoe is right for the sport or activity.

What might you say to a friend who bought a workout shoe based just on an advertisement?

Treating Injuries

Sometimes even when you are careful, injuries happen. Scrapes and cuts are common in sports. So is muscle soreness after a game or workout. When a muscle is stiff or aches, remember the word PRICE. The letters in **PRICE** stand for *protect, rest, ice, compress,* and *elevate.* The sooner the treatment is applied, the better. You should:

- **Protect** the injured part from further injury by keeping it still. Try not to move it too much. Moving it may make the pain worse.
- **Rest** the injured part.
- **Ice** the part using an ice pack.
- **Compress**, or put pressure on, the part using an elastic bandage. This will keep the injury from swelling. Just be careful not to wrap the bandage too tightly. This could cut off the flow of blood.
- **Elevate** the injured part above the level of the heart.

Weather-Related Injuries

Some activities are done in very cold or very hot temperatures. Both carry health risks. When you exercise or play during very hot weather, your temperature rises. Sweating increases to try to cool you down. Unless this water is replaced, dehydration can result. **Dehydration** is *a condition caused by too much water loss.* It can lead to other, more serious health problems. One of these is **heat exhaustion.** This is *an overheating of the body that can result from dehydration.* People with heat exhaustion often feel dizzy and have a headache. Their skin feels clammy when touched. If someone you know has these symptoms, find a cool, shady spot. Give the person plenty of fluids. If the symptoms don't clear up, call for help right away.

Similar precautions need to be taken in cold weather. Winter activities, such as ice-skating, skiing, and snowboarding, require protection

◀ When an injury occurs, the PRICE formula can be used to treat them. **What do the letters in PRICE stand for?**

134 Chapter 5: Physical Activity

Dealing with Sensitive Issues

Sports Injuries Students can sometimes feel internal or external pressure to continue a sport or physical activity in spite of pain or injury. Professional athletes are often praised in the media for their abilities to play while injured. Ask students to discuss reasons an injured athlete might feel pressure to continue playing (for example, wanting to play in the big game). Then have students discuss the possible consequences of playing with an injury (causing a permanent injury). Finally, have each student develop a slogan to promote the importance of resting an injury. **OL**

against snow and cold. To stay warm, dress in several layers of clothing. Layered clothing will trap warm air next to your body. A windproof jacket should be the outermost layer. Always wear a hat and gloves.

In the coldest weather, be alert to signs of **frostbite,** *freezing of the skin.* Frostbite usually affects the nose, ears, fingers, and toes. The area will be numb, pale, and stiff. Frostbite is a serious injury. Get the person inside right away. Treat the affected area by soaking it in warm, not hot, water. Get medical help as soon as possible.

 Wearing proper clothing can protect you during winter activities. **What are some health risks you face when participating in cold-weather sports or activities?**

 Reading Check **Explain** What causes dehydration?

Health *Online*

Visit **health.glencoe.com** and complete the Interactive Study Guide for Lesson 3.

Reading Check

Answer Dehydration is caused by too much water loss.

ASSESS

Assessment Resources

Lesson Review Quiz
- *ExamView*
- Fast Files Activities
- Online Quizzes and Activities

Reteaching

- Assign Concept Map 5-3 or Reteaching Activity 5-3 in the Fast Files.
- Have students rewrite each Main Idea in the form of a question and provide a short answer for each question.

Enrichment

- Assign Enrichment Activity 5-3 in the Fast Files.
- Ask students to develop a poster describing ways to avoid one type of weather-related sports injury. Have students present their posters to the class.

CLOSE

Have students list three steps for safe exercise.

Lesson 3 Review

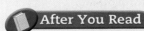 **After You Read**

Review this lesson for new terms, major headings, and Reading Checks.

What I Learned

1. *Vocabulary* What do the letters in *PRICE* stand for?

2. *Recall* Why is replacing lost water important during physical activity?

3. *List* Name two types of protective sports gear.

Thinking Critically

4. *Apply* Rey wants to play hockey, but he doesn't want to wear the face mask that players need to wear. What advice might you give Rey about the importance of sports gear?

5. *Apply* Maintain a three-day activity and exercise diary. How much of each did you do in this time period? What changes do you need to make to your routine?

Applying Health Skills

6. *Advocacy* Create a pamphlet titled *Five Things Teens Should Know Before Exercising.* Include five pieces of advice from the lesson, and put each in your own words.

 **Health** *Online* For more review questions for Lesson 3, go to **health.glencoe.com**.

Lesson 3: Safety in Sports and Physical Activities **135**

Lesson 3 Review Answers

1. They stand for *protect, rest, ice, compress,* and *elevate.*
2. It is important because the body loses water through perspiration.
3. Answers include any two of the following: helmets, protective pads, goggles, eyeguards.

4. Answers should emphasize that wearing such gear can prevent serious injury and even death.
5. Answers should reveal an understanding of the principles of activity and exercise and of maintaining a fitness log.

6. Check students' pamphlets to be certain that they include five pieces of advice from the lesson.

Developing a Personal Fitness Plan

SKILL
Goal Setting

Activating Prior Knowledge

Ask students to identify how careful planning can help in achieving a goal. Have them think about specific concepts they have learned about fitness planning in this chapter.

- **Objective** After completing the activity, students will be able to make a plan to achieve a health goal.
- **Time** 45 minutes
- **Materials** paper, pencil

Teacher Classroom Resources

📁 Building Health Skills
🖳 Transparency 1-5

Model

- Have students identify the steps Enrique followed to make his fitness plan. *make a specific goal, list the steps, break big goals into smaller tasks, get help from others, evaluate progress, reward yourself*

Building Health Skills

GOAL SETTING

Developing a Personal Fitness Plan

DIRECTIONS

Goal setting involves setting positive goals and taking steps to achieve them. Avoid risky behaviors. This activity will give you the opportunity to develop and master this important health skill. Here's a guide to the different parts of this activity:

❶ In the **Model** section, you will read about a teen who performs the health skill successfully. This "model" scenario will show you how the skill is done.

❷ The **Practice** section will help guide you in practicing the skill.

❸ In the **Apply** section, you will have a chance to perform the skill on your own. You can use the Self-Check to check your work.

To complete this activity, first read the scenario presented in the Model. Then move on to the Practice. Finally, go ahead and try the Apply.

❶ Model

In health class, Enrique learned about the importance of fitness. He has used his new knowledge of goal setting to help him create a fitness goal and a plan to meet his goal. The steps in his fitness plan appear below.

Step 1. Make your goal specific.

Enrique wants to build up his endurance.

Step 2. List the steps to reach your goal.

Enrique decides to play soccer as a way of achieving his goal. He is joining a local soccer team.

Step 3. Break big goals down into smaller tasks.

The team practices two weekdays for an hour. They have games on weekends.

Step 4. Get help from others.

When Enrique feels discouraged, his father and brother are there to cheer him on.

Step 5. Evaluate your progress.

As time goes by, Enrique finds he is able to play for longer periods of time. He is also improving his soccer skills.

Step 6. Reward yourself.

Enrique's coach gave him a certificate of achievement for his efforts.

Teaching Tips

Keys to Success Discuss how use of the goal-setting steps increases the likelihood of success. Explore how setting and achieving goals becomes more important through the teen years and into adulthood.

Ask students to suggest examples of long-term fitness goals and name the short-term goals that will help a person reach the long-term goal.

❷ Practice

Enrique began learning about other fitness measures. He is now interested in building his muscle strength. Enrique needs to choose one or more physical activities that will help him reach his goal, such as weight lifting or push-ups. He also needs to decide how to fit these activities into his weekly schedule. Map out the steps Enrique will need to take to achieve his new goal. Use these questions to help you develop an action plan.

Step 1. Who could help Enrique reach his goal?

Step 2. How could Enrique reward himself in the event he succeeds?

Skill Summary
GOAL SETTING

Goal setting steps include the following:
- Make your goal specific.
- List the steps to reach your goal.
- Break big goals down into smaller tasks.
- Get help from others.
- Evaluate your progress.
- Reward yourself.

❸ Apply

Think about a fitness goal you would like to set for yourself. Develop a personal fitness plan to help you reach your goal. Identify people who can help along the way. Decide how you will reward yourself once you successfully complete your plan.

Self-Check

- Did I set a realistic fitness goal?
- Did I identify people who could help me reach my goal?
- Did I use each of the goal-setting steps in my fitness plan?

Practice

- After students have read the Practice scenario, divide the class into small groups. Distribute six index cards to each group.
- Have students outline one step of an action plan for Enrique on each index card. Remind students to follow the six steps outlined in the Model section.
- Have each group share its results with the class.

Apply/Assess

- If students are having difficulty with their personal fitness plans, have them review the steps used in the Model and Practice activities.
- Have volunteers share their completed plans with the class.
- You may wish to distribute the Building Health Skills Activity in the Fast Files.

ASSESSMENT SCORING

Student work should meet all criteria to achieve the highest score.

Skill Student work demonstrates:
- a specific goal
- steps to reach the goal
- resources for help
- evaluation of progress
- a reward

Concepts Student work includes:
- a goal that improves fitness
- accurate linkage between the goal and improvement of physical, mental, or social health

137

How to Stay Fit For Life

Objectives

Students will be able to
- identify the recommended amount of each type of exercise
- compare the amount of exercise they get in one week to the recommended amount
- develop a health goal related to fitness and exercise

Motivator

Ask: What do ice-skating, dancing, and basketball have in common. *They are all forms of exercise.* Tell students that all forms of exercise have health benefits.

Teaching the Feature

- After students have read the feature, have them discuss the three types of exercise described in the table. Ask volunteers to name other examples of each type of exercise. List their responses on the board. **OL**
- Have students make a collage that shows some of the many forms of exercise. Students can use drawings, images from magazines or newspapers, and/or words. Have students display their completed collages for the class. Ask students to name the forms of exercise depicted in the collages. **BL**

TIME *health news*

How to Stay FIT FOR LIFE

Getting the right amount of exercise is key to staying healthy.

Kids are busier than ever before. They feel pressure to do well in school and to keep up with music lessons and other activities. But most kids' hectic schedules leave out one of the most important activities: exercise.

Nearly half of all young people in the United States are not active on a regular basis. This trend is a big factor in the rising rate of obesity among kids. School budget cuts and more emphasis on preparing for tests have led many schools to cut down on gym and recess time. So it's up to you to make sure you stay fit.

GOOD FOR YOUR MIND AND BODY

Along with building muscle and preventing health problems, staying fit can give you more energy to keep up with your packed daily schedule. Experts suggest that young people get a total of 60 minutes of exercise most days. Exercise can help you relax, respond better to stress, and boost your self-confidence.

You don't need to play competitive sports to stay in shape. Riding a bike or inline skating with your friends will provide results, too. Choose activities that are fun—you'll be more likely to keep doing them in the future!

A FORMULA FOR STAYING FIT

To stay strong and flexible, different parts of our bodies require different types of exercise.

EXAMPLE		BENEFIT	AMOUNT
Aerobic Exercise Running, basketball, jumping rope, dancing		Aerobic exercise increases your heart rate and makes you breathe harder. This strengthens your heart and lungs.	Thirty minutes of aerobic exercise most days
Strength Training Pull-ups, sit-ups, push-ups		Muscle strength is the ability of your muscles to exert a force. Muscle endurance is the ability to keep up a physical activity without becoming overly tired. Building both improves overall fitness.	Two or three days a week
Flexibility Training Sit and reach, yoga, gymnastics, Tai Chi		Jog or warm up for five to 10 minutes before you do light stretching. After exercise, do more stretching. This helps protect you from injury.	Before and after any workout

Activity *Media, Technology, and Culture*

Technology Give interested students an option to create a multimedia presentation to demonstrate the variety of exercises teens may participate in. Encourage students to incorporate digital photos, video clips, images downloaded from the Internet to illustrate the many forms of exercise. Be sure students include safety information as well as the health benefits of the exercises.

Reading Review

FOLDABLES™ Study Organizer

Foldables™ and Other Study Aids Take out the Foldable™ that you created for Lesson 1 and any graphic organizers that you created for Lessons 1–3. Find a partner, and quiz each other using these study aids.

Lesson 1 Physical Activity and Your Health

Key Ideas
- Physical benefits of regular physical activity include strengthening your muscles, heart, and lungs. Mental benefits include better concentration in school, and greater confidence in your abilities. Social benefits include building friendships and learning teamwork.
- Measures of physical fitness include strength, muscular endurance, heart and lung endurance, stamina, and flexibility.
- Aerobic exercise works the heart and strengthens the lungs, allowing you to breathe in more oxygen. Anaerobic exercises build strength and muscle endurance.

Vocabulary
- physical activity (p. 120)
- lifestyle activities (p. 121)
- physical fitness (p. 121)
- strength (p. 123)
- endurance (p. 123)
- stamina (p. 123)
- flexibility (p. 124)
- exercise (p. 125)

Lesson 2 Creating a Personal Fitness Plan

Key Ideas
- The parts of a fitness plan include setting fitness goals, measuring your fitness level, choosing activities, achieving your goals, creating a schedule, checking your heart rate, warming up, and cooling down.
- Warm-ups are gentle activities that prepare your body for exercise or sport. Cool-downs are gentle activities designed to slow your body down again after exercise.

Vocabulary
- FITT principle (p. 128)
- resting heart rate (p. 129)
- target heart rate (p. 130)
- recovery heart rate (p. 130)
- warm-up (p. 130)
- cool-down (p. 131)

Lesson 3 Safety in Sports and Physical Activities

Key Ideas
- Types of sports gear include helmets, protective pads, mouth guard, goggles, and shoes.
- Sports-related injuries are best treated using the PRICE formula, whose letters stand for *protect*, *rest*, *ice*, *compress*, and *elevate*.
- To avoid weather-related injuries, drink plenty of fluid, and wear layers of clothing in cold weather.

Vocabulary
- sports gear (p. 132)
- dehydration (p. 134)
- PRICE (p. 134)
- heat exhaustion (p. 134)
- frostbite (p. 135)

Chapter 5 Study Guide **139**

Assessment Resources

- Chapter 5 Summary and Activity
- Audio Summaries
- Reading Tutor
- Performance Assessment
- Chapter 5 Test
- *ExamView*
- Vocabulary PuzzleMaker
- Online Learning Center

Reading Review

Study Aids
- **Using the Dinah Zike Foldable™ Study Organizer** Have students use the Foldable™ to review the content of Lesson 1.

FOLDABLES™ Study Organizer

Key Ideas
- **Use the Figures and Captions** Have students review all of the figures in Chapter 5. Ask students to check to be sure they can answer all of the caption questions that accompany the figures.

Vocabulary Review
- **Vocabulary Quiz** Have each student prepare a 10-question vocabulary quiz using lesson vocabulary terms. Have students trade quizzes with a partner, and then trade back for grading.

Teaching Tips

Comprehension and Background Knowledge Students should connect their personal experience with what they are reading. Help students build their background knowledge by asking them what they know about the subject. Teach students important concepts they might be missing. Your own rich background knowledge can be a valuable resource to share. Model the way you refer to your own background knowledge while you are reading. Gather other materials, such as appropriate media resources, that tie in with what students are learning.

Reviewing Vocabulary and Main Ideas

1. Physical fitness
2. lifestyle activities
3. physical activity
4. resting heart rate
5. target heart rate
6. recovery heart rate
7. True
8. False, 8 ounces
9. False, PRICE formula
10. False, heat exhaustion

Thinking Critically

11. The two are similar in that both involve short periods of gentle activity. They are different in that warm-ups are done prior to a workout session, whereas cool-downs are done to return the body to its normal resting state.
12. The symptoms suggest that the person is suffering heat exhaustion. The person needs to be taken to a cool, shady spot and given plenty of fluids to drink. If the symptoms fail to clear up, emergency medical help should be summoned.

HEALTH QUIZ

Now that you have read the chapter, look back at your answers to the Health Quiz on the chapter opener. Would you change any of them? What would your answers be now?

Reviewing Vocabulary and Main Ideas

On a sheet of paper, write the numbers 1–6. After each number, write the term from the list that best completes each sentence.

- dehydration
- heat exhaustion
- lifestyle activities
- physical activity
- physical fitness
- recovery heart rate
- resting heart rate
- target heart rate

Lesson 1 Physical Activity and Your Health

1. _____ is the ability to handle everyday physical work and play without becoming tired.
2. Forms of physical activity that are part of your day-to-day routine or recreation are known as _____.
3. Any kind of movement that causes your body to use energy is called _____.

Lesson 2 Creating a Personal Fitness Plan

4. Your _____ is the number of times your heart beats per minute when you are relaxing.

5. The level at which your heart and lungs receive the most benefit from a workout is its _____.
6. Your _____ is how quickly your heart rate returns to normal right after exercise is stopped.

On a sheet of paper, write the numbers 7–10. Write True or False for each statement below. If the statement is false, change the underlined word or phrase to make it true.

Lesson 3 Safety in Sports and Physical Activities

7. Depending on the sport or activity, <u>safety equipment</u> can include helmets, protective pads, and goggles.
8. To replace water your body loses through sweat, you should drink about <u>20 ounces</u> of water every 30 minutes.
9. The <u>FITT technique</u> can be used to treat muscle soreness and other sports-related injuries.
10. Symptoms of <u>frostbite</u> include dizziness and clammy skin.

Thinking Critically

Using complete sentences, answer the following questions on a sheet of paper.

11. **Compare and Contrast** In what ways are warming up and cooling down similar? How are they different?
12. **Synthesize** Imagine you are playing softball on a hot day. One of your teammates becomes ill. There is no shade or water nearby. What should you do?

Health Online Visit health.glencoe.com and take the Online Quiz for Chapter 5.

Health Online

Have students visit **health.glencoe.com** to take the Chapter 5 Quiz.

HEALTH QUIZ Wrap-Up

Physical Activity Have students retake the Chapter Opener Health Quiz. Students may find that their answers have changed after reading the chapter. Ask: Name a specific idea from the chapter that changed one of your answers on the Health Quiz.

Sample answer: *I never used to worry about drinking enough water during hot-weather exercise, now I know to drink 8 ounces of water for every 30 minutes of exercise.*

Write About It

13. Practicing Healthful Behaviors Write a paragraph explaining the benefits of physical activity. In your paragraph, persuade other teens to be physically active by stating facts, using supporting evidence, and giving examples.

14. Injury Prevention Choose a physical activity or sport that you enjoy. Write a safety guide for players to refer to that tells them how to stay safe and prevent injury.

Write About It

13. Persuasive Writing Tell students to write their paragraphs in a persuasive writing style. This type of writing takes a stand, states a position, and states facts and opinions. Students' paragraphs will vary, but should include examples of benefits of physical activity.

14. Expository Writing Explain to students that expository writing shares knowledge to help others understand. Student safety guides will vary, but should explain appropriate sport or physical activity injury prevention strategies, which may include the use of appropriate sports gear, staying hydrated, and being prepared for the weather.

Standardized Test Practice

1. C
2. B

 Career Corner

Sports Medicine Have students visit the Career Corner at **health.glencoe.com** to gather more information about a career in sports medicine. Explain that students who are interested in careers in sports medicine should enjoy science and working with people. Encourage interested students to interview medical doctors about the training required for this career.

Standardized Test Practice

Reading

Read the passage and then answer the questions.

A moderate to high level of flexibility has many health benefits. It helps reduce muscle strains and lower-back problems. It also improves performance in most sports and activities.

Many different stretches can be used to improve flexibility. There are stretching exercises for all major joints of the body. A complete workout should include stretches for each.

While flexibility is important, you should know your limits. It is possible to overdo stretching. A joint that is overly stretched can become injured easily. It can also cause injuries in nearby muscles. An overly stretched shoulder joint, for example, can lead to a dislocated shoulder. This is a painful condition in which the entire shoulder moves out of its normal location.

> **TEST-TAKING TIP**
>
> Find the main idea in a reading passage. Then look for details that support this idea.

1. Which statement best sums up the main idea of the passage?

   A. Flexibility is important but impossible to measure.

   B. Flexibility helps reduce muscle strains and lower-back problems.

   C. Maintaining flexibility by stretching is important, but know your limits.

   D. A dislocated shoulder is a painful condition that can be prevented by stretching.

2. Which of the following is *not* included in the passage?

   A. An example of an injury that can occur when a joint is made overly flexible.

   B. Examples of stretching activities for all the different joints of the body.

   C. Support for the claim that flexibility has many health benefits.

   D. A warning that you should not overdo it when it comes to stretching.

CHAPTER 6 pp. 142–173	Standards		Skills and Activities
	National	**State/Local**	
	National Health Education Standards 3.1, 3.2, 3.3, 3.4		**IM EXPRESS**, *p. 143* **HANDS-ON-HEALTH** Observing the Eye, *p. 170* **BUILDING HEALTH SKILLS** *Accessing Information* Buyer Beware, *pp. 168–169*
Lesson 1 **Your Teeth, Skin, and Hair** pp. 144–150	National Health Education Standards 1.1, 1.2, 3.3, 3.4, 3.5, 3.6, 4.4, 5.3, 6.2, 6.3, 7.1, 7.4, 8.2, 8.4		**Connect To... SCIENCE** Teeth and Talking, *p. 146*
Lesson 2 **Protecting Your Eyes and Ears** pp. 151–154	National Health Education Standards 1.1, 1.6, 1.7, 2.3, 3.6, 5.3, 7.1, 7.4, 7.5, 8.2, 8.4		**Connect To... SCIENCE** Help for the Hearing Impaired, *p. 153*
Lesson 3 **Choosing Health Products** pp. 155–158	National Health Education Standards 2.2, 3.1, 3.3, 3.4, 3.5, 5.2, 5.3, 8.2, 8.4		**HEALTH SKILLS ACTIVITY** *Analyzing Influences* Persuasive Advertising, *p. 157*
Lesson 4 **Using Medicines Responsibly** pp. 159–162	National Health Education Standards 1.1, 1.6, 1.7, 2.3, 3.1, 3.2, 3.6, 5.2, 5.3, 7.1, 7.4, 7.6, 8.2		**DEVELOPING GOOD CHARACTER** Responsibility, *p. 162*
Lesson 5 **Health Care in Your Community** pp. 163–167	National Health Education Standards 1.1, 1.6, 1.7, 3.2, 3.4, 3.5, 3.6, 4.5, 7.1, 7.4, 8.2		**HEALTH SKILLS ACTIVITY** *Advocacy* Doing Your Part for Community Health, *p. 166*

PACING THE CHAPTER

Lesson 1	90 min	**Lesson 4**	90 min	**Chapter Review**	45 min
Lesson 2	45min	**Lesson 5**	45 min	**Hands-on Health**	20 min
Lesson 3	90 min	**Building Health Skills**	45 min		

BLOCK SCHEDULING

For block scheduling, assign students Building Health Skills feature *Buyer Beware,* pages 168–169, and Guided Reading and Writing. 📁

Planning Guide

Reproducible Resources	Assessment	Media and Technology
Chapter FAST FILE Resources Chapter Summaries and Activities **REVIEW** Building Health Skills Activity **TEACH** Performance Assessment Activity **EXTEND** Universal Access Activities **TEACH** Parent Letter and Activities **Student Activities Workbook** **TEACH** **Reading Tutor** **TEACH**	Building Health Skills Activity, *pp. 168–169* Chapter 6 Assessment, *pp. 172–173* **Chapter FAST FILE Resources** Performance Assessment Activity, *p. 4* Chapter 6 Test, *p. 7* ExamView® Test Generator	**TeacherWorks™** includes: • Interactive Teacher Edition • Lesson Planner with Calendar • Access to all blackline masters • Correlations to standards StudentWorks™ Plus Online Student Edition Dinah Zike's Teaching Health with Foldables™
Chapter FAST FILE Resources Concept Mapping Activity 6-1 **REVIEW** Decision-Making Activity 6-1 **EXTEND** Enrichment Activity 6-1 **EXTEND** Guided Reading and Writing 6-1 **TEACH** Lesson Plan 6-1 Reteaching Activity 6-1 **REVIEW**	Lesson 1 Review, *p. 150* Vocabulary PuzzleMaker ExamView® Test Generator	Vocabulary PuzzleMaker ExamView® Test Generator StudentWorks™ Plus Transparency 6-1 **Health Online**
Chapter FAST FILE Resources Concept Mapping Activity 6-2 **REVIEW** Cross-Curriculum Activity 6-2 **EXTEND** Enrichment Activity 6-2 **EXTEND** Guided Reading and Writing 6-2 **TEACH** Lesson Plan 6-2 Reteaching Activity 6-2 **REVIEW**	Lesson 2 Review, *p. 154* Vocabulary PuzzleMaker ExamView® Test Generator	Vocabulary PuzzleMaker ExamView® Test Generator StudentWorks™ Plus Transparency 6-2 **Health Online**
Chapter FAST FILE Resources Concept Mapping Activity 6-3 **REVIEW** Enrichment Activity 6-3 **EXTEND** Guided Reading and Writing 6-3 **TEACH** Health Lab 6-3 **EXTEND** Lesson Plan 6-3 Reteaching Activity 6-3 **REVIEW**	Lesson 3 Review, *p. 158* Vocabulary PuzzleMaker ExamView® Test Generator	Vocabulary PuzzleMaker ExamView® Test Generator StudentWorks™ Plus Transparency 6-3 **Health Online**
Chapter FAST FILE Resources Concept Mapping Activity 6-4 **REVIEW** Cross-Curriculum Activity 6-4 **EXTEND** Enrichment Activity 6-4 **EXTEND** Guided Reading and Writing 6-4 **TEACH** Lesson Plan 6-4 Reteaching Activity 6-4 **REVIEW**	Lesson 4 Review, *p. 162* Vocabulary PuzzleMaker ExamView® Test Generator	Vocabulary PuzzleMaker ExamView® Test Generator StudentWorks™ Plus Transparency 6-4 **Health Online**
Chapter Fast File Resources Concept Mapping Activity 6-5 **REVIEW** Decision-Making Activity 6-5 **EXTEND** Enrichment Activity 6-5 **EXTEND** Guided Reading and Writing 6-5 **TEACH** Lesson Plan 6-5 Reteaching Activity 6–5 **REVIEW**	Lesson 5 Review, *p. 167* Vocabulary PuzzleMaker ExamView® Test Generator	Vocabulary PuzzleMaker ExamView® Test Generator StudentWorks™ Plus Transparency 6-5 **Health Online**

Chapter and Lesson Resources

The *Teen Health* resources are designed for differentiated learning abilities. You may want to use the coded items in this way:

REVIEW—activities to review or reinforce content
TEACH—activities to teach basic concepts
EXTEND—activities to extend or enrich lesson content

OUT OF TIME?

Use Health Skills Activities *Persuasive Advertising,* page 157 and *Doing Your Part for Community Health,* page 166 or *Developing Good Character,* page 162.

Melanoma—Prevention and Detection

The risk of melanoma, a cancer of the skin cells, can be lowered by limiting exposure to ultraviolet (UV) light. Avoiding the sun between 10:00 a.m. and 4:00 p.m. is the most effective way to limit UV exposure. Wearing clothing that covers the skin and a hat that covers the ears are also ways to limit exposure to sunlight.

Regular skin examinations by a physician can identify moles that should be removed. Individuals can use the ABCDE guidelines to monitor moles in-between regular check-ups with a physician. These guidelines list characteristics of moles that should be checked by a physician.

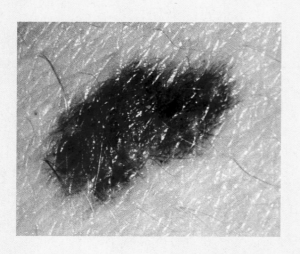

A Asymmetry: A mole that becomes lopsided.
B Border: A mole that suddenly develops an irregular border.
C Color: A mole that develops multiple colors.
D Diameter: A mole that rapidly increases in size.
E Elevated: A mole that develops a lump or nodule.
-or-
E Evolving: Any mole that undergoes a change in appearance.

Heath Insurance

There are many different types of health insurance available in the United States. Large companies usually offer group health insurance to their employees. Most employees of these companies pay a small fraction of the total cost of health insurance. Even that small fraction of the total cost can be prohibitive. According to a study by the Kaiser Family Foundation, the average employee pays more than $200.00 per month for family health insurance. Employees of small companies or those who are self-employed usually pay the entire cost of health insurance. Some working families are without health insurance due to the steep cost of premiums. In 2004, the average cost of health insurance for a family was between $9,000 and $10,000 per year.

Some examples of the different types of health insurance include:

- **Traditional Health Insurance:** This type of insurance allows patients to see whatever doctor they choose. At the appointment, the patient pays for the medical services, and is then partially or totally reimbursed by the insurance company.

- **Preferred Provider Organization (PPO)** A PPO is a type of managed care. By visiting an approved physician, members of a PPO pay only a small portion of the cost, called a co-pay.

- **Health Maintenance Organization (HMO)** An HMO is also a type of managed care. Members of an HMO also have reduced fees when visiting an in-network physician. HMOs differ from PPOs in that members cannot receive a reduced fee at a specialist unless they are referred by their primary care physician.

- **Catastrophic Health Insurance** This type of health insurance is less expensive, but has very limited coverage. Major illnesses and accidents are covered, but preventive and routine care are not.

Support for Teaching Reading

Reading Preview

Activating Background Vocabulary Ask students what comes to mind when they think of the words *hygiene* or *health*. Write their responses on the board. Direct students to sort their responses into categories such as care of teeth, skin care, hair care, protection of eyes, ears, and so on. Guide students in a discussion of appropriate personal hygiene.

FOLDABLES™ Study Organizer *Dinah Zike's Reading and Study Skills for Teen Health* provides interactive graphic organizers that help students comprehend and retain health concepts as they read. Use the Foldable™ on page 143 or find more Foldables™ activities for the chapter on **Personal Health** in the separate booklet, available in the TCR.

Lesson 1   Your Teeth, Skin, and Hair

Determining Main Ideas Have students restate the first heading in the lesson as a question, i.e. "What is **Looking Your Best?**" Guide students to find the main idea of the paragraph: looking your best means having good personal hygiene. Show students how to find supporting details about good hygiene, such as clean hair and teeth, and clean body.

Lesson 2   Protecting Your Eyes and Ears

Monitoring Comprehension Show students how to ask and answer their own questions during independent reading, such as: "What is my purpose in reading this? The title of the section is **Vision Problems.** My purpose must be to find the types of vision problems." Have students write the answers to their questions as they read (i.e. nearsighted, farsighted) and to reread a section if they can't find the answer.

Lesson 3   Choosing Health Products

Listen-Read-Discuss Present the lesson in a brief lecture to give students background information. Next, have students read silently, making a list of questions for clarification. Finally, stop students during reading and ask: "What do you understand most from what you have read so far? What do you understand least? What questions do you still have?"

Lesson 4   Using Medicines Responsibly

Compare and Contrast Illustrate a two-column chart on the board. Direct students to read independently to find out about using medicines responsibly. Have students record facts about the safe uses of medicine in one column of their charts and the improper uses of medicine in the other. Encourage students to compare their charts with a partner.

Lesson 5   Health Care in Your Community

3-2-1 Strategy Ask students to write a brief summary identifying **three** key points they found while reading the lesson (what is health care, who is a provider, how to pay). Next, have students list **two** things in the lesson they thought were interesting. Finally, ask students to write **one** question they still have. Have student pairs reread to find the answers.

Post Reading

Informational Presentations Have students use magazines, newspapers, and the Internet to gather more information on personal health and hygiene. Guide students to use speaking strategies effectively to convey meaning to the audience during an informational presentation.

Key for Using the Teacher Wraparound Edition

Use this key to help you identify the different types of prompts found in the Teacher Wraparound Edition.

R **Reading Strategies** activities help you teach reading skills and vocabulary.

C **Critical Thinking** strategies help students apply and extend what they have learned.

U **Universal Access** activities provide differentiated instruction for students learning to speak English, along with suggestions for teaching various types of learners.

HS **Health Skills Practice** activities reinforce Health Skills concepts and help students apply these skills in their everyday lives.

W **Writing Support** activities provide writing opportunities to help students comprehend the text.

AL **Active Learning** strategies provide a variety of activities for presenting lesson content, including Quick Demos and engaging classroom projects that get students actively involved.

Key to Ability Levels

Teaching Strategies and activities have been coded for ability level and appropriateness

AL Activities for students working above grade level

OL Activities for students working on grade level

BL Activities for students working below grade level

EL Activities for English Learners

Symbols

Transparencies

CD-ROM

health.glencoe.com

Print Resources

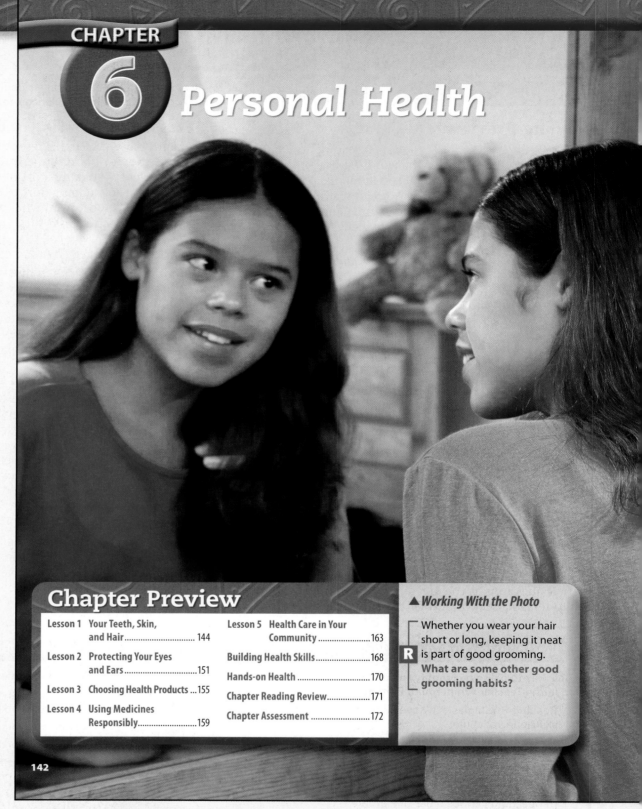

CHAPTER 6
Personal Health

Chapter at a Glance

Lesson 1 explains how to keep teeth healthy, identifies ways to care for skin, and describes hair and nail care.

Lesson 2 describes eye and ear care and explains how to protect hearing.

Lesson 3 identifies factors that influence consumer choices, explains ways to choose health-care products wisely, and identifies consumer skills that can be used to save money.

Lesson 4 explains the benefits of medicine, identifies information on medicine labels, and describes ways to avoid drug misuse.

Lesson 5 identifies different types of health-care providers and explains the importance of regular health checkups.

R Reading Strategy

Interpreting the Photo
Have students look at the photo of the student fixing her hair. Point out that keeping your hair neat is one example of a healthy grooming habit. Ask each student to make a bulleted list of five healthy grooming habits. Have volunteers share one entry from their lists with the class. **OL**

CHAPTER 6
Personal Health

Chapter Preview

Lesson 1 Your Teeth, Skin, and Hair 144

Lesson 2 Protecting Your Eyes and Ears 151

Lesson 3 Choosing Health Products ... 155

Lesson 4 Using Medicines Responsibly 159

Lesson 5 Health Care in Your Community 163

Building Health Skills 168

Hands-on Health 170

Chapter Reading Review 171

Chapter Assessment 172

142

▲ Working With the Photo

R Whether you wear your hair short or long, keeping it neat is part of good grooming. **What are some other good grooming habits?**

👥 Universal Access

Differentiated Learning Glencoe provides teacher support and student materials for all learners in the health classroom.

- Spanish *Glosario* and chapter summaries for the English Language Learners.
- *Reading Tutor* and related worksheets support reluctant readers.

- Universal Access strategies throughout the Teacher Wraparound Edition and Fast Files help you present materials for gifted students, at-risk students, physically impaired students and those with behavior disorders or learning disabilities.

Start-Up Activities

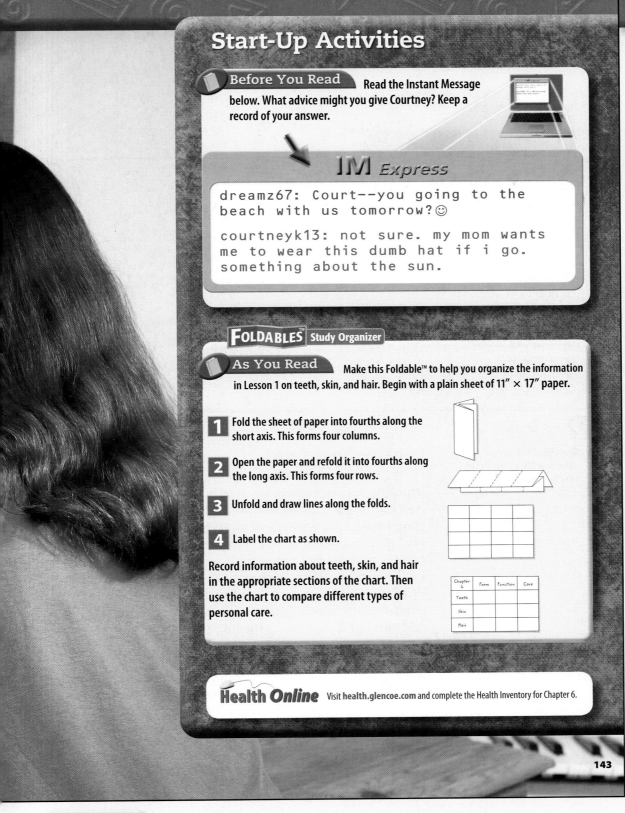

Before You Read

Read the Instant Message below. What advice might you give Courtney? Keep a record of your answer.

IM *Express*

dreamz67: Court--you going to the beach with us tomorrow?☺

courtneyk13: not sure. my mom wants me to wear this dumb hat if i go. something about the sun.

FOLDABLES™ Study Organizer

As You Read

Make this Foldable™ to help you organize the information in Lesson 1 on teeth, skin, and hair. Begin with a plain sheet of 11″ × 17″ paper.

1 Fold the sheet of paper into fourths along the short axis. This forms four columns.

2 Open the paper and refold it into fourths along the long axis. This forms four rows.

3 Unfold and draw lines along the folds.

4 Label the chart as shown.

Record information about teeth, skin, and hair in the appropriate sections of the chart. Then use the chart to compare different types of personal care.

Chapter 6	Form	Function	Care
Teeth			
Skin			
Hair			

Health Online Visit health.glencoe.com and complete the Health Inventory for Chapter 6.

143

143

FOCUS

Activating Prior Knowledge

What I Know Ask students to name ways that taking care of their skin, hair, or teeth could positively affect their health.

Guide to Reading

BUILDING VOCABULARY

- Explain that the word part *epi-* means "outer," and the word part *-dermis* means "layer of skin." Have students use this information to determine the definition for the term *epidermis.*
- Use Vocabulary Puzzle-Maker to reinforce vocabulary terms.

READING STRATEGY

FOLDABLES Have students use their Foldables™ as they read Lesson 1.

- **Predicting** Give students 5 minutes to read the headings in this lesson. Ask them to make a prediction for each section.

Quick Write

Remind students to include at least one care tip for each in their Quick Writes.

Academic Vocabulary

Maintain Students learn ways to *maintain* their health. Ask a volunteer to define the word *maintain.* Ask other volunteers to use the word *maintain* in a sentence.

144

Your Teeth, Skin, and Hair

Guide to Reading

● **Building Vocabulary**
In your own words, write definitions for the following terms. Check to make sure your definitions are correct as you read the chapter.

- hygiene (p. 144)
- plaque (p. 145)
- fluoride (p. 146)
- epidermis (p. 147)
- dermis (p. 147)
- sunscreen (p. 148)
- acne (p. 148)
- dandruff (p. 149)
- cuticle (p. 150)

● **Focusing on the Main Ideas**
In this lesson, you will learn to

- **recognize** ways to keep your teeth and gums healthy.
- **identify** ways to take care of your skin.
- **describe** how to care for hair and nails.
- **apply** the skill of advocacy to inform others about proper tooth and gum care.

● **Reading Strategy**
Predicting Read the major and minor headings throughout the lesson. Write a sentence about the kind of advice you think will be given for each heading.

FOLDABLES **Study Organizer** Use the Foldable™ on p. 143 as you read this lesson.

Quick Write

Describe the steps you take in caring for your teeth, skin, and hair.

Looking Your Best

Think about your appearance. Are your clothes neat and clean? Is your hair combed? Did you brush your teeth this morning? Caring for your appearance includes paying attention to your personal hygiene (HY·jeen). **Hygiene** includes the *actions you take to improve or maintain your health.* Keeping your body clean is an example of good hygiene. Your hygiene and resulting appearance affect all three sides of your health triangle. When you look your best, you feel good about yourself. This improves your mental/emotional health. You are more confident around others, strengthening your social health. Good hygiene also keeps your body physically healthy. For example, washing your hands helps prevent illness.

Reading Check **Define** What is *hygiene*?

Lesson 1 Resources

📂 **Chapter *FAST FILE* Resources**
Guided Reading and Writing 6-1
Concept Mapping Activity 6-1
Decision-Making Activity 6-1
Reteaching Activity 6-1
Enrichment Activity 6-1
Lesson Quiz 6-1

Technology
🔥 Transparency 6-1
🖱 Audio Summaries
💿 *ExamView*
🖱 Vocabulary PuzzleMaker
💿 StudentWorks™ Plus

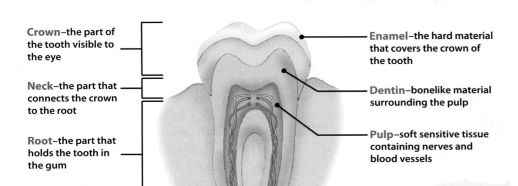

Crown–the part of the tooth visible to the eye

Neck–the part that connects the crown to the root

Root–the part that holds the tooth in the gum

Enamel–the hard material that covers the crown of the tooth

Dentin–bonelike material surrounding the pulp

Pulp–soft sensitive tissue containing nerves and blood vessels

Healthy Teeth and Gums

Your teeth and gums have important jobs. Your teeth make it possible for you to chew and grind food. They aid in forming certain speech sounds. Your teeth help shape and give structure to your mouth.

Your gums anchor your teeth in your mouth and keep them in place. About three fourths of each tooth is located below the gum line. **Figure 6.1** shows the parts of the tooth.

Tooth and Gum Problems

Proper care of your teeth and gums can prevent tooth decay. If this occurs and goes untreated, you can lose your teeth.

Tooth decay begins with the formation of plaque (PLAK). **Plaque** is *a soft, colorless, sticky film containing bacteria that grows on your teeth.* The germs in plaque cause bad breath. If left on the teeth, these germs combine with sugars to form an acid that causes tooth decay and gum disease. If plaque is not removed, it eventually hardens and becomes *tartar* (TAR·tuhr). Only a dentist or dental hygienist can remove tartar. **Figure 6.2** shows the stages in tooth decay.

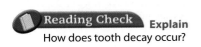

Reading Check Explain How does tooth decay occur?

▲ FIGURE 6.1

THE TOOTH

This figure illustrates the different parts of the tooth. Which part of the tooth do you see when you look at your smile in the mirror?

▼ FIGURE 6.2

TOOTH DECAY

Tooth decay and gum disease can both be prevented. What are some steps you can take to prevent these problems?

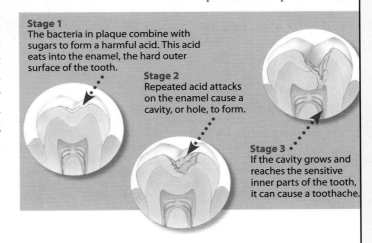

Stage 1
The bacteria in plaque combine with sugars to form a harmful acid. This acid eats into the enamel, the hard outer surface of the tooth.

Stage 2
Repeated acid attacks on the enamel cause a cavity, or hole, to form.

Stage 3
If the cavity grows and reaches the sensitive inner parts of the tooth, it can cause a toothache.

TEACH

R Reading Strategy

Analyzing a Graphic Have students prepare an outline from their reading and examine the stages of tooth decay shown in Figure 6.1. Then have students write a short paragraph that describes the sequence of steps in tooth decay. As an alternative, have interested volunteers prepare skits from their paragraphs and perform the skits for the class. **OL**

R Reading Strategy

Analyzing a Graphic Allow students to read the details in each stage of tooth decay presented in Figure 6.2. After students have examined the illustrations, have them read again the text about Healthy Teeth and Gums. Discuss the role of gums in relationship to teeth. Then ask: Why is good gum care important for the health of your teeth? *The gums protect several parts of the teeth.* **AL**

Reading Check

Answer, p. 144 actions you take to improve health

Reading Check

Answer Tooth decay occurs when the bacteria in plaque combine with sugars to form a harmful acid that eats into the tooth and forms a cavity.

Caption Answer

Figure Caption When you look at your smile, you see the crowns of your teeth.

TECHNOLOGY AND HEALTH

New Dental Technology Many new technologies have been introduced that make trips to the dentist easier and less painful. For example, computer digital radiography is a technology that can replace dental X rays. This technology reduces radiation exposure as compared to X rays, and can provide a better view of dental problems. Other technologies replace a traditional dental drill with an air abrasion system. Have students research new technologies being used in dental care. Have each student prepare a written paragraph about one new technology. **OL**

Connect To... Science

Teeth and Talking

Distribute small hand mirrors for students to use as they explore the importance of teeth in forming speech sounds. Have students observe the role of the teeth in the formation of various speech sounds by having them recite their names, the date, and other short phrases. Students should conclude that keeping their teeth healthy is important for clear speech.

AL Active Learning

Puppet Show Have students work in small groups to write and perform a puppet show to teach young children how to keep their teeth healthy. Allow students 15 minutes to write their puppet shows. Provide paper bags, markers, or other materials for puppet making. Have each group perform its puppet show for the class, and if possible, for younger students. **OL**

R Reading Strategy

Analyzing a Graphic After students have examined Figure 6.3, ask: Why is fluoride important for good dental health? *Fluoride fights tooth decay.* Ask: How often should you floss your teeth? *at least once a day* **OL**

Caption Answer

Figure Caption Proper brushing and regular dental checkups are ways to prevent tooth decay and gum disease.

Connect To... Science

Teeth and Talking

Without your teeth, you would have difficulty speaking. To see what that would be like, try making the *th* sound without letting your tongue touch your teeth. What happens? Studying how words are formed is part of a science called linguistics.

See if you can figure out which speech sounds the tongue and lips form.

▶ **FIGURE 6.3**

R **PROPER BRUSHING AND FLOSSING TECHNIQUES**

To reduce plaque build-up, brush at least twice a day and floss once a day. Why is it important to know how to brush and floss properly?

- You should brush using a soft-bristled brush. Use toothpaste that contains **fluoride** (FLAWR•ahyd), *a substance that fights tooth decay.* Brush the outer tooth surfaces first. Tilt the top of your toothbrush where your teeth and gums meet. Move your brush back and forth gently, using short strokes across your teeth. Then brush the inner tooth surfaces and your chewing surfaces. Finally, brush your tongue.

- Proper flossing begins with an 18-inch piece of dental floss. Wrap the ends around the middle finger of each hand. Hold the floss tightly between your thumbs and forefingers. Now gently slide the floss between your teeth. Move it up or down to the gum line, using a gentle sawing motion. Rub the side of the tooth, and bring the floss back out gently. Repeat the process between all of your teeth.

Keeping Teeth and Gums Healthy

You can help prevent tooth and gum problems by remembering to do three important things. Two of these, brushing and flossing, are illustrated in **Figure 6.3.** Brushing cleans the teeth, removes plaque, and stimulates the gums. Flossing removes food particles and plaque from between the teeth and under the gum line that the toothbrush cannot reach. Flossing also helps to clean underneath braces. **AL**

The third way you can maintain your dental health is by eating right. Choose foods that are high in the mineral calcium, such as yogurt and milk. You should also limit foods that are high in sugar, which can cause tooth decay. When you do eat sugary foods, brush your teeth as soon as you can.

HEALTH LITERACY

Tobacco's Effect on Dental Health
Cigarettes, cigars, and smokeless tobacco all affect the health of teeth, gums, and the tongue. For example, the use of smokeless tobacco is associated with damage to the gums, leading to exposure of tooth roots and loss of teeth. Tobacco products have also been linked to oral cancer. In fact, of the people diagnosed with oral cancer, more than 75 percent used tobacco. Have students research the effects of one type of tobacco product on dental health. Then have students make a poster showing what they learned. **OL**

Regular Dental Checkups

Another important way to protect your teeth and gums is to have dental checkups twice a year. The dentist or dental hygienist will clean your teeth to help prevent tooth decay and gum disease. The dentist will also examine your teeth for cavities or other problems.

If your teeth need straightening, your dentist may refer you to an *orthodontist.* This is a dentist who specializes in correcting irregularities of the teeth and jaw. The orthodontist may apply braces to straighten your teeth. This will make your teeth look better and easier to clean.

 **Reading Check** **List** Name three habits that promote healthy teeth and gums.

Healthy Skin

AL What's the biggest organ of your body? Believe it or not, the answer is your skin. The skin acts as a waterproof shield that defends your body against germs. It maintains your body temperature and allows you to feel and sense pressure and temperature.

The two main layers of the skin are shown in **Figure 6.4.** *The thinner outer layer of the skin* is called the **epidermis.** *The thicker inner layer of the skin* is the **dermis.**

Skin Care

The most important part of skin care is cleansing. As your body develops, sweat glands become more active. Bacteria can grow in areas where you sweat, such as under your arms. In large enough numbers, these germs give off an unpleasant odor. Washing sweat away keeps your skin clean and smelling fresh. You can also help control sweat and odor by using an antiperspirant or deodorant.

HS You should also protect your skin from the sun. The sun's ultraviolet (UV) rays can cause sunburn and wrinkles and can increase your risk of skin cancer. Avoid direct sunlight between the hours of 10:00 A.M. and 4:00 P.M. This is when the sun's UV rays are strongest. Whenever you do spend time in the sun,

▲ Dental braces are made of a variety of materials. **Why would someone need to wear braces?**

AL Active Learning

Game Show Divide the class into small groups. Allow 15 minutes for students to work in their groups to develop game-show style questions about skin care. Allow each group to quiz the remainder of the class with its questions. **OL**

HS Health Skills Practice

Advocacy Have students use the information in the text to make a collage showing ways to protect skin from the sun. With permission, display the completed collages in the school hallways. **OL**

Reading Check

Answer Eating foods with calcium, brushing and flossing, and getting regular dental checkups are all habits that promote healthy teeth and gums.

What Teens Want to Know

Is indoor tanning safe? Exposure to UV radiation, either from the sun or from tanning beds and lamps, can cause skin damage, premature aging, and melanoma. Some advertisements for indoor tanning state that because the tanning beds use UVA radiation, they are safer than the sun. This type of radiation is less likely to cause sunburn, but it is associated with skin damage and skin cancer. Many health experts advocate strict regulations on the use of indoor tanning by people under the age of 18. Have students research the potential hazards of indoor tanning.

Caption Answer

Photo Caption Braces correct irregularities, so a person would wear braces to make their teeth look better and easier to clean.

R Reading Strategy

Analyzing a Graphic After students have examined Figure 6.4, ask: How does your skin help your body regulate temperature? *Sweat glands secrete perspiration, which evaporates and cools the whole body.* **OL**

AL Active Learning

Newspaper Article Have students write a newspaper article about acne. Remind students that newspaper articles are written to give information about "who, what, where, when, and why." Be sure students proofread their work before turning it in. **OL**

Health Online

Helping Troubled Skin Show students how to fold a piece of paper in thirds to make a pamphlet. Have each student make a pamphlet about acne treatments using the information found at **health.glencoe.com**. Display the completed pamphlets in the classroom. **OL**

Reading Check

Answer Healthy skin helps you look and feel your best, and helps defend against bacteria and odor.

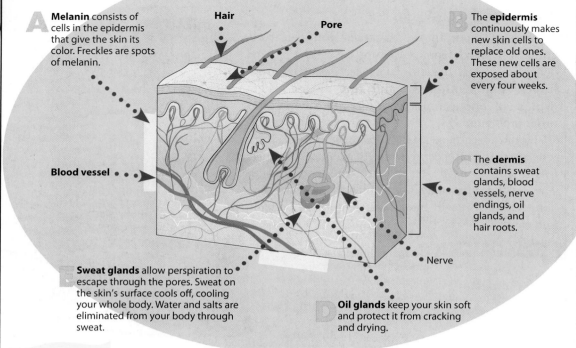

A **Melanin** consists of cells in the epidermis that give the skin its color. Freckles are spots of melanin.

Hair

Pore

B The **epidermis** continuously makes new skin cells to replace old ones. These new cells are exposed about every four weeks.

Blood vessel

C The **dermis** contains sweat glands, blood vessels, nerve endings, oil glands, and hair roots.

Nerve

E **Sweat glands** allow perspiration to escape through the pores. Sweat on the skin's surface cools off, cooling your whole body. Water and salts are eliminated from your body through sweat.

D **Oil glands** keep your skin soft and protect it from cracking and drying.

▲ **FIGURE 6.4**

THE SKIN

R Your skin is a very complex body organ. It has many parts. What is the outer layer of skin called?

Health Online

Topic: Helping Troubled Skin

Visit health.glencoe.com for Student Web Activities to learn more about dealing with acne.

Activity: Using the information provided at the link above, create a one-page fact sheet that lists the causes, effects, myths, and treatment of acne.

---

wear protective clothing and use a **sunscreen.** This is *a cream or lotion that filters out some UV rays.* Choose sunscreens with a sun protection factor (SPF) of 15 or higher. Reapply sunscreen about every two hours and after swimming.

Dealing with Acne

No matter how careful you are to keep your skin clean, some skin problems are hard to avoid. One of these problems is acne. **Acne** is *a skin condition caused by overly active oil glands.* This is due to increased hormone production during the teen years. The excess oil can clog pores, causing bumps on the skin's surface. Mild acne can usually be treated at home. Wash your face with mild soap, but do not scrub too hard. This can irritate skin and cause more acne. Also, avoid squeezing pimples, which can leave acne scars on your skin. For serious cases, you may need to see a *dermatologist* (DER·muh·TAH·luh·jist). This is a doctor who treats skin disorders. **AL**

Reading Check  **Explain** Explain the importance of keeping your skin clean.

HEALTH LITERACY

Comparing Products The ability to access information about acne medications or skincare and hair products is a skill that is important for all students to master. Use the following techniques to help all students with these concepts.

- Use real pamphlets and advertising flyers to let students analyze and compare products being advertised.
- Have students work with a partner to research and report to the class on facts about a product and how to determine where to access accurate information.

Healthy Hair

Your hair is made up of a substance called keratin. The roots of the hair are in the dermis, the deep inner layer of skin. They are housed in small pockets called *follicles*. As new hair cells are formed, old ones are forced out.

The part of the hair that you can see is the *shaft*. The shape of the hair shafts determines whether your hair is wavy, curly, or straight. Like living skin, hair gets its color from the pigment melanin. The color of your hair is determined by heredity.

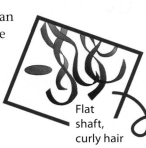

Flat shaft, curly hair

Round shaft, straight hair

Oval shaft, wavy hair

Hair Care

Keep your hair healthy by washing it regularly with a gentle shampoo and using a conditioner. If possible, let your hair dry by itself. If you use a blow dryer, use low heat. Styling irons and high heat from hair dryers can make hair dry, brittle, and faded. Brushing or combing daily removes dirt and helps spread natural scalp oils down the hair shaft.

Problem Hair and Hair Problems

Two conditions that can affect the health of your hair are dry or oily scalp. Either problem can be corrected by choosing the right shampoo. Read the label carefully. Different products are made for dry, oily, and normal hair. Chlorine in pool water can be another problem. Special shampoos can remove chlorine.

Another common scalp problem is **dandruff.** This is *flaking of the outer layer of dead skin cells.* Washing your hair regularly controls dandruff. If this does not work, try a dandruff shampoo.

Sometimes, an itchy scalp is caused by head lice. These tiny, wingless insects live in the hair. They are easy to catch from someone else. To prevent lice from spreading, avoid sharing hats, combs, and brushes. If you get lice, you can kill them with a medicated shampoo. You will also need to wash all your bedding, towels, combs, brushes, and clothing. Everyone else in your house will need to take these steps, too.

▲ No matter what kind of hair you have, it deserves proper treatment. **What are three steps you can take to keep your hair healthy?**

Reading Check **List** Give two steps that are part of good hair hygiene.

U Universal Access

English Learners Have students create a set of vocabulary flash cards for unfamiliar terms used on this page. List terms on the board: *keratin, follicles, shaft, brittle, dandruff, lice.* Students should write each term and a short definition in a notebook or on index cards. Encourage students to work in pairs with English-proficient students to look up the meaning of unfamiliar terms in a dictionary. Advanced students can practice using the terms in spoken and written sentences. Encourage students to expand their health glossaries to include these terms along with all of the chapter vocabulary terms. **EL**

Reading Check

Shampooing regularly and using conditioner are two parts of good hair hygiene.

Cultural Perspectives

Hair-Care Products When discussing hair-care products, such as shampoos and conditioners, include a variety of products that reflect specific care and considerations for individuals of a variety of cultures and ethnicities. Point out that different types of hair require different types of care. Have students examine the ingredients and instructions on the labels of various hair-care products. Ask students to identify any similarities and differences between the brands. **OL**

Caption Answer

Photo Caption Keeping your hair clean, using a conditioner, and avoiding styling irons can help keep your hair healthy.

Reading Check

Use a nail clipper. Fingernails should be rounded slightly. Cut toenails straight.

ASSESS

Assessment Resources

Lesson Review Quiz
- *ExamView*
- Fast Files Activities
- Online Quizzes and Activities

Reteaching

- Assign Concept Map 6-1 or Reteaching Activity 6-1 in the Fast Files.
- Have students name three ways to keep teeth and gums healthy.

Enrichment

- Assign Enrichment Activity 6-1 in the Fast Files.
- Have students prepare a video to teach steps of proper hygiene.

CLOSE

Ask students to name one new fact they learned about caring for skin, teeth, and hair.

Caption Answer

Photo Caption Keep nails trimmed; never bite nails.

▲ Proper nail care keeps your nails looking clean and healthy. **What are some steps you can take to improve the appearance of your nails?**

Health *Online*

Visit **health.glencoe.com** and complete the Interactive Study Guide for Lesson 1.

Your Nails

Like your hair, your fingernails and toenails are made of a tough substance called keratin. Around the nail is *a nonliving band of outer skin* called the **cuticle** (KYOO·ti·kuhl).

To keep nails healthy, soften your hands with warm water. Use a cuticle stick to push back the cuticle. Trim your nails using a nail clipper or small scissors. Cut your toenails straight across, so the nail is at or just beyond skin level. Use an emery board or nail file to round out the ends of your fingernails slightly and smooth out rough edges. Never bite your nails. Putting your fingers in your mouth can spread germs.

Reading Check **Identify** Describe how you should trim your fingernails and toenails.

Lesson 1 Review

 After You Read

Review this lesson for new terms, major headings, and Reading Checks.

What I Learned

1. *Vocabulary* What is *plaque?*

2. *Recall* Between what hours are the sun's UV rays strongest?

3. *Explain* What are two ways to treat acne?

Thinking Critically

4. *Hypothesize* What can happen to your teeth and gums if you do not floss regularly?

5. *Compare* In what ways are hair and nails similar? How are they different?

Applying Health Skills

6. *Advocacy* Create a booklet that explains the importance of proper tooth and gum care. Include original art, if you like, with step-by-step instructions. Distribute copies to students in other classes.

 **Health *Online*** For more review questions for Lesson 1, go to **health.glencoe.com**.

Lesson 1 Review Answers

1. Plaque is a soft, colorless, sticky film containing bacteria that grows on teeth.
2. They are strongest between 10:00 a.m. and 4:00 p.m.
3. *Sample answer:* Washing your face with soap and avoiding stressful situations are two ways to manage acne.

4. Food and plaque left on the teeth can cause tooth decay, gum disease, and eventually tooth loss.
5. Hair and nails are both made of dead cells and grow out of the dermis. They require different types of care.

6. Pamphlets should contain one or more of the tips for dental hygiene found in the lesson and at least one consequence of poor dental hygiene.

Protecting Your Eyes and Ears

Guide to Reading

● **Building Vocabulary**
Write the terms below in your notebook. As you read, write a definition for each.

■ farsightedness (p. 152)
■ nearsightedness (p. 152)
■ astigmatism (p. 152)

● **Focusing on the Main Ideas**
In this lesson, you will learn to

■ **describe** how to care for your eyes and ears.
■ **explain** how to protect your hearing.

● **Reading Strategy**
Organizing Information Copy the headings from the lesson onto a sheet of paper. Use these to make an outline of the lesson.

Healthy Eyes

Your eyes are your windows to the world. They allow you to take in millions of bits of information, which are sent to your brain. There the information is processed into shapes, colors, and movements. The many parts of the eye are shown in **Figure 6.5.**

Eye Care

The following tips can help you take care of your eyes:

- Take a break when using your computer, watching TV, and reading. Resting your eyes from time to time will help prevent eyestrain.

- Try not to sit too close to the TV or computer. The computer screen should be about two feet from your face.

- Read and watch TV in a well-lighted room. Light should come from above your reading material.

- Wear safety goggles during sports or science lab. Be especially careful when you are holding sharp objects.

- Wear sunglasses outdoors on sunny days. Buy sunglasses that have UV-approved lenses.

- If your eyes hurt or itch, don't rub them. You could have allergies or an infection. Tell a parent or guardian.

 uick Write

Write an original science fiction story about a visitor from another planet. The creature should have no ears or eyes. In your story, explain seeing and hearing to this visitor.

FOCUS

Activating Prior Knowledge

What I Know Ask students to name sources of loud sounds (for example, concerts or airplanes). Then have students name negative effects of listening to very loud sounds.

Guide to Reading

BUILDING VOCABULARY

■ Assign students to write each vocabulary term on the front of an index card and the definition of the term on the back of the card. Students can use these flashcards to practice the lesson vocabulary with a partner.

■ Use Vocabulary PuzzleMaker to reinforce vocabulary terms.

READING STRATEGY

Organizing Information Model the Reading Strategy activity for students by starting an outline on an overhead projector or on the board.

uick Write

Have students brainstorm phrases used to describe various sights and sounds. Record their answers on the board. Have students use the list of phrases as a resource as they write their stories.

Lesson 2 Resources

 Chapter *Fast File* Resources
Guided Reading and Writing 6-2
Concept Mapping Activity 6-2
Cross-Curriculum Activity 6-2
Reteaching Activity 6-2
Enrichment Activity 6-2
Lesson Quiz 6-2

Technology
⬇ Transparency 6-2
🥏 Audio Summaries
◉ *ExamView*
🥏 Vocabulary PuzzleMaker
◉ StudentWorks™ Plus

TEACH

R Reading Strategy

Analyzing a Graphic Begin by asking students to write three questions they have about the functions of the eye. Then after students have examined Figure 6.5, have them write a paragraph from the point of view of one of the parts of the eye explaining why that part serves an important function. **OL**

AL Active Learning

Video Have students work in small groups to write a script for a 3-minute video explaining one or more tips for eye care. Allow each group 15 minutes to write its script. Then allow time for practice and filming. After all groups have completed filming, share the videos with the class. **OL**

Reading Check

Answer A person who is farsighted can see distant objects clearly; a person who is nearsighted can see close objects clearly.

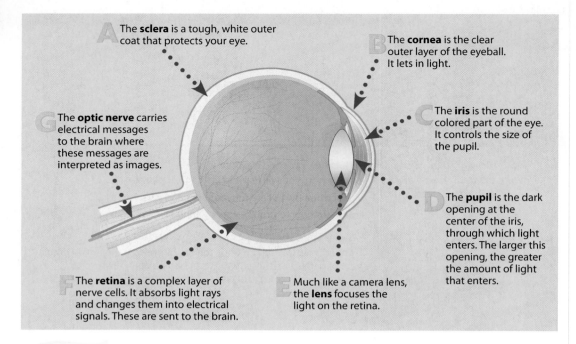

A The **sclera** is a tough, white outer coat that protects your eye.

B The **cornea** is the clear outer layer of the eyeball. It lets in light.

C The **iris** is the round colored part of the eye. It controls the size of the pupil.

D The **pupil** is the dark opening at the center of the iris, through which light enters. The larger this opening, the greater the amount of light that enters.

E Much like a camera lens, the **lens** focuses the light on the retina.

F The **retina** is a complex layer of nerve cells. It absorbs light rays and changes them into electrical signals. These are sent to the brain.

G The **optic nerve** carries electrical messages to the brain where these messages are interpreted as images.

▲ **FIGURE 6.5**

THE EYE

R The many parts of the eye work together to tell you about the world around you. How do the various parts interact to make vision possible?

- If you get something in your eye, try to blink to let tears wash it out. If this doesn't work, rinse the eye with water.
- Never share eye makeup or eye care products. Using someone else's products can spread germs.
- Get regular vision screenings and eye exams.

AL

Vision Problems

Two common vision problems are farsightedness and nearsightedness. **Farsightedness** is *the ability to see objects at a distance while close objects look blurry.* For example, if you are farsighted, the words on this page may look unclear. However, if you look at a sign on the wall across the room, the words will be in focus. The opposite will be true if you are **nearsighted.** This is *the ability to see objects close to you while distant objects look blurry.* A third common condition is **astigmatism** (ah·STIG·muh·tizm), *a misshaped cornea or lens causing objects to look wavy or blurred.*

Eye problems are usually corrected by using eyeglasses or contact lenses. Both help the lens of the eye focus light on the retina. An eye doctor can determine if you need corrective lenses.

Reading Check

Compare What is the difference between *nearsightedness* and *farsightedness*?

Caption Answer

Photo Caption The various parts of the eye work together to let in light, produce images, and send images to the brain.

TECHNOLOGY AND HEALTH

Corrective Eye Surgery There are several types of eye surgery that can correct eye problems and improve vision. In LASIK (laser-assisted in situ keratomileusis), LASEK (laser epithelial keratomileusis), and PRK (photorefractive keratectomy), a surgeon uses a laser to treat vision problems. These and other types of elective eye surgery are generally not performed on patients until they have reached the age of 18. Have students find out more about laser eye surgery by researching the procedure online. Have students share their findings with the class. **OL**

Healthy Ears

Like your eyes, your ears allow you to receive information. Your ears also help you keep your balance. Balance is controlled by the semicircular canals, tube-like structures in the inner ear. The different parts of the ear and what they do are shown in **Figure 6.6.**

Ear Problems

Infections in the middle ear are the most common ear problems. Germs from colds in the nose or throat can spread through the eustachian tube into the middle and inner ear. Ear infections can be treated by a doctor.

The most serious ear problems are hearing loss and deafness. These can result from injury, disease, and birth defects. Very loud noise can also cause hearing loss. Have you ever had a ringing in your ears after exposure to noise for a long period of time? This is called *tinnitus* (TIN·uh·tuhs). For some people, tinnitus is ongoing; the ringing is always present. Frequent or ongoing tinnitus is an early warning sign of inner-ear nerve damage.

Connect To... Science

Help for the Hearing Impaired

Medical science has developed a device that permits deaf and hearing-impaired people to communicate through sound. The device is called a *cochlear implant* and is placed under the skin behind the ear. Unlike a hearing aid, which makes sound louder, the device allows the person using it to identify speech sounds.

Using online or print resources, learn more about this technology. Share your findings in a short report.

Connect To... Science

Help for the Hearing Impaired

- Prepare in advance print resources about cochlear implants, or make a list of appropriate Web addresses to provide to students.
- If needed, have students work in small groups to share resources or computers.
- Have each student or group prepare a short report to share with the class.

R Reading Strategy

Analyzing a Graphic Have students examine Figure 6.6, which shows the parts of the ear. Give each student three index cards. Then have students organize the information in the following way: have students designate one index card for the inner ear, one for the outer ear, and one for the middle ear; have students write the headings "Structures" and "Functions" on each index card; then have students record the structures and functions of each part of the ear on their cards. **OL**

▼ FIGURE 6.6

R THE EAR

The ears carry sound to the brain and help you stay balanced. **Which parts of the ear are responsible for these two main functions?**

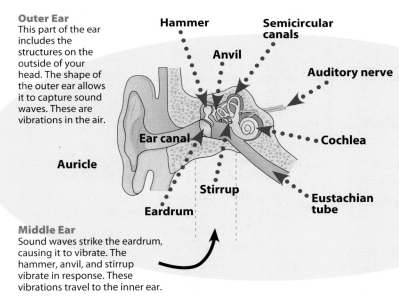

Outer Ear
This part of the ear includes the structures on the outside of your head. The shape of the outer ear allows it to capture sound waves. These are vibrations in the air.

Hammer

Anvil

Semicircular canals

Auditory nerve

Ear canal

Auricle

Cochlea

Stirrup

Eustachian tube

Eardrum

Middle Ear
Sound waves strike the eardrum, causing it to vibrate. The hammer, anvil, and stirrup vibrate in response. These vibrations travel to the inner ear.

Inner Ear
Sound
Tiny hair cells inside the cochlea move. This movement produces electrical messages in nerves deep inside the inner ear. These are sent to the brain along the auditory nerve. There, they are sorted out as speech sounds or nonspeech sounds. The sounds are then interpreted.

Balance
These canals are lined with tiny hairs and filled with fluid. When you move or change positions, the hairs and fluid also move. The brain senses these delicate movements. It tells your body which way to adjust your weight. This prevents you from falling over.

HEALTH LITERACY

American Sign Language Many people who are deaf or hearing-impaired communicate using American Sign Language (ASL). This language consists of hand motions, gestures, and facial expressions. Many people believe that sign language is spoken English translated into gestures. This is a misconception. ASL uses a different system of grammar and syntax than spoken English. Have students research some of the signs used in ASL. If possible, invite someone fluent in ASL to demonstrate this language to the class. **OL**

Caption Answer

Figure Caption The inner ear is responsible for balance and carrying sounds to the brain.

Reading Check

Answer Loud sound can damage hearing.

ASSESS

Assessment Resources

Lesson Review Quiz
* *ExamView*
* Fast Files Activities
* Online Quizzes and Activities

Reteaching

* Assign Concept Map 6-2 or Reteaching Activity 6-2 in the Fast Files.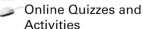
* Ask students to write a short paragraph that describes two ways to protect their hearing.

Enrichment

* Assign Enrichment Activity 6-2 in the Fast Files.
* Have each student create a poster that lists tips for eye care.

CLOSE

Ask students to name one strategy they can use to protect the health of their eyes or ears.

Caption Answer

Photo Caption People with hearing loss use sign language.

◄ People with hearing loss may wear hearing aids. These increase the loudness of sounds. **What are some other ways people with hearing loss can communicate?**

Ear Care

The best way to care for your ears is to protect them from loud sounds. The loudness of sounds is measured in units called *decibels* (DES·ih·belz). Normal conversation measures about 60 decibels. Repeated exposure to sounds above 85 decibels is harmful. When listening to music, especially with headphones, keep the volume down.

Never use cotton swabs to clean the inside of your ear. Putting anything inside your ear opening can damage your ear. Instead, clean the outside of the ears with water. Allow the insides of the ear to dry on their own.

Health *Online*

Visit **health.glencoe.com** and complete the Interactive Study Guide for Lesson 2.

Reading Check

Explain Why is it important to limit your exposure to loud sounds?

Lesson 2 Review

After You Read

Review this lesson for new terms, major headings, and Reading Checks.

What I Learned

1. *Vocabulary* What is *astigmatism?* How is it treated?

2. *Describe* List three habits that promote the health of your eyes.

3. *Recall* Name two jobs your ears perform.

Thinking Critically

4. *Apply* Frank is the equipment manager for a local band. What should Frank do to protect his ears while at work?

5. *Evaluate* Why might a person living near an airport need to take special care of his or her ears?

Applying Health Skills

6. *Decision Making* Eileen has learned that she needs glasses for a vision problem. She tried on several pairs and doesn't like any of them. What are Eileen's choices?

154 Chapter 6: Personal Health

Health *Online* For more review questions for Lesson 2, go to health.glencoe.com.

Lesson 2 Review Answers

1. It is a condition in which a misshaped cornea or lens causes objects to look blurred. It can be corrected by eyeglasses or contact lenses.
2. *Any three:* Take breaks when using a computer; do not sit too close to the television or computer; read in a well-lighted room; protect your eyes during sports, science lab, and shop class; avoid rubbing your eyes; never share eye-care products.
3. They help you hear and maintain your balance.
4. He should wear ear plugs to protect his ears.
5. A person living near an airport may be exposed to the loud sounds of airplanes taking off, which could cause hearing loss.
6. Eileen may be able to get contact lenses instead of glasses.

Choosing Health Products

Guide to Reading

● **Building Vocabulary**
Copy the terms below into your notebook.
As you come across each term in the lesson,
write its definition.

- consumer (p. 155)
- guarantee (p. 157)
- unit price (p. 157)
- coupons (p. 158)
- generic (p. 158)
- fraud (p. 158)

● **Focusing on the Main Ideas**
In this lesson, you will learn to

- **identify** factors that influence your consumer choices.
- **explain** ways to choose health products wisely.
- **analyze** how the media influences consumer choices.

● **Reading Strategy**
Predicting You probably make purchases already. Predict what kind of information would help you improve your shopping skills.

Consumer Skills

"I can't believe there are so many kinds of adhesive bandages," Marty remarked. He was finding it difficult to choose which product to buy. Having consumer skills would have made Marty's job easier. A **consumer** is *someone who buys products or services.* Consumer skills allow you to make informed choices when shopping.

Recognizing Influences

Many different factors influence your decisions as a consumer. One is your likes and dislikes. You might prefer one shampoo brand over another because it makes your hair shinier. Cost is also likely to be a factor.

Another factor that influences you is the media. This includes television, radio, the Internet, newspapers, and other information sources. One important influence you may not always be consciously aware of is advertising. Without knowing it, you might be tempted to buy an item that has a catchy ad.

 Quick Write

Make a list of health and beauty aids you use, such as shampoo and toothpaste. Explain how you decide what products to buy.

▶ There are many different health care products to choose from. **What influences your decisions as a consumer?**

Lesson 3: Choosing Health Products **155**

FOCUS

Activating Prior Knowledge

What I Know Have students recall the last time they had to choose between two or more products. Have volunteers name a factor that affected their decision. Tell students they will learn about consumer decisions in this lesson.

Guide to Reading

BUILDING VOCABULARY
- Ask students to name the meaning of the word *unit* in the term *unit price* (a *unit* is a single item).
- Use Vocabulary PuzzleMaker to reinforce vocabulary terms.

READING STRATEGY
Predicting Have each student list three techniques they would like to learn to improve his or her shopping skills.

Quick Write
After students have written their lists and explanations, have volunteers share their answers with the class.

Lesson 3 Resources

 Chapter *FAST FILE* **Resources**
Guided Reading and Writing 6-3
Concept Mapping Activity 6-3
Health Lab 6-3
Reteaching Activity 6-3
Enrichment Activity 6-3
Lesson Quiz 6-3

Technology
 Transparency 6-3
Audio Summaries
ExamView
Vocabulary PuzzleMaker
StudentWorks™ Plus

Caption Answer
Photo Caption An internal influence on consumer choices is likes and dislikes; an external influence is advertising.

TEACH

AL Active Learning

Connecting to the Real World Divide the class into small groups. Provide each group with advertisements and coupon circulars. Assign each group a type of health-care product, for example, soap or toothpaste. Challenge each group to find a sale or coupon for its assigned product. Ask: Is a product that is on sale or has a coupon always the best choice? Explain. *Sample answer: No, if a product does not meet your needs, it is not a good deal.* **OL**

R Reading Strategy

Analyzing a Graphic After students have examined Figure 6.7, ask: What can you learn from the indication section of a label? *what the product is used for* Ask: Why is it important to read the entire label on a health-care product? *Sample answer: In order to use the product effectively and properly, you need the information from each part of the label.* **OL**

Academic Vocabulary

Benefits The *benefits* of health-care products are mentioned on this page. Have students use the word *benefits* in a spoken sentence. Ask: What is the opposite of *benefit*? *disadvantage, drawback*

Caption Answer

Photo Caption This product would be used to treat cuts and scrapes.

Reading Product Labels

The first step in becoming a smart shopper is to understand what you're buying. With many products, this means reading the product label. Most product labels contain similar information. **Figure 6.7** shows a typical label on a health product. Take a moment to study the information on it.

AL Notice that the label tells you what the product is intended to do. This information appears first, under *indications*. What is the purpose of the product shown?

The label also gives directions. These tell you how much of the product to use and how often to use it. Use a product *only* as directed. If problems occur when you use the product, stop using it immediately and tell a trusted adult. There may be an ingredient in it that is causing the problem.

Comparison Shopping

When you compare two or more similar products by different manufacturers, you are comparison shopping. When comparing products, consider the benefits of one product over another. Which brand offers more of what you need and want? You should also consider the brand's reputation. Do you know anyone who has used and liked it? Finally, check to see if the

▼ FIGURE 6.7

WHAT PRODUCT LABELS CAN TELL
R YOU

Product labels contain important information. What do you think this product would be used for?

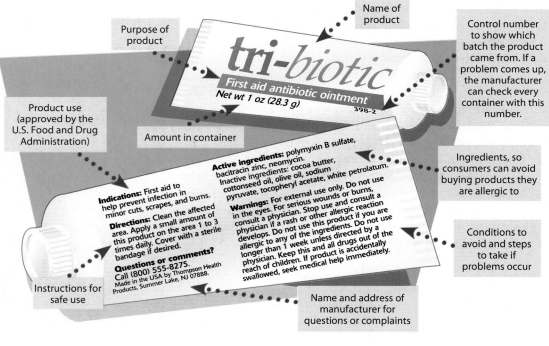

Purpose of product

Name of product

Control number to show which batch the product came from. If a problem comes up, the manufacturer can check every container with this number.

Product use (approved by the U.S. Food and Drug Administration)

Amount in container

Ingredients, so consumers can avoid buying products they are allergic to

Conditions to avoid and steps to take if problems occur

Instructions for safe use

Name and address of manufacturer for questions or complaints

156 Chapter 6: Personal Health

TECHNOLOGY AND HEALTH

Using a Spreadsheet Record comparison shopping results on a spreadsheet. Open a computer spreadsheet program. In cell A1 enter *Product;* cell B1 enter *Weight/Volume;* cell C1 enter *Price;* cell D1 enter *Per Unit Price.* In cell D2 enter the formula *=C2/B2.* Click cell D2; click Edit, Copy; Click D3; Click Edit, Paste. Click on next cell down (D4) then click Paste. Repeat pasting until you reach cell D23. Collect labels on 10 items you purchase regularly. Enter comparable products for each item listed. Be sure to save your files.

Health Skills Activity

Analyzing Influences

Persuasive Advertising

Advertisers often use the following techniques to persuade you to buy their items.

- **Hidden messages.** Sometimes messages are in the form of pictures. A picture may show attractive people smiling when they use a product. This is telling you that the product will make you happier and healthier.
- **Comments by previous users.** These ads show people who claim to have used the company's product and gotten great results. These people may be paid actors.
- **Celebrity backing.** Popular actors, athletes, or celebrities promote some products. Remember that these people are paid to promote these products.

With a Group

Find an example of an ad that uses one of the techniques described above. How might these ads influence your decision to try the product? Discuss your findings with the class.

Health Skills Activity

Analyzing Influences

Persuasive Advertising

Use the following strategies to help students complete the activity.

- Ask students to spend 5 minutes in their groups discussing familiar advertisements. Have students discuss the techniques used in these advertisements.
- Have the group select one of the ads that it has discussed to complete the activity.

R **Reading Strategy**

Analyzing a Graphic Have students examine Figure 6.8. Ask: Why are unit prices important for comparison shopping? *If products are in different-sized containers, unit prices are required to find out which is a better buy.* **OL**

product has a guarantee. A **guarantee** is *a promise to refund your money if the product doesn't work as claimed.* It shows that the company that makes the product actually believes in their product and is willing to stand behind it.

When comparing the costs of health products, one important factor is **unit price.** This is the *cost per unit of weight or volume.* Often, a product's unit price appears on a tab on the shelf beneath it. You can compute it yourself, if necessary.

1. Find the weight or volume given on each product container. (Make sure that both products are measured in the same type of units.)
2. Divide the price of the product by its weight or volume.
3. The result is the unit price.

For example, an 8-fluid-ounce bottle of lotion costs $3.89. Dividing $3.89 by 8 equals $0.49. The unit price is 49¢ per fluid ounce. What's the unit price of each bottle of liquid soap in **Figure 6.8**? Which costs less per fluid ounce? Which is a better value?

▲ **FIGURE 6.8**

USING UNIT PRICING

Comparing unit price can help you save money. **Which of these products is a better value?** **R**

HEALTH LITERACY

Identifying Health Fraud Have students develop a checklist that can help them spot health fraud and false claims. Have students work as a class to develop a list of tips for spotting false claims about health-care products. Some tips that students might include on their list are: avoid any product that claims to be a miracle cure, be wary of claims that are based solely on personal testimonials, and avoid products that claim to contain a secret ingredient. After completing the list of tips, have each student write a paragraph in the style of a newspaper article about avoiding health fraud. **OL**

Caption Answer

Photo Caption In this case, the Silky Soap on the left is the better value.
($2.89 ÷ 15 = 19¢)
($1.69 ÷ 7.5 = 22¢)

Answer Consumers can save by comparing unit prices and using coupons.

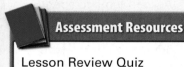
ASSESS

Assessment Resources

Lesson Review Quiz
- *ExamView*
- Fast Files Activities
- Online Quizzes and Activities

Reteaching

- Assign Concept Map 6-3 or Reteaching Activity 6-3 in the Fast Files.
- Have students name two ways to make wise choices about health-care products.

Enrichment

- Assign Enrichment Activity 6-3 in the Fast Files.
- Have each student write five true-or-false quiz questions about the main concepts and vocabulary terms of this lesson. Have students quiz each other using their prepared questions.

CLOSE

Ask students to name one piece of information from the lesson that could improve their shopping skills.

Saving Money

Comparing unit prices can help you save money. So does buying personal products at discount stores. Clipping coupons is another way to save. **Coupons** are *slips of paper that save you money on certain brands.* Coupons are found in many daily newspapers and store flyers. Another way to save is by selecting the store, or **generic** (juh·NEHR·ik), brand. These are *products that imitate name-brand products but are sold in plain packages.* They cost less because the product maker spends less money on advertising.

Spotting False Claims

Some ads and product labels make claims that sound too good to be true. Some companies go beyond making misleading claims. They commit the crime of fraud. **Fraud** is *deliberately trying to trick consumers into buying a product or service.* Health fraud is a serious issue. You can report suspicious health products at the Food and Drug Administration (FDA) Web site. Helping fight fraud allows you to use your skill as a health advocate.

Health Online

Visit **health.glencoe.com** and complete the Interactive Study Guide for Lesson 3.

Reading Check   **Explain** What are two ways consumers can save money?

Lesson 3 Review

After You Read

Review this lesson for new terms, major headings, and Reading Checks.

What I Learned

1. *Vocabulary* Define *consumer.*

2. *List* What are two types of information found on health product labels?

3. *Recall* What is the benefit of knowing a product's unit price?

Thinking Critically

4. *Apply* Jessica has poison ivy. She uses twice as much cream as the product label directs. Is this a good way of getting better faster?

5. *Synthesize* Why might a less expensive product not be the best product to buy? What other factors should you consider?

Applying Health Skills

6. *Analyzing Influences* Imagine that you are selecting a deodorant. What factors would influence your decision?

Health Online For more review questions for Lesson 3, go to **health.glencoe.com**.

Lesson 3 Review Answers

1. A consumer is a person who buys products or services.
2. Answers may include indications, directions, or any of the other label features noted in Figure 6.7 on page 156.
3. It allows the consumer to compare products of different sizes and prices.
4. No, it is not a good idea to use a product in a manner other than what is recommended in the directions.
5. Answers might include the idea that the product may not contain the same ingredients.
6. *Sample answers:* price, advertising, effectiveness

Using Medicines Responsibly

Guide to Reading

● Building Vocabulary
Arrange the terms below in a word web. Place what you believe is the *main* term at the center.

- medicines (p. 159)
- prescription medicines (p. 159)
- over-the-counter (OTC) medicines (p. 159)
- vaccines (p. 160)
- antibiotics (p. 160)
- side effect (p. 160)
- tolerance (p. 160)
- drug misuse (p. 162)

● Focusing on the Main Ideas
In this lesson, you will learn to

- **explain** how medicines help you.
- **identify** information on medicine labels.
- **access** reliable health information on medicines.

● Reading Strategy
Organizing Information As you read the lesson, make notes about what medicines do and how to use them safely.

What Are Medicines?

Medicines are *drugs used to treat, cure, or prevent diseases or other medical conditions.* In earlier times, medicines were taken from plant leaves. People would eat the leaves or drink tea brewed from them. Today most medicines are in the form of pills or liquids. Occasionally they are also injected into the bloodstream using needles, inhaled into the lungs, or rubbed into the skin.

There are two types of medicines. **Prescription** (prih·SKRIP·shuhn) **medicines** are *medicines sold only with a written order from a doctor.* **Over-the-counter (OTC) medicines** are *medicines available without a written order from a doctor.* These are also known as "nonprescription medicines." Prescription medicines require a doctor's supervision because they can carry more risks. However, OTC medicines should be used just as carefully.

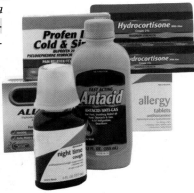

▶ Different medicines do different jobs. **Why do you think it is important to tell a new doctor what medicines you are taking?**

Q *uick Write*

Describe a TV commercial you have seen advertising a medicine. Tell what the medicine is supposed to do.

Lesson 4: Using Medicines Responsibly · **159**

Lesson 4 Resources

📁 **Chapter** *FAST FILE* **Resources**
Guided Reading and Writing 6-4
Concept Mapping Activity 6-4
Cross-Curriculum Activity 6-4
Reteaching Activity 6-4
Enrichment Activity 6-4
Lesson Quiz 6-4

Technology
👍 Transparency 6-4
💿 Audio Summaries
🔵 *ExamView*
💿 Vocabulary PuzzleMaker
🔵 StudentWorks™ Plus

FOCUS

Activating Prior Knowledge

What I Know Have students name ways that medicine can be used and misused. Write their answers in two lists on the board. Refer to this list to correct any misconceptions as students complete the lesson.

Guide to Reading

BUILDING VOCABULARY

- Explain that the word part *mis-* in the term *misuse* means "bad" or "wrong." Have students think of other words that have the word part *mis-* (mistake, misbehave).
- Use Vocabulary PuzzleMaker to reinforce vocabulary terms. 💿

READING STRATEGY
Organizing Information Have students prepare a piece of paper with two headings: "What Medicines Do," and "How to Use Medicines Safely." Have students make notes in both columns as they read the lesson.

Q *uick Write*

Lead a class discussion about advertising of prescription and non-prescription medicines to introduce the Quick Write activity.

159

TEACH

Academic Vocabulary

Interact The ways medicines *interact* with the body is described on this page. Explain that the word part *inter-* means "involving two or more." Have students list other terms that use the word part *inter-* (intercept, interface, intermission).

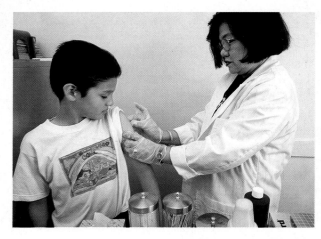

▲ Vaccines are medicines that prevent disease. **What are some common vaccines given today?**

What Medicines Do

Different medicines do different jobs. *Medicines that protect you from getting certain diseases* are known as **vaccines.** Some medicines cure diseases or kill germs. One type of germ-fighting medicines is **antibiotics** (an·tih·by·AH·tiks). These *kill or stop the growth of bacteria and other specific germs*. Still some medicines are used to manage *chronic*, or ongoing, conditions such as asthma. Other medicines relieve symptoms, such as itching, or pain.

U

Reading Check **List** Name three different kinds of medicine, and tell what job each does.

How Medicines Affect the Body

Because everyone's body is unique, medicines affect people in different ways. Factors that determine how a medicine affects you include age, weight, and general health. Combining medicines may also affect the way they work. Some medicines don't mix well with others and can cause harmful reactions. Some people are allergic to certain medicines and cannot take them at all.

Negative Reactions to Medicines

Even when used as directed, medicines can cause unwanted reactions. A **side effect** is *any reaction to a medicine other than the one intended.* Common side effects are drowsiness, dizziness, or upset stomach. Taking more than one medicine at a time can cause dangerous side effects if they are not supposed to be taken together. Make sure your doctor and pharmacist know *all* the medicines you are taking, including OTC medicines.

If you take a medicine for a long time, you may develop a **tolerance** (TAHL·ehr·uhns). This means *the body becomes used to the medicine and no longer has the same effect.* Greater amounts of the medicine are needed to get the same results. This can become a dangerous problem. If a medicine you are taking no longer seems to be working, tell a parent or guardian, and speak to your doctor.

Reading Check **Define** What does *side effect* mean?

What Teens Want to Know

Do I still need to get vaccines? Students often think of vaccines as something needed by babies and toddlers. Preteens and teens may be surprised to learn how vital booster shots are. Several important vaccines are required for those between the ages of 10 and 18. Most preteens and teens will need to receive a vaccine for diphtheria and tetanus, chicken pox (unless they have already had chicken pox), hepatitis B, measles, mumps, and rubella, and meningococcus. If possible, have the school nurse provide a sample immunization schedule for students to examine. **OL**

Using Medicines Safely

Before using OTC or prescription medicines, read the product label. The FDA requires makers of medicines to include certain information on medicine labels. Pharmacists are also required to include specific information on prescription labels. This includes the name of the patient and doctor, instructions for using the medicine, and the *dose*. This is how much of the medicine to take at one time. One especially important item on the label is the *expiration date of the medicine*. Find the expiration date on the sample prescription medicine label in **Figure 6.9**. All medicines have ingredients that can change over time and become less effective. The expiration date will tell you the date after which you can longer use the medicine.

Over-the-counter (OTC) medicines have both front and back labels. The front label contains the name of the product and type of medicine. It also lists the main ingredient. The back label lists *directions* for use, which are similar to dosage information on a prescription label. If you have questions about an OTC or prescription medicine, talk to your pharmacist or doctor.

▼ **FIGURE 6.9**

LABEL ON A PRESCRIPTION MEDICINE

Medicine labels include instructions on how to use the medicine safely. If you had questions about the use of this product, whom could you ask?

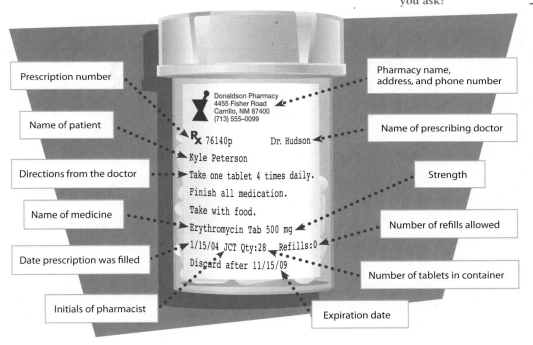

Prescription number

Name of patient

Directions from the doctor

Name of medicine

Date prescription was filled

Initials of pharmacist

Pharmacy name, address, and phone number

Name of prescribing doctor

Strength

Number of refills allowed

Number of tablets in container

Expiration date

Donaldson Pharmacy
4455 Fisher Road
Carrillo, NM 87400
(713) 555-0099

R~x~ 76140p   Dr. Hudson
Kyle Peterson
Take one tablet 4 times daily.
Finish all medication.
Take with food.
Erythromycin Tab 500 mg
1/15/04 JCT Qty:28 Refills:0
Discard after 11/15/09

Lesson 4: Using Medicines Responsibly **161**

CHAPTER 6
Lesson 4

AL **Active Learning**

Role-Plays Divide the class into small groups. Have each group spend 15 minutes writing a script for a role-play that demonstrates one or more of the tips for using medicines safely and avoiding drug misuse. Have each group perform its role-play for the class. **OL**

R **Reading Strategy**

Analyzing a Graphic After students have examined Figure 6.9, ask: How many refills of this prescription are allowed? *none* **OL**

DEVELOPING
Good Character

Responsibility Have students read the activity about Responsibility on the next page. Discuss other ways that a student their age could share information about the dangers of drug misuse. Record the students' suggestions on the board. Then have each student develop a slogan that could be used to communicate one of the suggestions.

Home, School, and Community

At School According to a study by the Partnership for a Drug-Free America®, teens are more likely to have abused a legal drug than they are to have tried an illegal drug. The study found that as many as 1 in 5 teens has abused painkillers, 1 in 10 teens has abused stimulants, and 1 in 11 teens has abused cough medicines. Invite the school counselor to discuss the abuse of over-the-counter and prescription drugs. Have students develop comic strips that warn of the dangers of abusing legal drugs. With permission, post students' comic strips throughout the school. **OL**

Caption Answer

Figure Caption A pharmacist could answer questions about the use of this product.

ASSESS

Assessment Resources

Lesson Review Quiz
- *ExamView*
- Fast Files Activities
- Online Quizzes and Activities

Reteaching

- Assign Concept Map 6-4 or Reteaching Activity 6-4 in the Fast Files.
- Have students compare and contrast prescription medicine and over-the-counter medicine, and how misuse can occur.

Enrichment

- Assign Enrichment Activity 6-4 in the Fast Files.
- Have students research the possible side effects of common pain relievers and write a short report.

CLOSE

Have students discuss ways that advertising of medications can be helpful or harmful.

Health Online

Visit **health.glencoe.com** and complete the Interactive Study Guide for Lesson 4.

Improper Use of Medicines

Medicines can do serious harm as well as good. This is why they should be taken with great care. *Taking medicine in a way that is not intended* is **drug misuse.** Taking more medicine than a doctor instructs is one example of drug misuse. To avoid misusing drugs, follow these guidelines.

- Talk to your doctor or pharmacist if you are not sure how to use a medicine.
- In the case of prescription medicines, take only medicines prescribed specifically for you.
- Use all medicines only as instructed. Make sure you understand the dose and how often it should be taken. Use exactly the amount indicated on the label.
- Don't use a medicine that was prescribed for an earlier illness without a doctor's approval.
- Don't use a medicine that has expired.

Using medicines in ways that are unhealthy is a form of drug abuse. You will learn more about drug abuse in Chapter 11.

 **Reading Check** **Give examples** What are three ways of avoiding drug misuse?

Lesson 4 Review

 After You Read

Review this lesson for new terms, major headings, and Reading Checks.

What I Learned

1. *Identify* What are three ways that medicines can enter the body?
2. *Recall* Name two items on an over-the-counter (OTC) medicine label.
3. *Vocabulary* Define *tolerance.*

Thinking Critically

4. *Hypothesize* Why might a doctor prescribe different medicines for two people with the same illness?

5. *Synthesize* Why do you think the number of refills allowed is important information to include on a medicine label?

Applying Health Skills

6. *Accessing Information* The Internet makes it easier than ever to get information about medicines. Under your teacher's supervision, visit a Web site that contains information about medicines. List the kinds of facts provided.

Health Online For more review questions for Lesson 4, go to **health.glencoe.com**.

Lesson 4 Review Answers

1. Answers include swallowing, injection, inhaling, and rubbing into the skin.
2. Answers, which will vary, can include any of the facts appearing in the appropriate part of Figure 6.9.

3. Tolerance is a condition in which the body becomes used to the medicine's effects.
4. The doctor's decision involves factors such as age, weight, allergies, and other medications being taken.

5. Students should recognize that limiting refills prevents misuse, abuse, and tolerance to the medication.
6. Students' answers will vary depending on the Internet site visited.

Health Care in Your Community

Guide to Reading

● **Building Vocabulary**
Define the familiar terms below in your notebook. Define the unfamiliar terms as you read the lesson.

- health care (p. 163)
- specialist (p. 164)
- voluntary health agencies (p. 165)
- health insurance (p. 166)
- managed care (p. 167)

● **Focusing on the Main Ideas**
In this lesson, you will learn to

- **identify** different types of health care providers.
- **explain** the importance of regular health checkups.
- **apply** the skill of advocacy to raise awareness of health problems.

● **Reading Strategy**
Classifying As you read the lesson, list the different health care providers, groups, and agencies. Find examples of each in your own community.

What Is Health Care?

Health care includes *any services provided to individuals or communities that promote, maintain, or restore health.* The health care industry is made up of a number of different health care providers, groups, and agencies. In this lesson, you will learn about the role each of these plays in your health.

Health Care Providers

Imagine you were feeling sick. Your parent or guardian might take you to see a doctor. Your doctor provides you with primary health care. Primary care includes the treatment of illnesses or diseases that do not require hospitalization. Primary care also includes *preventive care* such as regular health checkups and immunization against disease. Preventive care is any action that helps prevent the onset of disease or injury.

Different health professionals can provide primary care. This includes doctors, nurse practitioners, and physicians' assistants. All are trained to answer many health and medical questions and to give regular health checkups.

Quick Write

Explain in a paragraph why you think it's important to have regular medical checkups.

Activating Prior Knowledge

What I Know Have students name community resources where they have access to medical professionals. Explain that in this lesson students will learn more about health-care options.

 Guide to Reading

BUILDING VOCABULARY
- Explain that one of the meanings of the word *primary* is "first." Have students relate this to the meaning of the term *primary care giver. (The person you contact first when you have a medical problem.)*
- Use Vocabulary PuzzleMaker to reinforce vocabulary terms.

READING STRATEGY
Classifying Provide students with telephone directories or other resources with examples of different types of health-care providers in their community.

Quick Write

To help students get started on their Quick Write, have them identify some consequences of not receiving regular medical checkups.

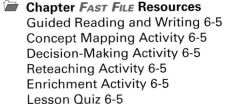 **Lesson 5 Resources**

📂 **Chapter *FAST FILE* Resources**
Guided Reading and Writing 6-5
Concept Mapping Activity 6-5
Decision-Making Activity 6-5
Reteaching Activity 6-5
Enrichment Activity 6-5
Lesson Quiz 6-5

Technology
🔌 Transparency 6-5
🎧 Audio Summaries
💿 *ExamView*
🎧 Vocabulary PuzzleMaker
💿 StudentWorks™ Plus

TEACH

Differentiate Have a class discussion of the role of preventive care in maintaining health. Then have students work as a class to list types of preventive care provided by health professionals (for example immunizations and vision screenings), and preventive care for which individuals are responsible (for example eating right and exercising). **OL**

AL Active Learning

Quick Demo Display a picture of a sports team from a newspaper, magazine, or school yearbook. Explain that the members of a sports team play different positions on the team, but all work toward the common goal of winning the game. In the same way, different types of health-care providers all do different jobs with a common goal of good health for their patients. **BL**

▶ Regular checkups can help you stay healthy. **Who are some of the different health professionals you could see for a checkup?**

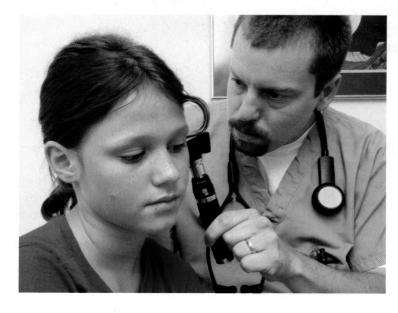

Annual Physical Checkups

C Getting regular checkups is one way to prevent health problems and maintain wellness. During a checkup, your health care provider will check your height and weight. He or she will also check your heart and lungs. Your vision and hearing may be tested. You may also receive any immunizations you need. These help your body resist getting certain common childhood diseases, such as measles.

Specialists and Other Health Care Providers

Sometimes the doctor or other health professional you see first will need to refer you to a **specialist** (SPEH·shuh·list). This is *a doctor trained to handle particular health problems.* Some specialists treat specific types of people. Other specialists treat specific conditions or body systems. **Figure 6.11** shows some of these specialists.

AL Health care today is largely a team effort. It involves more care providers than just your primary doctor and specialists. Think of the many health professionals you see. These probably include a dentist and/or dental hygienist. At school, you probably have a school nurse who can help you. You might see a counselor, either at school or in the community. All of these professionals play a role in keeping you healthy.

Caption Answer

Photo Caption Students should name health professionals listed in Figure 6.11 on page 165.

✦ Promoting Coordinated School Health

Health Care at School Most schools provide some health services to students. Be certain that students are familiar with the heath-care services available through the school. Explain the role of the school nurse in helping students maintain their health. Identify any screenings or preventive care available to students as well. Explain that the nurse also helps students manage chronic health conditions during the school day. Remind students that the school nurse is a valuable resource for health information.

Specialist	Specialty
Allergist	Asthma, hay fever, other allergies
Cardiologist	Heart problems
Dermatologist	Skin conditions and diseases
Oncologist	Cancer
Ophthalmologist	Eye diseases
Orthodontist	Tooth and jaw irregularities
Orthopedist	Broken bones and similar problems
Otolaryngologist	Ears, nose, and throat
Pediatrician	Infants, children, and teens

◀ **FIGURE 6.11**

SOME SPECIALISTS

Different specialists treat different conditions or types of people. Are there other specialties you have heard of?

Other Sources of Health Care

Your health care doesn't stop with the individuals who treat you personally. There are groups and organizations that contribute to your health. In this country, government agencies oversee the health of communities as a whole. They make sure that our food and water are safe to eat and drink. They also fund research to help treat and cure diseases and improve medical technology.

Other groups that play a role in health care include **voluntary health agencies,** *organizations that work to treat and eliminate certain diseases.* Two examples of these agencies are the American Heart Association and American Cancer Society. These groups are privately run. This means that they receive

◀ Volunteer health agencies often raise money by sponsoring community events such as races. **Are there any events like this in your community?**

Lesson 5: Health Care in Your Community **165**

R Reading Strategy

Analyzing a Chart Have students choose one of the types of health-care providers described in the text or the chart in Figure 6.11. Then using the provided description, have each student prepare a script for a 20-second radio advertisement describing the services provided by that particular health-care professional. **OL**

C Critical Thinking

Analyze Have students make a Venn diagram that compares the roles of health care professionals who treat individuals and organizations that monitor community health. Guide them in identifying details from the section on Other Sources of Health Care to complete their diagrams. **OL**

HEALTH LITERACY

The Red Cross The International Federation of Red Cross is the world's largest international humanitarian agency, providing aid during times of war and disaster to communities around the world. The Red Cross began in Switzerland in 1859, and today it represents a network of agencies in over 170 countries. The agency provides medical treatment, food, clothing, and shelter, facilitates communication, and offers counseling and assistance to those in need following disasters that include hurricanes, drought, earthquakes, or epidemics.

Caption Answer

Photo Caption Students should give examples of nonprofit events in your community.

Health Skills Activity

Advocacy

Doing Your Part for Community Health

Use the following strategies to help students complete the activity.

- Have students meet in small groups to read the suggestions for volunteering with health agencies.
- Then have each group choose a major disease or health problem. Be certain that each group selects a different topic.
- Provide materials for students to use for their research, or arrange for a class visit to the school library or media center.
- Have each group produce a poster and a pamphlet to raise community awareness and to encourage volunteering.

Academic Vocabulary

Ongoing This section mentions *ongoing* medical conditions. Explain that *ongoing* means "continuing" or "long-term." Have students list medical conditions that would be considered *ongoing*. Sample answers: *diabetes, asthma*

Health Skills Activity

Advocacy

Doing Your Part for Community Health

Volunteer health agencies need everyone's help to stamp out disease. How can you help? Here are some suggestions.

- A number of volunteer organizations have local chapters around the country. If there is a chapter in your community, contact them and ask how you can volunteer.
- Take part in a walk or run for a cure. These are held in many places across the country. Walkers or runners find sponsors before the event. Each sponsor donates a sum of money for every mile covered. The money collected from this effort goes toward research.

With a Group

Choose and research a major disease or health problem. Are there any local volunteer organizations for this health problem? Find out what volunteer opportunities they have for teens.

donations from individuals and groups, and not from the government, to pay for what they do. One of their most important jobs is to educate the public about diseases. They also conduct research to fight diseases.

 **Reading Check** **List** Name several different types of specialists, and tell what each does.

Paying for Health Care

Paying for health care can be difficult, especially if you have an ongoing illness. Surgery and hospital stays, for example, can cost thousands of dollars. Many people pay for health care by buying **health insurance.** This is *an insurance policy that covers most health-care costs*. These people pay a monthly fee to the health insurance company for the policy. Some employers help their employees pay the monthly fee. When a person goes to the doctor or hospital, their insurance will usually pay a large part of the health care cost. Health insurance will usually pay part of the cost of prescription medicines as well.

Reading Check

Answer A pediatrician treats children and teens; a pharmacist answers questions about medicines.

Dealing with Sensitive Issues

Uninsured Students Some students may have limited access to health care due to lack of health insurance. Many states offer low- or no-cost health insurance to children in families with incomes below a certain threshold. If your state offers such a program, gather relevant information, then incorporate this information into the lesson content. The school nurse may be able to assist you with this. Be certain all students have access to the materials you provide. **OL**

Because of rising costs, there are new options when choosing health insurance. One option is **managed care.** This is *a health insurance plan that saves money by limiting people's choice of doctors.* Patients save money when they visit doctors who participate in the managed care plan.

Two types of health insurance offered by the government are Medicaid and Medicare. Medicaid is for people with limited income. Medicare is for adults over the age of 65 and people of any age with certain disabilities.

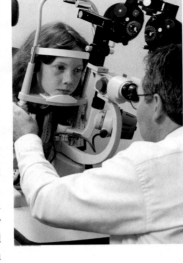

 Vision insurance is one type of health insurance that helps people pay for visits to the eye doctor. **What do you think dental insurance helps people pay for?**

 **Reading Check**

Explain Tell how a patient saves money with a managed care plan.

Health *Online*

Visit **health.glencoe.com** and complete the Interactive Study Guide for Lesson 5.

 Reading Check

Answer Participants in managed care can only visit participating doctors.

ASSESS

Assessment Resources

Lesson Review Quiz
* *ExamView*
* Fast Files Activities
* Online Quizzes and Activities

Reteaching

● Assign Concept Map 6-5 or Reteaching Activity 6-5 in the Fast Files.
● Ask students to name one type of health-care provider and describe the services they provide.

Enrichment

● Assign Enrichment Activity 6-5 in the Fast Files.
● Have students research a voluntary health agency, such as the American Cancer Society. Each student should prepare a written report describing the agency he or she has chosen to research.

CLOSE

Ask students to name and describe two sources of health care they have learned about.

 **Lesson 5 Review**

 **After You Read**

Review this lesson for new terms, major headings, and Reading Checks.

What I Learned

1. *Vocabulary* Define *health care.*

2. *Describe* Why is it important to have regular health checkups?

3. *Recall* What are some steps the government takes to oversee the health of Americans?

Thinking Critically

4. *Hypothesize* What kinds of information can a patient give to a primary care provider to help solve a health problem?

5. *Evaluate* How do volunteer health agencies contribute to our overall health?

Applying Health Skills

6. *Advocacy* Using the phone directory, make a list of health care resources for your community. Identify the kinds of health care each group offers. Convert your findings into a booklet. Share copies with other students.

Health *Online* For more review questions for Lesson 5, go to **health.glencoe.com**.   Lesson 5: Health Care in Your Community   **167**

Lesson 5 Review Answers

1. Health care includes any services provided to individuals or communities that promote, maintain, or restore health.
2. Regular checkups help you prevent and detect health problems and maintain wellness.

3. Answers include making sure drinking water is safe, inspecting food-handling facilities, and funding medical research.
4. Answers might include making a list of questions to ask, reporting all problems, and bringing a list of all medicines the person is taking.

5. Volunteer agencies teach about diseases and how to prevent them, and provide research for treatment and cures.
6. Provide phone directories for student use. Review students' booklets for accuracy and appropriate content before they are distributed.

Building Health Skills

ACCESSING INFORMATION

Buyer Beware!

SKILL
Accessing Information

Activating Prior Knowledge

Ask students to consider what they have learned in this chapter about choosing health-care products. Have them name one source of information they would use to make a decision when buying a health-care product.

- **Objective** After completing the activity, students will be able to identify and evaluate reliable sources of information about health-care products.
- **Time** 45 minutes
- **Materials** paper, pencil

Teacher Classroom Resources
📂 Building Health Skills
🔖 Transparency 6-5

Model

- Have students read the steps Lindsey followed to make an informed choice about buying sunglasses. Ask: Why did Lindsey determine she could trust the pharmacist's comment? *Sample answer: Pharmacists are medical professionals; they are highly qualified to give advice about health-care products.*

Buyer Beware!

DIRECTIONS

Accessing Information involves finding reliable information to make healthy choices. This activity will give you the opportunity to develop and master this important health skill. Here's a guide to the different parts of this activity:

❶ In the **Model** section, you will read about a teen who performs the health skill successfully. This "model" scenario will show you how the skill is done.

❷ The **Practice** section will help guide you in practicing the skill.

❸ In the **Apply** section, you will have a chance to perform the skill on your own. You can use the Self-Check to check your work.

To complete this activity, first read the scenario presented in the Model. Then move on to the Practice. Finally, go ahead and try the Apply.

168

❶ Model

The media influences what you choose to buy as a consumer. Think of the many advertisements you see, read, or hear every day. In addition, you may hear or read news reports, magazine articles, and other information about certain products.

Lindsey wanted a pair of sunglasses and read in a magazine that lenses with UV protection provide the best benefits over other types of sunglasses. At the pharmacy she saw several different styles of sunglasses that she liked. Lindsey picked up one style with UV lenses. She also picked up another style she really liked that did not have UV lenses. Lindsey asked the pharmacist for advice. The pharmacist confirmed that UV lenses would protect her eyes from potential damage from the sun.

Lindsey knew the pharmacist was a reliable source that she could trust. She felt confident choosing the sunglasses with UV lenses.

Teaching Tips

Advertising Techniques Review these advertising techniques: Bandwagon (*image:* groups of teens; *message:* other teens use this product so you should, too); Beautiful People (*image:* a glamorous person; *message:* you'll be like this person if you use this product); Good Times (*image:* teens having fun; *message:* you'll have fun if you use this product; Status (*image:* Designer Items); Symbols (*image:* well-known character; *message:* you'll be popular like this character if you use this product).

❷ Practice

Advertisements often make claims about a product's effectiveness. Lindsey's sister, Briana, has a sore throat. Lindsey's father asks her to help choose a product that would relieve Briana's symptoms. In the pharmacy ad, they see a sale on throat lozenges. "Lasts all day," the ad reads. Another product, a throat spray, advertises that it would provide "instant relief."

Using what you have learned about accessing information, answer these questions.

1. Are advertisements good sources of information?

2. What additional information might Lindsey and her father need to make a confident decision?

3. Where could they find more reliable information to help evaluate the different products?

Skill Summary
ACCESSING INFORMATION

Smart shopper tips:

■ Be cautious about product claims made in advertisements.

■ Read labels to learn what products contain, how they work, and how to use them.

■ If you want more information about a health product, talk to your parent or guardian or your local pharmacist.

❸ Apply

Working with a group, find three different advertisements for health products. Write down what claim each advertisement makes about the product. Does each claim seem believable? What additional information is needed?

Identify two sources where teens could find reliable information about these health products. Explain why these resources are reliable.

Self-Check

■ Did I find at least three different advertisements for health products?

■ Did I name two sources of reliable health information?

■ Did I explain why these resources are reliable?

Practice

● Have students read the introductory paragraph in the Practice activity.

● Then have students work in pairs to discuss the questions. Have each pair of students write a response to the questions.

● Lead a class discussion of the responses. Write the possible choices for answer 3 on the board. Record under each product name the number of student pairs that selected that product. Have students justify their answers.

Apply/Assess

● Provide newspaper advertisements or magazines for students to use as possible sources of information about health products.

● Be sure students explain specifically why the sources are reliable.

● You may wish to distribute the Building Health Skills Activity in the Fast Files. 📁

ASSESSMENT SCORING

Student work should meet all criteria to achieve the highest score:

Skills Student work identifies:

● two sources of reliable information about health products.

● reasons why these sources were chosen.

Concept Student work provides:

● a logical determination regarding the legitimacy of health claims.

● analysis of why the health claims are genuine or misleading.

Observing the Eye

Time: 20 minutes
Materials: pencil or pen, paper, one mirror for each student

Introducing Hands-on Health

● Have a class discussion in which students share what they already know about how their eyes respond to light. Ask students to recall what happens when they step out of a dark movie theater on a bright day.

Teaching the Activity

● Distribute the mirrors.
● Have students read the instructions for the activity.
● Turn off the lights for a two-minute period. Then turn on the lights.
● Have students record their observations.
● Then have students complete the color vision test and record their results.
● Have a class discussion about various ways to show the class data. Have students choose whether they will use a chart, a graph, or both.

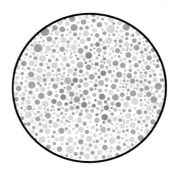 Writing Support

Descriptive Writing Have students complete their chart or graph. Then have students write a sentence that summarizes each set of class data. **OL**

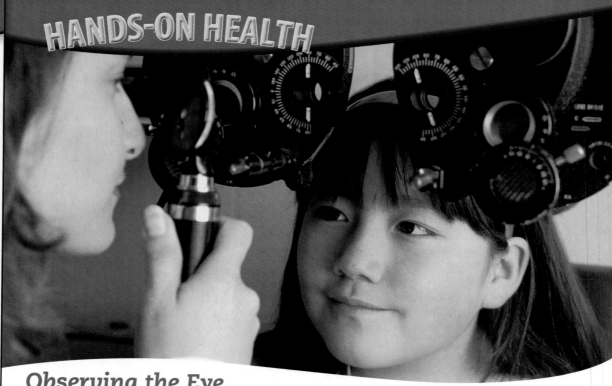

HANDS-ON HEALTH

Observing the Eye

Your eyes can adjust very quickly to different levels of light. The muscles inside the eye change so that more or less light comes in. Most people can also distinguish colors with their eyes. Some, however, are born without the ability to see certain colors. Try this activity to observe how your eyes react to light and color.

What You Will Need

■ Mirror
■ Pencil or pen
■ Paper

What You Will Do

1 Turn off the lights. Sit in the dark for two to three minutes.

2 Turn the lights back on, and quickly look at your eyes in the mirror. Watch what happens in the center of your eyes. Record what you saw.

3 Once your eyes have adjusted to the light, do the color vision test. Look at the circle shown on this page. Can you see a number in the circle? If not, you may have trouble distinguishing between the colors red and green.

Wrapping It Up

As a class, make a chart or graph that compares the results for all students. What do your findings show?

HANDS-ON HEALTH Assessment

Discussion After the class has had time to complete the activity, ask students to:
● Name a situation in which your eyes need to adjust quickly to a change from light to dark. Sample answer: *walking into a dark house from outdoors*

● Review Figure 6.5. What part of the eye controls the amount of light that comes in? *the pupil*

Reading Review

FOLDABLES Study Organizer

Foldables™ and Other Study Aids Take out the Foldable™ that you created for Lesson 1 and any graphic organizers that you created for Lessons 1–5. Find a partner and quiz each other using these study aids.

Lesson 1) Your Teeth, Skin, and Hair

Key Ideas

- Keep your teeth healthy by brushing and flossing, eating healthy, and seeing your dentist.
- Skin care includes daily cleansing and protecting the skin from the sun's UV rays.
- Hair care includes brushing and regular shampooing.
- Nail care includes trimming and pushing back the cuticles.

Vocabulary

- hygiene (p. 144)
- plaque (p. 145)
- fluoride (p. 146)
- epidermis (p. 147)
- dermis (p. 147)
- sunscreen (p. 148)
- acne (p. 148)
- dandruff (p. 149)
- cuticle (p. 150)

Lesson 2) Protecting Your Eyes and Ears

Key Ideas

- To care for your eyes, get regular eye checkups. Read and watch TV in a well-lighted room.
- Protect your ears by limiting their exposure to loud sounds.

Vocabulary

- farsightedness (p. 152)
- nearsightedness (p. 152)
- astigmatism (p. 152)

Lesson 3) Choosing Health Products

Key Ideas

- Factors that influence you as a consumer include personal likes and dislikes, cost, and the media.
- Consumer skills can help you become a smart shopper.

Vocabulary

- consumer (p. 157)
- guarantee (p. 157)
- unit price (p. 157)
- coupons (p. 158)
- generic (p. 158)
- fraud (p. 158)

Lesson 4) Using Medicines Responsibly

Key Ideas

- Information on medicine labels includes instructions on how to use the medicine.
- Drug misuse involves using medicines in ways other than those intended.

Vocabulary

- medicines (p. 159)
- prescription medicines (p. 159)
- over-the-counter (OTC) medicines (p. 159)
- vaccines (p. 160)
- antibiotics (p. 160)
- side effect (p. 160)
- tolerance (p. 160)
- drug misuse (p. 162)

Lesson 5) Health Care in Your Community

Key Ideas

- Health care providers include those who provide primary care and specialists.
- Health insurance helps many people pay for health care costs.

Vocabulary

- health care (p. 163)
- specialist (p. 164)
- voluntary health agencies (p. 165)
- health insurance (p. 166)
- managed care (p. 167)

Assessment Resources

- Chapter 6 Summary and Activity
- Audio Summaries
- Reading Tutor
- Performance Assessment
- Chapter 6 Test
- *ExamView*
- Vocabulary PuzzleMaker
- Online Learning Center

Reading Review

Study Aids

- **Using the Dinah Zike Foldable™ Study Organizer** Have students use the Foldable™ to review the content of Lesson 1. Have students name two ways that hair, skin, and teeth are similar.

FOLDABLES Study Organizer

Key Ideas

- **Use the Quick Writes** Have students review and discuss their completed Quick Write activities with a partner.

Vocabulary Review

- **Vocabulary** Stories Have students write a short story that correctly incorporates as many of the chapter vocabulary terms as possible. Have volunteers share their stories with the class.

Teaching Tips

Outlining Explain that outlining is an effective method for organizing information and focusing on the main ideas of the text. Model for students the structure of an outline, using the lesson title as the main head. List each major head from the lesson with space underneath. Explain to students that the space under each head should be used to record the main idea and supporting details found in that section of the text. Before students take a test, have them review their outlines to refresh their memories of the main ideas of the lesson.

Assessment

Reviewing Vocabulary and Main Ideas

1. Fluoride
2. acne
3. dermis
4. Nearsightedness
5. astigmatism
6. Farsightedness
7. True
8. False, guarantee
9. True
10. False, Antibiotics
11. False, tolerance
12. True
13. True
14. True
15. False, Medicaid

Thinking Critically

16. Answers, which will vary, might include endangering your health by not being able to hear car horns as you cross a street.
17. No, consumer skills can also enable the shopper to buy the health product best suited to his or her needs or problems.

Assessment

After You Read

IM Express

Now that you have read the chapter, review your answer to the I.M. Express on the chapter opener. Have your ideas changed? What would your answer be now?

Reviewing Vocabulary and Main Ideas

On a sheet of paper, write the numbers 1–6. After each number, write the term from the list that best completes each sentence.

- acne
- astigmatism
- dermis
- farsightedness
- fluoride
- nearsightedness
- health care
- specialist

Lesson 1 Your Teeth, Skin, and Hair

1. _____ is a substance that fights tooth decay.
2. A condition caused by overly active oil glands is called _____.
3. The thicker inner layer of the skin is known as the _____.

Lesson 2 Protecting Your Eyes and Ears

4. _____ is a condition in which near objects appear clear while those faraway look blurry.
5. A misshaped cornea or lens that causes objects to look wavy or blurred is known as _____.
6. _____ is a condition in which faraway objects appear clear while near objects look blurry.

*On a sheet of paper, write the numbers 7–15. Write **True** or **False** for each statement. If the statement is false, change the underlined word to make it true.*

Lesson 3 Choosing Health Products

7. <u>Comparison shopping</u> involves comparing different brands of a product.
8. A <u>unit price</u> is your promise of a refund of your money if the product doesn't work as claimed.
9. The store brand of an item is also known as a <u>generic</u> brand.

Lesson 4 Using Medicines Responsibly

10. <u>Vaccines</u> are medicines that kill or stop the growth of bacteria and other specific germs.
11. When you develop a <u>side effect</u> to a medicine, your body needs greater amounts.
12. Taking more of a medicine than the doctor instructs is an example of <u>drug misuse</u>.

Lesson 5 Health Care in Your Community

13. When a problem is beyond your doctor's training, he or she might suggest that you see a <u>specialist</u>.
14. <u>Voluntary health agencies</u> are organizations that work to help prevent and cure certain diseases.
15. <u>Managed care</u> is a program to help people with limited income get health care.

Health Online Visit health.glencoe.com and take the Online Quiz for Chapter 6.

Health Online

Have students visit **health.glencoe.com** to take the Chapter 6 Quiz.

IM Express Wrap-Up

Skin Care Have students reread the Chapter Opener IM Express. Some students may find that their answers have changed after reading the chapter. Ask students to reconsider their answers in light of the information they have learned while reading the chapter. Have volunteers share with the class how their answers have changed.

Thinking Critically

Using complete sentences, answer the following questions on a sheet of paper.

16. **Predict** If you don't treat a hearing problem how might it affect other areas of your health?

17. **Evaluate** Are consumer skills only good for saving money? Explain.

Write About It

18. **Advocacy** Imagine that you are writing an article about a volunteer health agency. Explain the kinds of things the volunteer health agency does. Tell how a teen can help.

 Career Corner

Dental Hygienist Would you like to help improve people's smiles? With just one to two years of training at a college or vocational/technical school, you can become a dental hygienist. These professionals assist dentists. They help clean teeth and gums, insert fillings, and take X-rays. Hygienists work with a variety of special tools. They also have a lot of contact with people. Learn more about this and other health careers by clicking on *Career Corner* at **health.glencoe.com**.

19. **Analyzing Influences** Write a short story about a teen who is trying to decide which health product to buy. Identify the factors that might influence the teen's decision.

Write About It

18. **Expository Writing** Explain to students that expository writing is writing that shares knowledge to help others understand. Student articles should inform others how to advocate for volunteer health agencies, which may include calling a local chapter, and taking part in a walk or run.

19. **Narrative Writing** Tell students that narrative writing tells a clear story arranged in a logical order. Remind them to develop interesting characters, describe the setting, and include a plot. Student stories will vary, but should identify factors that influence the teen's decision in choosing a health product.

Standardized Test Practice

1. C
2. B

 Career Corner

Dental Hygienist Have students visit the Career Corner at **health.glencoe .com** to gather more information about a career as a dental hygienist. Explain that a dental hygienist should have excellent communication skills, enjoy working with people, and like to help others. Have interested students interview a dental hygienist to learn more about this profession.

Standardized Test Practice

Math

Use the graph to answer the questions.

TEST-TAKING TIP

Make sure you understand the parts of a graph. Read the title. Look at the label next to the vertical (*y*) axis. Look at the label beneath the horizontal (*x*) axis.

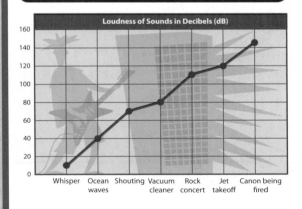

Loudness of Sounds in Decibels (dB)

Whisper, Ocean waves, Shouting, Vacuum cleaner, Rock concert, Jet takeoff, Canon being fired

1. If any noise above 85 dB is harmful, then all of the following sounds are harmful *except*
   A. a jet takeoff.
   B. a canon being fired.
   C. a vacuum cleaner running.
   D. a rock concert.

2. Based on the line graph, which inference can be made?
   A. Two people shouting are likely to be louder than a vacuum cleaner.
   B. Sounds under a whisper are probably too quiet to hear.
   C. Going to the beach can harm your hearing.
   D. Airport ground crews have hearing problems.

Chapter 6 Assessment **173**

Test-Taking Tips

Math Skills Remind students that some health test questions require the use of math skills. Tell students that they should write out calculations to help prevent errors. Remind students that most numerical answers also require a correct unit, and that they should be aware of multiple choice distractors with the correct number but the wrong unit.

CHAPTER 7 pp. 174–199	Standards		Skills and Activities
	National	**State/Local**	**HEALTH INVENTORY,** *p. 175*
	National Health Education Standards 7.1, 7.4, 7.5		TIME HEALTH NEWS The Mystery of Sleep, *p. 196* **BUILDING HEALTH SKILLS** *Practicing Healthful Behaviors* Maintaining Healthy Body Systems, *pp. 194–195*
Lesson 1 From Cells to Body Systems pp. 176–180	National Health Education Standards 1.1, 1.3, 1.6, 1.8, 5.3, 7.1, 7.5		**Connect To... LANGUAGE ARTS** Scientific Word Parts, *p. 178*
Lesson 2 Bones and Muscles pp. 181–184	National Health Education Standards 1.1, 1.3, 1.6, 7.5		**HEALTH SKILLS ACTIVITY** *Practicing Healthful Behaviors* Building Strong Bones, *p. 183*
Lesson 3 Digestion and Excretion pp. 185–187	National Health Education Standards 1.3, 8.2		
Lesson 4 Heart, Blood, Lungs, and Nerves pp. 188–193	National Health Education Standards 1.3, 8.2		**DEVELOPING GOOD CHARACTER** Citizenship, *p. 192*

PACING THE CHAPTER		
Lesson 1 45 min	**Lesson 4** 90 min	**Chapter Review** 45 min
Lesson 2 45 min	**Hands-on Health** 30 min	
Lesson 3 45 min	**Building Health Skills** 45 min	

BLOCK SCHEDULING

For block scheduling, assign Building Health Skills feature *Maintaining Healthy Body Systems*, pages 194–195, and Guided Reading and Writing. 📁

Planning Guide

Reproducible Resources	Assessment	Media and Technology
Chapter _FAST FILE_ Resources Chapter Summaries and Activities **REVIEW** Building Health Skills Activity **TEACH** Performance Assessment Activity **EXTEND** Universal Access Activities **TEACH** Parent Letter and Activities **Student Activities Workbook** **TEACH** **Reading Tutor** **TEACH**	Building Health Skills Activity, *pp. 194–195* Chapter 2 Assessment, *pp. 198–199* **Chapter _FAST FILE_ Resources** Performance Assessment Activity, *p. 4* Chapter 7 Test, *p. 7* 🔘 *ExamView® Test Generator*	**Teacher Works**™ includes: • Interactive Teacher Edition • Lesson Planner with Calendar • Access to all blackline masters • Correlations to standards 🔘 StudentWorks™ Plus 🗪 Online Student Edition Dinah Zike's Teaching Health with Foldables™
Chapter _FAST FILE_ Resources Concept Mapping Activity 7-1 **REVIEW** Decision-Making Activity 7-1 **EXTEND** Enrichment Activity 7-1 **EXTEND** Guided Reading and Writing 7-1 **TEACH** Lesson Plan 7-1 Reteaching Activity 7-1 **REVIEW**	Lesson 1 Review, *p. 180* 🗪 Vocabulary PuzzleMaker 🔘 *ExamView® Test Generator*	🗪 Vocabulary PuzzleMaker 🔘 *ExamView® Test Generator* 🔘 StudentWorks™ Plus 🗪 Transparency 7-1 🗪 **Health Online**
Chapter _FAST FILE_ Resources Concept Mapping Activity 7-2 **REVIEW** Cross-Curriculum Activity 7-2 **EXTEND** Enrichment Activity 7-2 **EXTEND** Guided Reading and Writing 7-2 **TEACH** Lesson Plan 7-2 Reteaching Activity 7-2 **REVIEW**	Lesson 2 Review, *p. 184* 🗪 Vocabulary PuzzleMaker 🔘 *ExamView® Test Generator*	🗪 Vocabulary PuzzleMaker 🔘 *ExamView® Test Generator* 🔘 StudentWorks™ Plus 🗪 Transparency 7-2 🗪 **Health Online**
Chapter _FAST FILE_ Resources Concept Mapping Activity 7-3 **REVIEW** Health Lab 7-3 **EXTEND** Enrichment Activity 7-3 **EXTEND** Guided Reading and Writing 7-3 **TEACH** Lesson Plan 7-3 Reteaching Activity 7-3 **REVIEW**	Lesson 3 Review, *p. 187* 🗪 Vocabulary PuzzleMaker 🔘 *ExamView® Test Generator*	🗪 Vocabulary PuzzleMaker 🔘 *ExamView® Test Generator* 🔘 StudentWorks™ Plus 🗪 Transparency 7-3 🗪 **Health Online**
Chapter _FAST FILE_ Resources Concept Mapping Activity 7-4 **REVIEW** Cross-Curriculum Activity 7-4 **EXTEND** Guided Reading and Writing 7-4 **TEACH** Lesson Plan 7-4 Reteaching Activity 7-4 **REVIEW**	Lesson 4 Review, *p. 193* 🗪 Vocabulary PuzzleMaker 🔘 *ExamView® Test Generator*	🗪 Vocabulary PuzzleMaker 🔘 *ExamView® Test Generator* 🔘 StudentWorks™ Plus 🗪 Transparency 7-4 🗪 **Health Online**

Chapter and Lesson Resources

The *Teen Health* resources are designed for differentiated learning abilities. You may want to use the coded items in this way:

REVIEW—activities to review or reinforce content
TEACH—activities to teach basic concepts
EXTEND—activities to extend or enrich lesson content

 OUT OF TIME?

Use Health Skills Activity *Building Strong Bones*, page 183, or *TIME health news*, page 196.

Physical Activity Benefits All Body Systems

Relate the content of Chapter 5, "Physical Activity," to the information in this chapter about body systems. Physical activity has a positive impact on every body system. However, the Centers for Disease Control and Prevention (CDC), reports that 33.4 percent of high school students get insufficient amounts of physical activity.

As the body systems are introduced in this chapter, take time to incorporate information about the benefits of regular physical activity.

- **Skeletal System** According to the National Institutes of Health, regular weight-bearing exercise can increase and help maintain bone density, which decreases the risk of fractures and osteoporosis.

- **Muscular System** Most students will be familiar with the idea that physical activity increases muscle mass. Remind students that physical activity can also increase flexibility.

- **Digestive and Excretory System** Food is moved more efficiently through the digestive system when a person takes part in physical activity. Exercise also reduces stress, which has negative effects on the digestive system.

- **Cardiovascular System** Exercise increases the strength of the heart and reduces cholesterol levels in the blood. Reduced cholesterol levels, in turn, reduce the risk of developing heart disease.

- **Nervous System** In studies, physically fit students are found to perform better at cognitive tasks and have higher levels of academic achievement.

Have students review the personal fitness plan they developed in the Building Health Skills Activity in Chapter 5. Then have students explain how the plan could positively affect each of their body systems. Have students set a goal to continue using their personal fitness plan to contribute to the good health of their body systems.

Maintaining Bone Health

According to the National Institutes of Health, people between the ages of 9 and 18 need 1,300 milligrams of calcium each day. This amount of calcium allows for growth and development of bones, as well as storage of calcium that is used later in life.

As students study the skeletal system, point out that calcium is added to bones until the late teen years. After that time, calcium is lost from bones. It can be helpful to use the analogy of bones as a bank, in which enough calcium must be deposited by age 18 to last for the rest of their lives. Taking in too little calcium in the teen years can lead to the development of osteoporosis, a debilitating condition characterized by fragile bones and frequent fractures.

Studies have shown that less than 20 percent of teen girls and less than 50 percent of teen boys get enough calcium each day. During the study of the skeletal system, be sure to stress the importance of calcium. Use the following activities to encourage students to apply information about calcium to their everyday food choices:

- Ask students to make a personal health goal to include calcium-rich foods in their diet. Have students track their progress toward their goal as they study Chapter 7.

- Have students develop consumer skills by reading nutrition labels to determine the calcium content of foods.

- Have students design a menu for one week that uses calcium-rich foods as part of a healthy eating plan.

- Have students identify calcium-rich food choices available in the school cafeteria.

Support for Teaching Reading

 Reading Support

Health Online

Academic Integration For additional academic integration strategies, visit the Teacher Center at **health.glencoe.com**.

Reading Preview

Activating Background Vocabulary In a class discussion, solicit all meanings of the terms 'tissues' and 'organs.' Point out that meanings differ when in reference to our bodies versus non-health topics. Direct students to read the text to find examples of these words in context within the lesson. Have students record the definitions in a vocabulary notebook.

FOLDABLES Study Organizer *Dinah Zike's Reading and Study Skills for Teen Health* provides interactive graphic organizers that help students comprehend and retain health concepts as they read. Use the Foldable™ on page 175 or find more Foldables™ activities for the chapter on **Your Body Systems** in the separate booklet, available in the TCR.

Lesson 1　From Cells to Body Systems

Previewing Show students how to read the title and skim through the entire lesson, reading headings and captions. Demonstrate how to look for key words, such as *cells* or *body systems*, to find specific information quickly. Based on their preview, have students write a sentence stating one thing they would like to learn while reading this lesson.

Lesson 2　Bones and Muscles

Classifying Ask students to name all the words they can think of that relate to bones and muscles. List these words on the board. Identify two categories: the skeletal system and the muscular system. In a class discussion, analyze the differences between the categories. As they read, have students determine which words belong in each category.

Lesson 3　Digestion and Excretion

Active Silent Reading Stop students during reading and have them close their books. Prompt students to recall what they have read about the digestive and excretory systems. Record responses on the board. Discuss the main ideas and key terms. Encourage student pairs to refer back to the text to clarify questions or correct misinformation.

Lesson 4　Heart, Blood, Lungs, and Nerves

Choral Reading Model reading aloud, using proper tempo, phrasing, and enunciation. Discuss how volume, stress, pacing, and pronunciation can affect comprehension while reading. Direct the entire class to read the first sentence of **The Circulatory System** paragraph. Correct any missteps, then have the class read the entire paragraph together.

Post Reading

Research Presentations Direct students to various library and Internet resources to locate and organize information for a research presentation on one of the body systems: skeletal, muscular, digestive, excretory, circulatory, and so on. Encourage students to produce final documents that have been edited for appropriate mechanics, usage, and punctuation.

Key for Using the Teacher Wraparound Edition

Use this key to help you identify the different types of prompts found in the Teacher Wraparound Edition.

R　**Reading Strategies** activities help you teach reading skills and vocabulary.

C　**Critical Thinking** strategies help students apply and extend what they have learned.

U　**Universal Access** activities provide differentiated instruction for students learning to speak English, along with suggestions for teaching various types of learners.

HS　**Health Skills Practice** activities reinforce Health Skills concepts and help students apply these skills in their everyday lives.

W　**Writing Support** activities provide writing opportunities to help students comprehend the text.

AL　**Active Learning** strategies provide a variety of activities for presenting lesson content, including Quick Demos and engaging classroom projects that get students actively involved.

Key to Ability Levels

Teaching Strategies and activities have been coded for ability level and appropriateness

AL　Activities for students working above grade level

OL　Activities for students working on grade level

BL　Activities for students working below grade level

EL　Activities for English Learners

Symbols

　Transparencies

　CD-ROM

　health.glencoe.com

　Print Resources

Your Body Systems

Chapter at a Glance

Lesson 1 identifies the body's building blocks, names the major body systems and identifies their functions, and lists ways to care for body systems.

Lesson 2 explains the parts and jobs of the skeletal system and identifies ways to protect bones and muscles.

Lesson 3 explains the parts and jobs of the digestive system, explains the parts and jobs of the excretory system, and identifies ways to maintain the health of the digestive and excretory systems.

Lesson 4 explains how blood moves through the body, describes how the nervous system controls body functions, and examines factors in the environment that influence respiratory health.

R Reading Strategy

Interpreting the Photo
Tell students this is a photo of teens viewing an exhibit at a science museum: Ask whether anyone in class has been to a similar museum, and let volunteers share their experience. Ask: What body systems are involved when you ride a bike? Sample answers: *skeletal, muscular, circulatory, respiratory* **OL**

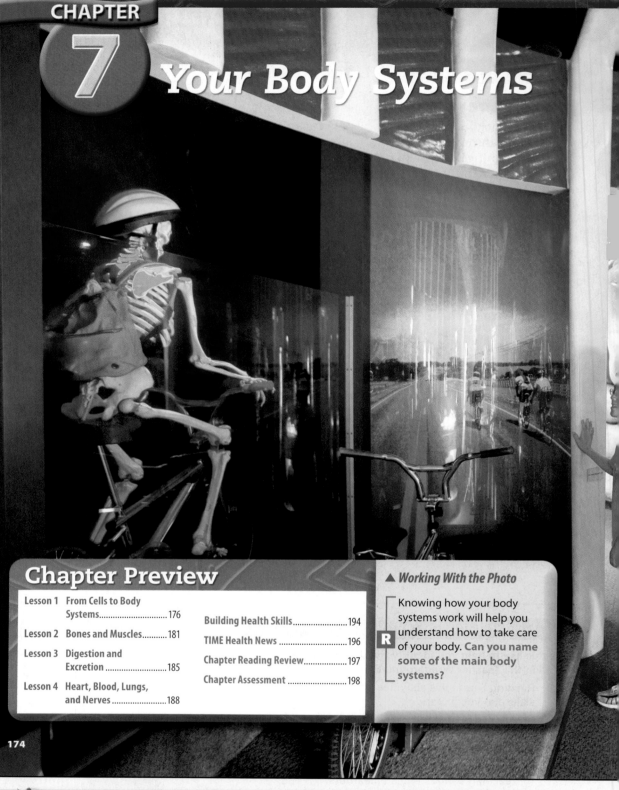

Chapter Preview

Lesson 1 From Cells to Body
         Systems..............................176

Lesson 2 Bones and Muscles...........181

Lesson 3 Digestion and
         Excretion 185

Lesson 4 Heart, Blood, Lungs,
         and Nerves.......................188

Building Health Skills........................194

TIME Health News 196

Chapter Reading Review..................197

Chapter Assessment 198

174

▲ *Working With the Photo*

R Knowing how your body systems work will help you understand how to take care of your body. **Can you name some of the main body systems?**

Universal Access

Differentiated Learning Glencoe provides teacher support and student materials for all learners in the health classroom.

● Spanish Glosario and chapter summaries for the English Language Learners.
● *Reading Tutor* and related worksheets support reluctant readers.

● Universal Access strategies throughout the Teacher Wraparound Edition and Fast Files help you present materials for gifted students, at-risk students, physically impaired students and those with behavior disorders or learning disabilities.

174

Start-Up Activities

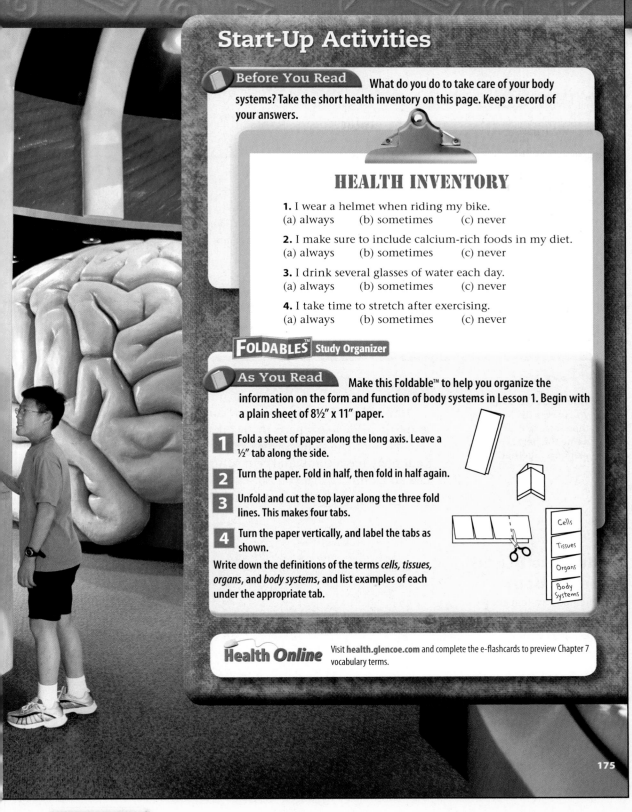

Before You Read What do you do to take care of your body systems? Take the short health inventory on this page. Keep a record of your answers.

HEALTH INVENTORY

1. I wear a helmet when riding my bike.
(a) always (b) sometimes (c) never

2. I make sure to include calcium-rich foods in my diet.
(a) always (b) sometimes (c) never

3. I drink several glasses of water each day.
(a) always (b) sometimes (c) never

4. I take time to stretch after exercising.
(a) always (b) sometimes (c) never

FOLDABLES Study Organizer

As You Read Make this Foldable™ to help you organize the information on the form and function of body systems in Lesson 1. Begin with a plain sheet of 8½" x 11" paper.

1 Fold a sheet of paper along the long axis. Leave a ½" tab along the side.

2 Turn the paper. Fold in half, then fold in half again.

3 Unfold and cut the top layer along the three fold lines. This makes four tabs.

4 Turn the paper vertically, and label the tabs as shown.

Write down the definitions of the terms *cells, tissues, organs,* and *body systems,* and list examples of each under the appropriate tab.

Cells

Tissues

Organs

Body Systems

Health Online Visit **health.glencoe.com** and complete the e-flashcards to preview Chapter 7 vocabulary terms.

175

FOCUS

Activating Prior Knowledge

What I Know Ask students to name body systems. Record their responses on the board. Then ask students to name a function of each listed body system.

Guide to Reading

BUILDING VOCABULARY
- Explain that a *system* is a group of parts that work together to perform a function. Ask students how this applies to the term *body systems*.
- Use Vocabulary PuzzleMaker to reinforce vocabulary terms.

READING STRATEGY

 Have students use their Foldables™ as they read Lesson 1.

- **Organizing Information** After completing their diagrams, ask students to list body systems that work together, such as the skeletal and muscular systems to move the body.

Quick Write

Have students develop lists of parts that work together as they form and release a fist. Ask volunteers to share one of the parts from their lists.

From Cells to Body Systems

Guide to Reading

● **Building Vocabulary**
Write each term below in your notebook. As you come across the term in your reading, write its definition.

- cells (p. 177)
- tissues (p. 177)
- organs (p. 177)
- body systems (p. 177)

● **Focusing on the Main Ideas**
In this lesson, you will be able to

- **identify** the body's building blocks.
- **name** the major body systems and identify their functions.
- **list** ways to care for your body systems.

● **Reading Strategy**
Organizing Information Make a bull's-eye diagram like the one to the right. Show how cells and other "building blocks" of the body relate.

 Use the Foldable™ on p. 175 as you read this lesson.

Quick Write

Watch your hand as you form a fist and then release it. Try to name the parts you see working together.

Parts of the Body

Have you ever looked inside a computer? If you have, you know there are many parts that work together. Each part does a separate job. The same is true of your body. Like the computer, your body has a command center. It gives instructions to muscles and joints so that you can raise your arms. It is instructing your eyes to read this page right now!

▶ **FIGURE 7.1**

R **BUILDING BLOCKS OF THE BODY**
The body system shown here is the nervous system. What is the most basic building block of the nervous system?

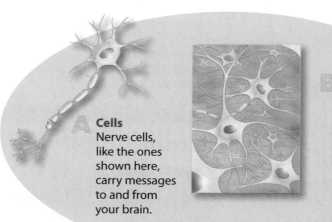

A **Cells**
Nerve cells, like the ones shown here, carry messages to and from your brain.

B **Tissues**
This tissue is made up of nerve cells.

Lesson 1 Resources

📁 **Chapter *Fast File* Resources**
Guided Reading and Writing 7-1
Concept Mapping Activity 7-1
Decision-Making Activity 7-1
Reteaching Activity 7-1
Enrichment Activity 7-1
Lesson Quiz 7-1

Technology
 Transparency 7-1
Audio Summaries
ExamView
Vocabulary PuzzleMaker
StudentWorks™ Plus

From Cells to Systems

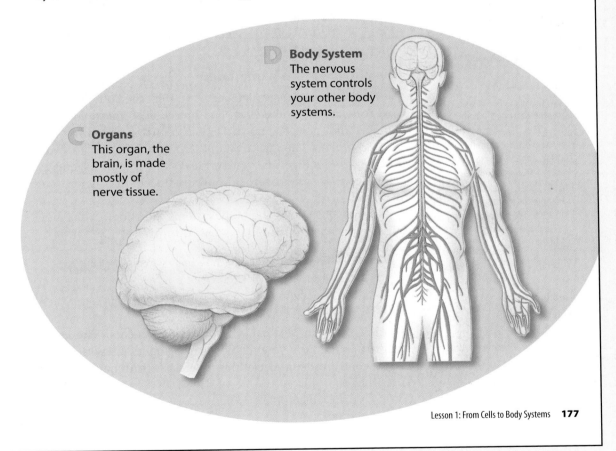

Your body is made up of many different kinds of cells, which vary in size and shape. **Cells** are *the basic building blocks of life.* Each cell does a specialized job. Nerve cells, for example, carry messages to and from your brain. Skin cells, on the other hand, are flat and rectangular. This allows them to spread out and cover the surface of your body.

Groups of similar cells that do the same kind of work are called **tissues.** For example, nerve cells such as those shown in **Figure 7.1** come together to form nerve tissue. Tissues come together to form organs. **Organs** are *structures made up of different types of tissues that all work together.* For example, your heart is an organ made up of muscle tissue, nerve tissue, and blood tissue. Organs perform specific jobs. Your brain is an organ that allows you to think and feel. Your stomach is an organ that stores and digests the food you eat. The next level up from organs is body systems. **Body systems** are *groups of organs that perform a body function.* For example, the digestive system breaks down food for energy.

D Body System
The nervous system controls your other body systems.

C Organs
This organ, the brain, is made mostly of nerve tissue.

Lesson 1: From Cells to Body Systems **177**

TEACH

R **Reading Strategy**

Analyzing a Graphic Have students examine Figure 7.1. Point out that all body systems are organized from cells, tissues, and organs. Explain that the body system shown in the infographic is just one example. Ask for four volunteers to each read one of the four parts of the nervous system, shown as A, B, C, and D. **OL**

W **Writing Support**

Expository Writing Have students write an expository paragraph that explains why care of all body systems is important to good health. Remind students that the purpose of an expository paragraph is to inform or teach others. Have students proofread their work and make any needed corrections before they turn it in. **OL**

Academic Vocabulary

Vary On this page, the text states that cells *vary* in size and shape. Have students name synonyms for the word *vary* (differ, change). Then randomly call on students to use the word *vary* in a sentence.

HEALTH LITERACY

Advocating for Healthy Lifestyles As students read about each body system, remind them of strategies for maintaining the health of all systems, for example, using a bicycle helmet and other safety equipment, avoiding tobacco, alcohol, and drug use, and making healthful food choices. Have each student research a strategy for protecting the health of body systems. Then have each student make a pamphlet that can be used to help other students learn about protecting their health. **OL**

Caption Answer

Figure Caption, p. 176
Cells are the basic building block.

R Reading Strategy

Analyzing a Chart After students have examined Figure 7.2, ask them to name body functions that require the actions of two or more body systems. Record their responses on the board. Have students add to the list as they read the chapter. **OL**

AL Active Learning

Small-Group Learning Divide the class into small groups. Assign each group one of the body systems shown in the chart. Challenge each group to develop an infomercial for its assigned body system that highlights the functions of that system. Have each group present its infomercial to the class. **OL**

Connect To... Science

Scientific Word Parts
Explain that the word part *-itis* means "inflammation of." Students should infer that the lungs are affected in bronchitis. Explain that the meaning of *dermatitis* is "inflammation of the skin." Ask: What word part could you add to the chart after knowing the meaning of this term? *derma, meaning skin*

Caption Answer

Figure Caption *Sample answer:* The skeletal and muscular systems work together.

▼ FIGURE 7.2

MAIN BODY SYSTEMS AND THEIR FUNCTIONS

The chart shows the main body systems. **Which of these work together?**

Body System	Jobs
Circulatory system	Brings food and oxygen to cells and takes away cell waste
Digestive system	Breaks down food for energy
Endocrine system	Produces hormones that regulate body functions
Excretory system	Gets rid of body wastes
Muscular system	Allows movement of body parts
Nervous system	Controls all body systems; sends and receives messages; and helps you see, hear, taste, smell, and feel
Reproductive system	Involved in producing *offspring*, or children
Respiratory system	Carries oxygen to blood and removes carbon dioxide
Skeletal system	Provides a hard cage to protect body organs, gives the body structure, and works with the muscular system to allow movement

R

AL

Connect To... Language Arts

Scientific Word Parts

Many diseases are named after the parts of the body they affect. Take, for example, the word *osteoporosis*. It is a disease that weakens the bones. The word's root, *"osteo"* means "bone." The ending, *"osis"* means "disease of." Other word parts named after the body are shown.

Optic	Eye
Neur(o)	Nerves or nervous system
Cardi(o)	Heart
Bronch(o)	Lungs

What body system do you think is affected by bronchitis?

The names and functions of the major body systems appear in **Figure 7.2.** This chapter will cover all of these systems except for the endocrine and reproductive systems. Those two systems will be discussed in Chapter 8.

AL

The Body Systems Work Together

The body systems work together to keep the body functioning. For example, the skeletal and muscular systems pair up to support and move the body. They also form a protective shell around organs. The digestive and excretory systems also work as a team. The digestive system breaks down food for energy. The excretory system gets rid of unused food from your body as waste.

Figure 7.3 shows the body systems in action. Notice how all systems relate during the act of running.

 **Reading Check** **List** Name three body systems, and tell what each does.

Care of the Body Systems

How can you take care of your body systems? The key is healthy living. You've already learned about habits that promote good health and wellness. Here is a summary of some useful ideas.

TECHNOLOGY AND HEALTH

Dialysis Helps Kidney Function Kidneys are organs that filter waste and extra liquid from the blood. Injury and illness, particularly diabetes, can damage a person's kidneys. Dialysis can be used to maintain the health of a person with damaged kidneys. Dialysis is a technology in which the blood is cleaned of salts, wastes, and extra water. Have students research to find information about other technologies that can temporarily or permanently perform the functions of a body organ. **OL**

► FIGURE 7.3

HOW THE BODY SYSTEMS RELATE

R The body systems depend on each other. How many systems are active when you run?

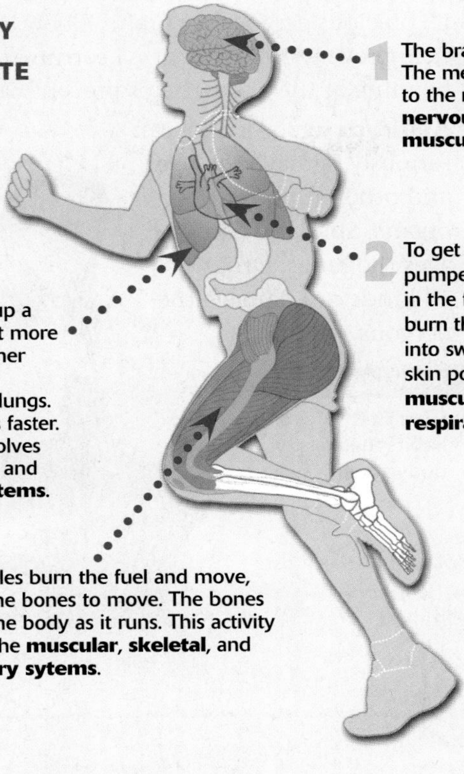

1 The brain sends out a message: Run! The message is carried through nerves to the muscles. This step involves the **nervous system** and the **muscular system**.

2 To get energy, muscles need blood that is pumped by the heart. Blood contains fuel in the form of sugar as well as oxygen to burn that fuel. As blood flows, wastes pass into sweat glands that release them through skin pores. These processes involve the **muscular, circulatory, digestive, respiratory,** and **excretory systems**.

4 Running burns up a lot of fuel. To get more oxygen, the runner gasps for breath provided by his lungs. His heart pumps faster. This process involves the **respiratory** and **circulatory systems**.

U

3 The muscles burn the fuel and move, causing the bones to move. The bones support the body as it runs. This activity involves the **muscular, skeletal,** and **circulatory sytems**.

- **Eat well.** Following a balanced eating plan is important to the care of most body systems. It will keep your heart and bloodstream healthy. Foods rich in calcium build strong bones. Drinking plenty of water aids your digestive and excretory systems.

- **Get plenty of physical activity.** Teens, as you learned, are advised to get an hour of physical activity most days. Physical activity makes muscles, bones, and joints stronger. Proper warm-ups and cool-downs are also important to muscle and bone health. Aerobic activity helps your heart and lungs work more efficiently.

- **Maintain a healthy weight.** This will put less stress on your bones and organs. It will also make it easier for your heart to pump blood through your body.

R **Reading Strategy**

Analyzing a Graphic After students have examined Figure 7.3, ask: Why is it important to practice healthy habits that maintain the health of all body systems? *The body systems are all interrelated, and the function of several systems is required for most activities.* Seven systems are active during running.

U **Universal Access**

Reluctant Readers and Writers Collect action photos of popular athletes from magazines or newspapers. Allow each student to choose one of the photos. Then have each student explain the body systems involved in the athlete's performance in a short oral report. **BL**

Reading Check

Answer, p. 178 The digestive system breaks down food for energy; the excretory system gets rid of wastes; and the muscular system allows movement of body parts.

What Teens Want to Know

What causes paralysis? In some cases, paralysis is the result of injury or disease that affects the nervous system. In the case of spinal cord injury, the nervous system loses the ability to send messages to the muscles. In the case of muscular disorders, such as muscular dystrophy, the muscular system loses the ability to respond to messages from the nervous system. Have students research diseases that affect the muscular system or nervous system. Have each student give a short oral report to the class. **OL**

Reading Check

Answer Eating well and getting plenty of physical activity promote the health of body systems.

ASSESS

Assessment Resources

Lesson Review Quiz
 ExamView
Fast Files Activities
Online Quizzes and Activities

Reteaching

- Assign Concept Map 7-1 or Reteaching Activity 7-1 in the Fast Files.
- Have each student name a major body system and write a sentence describing its function.

Enrichment

- Assign Enrichment Activity 7-1 in the Fast Files.
- Have students write a paragraph that describes how a cell's structure is related to its function.

CLOSE

Go around the room and call on students to describe cells, tissues, organs, and organ systems found in the human body.

 **Health Online**

Visit **health.glencoe.com** and complete the Interactive Study Guide for Lesson 1.

- **Play it safe.** Make sure to wear the right gear when you are physically active. A helmet can protect your skull and its precious cargo, your brain. Elbow and knee pads will help prevent broken bones. Learning to lift properly, by bending at the knees, helps prevent back injuries.

- **Avoid drugs.** Alcohol can seriously damage the liver and other important organs. Smoking damages the lungs. Drugs of all kinds can damage the nervous system.

 Reading Check

Give Examples Name two habits that keep your body systems healthy.

▶ Your brain is one of your body's most important organs. **How are these teens protecting their brains?**

Lesson 1 Review

 After You Read

Review this lesson for new terms, major headings, and Reading Checks.

What I Learned

1. **Vocabulary** Define *tissues*.

2. **Give Examples** What is the function of the circulatory system?

3. **Recall** Name some behaviors that keep the skeletal system healthy.

Thinking Critically

4. **Synthesize** Give an example of a risk a teen might take. Show how this behavior affects one or more body systems.

5. **Analyze** How might an injury to your nervous system affect your muscular system?

Applying Health Skills

6. **Accessing Information** Different types of safety helmets are used for different physical activities. Using reliable print or online resources, research different types of approved helmets. What kind of helmet would be best to wear while riding a bike? How about when you play football?

Health Online For more review questions for Lesson 1, go to **health.glencoe.com**.

Lesson 1 Review Answers

1. Tissues are groups of similar cells that do the same kind of work.
2. The circulatory system brings food and oxygen to cells and takes away cell wastes.
3. *Sample answers:* eating foods rich in calcium, getting exercise, and wearing protective gear

4. *Sample answer:* A teen might play sports without safety gear, leading to broken bones.
5. The nervous system sends messages to the brain, telling the muscles to move. Damage to the nervous system can make it difficult or impossible to move certain muscles.

6. Provide resources for students to use for research. Bicycle helmets should be approved by the Consumer Product Safety Commission.

Lesson 2

Bones and Muscles

Guide to Reading

● **Building Vocabulary**
Write each term below in your notebook. As you come across each term in your reading, write its definition.
■ skeletal system (p. 181)
■ joints (p. 182)
■ muscular system (p. 183)

● **Focusing on the Main Ideas**
In this lesson, you will be able to
■ **explain** the parts and functions of the skeletal system.
■ **explain** the parts and functions of the muscular system.
■ **determine** ways to protect the bones and muscles.

● **Reading Strategy**
Compare As you read, look for similarities and differences between the skeletal system and the muscular system.

The Skeletal System

Your bones are living tissue that make up the organs of your **skeletal system.** This is *a body system consisting of bones and the tissues connecting them.* Your bones are like the steel girders that support a skyscraper. They form your body's framework. They protect its soft parts from injury. Your bones also allow you to stand and move, with the help of your muscles. Adults have 206 separate bones in their bodies.

Bones

The bones inside your body are made up of living tissue and cells. Because bone tissue is alive, it is always being destroyed and remade to keep your bones strong. Bones are hard on the outside and have spongy tissue on the inside. This tissue produces blood cells for the circulatory system. Bones also store minerals such as calcium. Calcium strengthens your bones and teeth. When your body needs calcium, the bones release small amounts into the blood. The blood takes the calcium to where it is needed in the body.

Quick Write

Write a paragraph describing why you think muscles sometimes get sore after exercise or other physical activity.

▶ Regular physical activity helps keep your bones healthy. **What is another way to strengthen your bones?**

Lesson 1: From Cells to Body Systems **181**

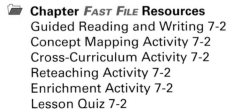

Lesson 2 Resources

📂 **Chapter FAST FILE Resources**
Guided Reading and Writing 7-2
Concept Mapping Activity 7-2
Cross-Curriculum Activity 7-2
Reteaching Activity 7-2
Enrichment Activity 7-2
Lesson Quiz 7-2

Technology
🔦 Transparency 7-2
💿 Audio Summaries
💿 *ExamView*
💿 Vocabulary PuzzleMaker
💿 StudentWorks™ Plus

FOCUS

Activating Prior Knowledge

What I Know Write two headings on the board: "Skeletal System" and "Muscular System." Have students state facts about each system. Record their answers under the correct heading on the board.

Guide to Reading

BUILDING VOCABULARY
■ Have students skim the lesson to find the definitions of the vocabulary terms. Ask volunteers to define each of the terms using their own words.
■ Use Vocabulary PuzzleMaker to reinforce vocabulary terms. 🖱

READING STRATEGY
Compare Help students with the reading strategy by pointing out several ways that these systems are similar. Then have students note differences between the two systems as they read the lesson.

Quick Write

Before students begin their Quick Write, ask them to recall a time when their muscles felt sore after exercise.

Caption Answer

Photo Caption Eating foods rich in calcium strengthens bones.

181

TEACH

R Reading Strategy

Analyzing a Graphic Direct students' attention to Figure 7.4. Have them identify the major bones and joints illustrated. Ask students to point out examples of each type of joints using the illustration. **OL**

AL Active Learning

Quick Demo If a skeleton model is available, let students work in groups to identify the bones and joints on the model. Ask volunteers to identify which part of the skeletal system protects the brain. *the skull* Point out that the lungs are located inside the chest. Ask: Which part of the skeletal system protects the lungs? *the rib cage* **AL**

> **Reading Check**
>
> **Answer** The skeletal system is a body system consisting of bones and the tissues connecting them.

Joints

Joints are *places where one bone meets another.* Different joints move in different ways. Some joints pivot, like your neck. The end of one bone rotates inside a ring formed by another. This joint can move up and down and from side to side. A hinge joint moves in only one direction like a door hinge. Your knee is an example of a hinge joint.

In ball-and-socket joints, the round end of one bone moves inside another's cup-shaped opening. A ball-and-socket joint can move in all directions. Your hip is an example of a ball-and-socket joint. Gliding joints allow one part of a bone to slide over another bone. They also move in a back-and-forth motion. Gliding joints are found in your wrists and ankles. **Figure 7.4** shows the four major types of joints as well as important bones.

> **Reading Check** **Define** What is the *skeletal system*?

▼ **FIGURE 7.4**

THE SKELETAL SYSTEM

R Notice the different shapes of different bones. Which of these bones have joints that pivot? Which have hinge joints?

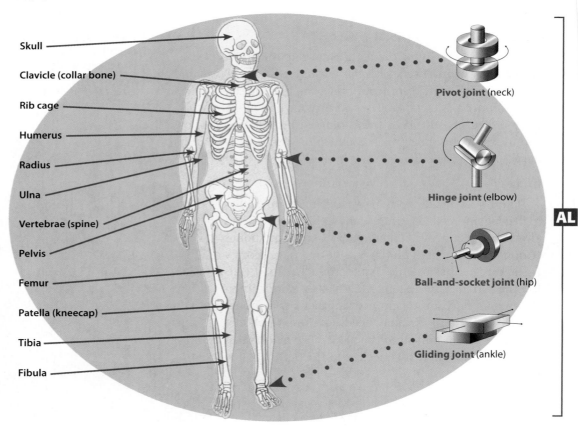

- Skull
- Clavicle (collar bone)
- Rib cage
- Humerus
- Radius
- Ulna
- Vertebrae (spine)
- Pelvis
- Femur
- Patella (kneecap)
- Tibia
- Fibula

Pivot joint (neck)

Hinge joint (elbow)

Ball-and-socket joint (hip)

Gliding joint (ankle)

AL

Caption Answer

Figure Caption A pivot joint is found in the neck. The knee is an example of a hinge joint.

HEALTH LITERACY

Osteoporosis The most common bone disease affects older adults, especially women. Osteoporosis means "porous bones." As a person ages, bones may lose some minerals and bones become less dense. This causes bones to become brittle and more likely to break. Although osteoporosis develops later in life, healthy habits during the teen years can help prevent this debilitating disease. Healthy habits include avoiding smoking and alcohol consumption, getting plenty of exercise, and consuming calcium-rich foods. **OL**

Health Skills Activity

Practicing Healthful Behaviors

Building Strong Bones

Your body needs plenty of calcium to keep your bones strong. Calcium is a mineral that makes bones hard. As a teen, your body is storing calcium to keep your bones healthy and strong as you get older. By eating calcium-rich foods, you help your body prepare for adulthood. The foods in the picture are all good sources of calcium.

With a Group

Create a plan for a meal that is rich in calcium. Share your meal plan with the other groups so each student in class will have a variety of calcium-rich meals to choose from.

The Muscular System

Your **muscular system** is made up of *all the muscles in your body.* Your muscles do several important things. They move the bones, pump your blood, and move food through the stomach and intestines.

There are three main types of muscles: skeletal, cardiac, and smooth. Skeletal muscles connect to and move your bones. You have this type of muscle in your arms, face, abdomen, back, and legs. They are considered *voluntary muscles* because you are able to control them. You are able to run, for example, by controlling the skeletal muscles in your legs.

Cardiac muscles are located only in the heart. They pump blood into and out of your heart. Cardiac muscles are *involuntary*. They move automatically without you having to think about them.

Smooth muscles are found in many of your internal organs. The stomach, intestines, bladder, and blood vessels all have smooth muscles. Like cardiac muscles, smooth muscles are **R** *involuntary* muscles. They slowly contract and relax on their own. **Figure 7.5** shows important muscle groups of the body.

Health Skills Activity

Practicing Healthful Behaviors

Building Strong Bones

● Ask students to spend 10 minutes in their groups planning menus. Have a representative from each group share the prepared menu.
● Extend the activity by providing labels from many foods, such as breakfast cereals, snack foods, and canned foods. Ask students to locate information about serving sizes and calcium content on the nutrition facts label. Have students review Chapter 4 on nutrition if they are having difficulty finding this information.

R Reading Strategy

Analyzing a Graphic Have students examine Figure 7.5 on page 184, which shows the muscular system. Ask: Which type of muscle are the triceps and deltoids? *skeletal muscle* **OL**

Academic Vocabulary

Located The text explains that cardiac muscles are *located* only in the heart. Tell students that the word *located* refers to the place where something is found. Have students relate this to the meaning of the words *location* and *local.*

What Teens Want to Know

How can I safely build muscle mass? Teens interested in weight lifting to build muscle mass should work with a coach or trainer who understands that teens have different requirements than adults. According to the American Academy of Pediatrics, creatine and other supplements promoted to increase athletic performance in sports should be avoided. These supplements can have serious health consequences such as dehydration, liver damage, and kidney problems. Have interested students discuss safe ways to build muscle mass with a physical education teacher. **OL**

Caption Answer

Figure Caption skeletal, cardiac, and smooth

ASSESS

Assessment Resources

Lesson Review Quiz
ExamView
Fast Files Activities
Online Quizzes and
Activities

Reteaching

● Assign Concept Map 7-2 or Reteaching Activity 7-2 in the Fast Files.
● Have students work with a partner to review the parts and jobs of the skeletal and muscular systems.

Enrichment

● Assign Enrichment Activity 7-2 in the Fast Files.
● Have students research minerals other than calcium that are needed to for good bone health, for example, phosphorus, zinc, and magnesium. Have students write a short report of their findings.

CLOSE

Call on random students to read and answer each of the reading checks found throughout the lesson.

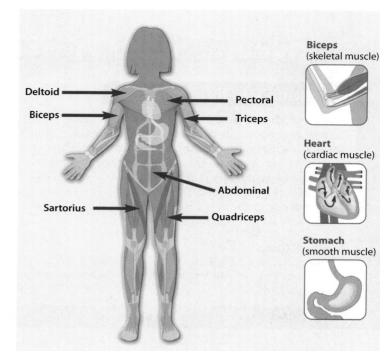

▶ **FIGURE 7.5**

R **THE MUSCULAR SYSTEM**

Muscles do many different jobs in the body. What are the three major types of muscles?

Deltoid

Biceps

Sartorius

Pectoral

Triceps

Abdominal

Quadriceps

Biceps
(skeletal muscle)

Heart
(cardiac muscle)

Stomach
(smooth muscle)

Health Online

Visit health.glencoe.com and complete the Interactive Study Guide for Lesson 2.

Lesson 2 Review

 **After You Read**

Review this lesson for new terms, major headings, and Reading Checks.

What I Learned

1. *Vocabulary* What is the *skeletal system*? What does this system do?

2. *Identify* Name the four types of joints. Briefly describe each.

3. *Explain* Tell the difference between voluntary and involuntary muscles.

Thinking Critically

4. *Apply* Juan slipped on the ice. When he stood up, his leg looked fine yet it hurt. Why do you suppose this was the case?

5. *Analyze* Do you think the muscles responsible for activities such as breathing and digesting food are voluntary or involuntary? Are they smooth or skeletal muscles?

Applying Health Skills

6. *Practicing Healthful Behaviors* During most sports, your body parts are frequently in motion. Think of a sport, then list ways to protect the bones and muscles from injury when playing that sport.

Health Online For more review questions for Lesson 2, go to **health.glencoe.com**.

Lesson 2 Review Answers

1. It is a body system consisting of bones and the tissues connecting them. It provides your body's framework, protects the soft parts, and allows you to stand and move.
2. Pivot joints move up and down and side to side; hinge joints move in only one direction;

ball-and-socket joints move in all directions; and gliding joints move across connecting surfaces. They also move in a back-and-forth motion.
3. Voluntary muscles can be controlled. Involuntary muscles work automatically, without a person's control.

4. Answers, which will vary, should emphasize the likelihood that he injured a bone.
5. Involuntary muscles are responsible for breathing and digesting food. They are smooth muscles.
6. *Sample answer:* I use shin guards to protect my bones when playing soccer.

Digestion and Excretion

Guide to Reading

● **Building Vocabulary**
Look for ways the words below are related. Keep these connections in mind as you read the lesson.

■ digestion (p. 185)
■ digestive system (p. 185)
■ excretory system (p. 186)

● **Focusing on the Main Ideas**
In this lesson, you will be able to

■ **explain** the parts and functions of the digestive system.
■ **explain** the parts and functions of the excretory system.
■ **apply** the skill of advocacy to promote ways to care for the digestive and excretory systems.

● **Reading Strategy**
Sequencing Create a flowchart that shows the path of food as your body digests it.

The Digestive System

As explained in Chapter 4, the foods you eat contain nutrients. Nutrients are substances that nourish and provide energy for the body. *The process by which your body breaks down food into small nutrient particles* is called **digestion.** *The body system that controls this process* is the **digestive** (dy·JES·tiv) **system.** The digestive system has eight main parts, which are shown in **Figure 7.6.** The arrow shows the order in which the different parts enter into the process of digestion.

The Digestive Process

The digestive process begins in your mouth. When you bite into an apple, for example, your teeth begin grinding the bite of apple into small bits. Chemicals in your saliva (suh·LY·vuh) called *enzymes* (EN·zymz) break down the apple further.

uick Write

Write a short paragraph explaining how you think digestion and excretion are related.

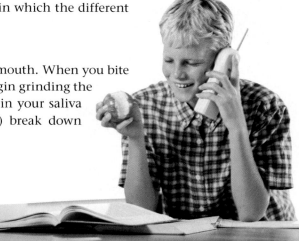

▶ The process of digestion begins in your mouth. **How can eating healthy foods help your digestive system?**

Lesson 3 Resources

📁 **Chapter FAST FILE Resources**
Guided Reading and Writing 7-3
Concept Mapping Activity 7-3
Health Lab 7-3
Reteaching Activity 7-3
Enrichment Activity 7-3
Lesson Quiz 7-3

Technology
🔌 Transparency 7-3
💿 Audio Summaries
⚙ *ExamView*
💿 Vocabulary PuzzleMaker
⚙ StudentWorks™ Plus

FOCUS

Activating Prior Knowledge

What I Know Have students name different parts of the digestive system. Tell students they will learn about digestion in this lesson.

Guide to Reading

BUILDING VOCABULARY
■ Ask students to write a sentence that shows the relationship between the terms *digestion* and *digestive system*.
■ Use Vocabulary PuzzleMaker to reinforce vocabulary terms.

READING STRATEGY
Sequencing Students' flowcharts should include the following steps: mouth, esophagus, stomach, small intestine, and large intestine.

uick Write

To help students get started on their Quick Write, ask them to consider whether their body uses every part of the foods they eat.

Academic Vocabulary

Process The *process* of digestion is mentioned on this page. Explain that a process is a series of steps leading to a result. Ask students to name other processes with which they are familiar.

TEACH

AL Active Learning

Game Show Have each student prepare three game-show style questions about the digestive system. Then have students work in pairs and quiz their partners using their prepared questions. For each missed question, have them write a sentence explaining the correct answer. Call on random pairs of students to identify missed questions and explain the correct response. **OL**

R Reading Strategy

Analyzing a Graphic After students have examined Figure 7.6, which shows the digestive system, ask: Which organ is also called the large intestine? *colon* Ask: Which organ stores bile? *gallbladder* Note that the digestive process begins in the mouth. **OL**

Reading Check

Answer Enzymes are chemicals that break down food in the process of digestion.
Answer, p. 187 Two organs of the excretory system are the kidneys and the bladder.

Caption Answers

Figure Caption Digestion begins in the mouth.
Photo Caption, p. 187
Sample answer: Drinking plenty of water helps you avoid the fatigue that results from dehydration.

When you swallow, the crushed apple passes into your throat. Muscles contract and relax to push the fruit down the esophagus and into the stomach. The esophagus is a muscular tube that connects the mouth to the stomach. Strong acid,  enzymes, and churning muscles in your stomach break down the food particles even further. The food particles move next into the small intestine. There, digestion breaks down the food particles into nutrients that are absorbed into the blood. The blood carries these nutrients throughout the body.

Reading Check **Explain** What are enzymes? What is their role?

The Excretory System

Your **excretory** (EK·skruh·tohr·ee) **system** *gets rid of some of the wastes your body produces and also maintains fluid balance.* The parts of the apple that can't be absorbed through digestion

▼ FIGURE 7.6

R THE DIGESTIVE PROCESS

The digestive system involves many different body parts. Where does this process begin?

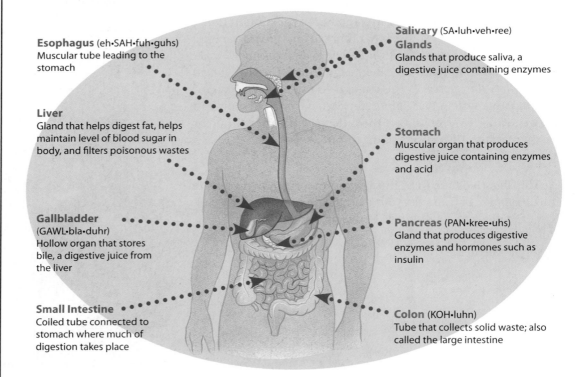

Esophagus (eh·SAH·fuh·guhs)
Muscular tube leading to the stomach

Liver
Gland that helps digest fat, helps maintain level of blood sugar in body, and filters poisonous wastes

Gallbladder (GAWL·bla·duhr)
Hollow organ that stores bile, a digestive juice from the liver

Small Intestine
Coiled tube connected to stomach where much of digestion takes place

Salivary (SA·luh·veh·ree) **Glands**
Glands that produce saliva, a digestive juice containing enzymes

Stomach
Muscular organ that produces digestive juice containing enzymes and acid

Pancreas (PAN·kree·uhs)
Gland that produces digestive enzymes and hormones such as insulin

Colon (KOH·luhn)
Tube that collects solid waste; also called the large intestine

---

What Teens Want to Know

Why do I get an upset stomach when I'm stressed? Everyone has experienced the feeling of butterflies in their stomach. Stress can also lead to upset stomach, nausea, diarrhea, or constipation. Explain that when the body is stressed, blood flow to the digestive system is decreased. Food sits in the stomach longer. The production of stomach acid is increased, often irritating the lining of the stomach. Stress also causes the colon to contract, which can lead to diarrhea. Have students research stress management techniques they can try. **OL**

become waste and are excreted or *removed* from the body. Your respiratory system and skin are also part of the excretory system. The respiratory system gets rid of carbon dioxide when you exhale. Your skin releases liquid waste and salt in the form of sweat. Your body needs to get rid of wastes to remain healthy. If wastes are not removed, they can build up in the body and damage organs.

Parts of the Excretory System

The major organs of the excretory system are the colon, kidneys, and bladder. Food particles that can't be absorbed in the small intestine are sent to the colon. There, most of the water is removed and absorbed by the body. When the colon fills up, the brain sends a message to the muscles in the colon telling them to contract. This action removes solid waste from the body.

The kidneys have several jobs. They filter the blood, remove water and waste, and maintain the body's fluid balance. When your brain detects too much water in your blood, your kidneys remove the excess water as liquid waste. Liquid waste from the kidneys, or *urine* (YOO·rihn), is stored in the bladder. When the bladder is full, the urine is passed out of the body.

 Reading Check **List** Name two organs of the excretory system.

▲ Drinking water helps the digestive and excretory systems function. **What is another health benefit of drinking water each day?**

Health *Online*

Visit **health.glencoe.com** and complete the Interactive Study Guide for Lesson 3.

ASSESS

Assessment Resources

Lesson Review Quiz
ExamView
Fast Files Activities
Online Quizzes and Activities

Reteaching

● Assign Concept Map 7-3 or Reteaching Activity 7-3 in the Fast Files 📁
● Have students work in teams to name the three major organs of the excretory system and explain their functions.

Enrichment

● Assign Enrichment Activity 7-3 in the Fast Files. 📁
● Have students do research to find out why their stomach growls when they are hungry, and what organs of the digestive system are involved. Have students share their findings with the class.

CLOSE

Go around the room and have students name an organ that is a part of the digestive system and identify its function.

Lesson 3 Review

 After You Read

> *Review this lesson for new terms, major headings, and Reading Checks.*

What I Learned

1. *Vocabulary* Define *digestion*, and use it in an original sentence.

2. *Recall* Once food is in the throat, how does it reach the stomach?

3. *List* Name two functions of the kidneys.

Thinking Critically

4. *Analyze* Do you think it would take your body longer to digest a large piece of food or one that has been cut into small pieces? Explain.

5. *Hypothesize* What do you think would happen if a person's kidneys were not working properly?

Applying Health Skills

6. *Advocacy* One way to maintain the health of the digestive system is to eat slowly. Research other ways to keep your digestive and excretory systems healthy. Make a list of your findings. Share this list with family members.

Health *Online* For more review questions for Lesson 3, go to **health.glencoe.com**.

Lesson 3: Digestion and Excretion **187**

Lesson 3 Review Answers

1. Digestion is the process used to break down foods. Sentences will vary.
2. Muscles in the throat contract and relax, pushing the food along.

3. *Sample answers:* filtering the blood, removing water and waste, and maintaining the body's fluid balance
4. Your body can break down smaller pieces easier and faster.

5. *Sample answer:* The person's body would have a hard time discharging liquid waste.
6. *Sample answers:* drinking plenty of water, eating foods that contain fiber

FOCUS

Activating Prior Knowledge

What I Know Ask students to identify what is happening when their heart beats.

Guide to Reading

BUILDING VOCABULARY

■ Have students write a sentence describing the relationship between the terms *neurons, spinal cord,* and *nervous system.*

■ Use Vocabulary PuzzleMaker to reinforce vocabulary terms.

READING STRATEGY

Classifying Have students fold a piece of paper in thirds horizontally. Have students label each section with the name of one of the body systems discussed in the lesson. Then as they read, students can record the parts of each system and the roles of each part.

ℚuick Write

Before students begin the Quick Write activity, remind them that most body functions are the result of several body systems working together.

Caption Answer

Photo Caption Blood provides oxygen to muscles because they use more oxygen during exercise.

Heart, Blood, Lungs, and Nerves

Guide to Reading

● **Building Vocabulary**
How are the terms below related? Which terms are muscles? Which terms are body systems?

■ circulatory system (p. 188)
■ heart (p. 189)
■ blood pressure (p. 189)
■ respiratory system (p. 191)
■ lungs (p. 191)
■ diaphragm (p. 191)
■ nervous system (p. 192)
■ neurons (p. 192)
■ spinal cord (p. 192)

● **Focusing on the Main Ideas**
In this lesson, you will be able to

■ **explain** how blood moves through the body.
■ **understand** how your nervous system controls body functions.
■ **analyze** factors in the environment that influence respiratory health.

● **Reading Strategy**
Classifying As you read the lesson, list the parts of each body system discussed. Briefly describe the role of each part.

ℚuick Write

Take a deep breath. Feel your heart beating in your chest. Write the names of the body systems that make these actions possible.

The Circulatory System

Every modern building has pipes and wires inside the walls that carry water and energy throughout the building. Although these pipes and wires are hidden, each does an important job. The same is true of your body's **circulatory system.** This system *allows the body to move blood to and from tissues.* The blood delivers oxygen, food, and other materials to the cells. It also carries waste products away from the cells. The circulatory system, or *cardiovascular system*, consists of the heart, blood vessels, and blood. See **Figure 7.7.**

◀ During exercise, your circulatory system pumps extra blood to and from your body's cells. **Why do your cells need extra blood during exercise or other physical activity?**

Lesson 4 Resources

📁 **Chapter** *FAST FILE* **Resources**
Guided Reading and Writing 7-4
Concept Mapping Activity 7-4
Cross-Curriculum Activity 7-4
Reteaching Activity 7-4
Enrichment Activity 7-4
Lesson Quiz 7-4

Technology
👍 Transparency 7-4
🖴 Audio Summaries
⚙ *ExamView*
🖴 Vocabulary PuzzleMaker
💿 StudentWorks™ Plus

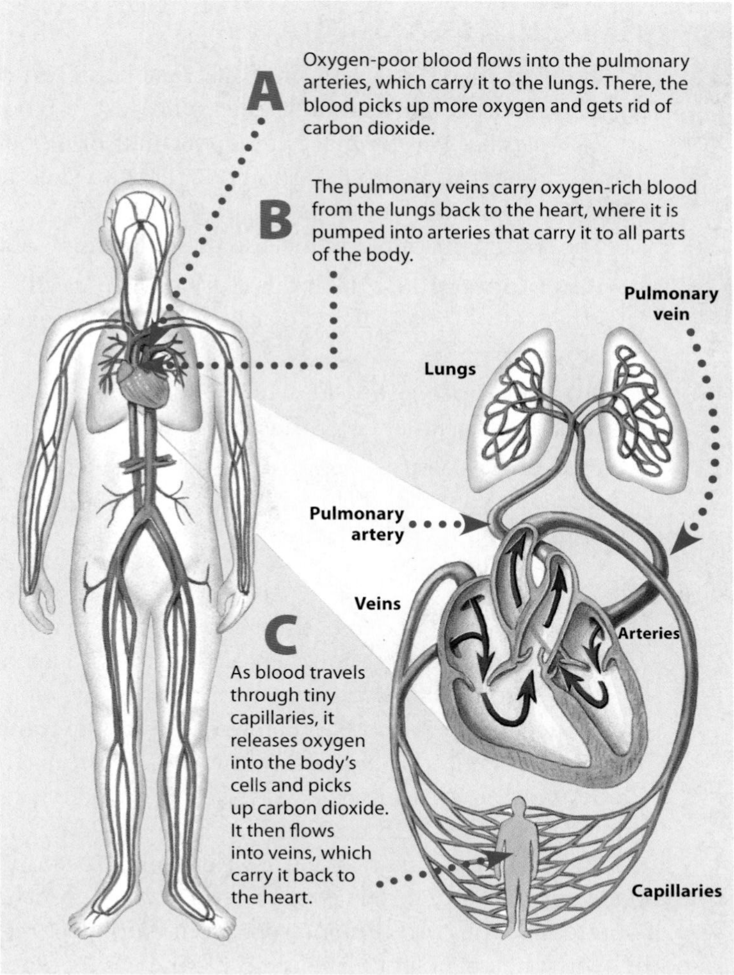

◀ FIGURE 7.7

THE CIRCULATORY SYSTEM

The blood vessels shown in blue carry oxygen-poor blood toward the heart and lungs. The red blood vessels carry oxygen-rich blood from the lungs to the heart. They also carry the blood to the rest of the body. Why are the pulmonary arteries shown in blue? **R**

A Oxygen-poor blood flows into the pulmonary arteries, which carry it to the lungs. There, the blood picks up more oxygen and gets rid of carbon dioxide.

B The pulmonary veins carry oxygen-rich blood from the lungs back to the heart, where it is pumped into arteries that carry it to all parts of the body.

Pulmonary vein

Lungs

Pulmonary artery

Veins

Arteries

C As blood travels through tiny capillaries, it releases oxygen into the body's cells and picks up carbon dioxide. It then flows into veins, which carry it back to the heart.

Capillaries

The Heart: The Body's Pump

The muscle that acts as the pump for the circulatory system is the **heart.** It pushes blood through tubes called blood vessels. There are three different types of blood vessels. *Arteries* carry blood away from the heart. *Veins* return blood to the heart. Between the arteries and veins are tiny blood vessels known as *capillaries* (KAP·uh·layr·eez). The capillaries deliver oxygen and nutrients in the blood directly to the body's cells.

The force of blood pushing against the blood vessel walls is called **HS** **blood pressure.** Blood pressure is greatest when the heart contracts, or pushes out blood. It is lowest between heartbeats, when the heart relaxes.

Health *Online*

Topic: Keeping Track of Your Pulse

Visit **health.glencoe.com** for Student Web Activities that will teach you how to test your heart rate, or pulse.

Activity: Using the information provided at the link above, take your pulse three times a day —when you first get up, at noon before lunch, and before you go to bed—to see when your heart is working hardest.

TEACH

R Reading Strategy

Analyzing a Graphic Direct students' attention to Figure 7.7. Ask: How does the circulatory system interact with the respiratory system? Sample answer: *The circulatory system delivers the oxygen taken in by the respiratory system to the body's cells.* Ask: How does the circulatory system interact with the digestive system? Sample answer: *The circulatory system delivers the nutrients that are the result of the digestive process.* **OL**

HS Health Skills Practice

Accessing Information High blood pressure, or hypertension, affects many people, including some children and teens. Although this condition often has no symptoms, it damages the heart, arteries, kidneys, and other organs. Have students use online and print resources to find information about high blood pressure in teens. Students' research should include the negative effects of high blood pressure, and ways that young people can reduce their risk of developing high blood pressure. Have students prepare a short report of their findings. **OL**

🏠 Home, School, and Community

At Home Discuss with students ways to maintain the health of the circulatory system. For example, exercise and a healthy diet are important to the heath of the circulatory system. Have students brainstorm other ways, such as choosing to play outside instead of sitting in front of the television, or choosing healthy snacks instead of potato chips. After students have worked as a class to develop a list of suggestions, have each student write a public service announcement highlighting one way to maintain the health of the circulatory system. **OL**

Caption Answer

Figure Caption The pulmonary arteries are shown in blue because they carry oxygen-poor blood.

Academic Vocabulary

Monitored This page mentions that all blood donations are *monitored.* Explain that, in this instance, the word *monitor* is a verb that means "to watch or to check." Have students relate this to the word *monitor* used as a noun, for example, in the term *hall monitor.*

Reading Check

Answer The main parts of the circulatory system are the heart, blood vessels, and the blood.

Caption Answer

Photo Caption Red blood cells carry oxygen to the other cells of the body and carry away some waste products. White blood cells destroy disease-causing germs that enter the body.

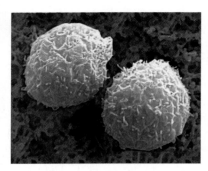

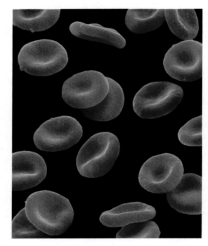

▲ This picture shows blood cells magnified many times. **What does each type of blood cell do?**

Parts of the Blood

Blood is made up of several different parts. These include solids as well as liquid. The liquid part of blood is *blood plasma.* Plasma makes up about half of blood's total volume. Plasma itself is about 92 percent water. Its job is to transport blood cells and dissolved food.

The solid parts of blood include the following:

- **Red blood cells.** These cells carry oxygen to all other cells of the body. They carry away some waste products.
- **White blood cells.** These help destroy disease-causing germs that enter the body.
- **Platelets.** These are small, disk-shaped structures that help your blood clot. Clotting keeps you from losing too much blood when you have a cut.

Blood Types

When a person undergoes surgery, he or she may lose blood during the operation. Blood that is lost can be replaced through a *transfusion.* This is transferring blood from one person to another. Before blood can be transfused, doctors need to make sure the *blood types* match. Blood types are classifications based on the kind of protein the red blood cells contain.

There are four main blood types: A, B, AB, and O. Everyone is born with one type or another. During a transfusion, if you receive the correct blood type, your blood will mix smoothly with the new blood. If you receive the wrong blood type, your blood cells will clump together with the new cells. This can cause serious health problems, even death.

Blood may also contain something called an Rh factor. Blood is either Rh-positive or Rh-negative. People with Rh-positive blood can receive blood from Rh-positive or Rh-negative donors. People with Rh-negative blood can only receive blood from people who are also Rh-negative.

Today, all blood donations are carefully monitored. When a person donates blood, his or her blood type and Rh factor are checked and carefully labeled. The blood is stored in a blood bank until needed.

Reading Check

 **Identify** Name the main parts of the circulatory system.

Cultural Perspectives

Sickle Cell Disease Some diseases are more prevalent in a particular racial or ethnic group. Sickle cell disease is a genetic disorder that affects the circulatory system. In the United States, it primarily affects African Americans, occurring in 1 of 500 births. In sickle cell disease, some of the red blood cells produced by the body are misshapen. These misshapen blood cells damage tiny blood vessels as they pass through and cause damage to organs such as the liver.

The Respiratory System

Your **respiratory system** *enables you to breathe*. Breathing in, or inhaling, brings oxygen into your lungs. Oxygen is needed by the body for survival. The **lungs** are *the main organs of the respiratory system*. When you breathe out, or exhale, the lungs get rid of carbon dioxide gas. The parts of the respiratory system and their functions are shown in **Figure 7.8.**

How You Breathe

Breathing begins with the **diaphragm** (DY·uh·fram). This is *a large muscle at the bottom of the chest*. When you breathe in, the diaphragm contracts. This tightening of the diaphragm allows the lungs to expand and fill with air. When you breathe out, the diaphragm expands. As it enlarges, it pushes on the lungs, forcing out the air.

Reading Check **Explain** What do your lungs do?

▼ **FIGURE 7.8**

THE RESPIRATORY SYSTEM

The respiratory system is divided into upper and lower sections. Each performs a different job. In which section are the alveoli found?

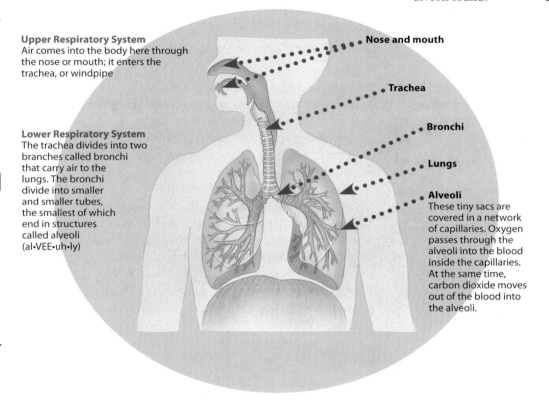

Upper Respiratory System
Air comes into the body here through the nose or mouth; it enters the trachea, or windpipe

Lower Respiratory System
The trachea divides into two branches called bronchi that carry air to the lungs. The bronchi divide into smaller and smaller tubes, the smallest of which end in structures called alveoli (al·VEE·uh·ly)

Nose and mouth

Trachea

Bronchi

Lungs

Alveoli
These tiny sacs are covered in a network of capillaries. Oxygen passes through the alveoli into the blood inside the capillaries. At the same time, carbon dioxide moves out of the blood into the alveoli.

R Reading Strategy

Analyzing a Graphic As students examine Figure 7.8, have a volunteer describe the path of air into and out of the body. Have them refer to the illustration and labels as they describe to the rest of the class. **OL**

AL Active Learning

Role-Plays After students read about the breathing process and how the respiratory works, divide the class into small groups. Have each group spend 15 minutes writing a script for a role-play demonstrating ways that smoking can adversely affect the health of the respiratory system. Role-plays should include a part in which students practice refusing to smoke cigarettes. **OL**

U Universal Access

English Learners Write the word *diaphragm* on the board. Underline the *ph* in this word. Explain that, in English, *ph* is often pronounced with the *f* sound. Have students practice pronouncing this word and using it in a spoken sentence. **OL**

Reading Check

Answer The lungs are the main organs of the respiratory system. These are the organs in which gas exchange occurs.

Caption Answer

Figure Caption The alveoli are a part of the lower respiratory system.

What Teens Want to Know

What causes hiccups? Hiccups are loud, involuntary, and can be embarrassing! The diaphragm is the cause of hiccups. Occasionally the diaphragm has spasms that cause air to be taken in or pushed out rapidly. The sound of a hiccup is caused by the sudden rush of air being stopped by the vocal cords. Some of the known triggers for hiccups include eating a big meal, swallowing air, stress, or excitement. There are many methods people use to get rid of hiccups. Have students describe any of these hiccup cures with which they are familiar. **OL**

R Reading Strategy

Analyzing a Graphic Have students look at Figure 7.9 on the facing page. Ask: Name two parts of the central nervous system. *the brain*

DEVELOPING
Good Character

Citizenship
Have students discuss ways that a student their age could promote healthy choices. Record students' suggestions on the board. Have each student choose one suggestion to incorporate into a poster. Display the posters throughout the school.

U Universal Access

Learning Styles Tell students that the nervous system carries messages about sounds, sights, smells, feel, and tastes to the brain. Review with students the five senses (hearing, sight, smell, touch, taste). Spray some air freshener in the air. Tell students that their nervous system carries the message about the smell from their nose to their brain. Then clap loudly, and explain that the nervous system carries the message about the sound from their ear to their brain. **OL**

Reading Check

Answer central nervous system and peripheral nervous system

DEVELOPING
Good Character

Citizenship

You can demonstrate good citizenship by sharing what you learn about protecting your health with others. For example, encourage family members to protect their brain by always wearing a helmet when riding a bike. What are some other ways you could promote healthy choices in your family or neighborhood?

The Nervous System

The **nervous system** is *the control and communication system of the body.* Its command center is the brain. The human brain does several important jobs. It processes thoughts and feelings. It also helps your body process and respond to information it receives from your senses. For example, when you smell fresh-baked cookies, your brain responds to the aroma by telling your tongue to produce saliva.

The brain is made up of billions of **neurons** (NOO·rahnz). These are *cells that carry electrical messages,* the language of the nervous system. There are three types of neurons: sensory neurons, connecting neurons, and motor neurons. Sensory neurons receive information from the outside world. For example, the smell of the fresh-baked cookies would be picked up by sensory neurons in the nose. Connecting neurons take the information picked up by the sensory neurons and pass them on to the motor neurons. The motor neurons send messages to the muscles and glands, telling them how to respond. If you like the smell of fresh-baked cookies, they will probably tell the glands in your mouth to produce saliva.

U

Parts of the Nervous System

The nervous system consists of the central nervous system and the peripheral nervous system. The *central nervous system* is made up of the brain and the spinal cord. The **spinal cord** is *a tube of neurons that runs along the spine.* The brain is made up of many parts. Each part has a different function. The largest part of the brain is the cerebrum (suh·REE·bruhm). This is where thinking takes place.

The *peripheral* (puh·RIF·uh·ruhl) *nervous system* is made up of nerves branching out from the brain and spinal cord. It handles both your voluntary and involuntary movements. Voluntary movements are ones you control. Lifting your arm to throw a ball is a voluntary movement. Involuntary movements are those you cannot control. The beating of your heart is an example of an involuntary movement. The parts of both the central nervous system and the peripheral nervous system are shown in **Figure 7.9.**

 **Reading Check**

Identify Name the two main parts of the nervous system.

Dealing with Sensitive Issues

Stem Cell Research Students might have heard about the use of stem cells as a way to treat those who are paralyzed. Because stem-cell research is often mentioned on the news and by political figures, students may have questions about this topic. Stem cells are cells in the body that have the potential to develop into a variety of types of cells, including neurons. If students ask about the ethics of stem-cell research, suggest that they research and discuss the issue with their families. **OL**

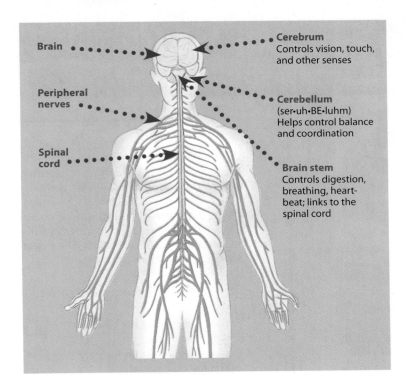

Brain

Peripheral nerves

Spinal cord

Cerebrum Controls vision, touch, and other senses

Cerebellum (ser·uh·BE·luhm) Helps control balance and coordination

Brain stem Controls digestion, breathing, heartbeat; links to the spinal cord

◀ **FIGURE 7.9**

THE NERVOUS SYSTEM

The central nervous system, shown in yellow, contains the brain and spinal cord. They work together to send messages to the peripheral nervous system, shown in blue. Which part of the brain controls your sense of smell?

R

ASSESS

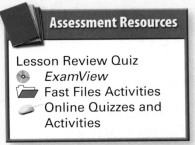

Assessment Resources

Lesson Review Quiz
◉ *ExamView*
📁 Fast Files Activities
🖱 Online Quizzes and Activities

Reteaching

● Assign Concept Map 7-4 or Reteaching Activity 7-4 in the *Fast Files*. 📁
● Have students name the two main parts of the nervous system.

Enrichment

● Assign Enrichment Activity 7-4 in the *Fast Files*. 📁
● Have students research to find out how the circulatory and respiratory systems work together. Research should include the role of hemoglobin in carrying oxygen. Have students create an illustrated report to share their findings.

CLOSE

Ask students to explain why the nervous system, the circulatory system, and the respiratory system all must work together in the body.

Caption Answer
Figure Caption the cerebrum

Lesson 4 Review

 After You Read

Review this lesson for new terms, major headings, and Reading Checks.

What I Learned

1. *Recall* What are the three types of blood vessels? What are their functions?

2. *Vocabulary* What is the *diaphragm*?

3. *List* Name two types of neurons, and tell what each does.

Thinking Critically

4. *Analyze* When Nick's father went to give blood, he was tested for his blood type. Why?

5. *Synthesize* Think about the movement of your chest as your lungs take in air. Is this voluntary or involuntary movement? Which part of the nervous system controls this action?

Applying Health Skills

6. *Analyzing Influences* A number of factors in the environment might influence respiratory health. Make a list of these factors and discuss their role in the health of the community.

Health Online For more review questions for Lesson 4, go to **health.glencoe.com**.

Lesson 4: Heart, Blood, Lungs, and Nerves **193**

Lesson 4 Review Answers

1. Arteries carry blood away from the heart. Veins return blood to the heart. Capillaries are tiny vessels that deliver oxygen and nutrients to the cells.

2. The diaphragm is a muscle at the bottom of the chest that aids in respiration.

3. *Sample answers:* sensory neurons, which receive information from the outside world; connecting neurons, which send messages between sensory neurons and motor neurons; motor neurons, which send messages to muscles and glands

4. Blood type is important when matching donated blood to recipients.

5. It is an involuntary movement controlled by the peripheral nervous system.

6. Pollution and cigarette smoke can negatively influence the health of the respiratory system.

Building Health Skills

PRACTICING HEALTHFUL BEHAVIORS

Maintaining Healthy Body Systems

SKILL
Practicing Healthful Behaviors

Activating Prior Knowledge

Ask students to name one way to improve the health of a body system. Then have students explain how the health of one body system can affect the health of the whole body.

- **Objective** After completing the activity students will be able to describe habits that can improve the health of a body system.
- **Time** 45 minutes
- **Materials** paper, pencil

Teacher Classroom Resources
📁 Building Health Skills
🖱 Transparency 7-1

Model

- Have students read about the steps that Stacy follows to maintain the health of her body systems. Ask: What body systems are positively affected by Stacy walking or riding her bike each day? *Sample answer: the circulatory system, the respiratory system, the muscular system*

National Health Standards Addressed
- - - - - - - - - - - - - -
7.1, 7.4, 7.5

Maintaining Healthy Body Systems

DIRECTIONS

Practicing healthful behaviors involves taking specific actions to stay healthy and avoid risky behaviors. This activity will give you the opportunity to develop and master this important health skill. Here's a guide to the different parts of this activity:

❶ In the **Model** section, you will read about a teen who performs the health skill successfully. This "model" scenario will show you how the skill is done.

❷ The **Practice** section will help guide you in practicing the skill.

❸ In the **Apply** section, you will have a chance to perform the skill on your own. You can use the Self-Check to check your work.

To complete this activity, first read the scenario presented in the Model. Then move on to the Practice. Finally, go ahead and try the Apply.

❶ Model

The different body systems work together to keep the body functioning properly. As a result, the health of one body system affects the health of others. Stacy knows that keeping her body systems healthy is important to good total health. She made a list of healthful habits to keep her body systems healthy:

1. I will eat healthy foods and drink plenty of water.
2. I will walk or ride my bike to school whenever I can.
3. I will try to get eight hours of sleep at night.
4. I will brush and floss my teeth regularly.
5. I will wear a helmet when riding my bike.

194 Chapter 7: Your Body Systems

▶ **Teaching Tips**

Providing Examples Before students begin working on the Apply section, it may be helpful to provide students with examples of articles or pamphlets on health care for a variety of body systems, such as skeletal system or digestive system. Let students look through the articles to see how they may want to organize or illustrate their reports.

❷ Practice

Stacy wants to try out for the track team at school. Because running requires strong lungs, she wants to develop some healthful habits that will benefit her respiratory system. Help Stacy by answering the following questions:

1. What are two habits Stacy can practice to take care of her respiratory system?

2. Will these habits help Stacy take care of any other body systems?

Skill Summary
PRACTICING HEALTHFUL BEHAVIORS

Caring for your body systems includes:

- Staying physically active
- Eating well
- Drinking plenty of water
- Avoiding harmful substances
- Taking care of illnesses
- Getting enough rest
- Wearing protective gear during sports

❸ Apply

Working with a group, choose a body system you learned about and create a report explaining how to care for this body system. Describe why caring for this body system is important. Identify at least four actions to keep this body system healthy. Explain how these actions can benefit your chosen body system. Do these actions benefit other body systems? Present your report to the class.

Self-Check

- Did we tell why care of our chosen body system is important?
- Did we identify at least four actions that will benefit our chosen body system?
- Did we explain how these actions benefit our chosen body system?

Practice

- Have students read the introductory paragraph in the Practice activity.
- Then have students work in small groups to answer the questions.
- Go around the room and call on groups to share answers to the questions.

Apply/Assess

- Check with each group to be sure the members have chosen a body system.
- Remind each group to identify the importance of caring for the chosen body system, three actions to keep the body system healthy, and an explanation of how each of those actions positively affects the chosen body system.
- Have each group share its report with the class.
- You may wish to distribute the Building Health Skills Activity in the Fast Files.

ASSESSMENT SCORING

Student work should meet all criteria to achieve the highest score.

Skills Student work describes:
- at least three behaviors that benefit body systems.
- how these behaviors benefit specific body systems.

Concepts Student work provides:
- accurate information about body systems.
- an explanation of the relationships between body systems.

The Mystery of Sleep

Objectives

After completing this activity, students will be able to

- Describe how different body systems benefit from sleep
- Identify ways to get a good night's sleep

Motivator

Write the word *sleep* on the board. Ask students to describe how a good night's sleep makes them feel. Record their responses on the board.

Teaching the Feature

- Have students read the feature. Encourage them to think beyond the text and use inference to consider the following. Explain that people who travel to other time zones often experience a set of symptoms called jet lag. Ask: Why does jet lag affect travelers who cross into different time zones? *because the body's 24-hour sleep cycle is disrupted when adapting to a new time zone* OL

- Have each student draw a large health triangle on a blank sheet of paper and label the sides physical health, mental/emotional health, and social health. Have students identify ways sleep can positively affect each side of the health triangle. Have them record answers on the appropriate sides of their triangles. OL

TIME *health news*

The Mystery of SLEEP

You'll spend a third of your life sleeping, but that helps keep your body in shape.

Everyone knows that you can't live without sleep, but no one knows exactly why or precisely how sleep works. Some researchers, such as Dr. Terrence Sejnowski, are working on a theory. He says the brain uses deep slumber to "shut off" so that it can process memories of the day. "It's like when you move out of your house so workers can renovate the kitchen," Dr. Sejnowski says. According to Sejnowski, sleep gives your brain time to refresh itself. In the morning, your brain is ready to go to work.

Scientists such as Dr. Sejnowksi may have different ideas about how sleep works to keep your organs in good working order. All scientists agree, however, that just as eating right and getting enough exercise are important, sleep is something your body needs to keep going strong. During sleep many of your body's major organs and regulatory systems continue to work actively. Some parts of your brain actually increase their activity while you are making zzzz's, and your body produces more of certain hormones that you need.

Did you know that you have an internal biological clock that regulates the timing of sleep? It programs each person to feel sleepy during nighttime hours and to be active during the day. Natural light sets your biological clock to the 24-hour cycle of day and night. And like some clocks, you wind down at the end of the day. That's when your body says it's time to get a good night's rest.

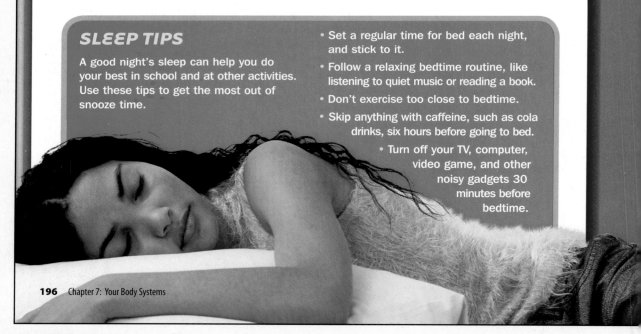

SLEEP TIPS

A good night's sleep can help you do your best in school and at other activities. Use these tips to get the most out of snooze time.

- Set a regular time for bed each night, and stick to it.
- Follow a relaxing bedtime routine, like listening to quiet music or reading a book.
- Don't exercise too close to bedtime.
- Skip anything with caffeine, such as cola drinks, six hours before going to bed.
- Turn off your TV, computer, video game, and other noisy gadgets 30 minutes before bedtime.

196 Chapter 7: Your Body Systems

Activity *Media, Technology, and Culture*

Developing a PSA Have students brainstorm ways to encourage others to recognize the importance of sleep to good health. Have them work in small groups to write scripts for 30-second public service announcements (PSA) promoting sleep. The PSAs should include the benefits of sleep and tips for getting a good night's sleep. Allow time for students to rehearse. Allow each group to present its PSA for the class. If possible, make a video recording of the presentations and share them with other students in the school.

Reading Review

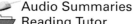

FOLDABLES™ | Study Organizer

Foldables™ and Other Study Aids Take out the Foldable™ that you created for Lesson 1 and any graphic organizers that you created for Lessons 1–4. Find a partner, and quiz each other using these study aids.

Lesson 1 From Cells to Body Systems

Key Ideas

- The body's building blocks include cells, tissues, and organs that make up body systems.
- The main body systems are the circulatory system, digestive system, endocrine system, excretory system, muscular system, nervous system, reproductive system, respiratory system, and skeletal system.
- The body systems work together to keep the body functioning.

Vocabulary

- cells (p. 177)
- tissues (p. 177)
- organs (p. 177)
- body systems (p. 177)

Lesson 2 Bones and Muscles

Key Ideas

- The skeletal system supports the body and protects the soft parts from injury.
- The muscular system makes movement possible. The three types of muscle are skeletal, cardiac, and smooth.

Vocabulary

- skeletal system (p. 181)
- joints (p. 182)
- muscular system (p. 183)

Lesson 3 Digestion and Excretion

Key Ideas

- The digestive system, which includes the mouth, esophagus, stomach, and intestines, is responsible for converting food to energy.
- The excretory system, which includes the colon, kidneys, and bladder, eliminates body waste and maintains fluid balance.

Vocabulary

- digestion (p. 185)
- digestive system (p. 185)
- excretory system (p. 186)

Lesson 4 Heart, Blood, Lungs, and Nerves

Key Ideas

- Blood moves through the body by means of the circulatory system, which consists of the heart, blood vessels, and blood.
- The respiratory system, which includes the nose, trachea, and lungs, makes breathing possible.
- Your nervous system controls body functions by sending signals around the body.

Vocabulary

- circulatory system (p. 188)
- heart (p. 189)
- blood pressure (p. 189)
- respiratory system (p. 191)
- lungs (p. 191)
- diaphragm (p. 191)
- nervous system (p. 192)
- neurons (p. 192)
- spinal cord (p. 192)

Assessment Resources

- Chapter 7 Summary and Activity
- Audio Summaries
- Reading Tutor
- Performance Assessment
- Chapter 7 Test
- *ExamView*
- Vocabulary PuzzleMaker
- Online Learning Center

Reading Review

Study Aids

- **Using the Dinah Zike Foldable™ Study Organizer** Have students use the Foldable™ to review the content of Lesson 1. Have students name a body system and describe some of the tissues and organs that make up that system.

Key Ideas

- **Use the Lesson Openers** Have students review the Focusing on the Main Ideas section on each of the lesson opener pages with a partner.

Vocabulary Review

- **Vocabulary Puzzles** Have students make a word search or crossword puzzle that uses chapter vocabulary terms. Have students trade puzzles with a partner.

Teaching Tips

Citing Internet Sources Students can access up-to-date health information for use in written reports by using the links provided at **health.glencoe.com**. Remind students that, like information from print sources, information from Internet sources must be cited properly. Tell students that directly copying information or images from an Internet source is plagiarism. Provide students with the format for citing an Internet source, and have students use that format when preparing a report based on Internet research.

Assessment

Reviewing Vocabulary and Main Ideas

1. organs
2. tissues
3. body systems
4. Joints
5. skeletal system
6. muscular system
7. c
8. b
9. b
10. d
11. a
12. e

Thinking Critically

13. Answers, which will vary, might mention the skeletal and muscular systems, which are both involved in movement.
14. *Sample answer:* Wearing a bicycle helmet helps protect the brain.

Assessment

 After You Read

HEALTH INVENTORY
Look back at your answers to the health inventory in the chapter opener. Is there anything you should do differently?

Reviewing Vocabulary and Main Ideas

On a sheet of paper, write the numbers 1–6. After each number, write the term from the list that best completes each sentence.

- blood pressure
- body systems
- excretory system
- joints
- muscular system
- nervous system
- organs
- skeletal system
- tissues

Lesson 1 From Cells to Body Systems

1. Structures within the body made of tissues and which carry out specific jobs are called _____.
2. Groups of similar cells that do the same kind of work form _____.
3. Taking care of your _____ is important for good total health.

Lesson 2 Bones and Muscles

4. _____ are places where one bone meets another.
5. The body system consisting of bones and the tissues connecting them is the _____.
6. Your _____ is made up of all the muscles in your body.

On a sheet of paper, write the numbers 7–12. For each phrase, write the letter of the body system that matches.

Lesson 3 Digestion and Excretion

a. Circulatory system
b. Digestive system
c. Excretory system
d. Nervous system
e. Respiratory system

7. Eliminates body wastes.
8. Breaks down food for energy.
9. Includes your liver, gallbladder, and stomach.

Lesson 4 Heart, Blood, Lungs, and Nerves

10. Its command center is the brain.
11. Includes blood vessels.
12. Makes breathing possible.

Thinking Critically

Using complete sentences, answer the following questions on a sheet of paper.

13. **Analyze** Which two body systems do you think are most closely related in their functions?
14. **Evaluate** Brainstorm ways of caring for the nervous system.

Health Online Visit health.glencoe.com and take the Online Quiz for Chapter 7.

Health Online

Have students visit **health.glencoe.com** to take the Chapter 7 quiz.

HEALTH INVENTORY WRAP-UP

Caring for Body Systems Have students reread the Health Inventory found on the chapter opener pages. Some students may find that their answers have changed after reading the chapter. Have students write a paragraph explaining if any of their answers have changed after reading the chapter. If students' answers have not changed, have them write a paragraph describing one new fact they learned while reading the chapter.

Write About It

15. **Analyzing Influences** Write an article for a health magazine about the factors that can influence a teen's health habits. Explain whether these factors are a positive or negative influence.

16. **Practicing Healthful Behaviors** Write a paragraph that describes a behavior that can benefit more than one body system. Explain how this behavior benefits each body system.

Write About It

15. **Expository Writing** Explain to students that expository writing is writing that shares knowledge to help others understand. Student articles will vary and may include factors such as family, friends, peers, and the media.

16. **Descriptive Writing** Explain to students that descriptive writing presents a clear picture, attracts the reader, and presents broad views or focuses on details. Student paragraphs will vary but should describe a behavior that benefits more than one body system. For example, exercise benefits the skeletal, muscular, and circulatory systems.

Standardized Test Practice

Reading

Read the passage and then answer the questions.

Blood pressure is an important measure of heart health. What exactly is blood pressure, and why is it important?

An answer to the first question requires understanding how the heart beats. When you rest, your heart beats about 60 to 70 times a minute. Each time your heart beats, it pumps blood into the arteries. At these moments, your heart is pushing blood. Between beats, your heart relaxes. It does not push blood. Your blood pressure is a measurement of these two states of your heart. It is shown as a fraction, such as 120/80. The top number represents the state of your heart during pushes. The bottom number is your heart when it is not pushing.

A trained medical professional can measure your blood pressure using an instrument called a *sphygmomanometer*. If your blood pressure is high, your doctor will do other tests to determine why. To lower your blood pressure, the doctor may recommend changes in lifestyle. These include getting regular exercise and eating healthy foods.

> **TEST-TAKING TIP**
>
> When interpreting facts or formulas in a passage, make sure you understand the concepts.

1. The author's purpose includes all of the following *except*:
   A. explaining blood pressure.
   B. telling why blood pressure is important as a measure of health.
   C. suggesting ways of keeping your heart healthy.
   D. telling about medications that reduce high blood pressure

2. Which of the following can be inferred from the passage?
   A. A blood pressure of 120/80 is better than a blood pressure of 120/70.
   B. High blood pressure is a sign of possible heart problems and may require require lifestyle changes.
   C. As a teen, your blood pressure should be lower than that of an adult.
   D. Blood pressure cannot be determined in teens.

Chapter 7 Assessment **199**

Standardized Test Practice

1. D
2. B

Test-Taking Tips

Making Inferences Tell students that they may be asked to make an inference based on a reading passage. Remind students to use details from the passage to form their inference. They should be sure that information in the passage supports their inference. Tell students that there might be more than one answer that is a true, correct statement, but their job is to determine which answer choice could be inferred from the passage.

CHAPTER 8 pp. 200–219	Standards		Skills and Activities
	National	**State/Local**	**IM EXPRESS,** *p. 201*
	National Health Education Standards 3.1, 3.2, 3.4, 3.6		**HANDS-ON HEALTH** Looking Ahead, *p. 216* **BUILDING HEALTH SKILLS** *Accessing Information* Coping with Changes During Puberty, *pp. 214–215*
Lesson 1 **Adolescence: A Time of Change** pp. 202–205	National Health Education Standards 1.2, 1.3, 1.4, 2.4, 5.2, 8.2		
Lesson 2 **Human Reproduction** pp. 206–209	National Health Education Standards 1.1, 1.6, 5.2, 5.3, 7.1, 7.4, 7.5, 8.2		**HEALTH SKILLS ACTIVITY** *Practicing Healthful Behaviors* Care of the Reproductive System, *p. 209*
Lesson 3 **Heredity and the Life Cycle** pp. 210–213	National Health Education Standards 1.1, 1.8, 6.1, 6.3		**DEVELOPING GOOD CHARACTER** Responsibility, *p. 212*

PACING THE CHAPTER

Lesson 1	45 min	Chapter Review	45 min
Lesson 2	45 min	Hands-on Health	20 min
Lesson 3	45 min	Building Health Skills	45 min

BLOCK SCHEDULING

For block scheduling, assign students Building Health Skills feature *Coping with Changes During Puberty,* pages 214–215, and Guided Reading and Writing.

Planning Guide

Glencoe Exclusive!
TeacherWorks™
All-In-One Planner and Resource Center

Reproducible Resources	Assessment	Media and Technology
Chapter FAST FILE Resources Chapter Summaries and Activities REVIEW Building Health Skills Activity TEACH Performance Assessment Activity EXTEND Universal Access Activities TEACH Parent Letter and Activities **Student Activities Workbook** TEACH **Reading Tutor** TEACH	Building Health Skills Activity, *pp. 214–215* Chapter 8 Assessment, *pp. 218–219* **Chapter FAST FILE Resources** Performance Assessment Activity, *p. 4* Chapter 8 Test, *p. 7* *ExamView® Test Generator*	**TeacherWorks™** includes: • Interactive Teacher Edition • Lesson Planner with Calendar • Access to all blackline masters • Correlations to standards StudentWorks™ Plus Online Student Edition Dinah Zike's Teaching Health with Foldables™
Chapter FAST FILE Resources Concept Mapping Activity 8-1 REVIEW Decision-Making Activity 8-1 EXTEND Enrichment Activity 8-1 EXTEND Lesson Plan 8-1 Guided Reading and Writing 8-1 TEACH Reteaching Activity 8-1 REVIEW	Lesson 1 Review, *p. 205* Vocabulary PuzzleMaker *ExamView® Test Generator*	Vocabulary PuzzleMaker *ExamView® Test Generator* StudentWorks™ Plus Transparency 8-1 Health **Online**
Chapter FAST FILE Resources Concept Mapping Activity 8-2 REVIEW Cross-Curriculum Activity 8-2 TEACH Enrichment Activity 8-2 EXTEND Lesson Plan 8-2 Guided Reading and Writing 8-2 TEACH Reteaching Activity 8-2 REVIEW	Lesson 2 Review, *p. 209* Vocabulary PuzzleMaker *ExamView® Test Generator*	Vocabulary PuzzleMaker *ExamView® Test Generator* StudentWorks™ Plus Transparency 8-2 Health **Online**
Chapter FAST FILE Resources Concept Mapping Activity 8-3 REVIEW Health Lab 8-3 EXTEND Enrichment Activity 8-3 EXTEND Lesson Plan 8-3 Guided Reading and Writing 8-3 TEACH Reteaching Activity 8-3 REVIEW	Lesson 3 Review, *p. 213* Vocabulary PuzzleMaker *ExamView® Test Generator*	Vocabulary PuzzleMaker *ExamView® Test Generator* StudentWorks™ Plus Transparency 8-3 Health **Online**

Chapter and Lesson Resources

The *Teen Health* resources are designed for differentiated learning abilities. You may want to use the coded items in this way:

REVIEW —activities to review or reinforce content

TEACH —activities to teach basic concepts

EXTEND —activities to extend or enrich lesson content

 OUT OF TIME?

Use Health Skills Activity *Care of the Reproductive System,* page 309 or Developing Good Character, page 212.

Meiosis

As you present Lesson 2 on Human Reproduction, it may be helpful to provide students with more information on meiosis, the process by which human egg and sperm cells are formed. In humans, reproductive cells formed be meiosis have 23 chromosomes, rather than the 46 chromosomes found in a typical body cell.

Meiosis occurs in two steps: meiosis I and meiosis II. During meiosis I, a cell's chromosomes are duplicated. The cell then divides, with one full set of 46 chromosomes going to each of the two resulting cells. In meiosis II, these two cells again undergo division, this time without a duplication of the chromosomes. After meiosis II, there are a total of four cells, each with half the number of chromosomes as the original cell.

In males, sperm production by the process of meiosis begins during puberty. Cells in the testes called spermatagonia undergo meiosis I and meiosis II. Each spermatagonia produces four sperm cells. Each sperm cell contains 23 chromosomes.

Egg production in females starts before birth. Egg cells in a developing female fetus begin developing and complete most of the steps of meiosis I. Egg production then stops. When puberty occurs, egg production resumes. Each month one or more eggs resume meiosis and complete meiosis I. One of the resulting cells is called a primary oocyte. The other resulting cell, called the first polar body, disintegrates. The primary oocyte then begins the process of meiosis II; however, meiosis II is not completed unless the cell is fertilized. If the cell is fertilized and meiosis II is completed, one of the resulting cells is the developing zygote, and the other cell, called the second polar body, disintegrates.

When fertilization occurs, 23 chromosomes are contributed by the sperm and 23 chromosomes are contributed by the egg. In most cases, the resulting zygote has 46 chromosomes. An exception occurs in the case of individuals with Down Syndrome, a condition caused by an extra copy of chromosome 21.

Teaching Heredity to Students in Nontraditional Families

Heredity is the study of traits passed from one generation to the next. DNA is the biological molecule that codes for traits. DNA is passed from one generation to the next on chromosomes. Some of an individual's traits are determined only by the hereditary information in their cells. Other traits are determined only by a person's environment. However, the vast majority of a person's traits are formed by a combination of genetic information and environmental influence.

Heredity and genetics can be a sensitive issue for students who do not live with two biological parents. In the United States, more than 2 million children are adopted, and another ½ million are in foster care. Many other children live with just one biological parent and have little or no contact with the other biological parent. It is important for teachers to be sensitive when discussing traits passed down through families or family resemblances. Avoid assignments that use a "family tree" to show how a particular trait has been passed to a student. Refrain from asking questions such as "What genetic traits do you share with your family?" or "In what ways do you resemble others in your family?" Also avoid pointing out a biological characteristic of a student and making an assumption about parents, such as "Your parents must have red hair, too."

When teaching heredity and genetics, use magazine pictures or pictures in the text for students to point out traits and family resemblances. Do not ask students to use pictures of their own families for this task. Be certain to use inclusive and unbiased language when describing families.

Support for Teaching Reading

 Reading Support   **Health Online**   Academic Integration For additional academic integration strategies, visit the Teacher Center at **health.glencoe.com**.

Reading Preview

Activating Background Vocabulary Have student pairs create a concept definition map for the word *adolescence*. Discuss the questions the map should answer: What is adolescence? (definition) What is it like? (characteristics) What are some examples of it? Encourage students to revise their maps as they read and gather more information.

FOLDABLES Study Organizer *Dinah Zike's Reading and Study Skills for Teen Health* provides interactive graphic organizers that help students comprehend and retain health concepts as they read. Use the Foldable™ on page 201 or find more Foldables™ activities for the chapter on **Growth and Development** in the separate booklet, available in the TCR.

Lesson 1   Adolescence: A Time of Change

Responding Have students stop at any point while reading and discuss with a partner what they find interesting or surprising about what they have read so far. Direct students to the paragraph that states that hormones cause physical, mental/emotional, and social changes during puberty. Have students write a journal entry, describing their thoughts about these changes.

Lesson 2   Human Reproduction

Directed Reading/Thinking Activity (DR/TA) Direct students to divide a paper into 4 columns titled, 'What I know,' 'What I think I know,' 'What I think I'll learn,' and 'What I know I learned.' Have students fill out the first three sections of the chart and discuss. Have students complete the chart while they read about the human reproductive systems.

Lesson 3   Heredity and the Life Cycle

Identifying Sequence Direct students to look at the section on **The Life Cycle**. Have them look for words that point to time order or steps in a process and identify the logical order of events. Have students read the section, then create a time line of the life cycle. Encourage student pairs to work together to revise their time lines as they gain information.

Post Reading

Nonverbal Presentations Guide students to use movement, placement, gestures, facial expressions, and other nonverbal cues to convey meaning to an audience in an informational presentation on the stages of the life cycle. Encourage students to use their time lines to help organize and structure their presentation to the class.

Key for Using the Teacher Wraparound Edition

Use this key to help you identify the different types of prompts found in the Teacher Wraparound Edition.

R **Reading Strategies** activities help you teach reading skills and vocabulary.

C **Critical Thinking** strategies help students apply and extend what they have learned.

U **Universal Access** activities provide differentiated instruction for students learning to speak English, along with suggestions for teaching various types of learners.

HS **Health Skills Practice** activities reinforce Health Skills concepts and help students apply these skills in their everyday lives.

W **Writing Support** activities provide writing opportunities to help students comprehend the text.

AL **Active Learning** strategies provide a variety of activities

Key to Ability Levels

Teaching Strategies and activities have been coded for ability level and appropriateness

AL Activities for students working above grade level

OL Activities for students working on grade level

BL Activities for students working below grade level

EL Activities for English Learners

Symbols

⬇ Transparencies

◉ CD-ROM

✎ health.glencoe.com

📁 Print Resources

Growth and Development

Chapter at a Glance

Lesson 1 describes the three kinds of changes that happen during the teen years, identifies the structure and function of the endocrine system, and analyzes how teens are influenced by peers.

Lesson 2 identifies the parts and functions of the reproductive system and explains how to care for the reproductive system.

Lesson 3 explains how inherited traits are passed along, identifies changes to a developing baby, and recognizes stages in the life cycle.

R Reading Strategy

Interpreting the Photo Have students look at the photo that shows teens at differing stages of growth. Ask: What social, emotional, or mental changes do you think Troy has undergone? *Sample answer: Troy has probably become more mature and responsible.* **OL**

Growth and Development

Chapter Preview

Lesson 1	Adolescence: A Time of Change	202
Lesson 2	Human Reproduction	206
Lesson 3	Heredity and the Life Cycle	210

Building Health Skills	214
Hands-on Health	216
Chapter Reading Review	217
Chapter Assessment	218

▲ *Working With the Photo*

R During the teen years, your body will go through many changes. **What mental and emotional changes will you experience?**

200

Universal Access

Differentiated Learning Glencoe provides teacher support and student materials for all learners in the health classroom.
● Spanish Glosario and chapter summaries for the English Language Learners.
● *Reading Tutor* and related worksheets support reluctant readers.

● Universal Access strategies throughout the Teacher Wraparound Edition and Fast Files help you present materials for gifted students, at-risk students, physically impaired students, and those with behavior disorders or learning disabilities.

Start-Up Activities

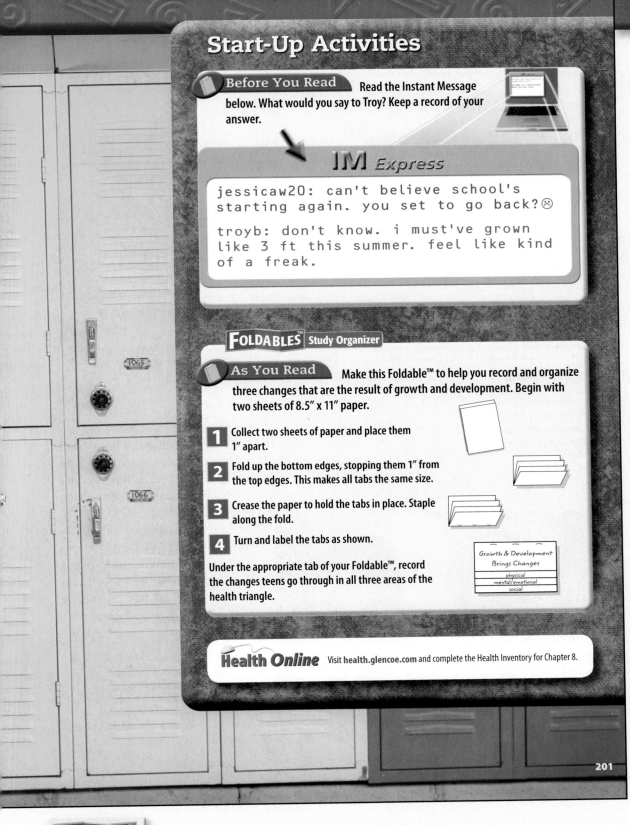

Before You Read

Read the Instant Message below. What would you say to Troy? Keep a record of your answer.

IM Express

jessicaw20: can't believe school's starting again. you set to go back? ☹

troyb: don't know. i must've grown like 3 ft this summer. feel like kind of a freak.

FOLDABLES™ Study Organizer

As You Read

Make this Foldable™ to help you record and organize three changes that are the result of growth and development. Begin with two sheets of 8.5" x 11" paper.

1 Collect two sheets of paper and place them 1" apart.

2 Fold up the bottom edges, stopping them 1" from the top edges. This makes all tabs the same size.

3 Crease the paper to hold the tabs in place. Staple along the fold.

4 Turn and label the tabs as shown.

Under the appropriate tab of your Foldable™, record the changes teens go through in all three areas of the health triangle.

Growth & Development Brings Changes

physical
mental/emotional
social

Health Online Visit health.glencoe.com and complete the Health Inventory for Chapter 8.

201

FOCUS

Activating Prior Knowledge

What I Know Ask volunteers to define the term *adolescence*. Explain that students will be discussing changes during adolescence as they read this lesson.

Guide to Reading

BUILDING VOCABULARY

- Have students write a definition of each vocabulary term in their own words.
- Use Vocabulary PuzzleMaker to reinforce vocabulary terms.

READING STRATEGY

 Have students use their Foldables™ as they read Lesson 1.

- **Organizing Information** Tell students they may use their Foldable™ or make a three-column table. As students read, remind them to note changes during adolescence that affect all three sides of the health triangle.

*Q*uick Write

Introduce the Quick Write by asking students if they could comfortably use the same desk and chair now that they used in first grade. In order to maintain privacy, do not ask students to share their completed Quick Writes.

Lesson 1

Adolescence: A Time of Change

Guide to Reading

● **Building Vocabulary**
As you read the lesson, write the definition for each of the following terms.

- adolescence (p. 202)
- endocrine system (p. 203)
- puberty (p. 203)

● **Focusing on the Main Ideas**
In this lesson, you will be able to

- **describe** three kinds of changes you go through during the teen years.
- **identify** the structure and function of the endocrine system.
- **analyze** how a teen is influenced by peers.

● **Reading Strategy**
Organizing Information Divide a sheet of paper into three columns. Name each column for one of the sides of the health triangle. Write two changes that occur on each side.

 Use the Foldable™ on p. 201 as you read this lesson.

*Q*uick Write

Think about ways your body has changed in the past few years. Make a list of some of these changes.

Changes During Adolescence

Look at any group of teens, and you'll probably see big differences between the individuals. One teen may be a head taller than another who is the same age. Some teens may look younger or older than they really are. These differences are caused by the changes teens go through during **adolescence** (a·duhl·EH·suhns). This is *the period between childhood and adulthood.* Although all teens experience these changes, they occur at different times and speeds for everyone. You are just beginning your adolescent years now.

◀ Mood swings are a normal part of adolescence. **What causes mood swings?**

Lesson 1 Resources

📁 **Chapter *FAST FILE* Resources**
Guided Reading and Writing 8-1
Concept Mapping Activity 8-1
Decision-Making Activity 8-1
Reteaching Activity 8-1
Enrichment Activity 8-1
Lesson Quiz 8-1

Technology
🔦 Transparency 8-1
💿 Audio Summaries
⊙ *ExamView*
💿 Vocabulary PuzzleMaker
⊙ StudentWorks™ Plus

▼ FIGURE 8.1

R THE ENDOCRINE SYSTEM

The glands that make up this system perform many different jobs in your body. Which glands regulate growth?

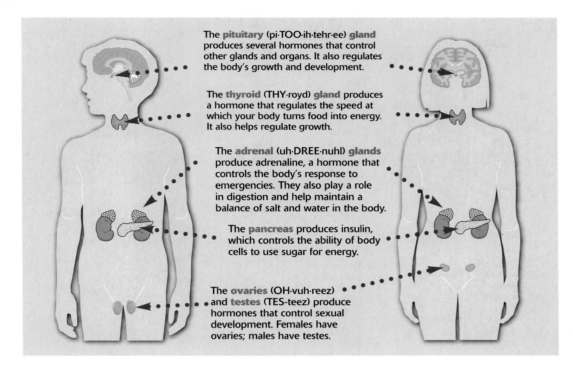

The **pituitary** (pi·TOO·ih·tehr·ee) **gland** produces several hormones that control other glands and organs. It also regulates the body's growth and development.

The **thyroid** (THY·royd) **gland** produces a hormone that regulates the speed at which your body turns food into energy. It also helps regulate growth.

The **adrenal** (uh·DREE·nuhl) **glands** produce adrenaline, a hormone that controls the body's response to emergencies. They also play a role in digestion and help maintain a balance of salt and water in the body.

The **pancreas** produces insulin, which controls the ability of body cells to use sugar for energy.

The **ovaries** (OH·vuh·reez) and **testes** (TES·teez) produce hormones that control sexual development. Females have ovaries; males have testes.

Adolescence brings changes in all three areas of your health triangle. You develop physically, mentally/emotionally, and socially. Many of these changes are caused by *hormones.* As noted in Chapter 2, hormones are chemicals made by the body. Specifically, they are produced in the **endocrine** (EN·duh·krin) **system.** This is *a body system containing glands that regulate growth and other important activities.* **Figure 8.1** describes many important functions of the endocrine system.

Physical Changes

Over the past summer, Phil noticed his voice beginning to change. Acne is appearing on Marie's face. Changes such as these **HS** signal the arrival of **puberty** (PYOO·bur·tee). This is *the time when you start developing the physical characteristics of adults of your gender.* Other changes that occur during puberty include the growth of body hair and increased sweating, or perspiration.

Lesson 1: Adolescence: A Time of Change   **203**

CHAPTER 8

Lesson 1

TEACH

R Reading Strategy

Analyzing a Graphic Encourage students to examine Figure 8.1. Ask: Which gland regulates the body's growth and development? *the pituitary gland* Then ask: If a person had a growth spurt, what glands would be working together to accomplish this? *the pituitary, and thyroid* **OL**

HS Health Skills Practice

Accessing Information Ask: Why is using deodorant important for both boys and girls during adolescence? Sample answer: *Both boys and girls experience an increase in perspiration during adolescence.* Review with students the section on consumer choices in Chapter 6, Personal Health, and discuss ways to make wise decisions when choosing health products such as antiperspirants and deodorants. **OL**

Caption Answers

Photo Caption, p. 202 Adolescent changes and hormones cause mood swings.
Figure Caption The pituitary and thyroid glands regulate growth.

Cultural Perspectives

Early Onset of Puberty "Early" puberty in American females is a commonly discussed topic in the media. Puberty before the age of 7 is called precocious puberty. Studies indicate the onset of puberty now ranges from 10 to 13, with some females entering puberty at 8 years of age. This has changed from the average age of 12 to 14 in the 1960s and 1970s. Studies of the causes of early puberty have not identified a clear cause. According to the American Academy of Pediatrics, one contributing factor in early puberty is obesity. **OL**

203

R Reading Strategy

Analyzing a Graphic As a class, examine Figure 8.2 on Physical Changes During Adolescence. On the board, draw two overlapping circles to create a Venn diagram. Label one circle "male changes" and the other "female changes." Ask students to note changes that are experienced by both males and females *increased perspiration, acne, underarm hair, enlargement of external genitals* record these in the overlapping section of the diagram. Then ask: Which changes are similar in males and females? *increased levels of hormones, production of reproductive cells*

W Writing Support

Persuasive Writing Remind students that all teens feel awkward at some point during adolescence. Have students write a persuasive paragraph explaining why it is important to treat others with respect, especially those who are growing and developing at a different rate than their classmates. Remind students that a persuasive paragraph uses information to support an opinion. Have students proofread their paragraphs and correct any errors before turning them in. **OL**

Academic Vocabulary

Temporary On this page situations in puberty are described as *temporary*. Tell students that *temporary* means "for a limited time." Have students identify words that have the opposite meaning. *permanent, long-lasting*

▼ **FIGURE 8.2**

R PHYSICAL CHANGES DURING ADOLESCENCE

Notice that boys and girls go through some similar changes. Give an example of a change both boys and girls go through.

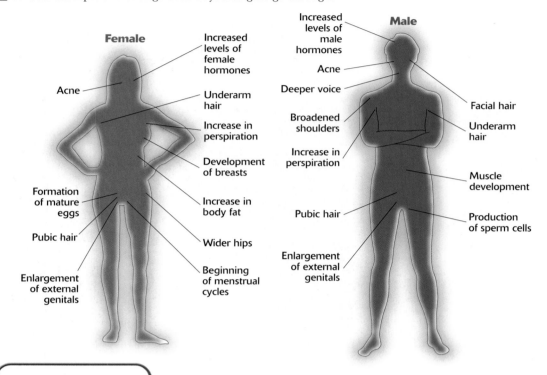

Female

Acne — Increased levels of female hormones

Underarm hair

Increase in perspiration

Development of breasts

Formation of mature eggs

Increase in body fat

Pubic hair

Wider hips

Enlargement of external genitals

Beginning of menstrual cycles

Male

Increased levels of male hormones

Acne

Deeper voice

Broadened shoulders

Increase in perspiration

Pubic hair

Enlargement of external genitals

Facial hair

Underarm hair

Muscle development

Production of sperm cells

Health Online

Topic: Understanding Puberty

Visit health.glencoe.com for Student Web Activities to get answers to questions teens are asking about growth and development.

Activity: Using the information provided at the link above, create a small card that has three resources printed on it where teens can access reliable information on growth and development.

The shape of your body changes, and you grow taller. These and other changes are shown in **Figure 8.2.**

Puberty begins at different times for different people. Typically, it starts between the ages of 8 and 14. During puberty, some body parts may grow faster than other parts. This is especially true of the hands and feet. These changes may make some teens feel awkward or self-conscious. Others, for whom puberty comes later, can feel "left behind." Although these situations can be troubling, remember that they are only temporary. **W**

Mental/Emotional Changes

During adolescence, you begin to think about things in new ways. You learn to appreciate different opinions or points of view. You will begin to identify your own values and beliefs. You will also become aware of how your opinions, decisions, and actions affect others.

What Teens Want to Know

How can I deal with mood swings? The hormones that cause changes in puberty can trigger mood swings. As a class, have students brainstorm a list of healthy ways to deal with mood swings, for example taking a walk, relaxing with a book, or talking with friends. Remind students that getting enough sleep and physical activity can help reduce mood swings. Explain that while most teens experience mood swings, some teens suffer from depression and other serious emotional problems. Teens should be encouraged to talk to a trusted adult about their feelings. **OL**

Changes in hormones can affect your feelings as well as your thoughts. You may feel strong emotions that you do not always understand. You might be happy one moment and sad the next. These sudden shifts in emotion are called mood swings and are common in adolescence. Talk about your feelings with others. This will help you manage your feelings in a healthy way.

Social Changes

Adolescence brings about changes in the way you relate to others. You become more independent. Your parents may give you more responsibility. For example, you may be asked to help care for a younger sibling or to prepare meals.

During this time, your friends can become very important. Like you, they are going through changes and can understand how you feel. As a result, their opinions and actions may influence you without you even knowing it. Choose friends that support you and influence you in a positive way. This will help you make good choices during your teen years.

 Reading Check **Identify** What is puberty?

Health Online

Visit **health.glencoe.com** and complete the Interactive Study Guide for Lesson 1.

Lesson 1 Review

 After You Read

Review this lesson for new terms, major headings, and Reading Checks.

What I Learned

1. **Vocabulary** Define *endocrine system*.

2. **Recall** Name two physical changes that occur during puberty.

3. **Identify** What are some social changes that occur during adolescence?

Thinking Critically

4. **Apply** Richard feels funny about his voice changing. What advice might you give him to make him feel less awkward?

5. **Evaluate** How do you think the changes you experience during puberty help you prepare for adulthood?

Applying Health Skills

6. **Analyzing Influences** Peers can have a strong influence on your actions during adolescence. Give one example of how this can be positive. Give another example of how it can be negative.

Health Online For more review questions for Lesson 1, go to **health.glencoe.com**. Lesson 1: Adolescence: A Time of Change **205**

Reading Check

Answer Puberty is the time when you start developing the physical characteristics of adults of your gender.

ASSESS

Assessment Resources

Lesson Review Quiz
- *ExamView*
- Fast Files Activities
- Online Quizzes and Activities

Reteaching
- Assign Concept Map 8-1 or Reteaching Activity 8-1 in the Fast Files.
- Have students write sentences that describe the function of the endocrine system. Allow students to use their text to verify their work and share it with each other and with the teacher.

Enrichment
- Assign Enrichment Activity 8-1 in the Fast Files.
- Have students write a short play about the social changes that occur during adolescence. Encourage students to share their plays with the class.

CLOSE

Have each student list five changes of adolescence.

Lesson 1 Review Answers

1. It is a body system containing glands that regulate growth and other activities.
2. Answer should include any of the changes listed in Figure 8.2.
3. *Sample answers:* becoming more independent, having more responsibility, spending more time with friends, and experiencing the influence of peers
4. *Sample answer:* These changes are normal for teen boys entering puberty.
5. Answers, which will vary, should show an understanding of the changes that occur during puberty.
6. *Sample answer:* A positive example is a friend encouraging you to study. Pressure to use alcohol is a negative influence.

FOCUS

Activating Prior Knowledge

What I Know Ask students to name the purpose of the reproductive system.

Guide to Reading

BUILDING VOCABULARY

- Explain that the word part *-ation* means "the process of." Have students relate this to the meaning of the words *fertilization* and *menstruation*.
- Use Vocabulary PuzzleMaker to reinforce vocabulary terms.

READING STRATEGY

Comparing and Contrasting Suggest students use a two-column chart to note details they read in the lesson about the male and female reproductive systems. Refer them to Figures 8.3 and 8.4 for specific examples. Review similarities and differences with the class at the end of the lesson.

Quick Write

To introduce the Quick Write, have students brainstorm healthy habits that could positively affect any of their body systems.

Human Reproduction

Guide to Reading

● **Building Vocabulary**
Create a word web for the terms below. Decide which term belongs at the center.

- reproductive system (p. 206)
- egg cell (p. 206)
- fertilization (p. 207)
- menstruation (p. 207)
- sperm (p. 208)

● **Focusing on the Main Ideas**
In this lesson, you will be able to

- **identify** the parts and functions of the male and female reproductive systems.
- **explain** how to care for the reproductive system.

● **Reading Strategy**
Comparing and Contrasting As you read the lesson, compare the female and male reproductive systems.

Quick Write

Write about what you think teens can do to care for their reproductive systems.

▼ Talking to a trusted adult can help you feel better about the changes you are experiencing. **Who are some adults you could talk to about reproductive health?**

Human Reproduction

So far, all the body systems you've learned about are the same for females and males. The **reproductive system,** however, is different. This is *the body system that makes it possible to create offspring*, or have babies. During puberty, the female and male reproductive systems undergo changes.

The Female Reproductive System

The female reproductive system, shown in **Figure 8.3,** has two main functions. One is to store egg cells. An **egg cell,** also called an *ovum*, is *the female reproductive cell*. The second function is to reproduce, to create offspring. This process begins when the egg cell joins with a male reproductive cell. The *ovaries* (OH·vuh·reez) are the two female reproductive glands that store the egg cells. The ovaries also release hormones that control growth and play a role in the proper functioning of the reproductive system. During puberty, the egg cells begin to mature. The ovaries begin to release eggs cells. If an egg cell is fertilized, a baby will

Lesson 2 Resources

📁 **Chapter *FAST FILE* Resources**
Guided Reading and Writing 8-2
Concept Mapping Activity 8-2
Cross-Curriculum Activity 8-2
Reteaching Activity 8-2
Enrichment Activity 8-2
Lesson Quiz 8-2

Technology
👆 Transparency 8-2
🧽 Audio Summaries
💿 *ExamView*
🧽 Vocabulary PuzzleMaker
💿 StudentWorks™ Plus

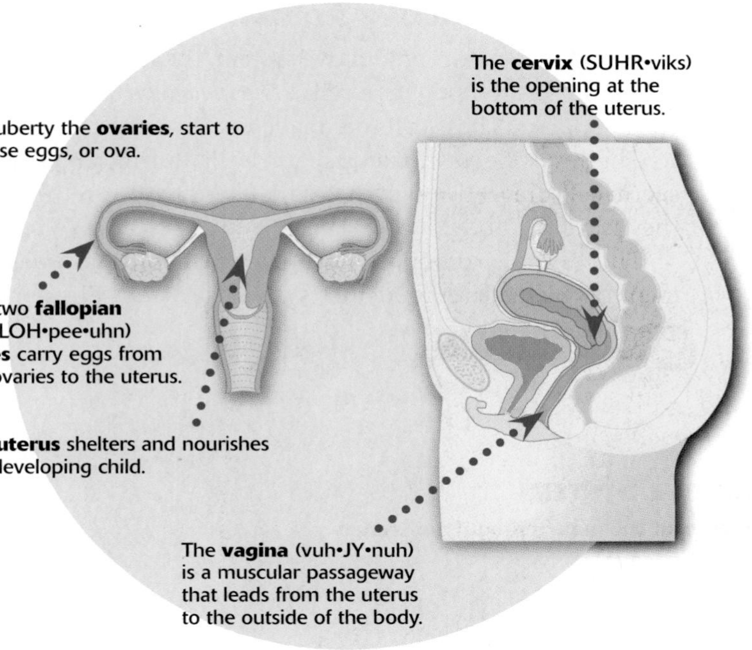

At puberty the **ovaries**, start to release eggs, or ova.

The two **fallopian** (fuh•LOH•pee•uhn) **tubes** carry eggs from the ovaries to the uterus.

The **uterus** shelters and nourishes the developing child.

The **vagina** (vuh•JY•nuh) is a muscular passageway that leads from the uterus to the outside of the body.

The **cervix** (SUHR•viks) is the opening at the bottom of the uterus.

◀ FIGURE 8.3

THE FEMALE REPRODUCTIVE SYSTEM R

This illustration shows the parts of the female reproductive system. What is the function of this system?

TEACH

R Reading Strategy

Analyzing a Graphic Have students examine Figure 8.3, which shows the female reproductive system. Ask: What are two functions of the ovaries? *Ovaries store eggs and release hormones.* Ask volunteers to identify problems that might occur with this system. OL

AL Active Learning

Pamphlet Have students work in small groups to make pamphlets that give basic facts about menstruation. Remind them to include sources of help for students who have questions or concerns about menstruation (parents or guardian, school nurse). OL

Reading Check

Answer Menstruation is the breakdown and flow of blood, tissue, and unfertilized egg from the body.

eventually grow from it. **Fertilization** is *the joining of a female egg cell with a male reproductive cell.* A newly fertilized egg will travel to the uterus (YOO·tuh·ruhs), the organ in which the baby will develop.

Menstruation

Each month, the uterus forms a lining of nutrient-rich blood and tissue to prepare for pregnancy. If fertilization does not occur, the lining breaks down. *Blood, tissue, and the unfertilized egg flow out of the body.* This flow is called **menstruation** (men·stroo·AY·shuhn).

Menstruation is often referred to as a "period." A period usually happens about once a month. It may last for three to five days, or as long as seven days. Most girls can expect to begin menstruation anywhere from age 9 through 16. However, this differs from female to female.

During menstruation, change sanitary pads or tampons several times a day. You may also experience some cramping. Exercise can sometimes ease the pain of cramps. Talk to your doctor if you have unusual pain or heavy bleeding.

Reading Check **Explain** What is menstruation?

Lesson 2: Human Reproduction **207**

Promoting Coordinated School Health

School Nurse The school nurse is an excellent resource for students who have questions or concerns about menstruation. Invite the school nurse to speak to the class and to answer students' questions. (To avoid embarrassment, students could anonymously write their questions for the nurse to answer.) The nurse may also have pamphlets or other literature about puberty that could be shared with the class. Remind students that the school nurse is available to answer questions throughout the year. OL

Caption Answers

Photo Caption, p. 206 A parent, guardian, school nurse, or doctor are good resources.
Figure Caption The main functions of the female reproductive system are to store eggs cells and to create offspring, or reproduce.

R Reading Strategy

Analyzing a Graphic Have students study Figure 8.4, which shows the male reproductive system. Ask: Why are the testes considered to be a part of both the reproductive system and the endocrine system? *The testes produce reproductive cells as well as hormones.* **OL**

Health Skills Activity

Practicing Healthful Behaviors

Care of the Reproductive System

After reading the feature on the next page, ask the class to brainstorm a list of healthful behaviors involving reproductive system health. Encourage teens to ask a parent, guardian, or medical professional for advice when questions arise. **OL**

Reading Check

Answer The testes make sperm cells.

Health Online

Visit **health.glencoe.com** and complete the Interactive Study Guide for Lesson 2.

Male Reproductive System

Like the female reproductive system, the male reproductive system makes reproductive cells. *The male reproductive cells are* called **sperm.** These cells are made inside the testes.

The testes begin making sperm cells during puberty. The sperm cells travel through the vas deferens to the urethra where they leave the body.

The testes also produce a hormone that controls the development of the male reproduction system shown in **Figure 8.4.**

Reading Check **Explain** What do the testes do?

▼ **FIGURE 8.4**

R THE MALE REPRODUCTIVE SYSTEM

This illustration shows the parts of the male reproduction system. What is the job of the male reproductive system?

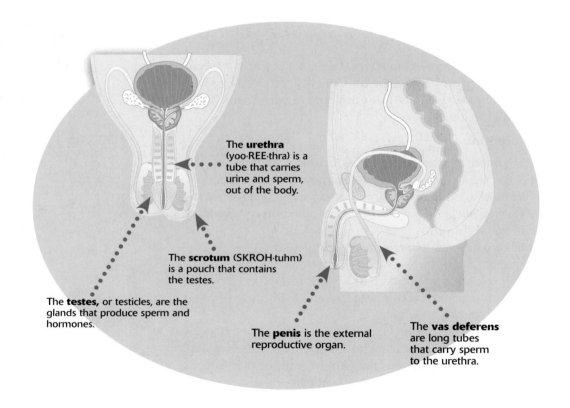

The **urethra** (yoo·REE·thra) is a tube that carries urine and sperm, out of the body.

The **scrotum** (SKROH·tuhm) is a pouch that contains the testes.

The **testes,** or testicles, are the glands that produce sperm and hormones.

The **penis** is the external reproductive organ.

The **vas deferens** are long tubes that carry sperm to the urethra.

Caption Answer

Figure Caption The function of the male reproductive system is to produce reproductive cells.

HEALTH LITERACY

Steroids and Reproductive Health According to a study by the Centers for Disease Control and Prevention (CDC), it has been documented that more than 6 percent of all high school students have used anabolic steroids. The use of anabolic steroids can have a negative impact on the reproductive health of both males and females. Anabolic steroids can cause the development of breasts, reduced sperm production, and shrunken testicles in males. In females, steroid use can result in reduced breast size and disruption or discontinuation of menstruation. **OL**

Health Skills Activity

Practicing Healthful Behaviors

Care of the Reproductive System

Like any body system, the reproductive system needs care. You can protect the health of your reproductive system by practicing the following healthful behaviors:

- Practice good hygiene, this includes showering or bathing regularly.
- Avoid wearing clothing or underwear that is too tight.
- Visit your doctor for regular checkups.
- Practice abstinence to prevent sexually transmitted diseases.
- Males who play contact sports should always wear protective gear.
- If you have questions about your reproductive health, talk to your parent or guardian, your doctor, or another trusted adult.

On Your Own
Make a list of other healthful behaviors you can practice that will help you look and feel your best during adolescence.

ASSESS

Assessment Resources

Lesson Review Quiz
ExamView
Fast Files Activities
Online Quizzes and Activities

Reteaching

- Assign Concept Map 8-2 or Reteaching Activity 8-2 in the Fast Files.
- Ask students to list three parts of the male reproductive system and their functions and three parts of the female reproductive system and their functions.

Enrichment

- Assign Enrichment Activity 8-2 in the Fast Files.
- Challenge students to research diseases that affect the reproductive system. Have them write a short report of their findings.

CLOSE

Have students work with a partner to review the definitions of the lesson vocabulary terms.

Lesson 2 Review

After You Read

Review this lesson for new terms, major headings, and Reading Checks.

What I Learned

1. *Recall* Name two functions of the female reproductive system.

2. *Vocabulary* Define *fertilization*?

3. *Identify* Where in the male reproductive system are sperm made?

Thinking Critically

4. *Compare* How are the female and male reproductive systems similar? How are they different?

5. *Analyze* James will be catcher this year for his baseball team. What special precautions should James take to prevent injury to his reproductive system? Give details to explain your answer.

Applying Health Skills

6. *Advocacy* Caring for your body during puberty is important. With a small group, design and print a pamphlet that explains the kinds of care needed.

Health Online For more review questions for Lesson 2, go to **health.glencoe.com**.

Lesson 2: Human Reproduction **209**

Lesson 2 Review Answers

1. Two functions of the female reproductive system are to produce hormones and reproductive cells.

2. Fertilization is the joining of an egg cell and a sperm cell.

3. Sperm are made in the testes.

4. They are alike in that both produce and store reproductive cells, but they have different structures.

5. He should wear a protective cup. Injury to male reproductive organs could cause sterility.

6. Pamphlets should include suggestions from the lesson.

FOCUS

Activating Prior Knowledge

What I Know Ask students to name stages of life and to identify what happens during each stage.

Guide to Reading

BUILDING VOCABULARY
- Point out that the word part *pre-* means "before." Ask students how this applies to the definition of the word *prenatal*.
- Use Vocabulary PuzzleMaker to reinforce vocabulary terms.

READING STRATEGY
Analyzing a Graphic
Students' diagrams should include any of the facts shown in Figure 8.5

Quick Write

To introduce the Quick Write, explain that traits are inherited characteristics, such as eye color. Point out that characteristics such as knowing another language are not inherited traits but are learned.

Caption Answer

Photo Caption Hair color and body build are hereditary.

210

Heredity and the Life Cycle

Guide to Reading

● **Building Vocabulary**
Review the terms below. See if you know which term represents a part of another term.
- chromosomes (p. 210)
- genes (p. 210)
- fetus (p. 212)
- prenatal care (p. 212)

● **Focusing on the Main Ideas**
In this lesson, you will be able to
- **explain** how inherited traits are passed along.
- **identify** changes to the developing baby.
- **recognize** stages in the life cycle.

● **Reading Strategy**
Analyzing a Graphic Using the diagram to the right as a guide, describe the stages of development before birth.

The Developing Baby

After 3 months:
↓
| After 6 months: |
↓
| After 9 months: |

Quick Write

Observe physical traits in your class, such as eye and hair color. Write a short paragraph noting which traits are most common and why you believe this.

Heredity

Do you remember reading about heredity in Chapter 1? This is the process by which parents pass certain traits to their children. Hair color and body build are two examples of inherited traits. Children may also inherit talents and abilities from parents. The likelihood of developing certain diseases and health problems is also passed along.

Traits are passed along by chromosomes (KROH·muh·sohmz). **Chromosomes** are *tiny strands of matter that carry the codes for inherited traits*. They are arranged in pairs in your body's cells. One chromosome in each pair comes from your father. The other is from your mother. Chromosomes are made up of smaller bits of matter called genes (JEENZ). **Genes** are *the basic units of heredity*. Each gene defines a particular trait.

◀ Parents and their offspring often have similar characteristics because of heredity. **What are some characteristics that can be passed along through heredity?**

210 Chapter 8: Growth and Development

Lesson 3 Resources

📁 **Chapter** *FAST FILE* **Resources**
Guided Reading and Writing 8-3
Concept Mapping Activity 8-3
Health Lab 8-3
Reteaching Activity 8-3
Enrichment Activity 8-3
Lesson Quiz 8-3

Technology
🔹 Transparency 8-3
🔹 Audio Summaries
🔹 *ExamView*
🔹 Vocabulary PuzzleMaker
🔹 StudentWorks™ Plus

Chromosomes and Fertilization

Every type of cell in the human body except one contains 46 chromosomes. That one exception is the reproductive cell. Egg cells and sperm cells each have half the usual number of chromosomes. Each has exactly 23. When these cells unite during fertilization, their chromosomes are joined. The newly fertilized egg cell has 46 chromosomes.

Among each sperm's 23 chromosomes, one alone determines the gender of the fertilized egg cell. This chromosome is represented by the letter *X* or *Y*. If a sperm carries an X chromosome, a female will result. If the sperm has a Y chromosome, a male will result.

▲ Female egg cells carry only an X chromosome. **Which of the two unions shown in this illustration will produce a boy?**

Reading Check **Define** What are genes?

Development Before Birth

A female becomes pregnant when one of her egg cells is fertilized by a male sperm cell. Much happens during the first days of pregnancy. The newly fertilized cell travels down the fallopian tube to the uterus. It attaches itself to the wall of the uterus. There it begins to divide, first into two cells, then into four. This process of doubling, or cell division, continues millions of times. From theses cells, the tissues, organs, and body systems are eventually formed. **Figure 8.5** shows the stages of development from fertilization through birth. **AL**

▼ FIGURE 8.5

 THE DEVELOPING BABY

After fertilization, it takes about nine months before a baby is born. About how much does a baby weigh at birth?

Time	Size	Features	Development
fertilization	microscopic	single cell	undeveloped
3 months after fertilization	about 3 inches long; weighs about 1 ounce	arms, legs, fingers toes, eyes, ears	heart is beating, nervous system is forming; cannot survive outside uterus
6 months after fertilization	about 14 inches long; weighs about 2 pounds	hair, eyebrows, fingernails, toenails	can move and kick, sucks thumb, can hear sounds; might survive outside uterus
9 months after fertilization	18–20 inches long; weights 7–9 pounds	smooth skin, fully developed organs	eyes open and close, fingers can grasp, body organs and systems can now work on their own; ready for birth

TECHNOLOGY AND HEALTH

Prenatal Surgery Explain to students that ultrasound imaging can be used to detect some disorders present in a developing fetus. Some of these disorders can be treated with surgery while the fetus is still developing. Spina bifida, for example, is a condition in which the spinal cord is not entirely enclosed. Fetal surgery can sometimes be used to close the "hole" in the spine. The goal of this surgery is to prevent some of the nerve damage that occurs before birth. Have students research the use of technology in prenatal care. **OL**

DEVELOPING

Good **Character**

Behaving Responsibly
After students have read the feature, lead a class discussion on ways to behave responsibly. Challenge students to name ways to show responsible behavior in the home, at school, and in the community.

W Writing Support

Descriptive Writing Have students write a poem that describes one of the stages in the human life cycle. Remind students that poems use vivid language and that not all poems rhyme. Before students turn in their poems, have them proofread their work. **OL**

Academic Vocabulary

Ensure The text explains that special care is needed to *ensure* a developing baby's health. Ask volunteers to define the word *ensure* and name synonyms (*assure*, *guarantee*).

Reading Check

Answer A fertilized egg cell divides by doubling, or cell division.

Caption Answer

Photo Caption Good communication and being responsible can contribute to a healthy, happy family.

DEVELOPING

Good **Character**

Responsibility

Independence is an important goal for many teens, but with it comes added responsibility. There are lots of ways you can show you are responsible and ready for more independence. For example, you could offer to help with extra chores at home. **What are some other ways you could show you are responsible?**

▼ Spending time with different generations of your family is one way to build strong family relationships. **What are some other ways?**

In the uterus, the developing baby receives oxygen and nutrients through a tube called the *umbilical cord*. Waste products are also removed through this cord. *The developing unborn baby, from the eighth week until birth,* is known as a **fetus.**

Pregnancy is a time of change for both parents-to-be. Having a child is a joyful event, but it also means added responsibility. Preparations must be made to care for the baby when it arrives and for his or her future. For the mother, changes are taking place in her body that affect her shape, weight, and emotions. Once the baby is born, he or she requires a lot of attention and care. New parents often don't get a lot of sleep and may experience added stress or other emotional changes.

Throughout pregnancy, an expectant mother needs **prenatal care.** This is *special care to ensure that the mother and her baby remain healthy*. Prenatal care includes eating healthy foods, getting enough rest, and seeing the doctor regularly. The mother-to-be also should avoid using tobacco, alcohol, and other drugs not prescribed by her doctor.

Reading Check

Explain Describe the way a fertilized egg cell divides.

The Life Cycle

Being born is the first step in a life-long journey full of new experiences and change. The entire journey is often called the "life-cycle." It is divided into six main parts or stages: **W**

• **Infancy.** During their first year of life, infants grow very fast. Their height can double and weight triple. Babies also grow mentally and emotionally during this time. Infants need loving care and attention to prepare them for childhood.

• **Childhood.** This period lasts from age 1 through 11. During this time children are busy taking in all sorts of new information. Encouragement and support from others during this stage builds positive self-esteem.

• **Adolescence.** Adolescence begins at age 12 and ends around age 18. This is a time of transition from child to adult. Skills such as decision making, goal setting, and good communication help prepare adolescents for adulthood.

212 Chapter 8: Growth and Development

Cultural Perspectives

Late Adulthood The stage of life known as late adulthood is perceived in different ways by those of different cultures. In American culture, it is typical for older adults to live apart from their extended families, either on their own or in an assisted-living facility. In many cultures, they live with their children and grandchildren. For example, older adults in Japan, Mexico, and China are treated with great honor and respect. Native American culture also has a revered view of older adults. Ask students what positive qualities they associate with older adults. **OL**

- **Early adulthood.** Early adulthood lasts from age 19 until around age 30. Many young adults are busy pursuing an education or training for a career. They may choose to get married and start a family during this time. Working to achieve career and family goals often extends into middle adulthood.

- **Middle adulthood.** This stage begins in the 30s and continues until roughly age 60. People in this life stage may begin looking for ways to contribute to their communities. For example, they may volunteer to coach youth sports or raise money for charity. They may also begin planning for retirement.

- **Late adulthood.** This stage begins around age 60 when adults are beginning to think of retirement. Retirement gives some people the opportunity to develop new interests or spend more time with family members. Maintaining good health will help you stay active during late adulthood.

 Reading Check **Identify** Name two stages in the life cycle.

 **Health Online**

Visit **health.glencoe.com** and complete the Interactive Study Guide for Lesson 3.

Reading Check

Answer *Sample answer:* Infancy and childhood are two stages in the human life cycle.

ASSESS

Assessment Resources

Lesson Review Quiz
- *ExamView*
- Fast Files Activities
- Online Quizzes and Activities

Reteaching
- Assign Concept Map 8-3 or Reteaching Activity 8-3 in the Fast Files.
- Have students create a flow chart of the stages in the human life cycle.

Enrichment
- Assign Enrichment Activity 8-3 in the Fast Files.
- Have students research the number of chromosomes present in the cells of living things other than humans. Students can create a poster of their findings.

CLOSE

Go around the room and ask students to describe some of the changes that take place in a developing fetus.

 **Lesson 3 Review**

After You Read

Review this lesson for new terms, major headings, and Reading Checks.

What I Learned

1. *Vocabulary* Define *chromosomes*.

2. *Recall* How many chromosomes are there in most cells of the human body? What is the one exception?

3. *Identify* Name two developments that may take place during early adulthood.

Thinking Critically

4. *Explain* What determines whether a baby will be male or female?

5. *Apply* Yvonne hopes to become a lawyer when she reaches adulthood. What skills can she develop now during her teens to help her achieve her career goals?

Applying Health Skills

6. *Accessing Information* Sometimes a missing or defective gene causes a health problem known as a genetic disorder. With a group, research different genetic disorders. Share your findings in an oral group report.

Health Online For more review questions for Lesson 3, go to **health.glencoe.com**.

Lesson 3: Heredity and the Life Cycle **213**

Lesson 3 Review Answers

1. Chromosomes are tiny strands of matter that carry the codes for inherited traits.
2. There are 46 chromosomes in all body cells except for the reproductive cells, which have 23 chromosomes.
3. *Sample answer:* advancing one's education, planning or beginning a career, getting married, starting a family
4. The presence of an X or Y chromosome in the sperm cells determines this. An X chromosome means that a female will result, while a Y chromosome means that a male will result.
5. *Sample answers:* learning and practicing communication skills, achieving good grades
6. Students' reports should include accurate information about genetic disorders.

Building Health Skills

ACCESSING INFORMATION

Coping with Changes During Puberty

Skill
Accessing Information

Activating Prior Knowledge

Ask students to name some of the changes associated with puberty and classify each change as a physical, social, or mental/emotional change.

- **Objective** After completing the activity, students will be able to access reliable sources of help for problems experienced during adolescence.
- **Time** 45 minutes
- **Materials** paper, pencil

Teacher Classroom Resources

📁 Building Health Skills
🖨 Transparency 6-5

Model

- Have students read about the steps Shaun took to find information about his problem. Ask: Why did Shaun use more than one source to get information. *Sample answer: Each source was able to give information from a different point of view.*

National Health Standards Addressed

3.1, 3.2, 3.4, 3.6

Coping With Changes During Puberty

DIRECTIONS

Accessing information involves finding reliable information to make healthy choices. This activity will give you the opportunity to develop and master this important health skill. Here's a guide to the different parts of this activity:

❶ In the **Model** section, you will read about a teen who performs the health skill successfully. This "model" scenario will show you how the skill is done.

❷ The **Practice** section will help guide you in practicing the skill.

❸ In the **Apply** section, you will have a chance to perform the skill on your own. You can use the Self-Check to check your work.

To complete this activity, first read the scenario presented in the Model. Then move on to the Practice. Finally, go ahead and try the Apply.

❶ Model

When Shaun returned to school in the fall, he was surprised to find that most of his classmates had grown a lot during the summer. Suddenly, he was the shortest one in his group. He began to worry that something might be wrong with him. Why wasn't he growing as fast as his friends? Finally, Shaun decided to get some help with his concerns.

Shaun talked to his older brother, Greg. Like Shaun, Greg had grown slower than his classmates. Greg told him to be patient, that he would eventually catch up with the rest of his class.

Next Shaun decided to talk to his dad, who told him that different people grow at different rates. His dad also pointed out that he and Shaun's mother were both tall. This, he explained, meant that Shaun had a good chance of being tall, too.

Teaching Tips

- Brainstorm Common Teen Concerns At Puberty. List these on the board so students can choose which problems to investigate and present on. Be prepared to suggest others so that presentations are on appropriate topics.

- Troubleshoot problems quickly by moving around the room and getting students to start writing. Near the end of this activity, identify exemplary papers and have students read these aloud.

❷ Practice

A while later, Shaun began developing acne on his face. At first, it was just a few small blemishes, but then it seemed to get worse. Shaun knew that many teens get acne. He saw several kids at school with acne, too. Shaun wanted to know what he could do to clear up his acne. Using what you know about accessing information, answer the following questions.

1. Where could Shaun get reliable information about treating acne?

2. Name a person Shaun could speak to for help with his acne?

Skill Summary
ACCESSING INFORMATION

Accessing Information includes:

■ Speaking with people you feel will understand you and try to help.

■ Speaking with a trusted adult.

■ Checking reliable sources of information.

❸ Apply

With a partner, plan a brief presentation about another problem some teens might experience during puberty. The problem might relate to emotional or social changes that occur during adolescence. Discuss how a teen can get help for the problem. Include a list of reliable sources to go to for help.

Self-Check

■ Is our problem related to adolescence?

■ Did we discuss how to get help for the problem?

■ Did we include a list of reliable sources?

Practice

● Divide the class into small groups. Have students read the introductory paragraph in the Practice activity.

● Then have students work in their groups to answer the questions.

● Have each group share its answers with the class.

Apply/Assess

● Check that each pair of students has chosen an appropriate problem as the topic of its presentation.

● Help students locate reliable sources to include in their presentations.

● Have each pair of students share its presentation with the class.

● You may wish to distribute the Building Health Skills Activity in the Fast Files.

ASSESSMENT SCORING

Student work should meet all criteria to achieve the highest score.

Skills Student work provides:
● at least 2 reliable sources for the problem.
● a list of reliable sources.

Concepts Student work includes:
● a health problem common to teens.
● accurate information about the health problem.

Looking Ahead

Time: 20 minutes
Materials: pencil or pen, paper

Introducing Hands-on Health

● Have students name ways in which they are more mature and responsible than they were as a 5-year-old.

Teaching the Activity

● Have each student number his or her paper from 1 to 10.
● Tell students that they will be allowed to keep their answers confidential.
● Allow students 10 minutes to answer the questions.
● After students have completed the survey, ask volunteers to share their answers.
● Have a class discussion of other ways to demonstrate mature and responsible behavior.

HANDS-ON HEALTH

Looking Ahead

Preparing for adulthood also involves behaving in a more mature and responsible way. This activity will give you a chance to do some adult-like thinking and see how you feel about questions that you may face as an adult.

What You Will Need

■ pencil or pen
■ paper

What You Will Do

Number a sheet of paper from 1–10. For each statement below, decide whether you would answer each statement as "always," "sometimes," or "rarely." Then write your answer next to each numbered item.

1 I try to think through problems, looking at all possible solutions.

2 I am able to communicate well with my parents or other adults.

3 I am able to list my four most important beliefs.

4 I think about the consequences before I act.

5 I like who I am; I don't try to be something I'm not.

6 I do some things alone or with friends that I used to do with my family.

7 I listen to other people's ideas even when they are different from mine.

8 I am concerned about problems in the world today.

9 I have one or two close friends with whom I can talk about almost anything.

10 I think about how my actions affect other people.

Wrapping It Up

When you are finished, look at how many questions you answered "always" and "sometimes." This shows that you are already beginning to think and act in a mature and responsible way. As a class, brainstorm some others ways you can demonstrate mature and responsible behavior.

216 Chapter 8: Growth and Development

HANDS-ON HEALTH Assessment

Discussion Ask students:
● What is one way to show mature and responsible behavior at home? Sample answer: *helping care for younger siblings*

● What is one way to demonstrate mature and responsible behavior at school? Sample answer: *by turning in assignments on time*

Reading Review

FOLDABLES™ Study Organizer

Foldables™ and Other Study Aids Take out the Foldable™ that you created for Lesson 1 and any graphic organizers that you created for Lessons 1–3. Find a partner, and quiz each other using these study aids.

Lesson 1 Adolescence: A Time of Change

Key Ideas
- During adolescence, you undergo physical, mental/emotional, and social changes.
- Your endocrine system contains glands that regulate growth and other important activities within the body.

Vocabulary
- adolescence (p. 202)
- endocrine system (p. 203)
- puberty (p. 203)

Lesson 2 Human Reproduction

Key Ideas
- The female reproductive system has two main functions: to store egg cells and to reproduce.
- The male reproductive system makes sperm, which fertilizes a female's egg cell to create offspring.
- Reproductive care includes good hygiene and regular checkups. For males, protection should be used during contact sports.

Vocabulary
- reproductive system (p. 206)
- egg cell (p. 206)
- fertilization (p. 207)
- menstruation (p. 207)
- sperm (p. 208)

Lesson 3: Heredity and Childbirth

Key Ideas
- Inherited traits are passed along by chromosomes and the genes they contain.
- A baby begins as a fertilized egg cell. This cell divides many times, ultimately forming tissues, organs, and body systems.
- The life cycle is a series of stages of development that occur throughout life. These stages include infancy, childhood, adolescence, early adulthood, middle adulthood, and late adulthood.

Vocabulary
- chromosomes (p. 210)
- genes (p. 210)
- fetus (p. 212)
- prenatal care (p. 212)

Assessment Resources

- Chapter 8 Summary and Activity
- Audio Summaries
- Reading Tutor
- Performance Assessment
- Chapter 8 Test
- *ExamView*
- Vocabulary PuzzleMaker
- Online Learning Center

Reading Review

Study Aids
- **Using the Dinah Zike Foldable™ Study Organizer** Have students use the Foldable™ to review the content of Lesson 1. **FOLDABLES™** Study Organizer

Key Ideas
- **Use the Lesson Reviews** Have students look back at the Lesson Reviews to be sure that they can answer each of the questions.

Vocabulary Review
- **Definition Cards** Have students write the definition of each vocabulary term on an index card. Then have students identify the vocabulary word associated with each definition.

Teaching Tips

Increasing Comprehension Previewing is an important tool that can increase understanding of the reading material. Explain that previewing means looking through a lesson before they read, noting the boldface heads, the figures and captions, the reading checks, and the lesson review questions. After students have previewed a lesson, have them prepare an outline of the bold-faced heads in the section, with space below each head in which they can write the main ideas of that section.

Assessment

Assessment

Reviewing Vocabulary and Main Ideas

1. Adolescence
2. puberty
3. endocrine system
4. reproductive system
5. egg cell
6. sperm
7. c
8. b
9. b

Thinking Critically

10. Students might observe that physical changes can cause emotional changes. As an example, being short or tall can lead to feelings of awkwardness or that one doesn't blend in with peers.
11. *Sample answer:* Both the body and the mind are changing during this time, so most teens are not stable enough to become parents. Also, childbirth can be difficult for teen mothers.

 After You Read

IM *Express*

Look back at your answer to the Instant Message on the chapter opener. Now that you have read the chapter, have your ideas changed? If so, how?

Reviewing Vocabulary and Main Ideas

On a sheet of paper, write the numbers 1–6. After each number, write the term from the list that best completes each sentence.

- adolescence
- chromosomes
- egg cell
- endocrine system
- genes
- reproductive system
- puberty
- sperm

Lesson 1 Adolescence: A Time of Change

1. _____ is the period between childhood and adulthood.

2. The time when you start developing physical characteristics of adults of your gender is _____.

3. The _____ is a body system containing glands that regulate growth and other important activities.

Lesson 2 Human Reproduction

4. The body system that makes it possible to create offspring is the _____.

5. The female reproductive cell is known as the _____.

6. The male reproductive cells are known as _____.

Lesson 3 Heredity and the Life Cycle

On a sheet of paper, write the numbers 7–9. Choose the letter of the word or phrase that best completes each statement or question.

7. Which statement about genes is TRUE?
   a. They are made up of chromosomes.
   b. They are tiny strands of matter that carry the codes for inherited traits.
   c. They define particular traits.
   d. They are different for identical twins.

8. Which of the following is part of pre-natal care?
   a. The newly fertilized cell travels down the fallopian tube to the uterus.
   b. The mother-to-be eats healthfully and gets enough rest.
   c. The baby is born.
   d. None of the above.

9. The stage of the life cycle in which many people begin training for a career is
   a. adolescence.
   b. early adulthood.
   c. middle adulthood.
   d. late adulthood.

Health *Online* Visit health.glencoe.com and take the Online Quiz for Chapter 8.

Health *Online*

Have students visit **health.glencoe.com** to take the Chapter 8 Quiz.

IM *Express Wrap-Up*

Adolescent Changes Have students reread the IM Express in the chapter opener. Ask students to explain why Troy should not feel uncomfortable about for having a growth spurt. Challenge students to write a new response to Troy based on the information in the chapter.

Thinking Critically

Using complete sentences, answer the following questions on a sheet of paper.

10. **Analyze** In what ways are emotional and physical changes during adolescence related? Give an example to support your views.

11. **Synthesize** Why do you think the teen years are not a good time for becoming a parent?

Write About It

Using complete sentences, answer the following questions on a sheet of paper.

12. **Communication Skills** Write a paragraph persuading teens to use good

Career Corner

Pediatrician Pediatricians are medical doctors who specialize in the care of children through adolescence. To become a pediatrician, you need a four-year college degree. After that, you need to attend four years of medical school. Finally, you need to have three years of residency training. For more on this career, visit *Career Corner* at **health.glencoe.com**.

communication skills to help cope with mood swings.

13. **Practicing Healthful Behaviors** Explain the importance of practicing healthful behaviors during adolescence.

Write About It

12. **Persuasive Writing** This writing activity should state a position, facts, opinions, and give examples. Answers may explain that a teen with good communication skills will know it is important to think before speaking and, thus, would be less likely to lash out at others.

13. **Expository Writing** This writing activity shares knowledge to help others understand. During puberty, a teen's sweat glands become more active. This can result in increased body odor. To offset this odor, a teen should shower or bathe regularly and use a deodorant. Other behaviors such as brushing teeth and combing hair will help a teen look and feel their best and stay healthy.

Standardized Test Practice

1. C
2. B

Career Corner

Pediatrician Have students visit the Career Corner at **health.glencoe.com** to gather more information about a career as a pediatrician. Pediatricians should enjoy working with infants, children, and teens. Explain that pediatricians can further specialize, for example, pediatric surgeons operate only on children.

Standardized Test Practice

Reading

Read the passage and then answer the questions.

Gregor Mendel was born in 1822 in what is now the Czech Republic. He developed an interest in gardening on his father's farm. As a young man, Mendel studied to become a priest. His teachers noticed his great interest in nature, especially plants. They urged him to become a teacher himself. In 1854, he earned a degree from the University of Vienna and became a teacher. In his spare time, Mendel continued to garden. One day, he noticed differences in pea plants in his garden. Some appeared shriveled, but others did not. Mendel wondered about this. As a result, he tested 28,000 different plants. His experiments led him to identify laws of heredity. Today, Mendel is still considered to be the father of this science.

TEST-TAKING TIP

Cause-and-effect relationships can be determined by word clues. Some of these clues are single words, for example, *because*. Others are phrases. Examples include *due to* and *as a result*.

1. Gregor Mendel's interest in gardening led to
   A. his becoming a teacher.
   B. his attending the University of Vienna.
   C. his noticing differences in pea plants in his garden.
   D. his returning to his homeland after finishing college.

2. Which best sums up the main idea of the passage?
   A. Most scientific breakthroughs happen by accident.
   B. Gregor Mendel's love of gardening led him to discover the laws of heredity.
   C. Gregor Mendel was a better teacher than a priest.
   D. Gregor Mendel was a better scientist than a teacher.

Chapter 8 Assessment **219**

Test-Taking Tips

Finding the Main Idea Tell students that they may be asked to find the main idea of a reading passage. In this case, all four of the answer choices might contain information from the reading passage.

Students should read each answer choice and determine which best sums up the major point of the reading passage, rather than marking the first answer choice that matches information from the passage.

	Standards		Skills and Activities
	National	**State/Local**	
CHAPTER 9 *pp. 220–239*			**HEALTH QUIZ,** *p. 221* TIME HEALTH NEWS Kick Butts, *p. 236* **BUILDING HEALTH SKILLS** *Refusal Skills* Taking a Stand Against Tobacco, *pp. 234–235*
	National Health Education Standards 4.6, 7.1, 7.4, 7.6		
Lesson 1 **Tobacco:** **A Harmful Drug** *pp. 222–226*	National Health Education Standards 1.1, 1.3, 1.4, 1.6, 1.8, 2.4, 3.1, 5.3, 7.1, 7.2, 8.2		**Connect To... MATH** Just Do the Math, *p. 223*
Lesson 2 **Teens and** **Tobacco** *pp. 227–229*	National Health Education Standards 1.4, 1.5, 1.8, 2.2, 2.3, 2.4, 3.3, 3.4, 5.2, 7.6, 8.1, 8.2		**MEDIA WATCH** The Truth About Tobacco, *p. 228*
Lesson 3 **Staying** **Tobacco Free** *pp. 230–233*	National Health Education Standards 1.1, 1.4, 1.5, 1.6, 1.8, 3.1, 3.2, 3.4, 4.3, 4.4, 4.6, 5.3, 7.4, 8.1, 8.2, 8.3		**DEVELOPING GOOD CHARACTER** Good Citizenship, *p. 231* **HEALTH SKILLS ACTIVITY** *Advocacy* Spreading the Word About Tobacco, *p. 232*

PACING THE CHAPTER

Lesson 1	45 min	**Chapter Review**	45 min
Lesson 2	30 min	**TIME Health News**	20 min
Lesson 3	45 min	**Building Health Skills**	45 min

BLOCK SCHEDULING

For block scheduling, assign students Building Health Skills feature *Taking a Stand Against Tobacco*, pages 234–235, and Guided Reading and Writing. 📁

Glencoe Exclusive!

All-In-One Planner and Resource Center

Reproducible Resources	Assessment	Media and Technology

Chapter FAST FILE Resources
  Chapter Summaries and Activities REVIEW
  Building Health Skills Activity TEACH
  Performance Assessment Activity EXTEND
  Universal Access Activities TEACH
  Parent Letter and Activities
Student Activities Workbook TEACH
Reading Tutor TEACH
	Building Health Skills Activity, pp. 234–235
	Chapter 9 Assessment, pp. 238–239
	Chapter FAST FILE Resources
	Performance Assessment Activity, p. 4
	Chapter 9 Test, p. 7
	  ExamView® Test Generator
		TeacherWorks™ includes:
		  • Interactive Teacher Edition
		  • Lesson Planner with Calendar
		  • Access to all blackline masters
		  • Correlations to standards
		  StudentWorks™ Plus
		  Online Student Edition
		Dinah Zike's Teaching Health with Foldables™

Chapter FAST FILE Resources
  Concept Mapping Activity 9-1 REVIEW
  Cross-Curriculum Activity 9-1 EXTEND
  Enrichment Activity 9-1 EXTEND
  Lesson Plan 9-1
  Guided Reading and Writing 9-1 TEACH
  Reteaching Activity 9-1 REVIEW
	Lesson 1 Review, p. 226
	  Vocabulary PuzzleMaker
	  ExamView® Test Generator
		Vocabulary PuzzleMaker
		  ExamView® Test Generator
		  StudentWorks™ Plus
		  Transparency 9-1
		  Health Online

Chapter FAST FILE Resources
  Concept Mapping Activity 9-2 REVIEW
  Health Lab 9-2 EXTEND
  Enrichment Activity 9-2 EXTEND
  Lesson Plan 9-2
  Guided Reading and Writing 9-2 TEACH
  Reteaching Activity 9-2 REVIEW
	Lesson 2 Review, p. 229
	  Vocabulary PuzzleMaker
	  ExamView® Test Generator
		Vocabulary PuzzleMaker
		  ExamView® Test Generator
		  StudentWorks™ Plus
		  Transparency 9-2
		  Health Online

Chapter FAST FILE Resources
  Concept Mapping Activity 9-3 REVIEW
  Decision-Making Activity 9-3 EXTEND
  Enrichment Activity 9-3 EXTEND
  Lesson Plan 9-3
  Guided Reading and Writing 9-3 TEACH
  Reteaching Activity 9-3 REVIEW
	Lesson 3 Review, p. 233
	  Vocabulary PuzzleMaker
	  ExamView® Test Generator
		Vocabulary PuzzleMaker
		  ExamView® Test Generator
		  StudentWorks™ Plus
		  Transparency 9-3
		  Health Online

Chapter and Lesson Resources

The *Teen Health* resources are designed for differentiated learning abilities. You may want to use the coded items in this way:

REVIEW —activities to review or reinforce content

TEACH —activities to teach basic concepts

EXTEND —activities to extend or enrich lesson content

 OUT OF TIME?

Use Health Skills Activity *Spreading the Word About Tobacco,* page 232 or Developing Good Character, page 231.

Nicotine's Effects on the Body

Students may be interested to learn how nicotine affects the brain and what causes smokers to become addicted to cigarettes.

The nicotine in cigarette smoke moves within seconds from the lungs into the blood. It is then carried throughout the body and reaches the brain just seconds later. In the brain, nicotine causes the release of the hormone epinephrine, which many people know by the name adrenaline. The body releases adrenaline naturally in the "fight-or-flight" response; the release caused by nicotine has the same effect on the body. Respiration rate and heart rate increase. Blood pressure rises. A rapid release of glucose into the body occurs when the endocrine glands are stimulated by epinephrine. In addition, epinephrine signals the pancreas to decrease insulin output. These biochemical responses to nicotine cause the initial "rush" a person feels when using tobacco.

Nicotine also causes the release of chemicals that are associated with the sense of pleasure and reward. Dopamine and endogenous opioids both are released in response to nicotine. These brain chemicals are also released by the use of drugs such as cocaine and heroin. This response is thought to be the key to nicotine addiction.

The human body naturally produces a chemical called acetylcholine, a neurotransmitter that affects nervous system function. Nicotine is shaped very much like acetylcholine; in fact it can "fit" into the body's highly specific acetylcholine receptors. This affects mood, and explains why nicotine addicts feel anxious if they try to quit using tobacco.

Nicotine does not last in the body, so tobacco users feel the need for another cigarette as the nicotine level in their body drops. Nicotine users also develop a tolerance, or need for increased amounts of nicotine over time.

Methods for Quitting Smoking

Although most smokers are aware of the health consequences of smoking and many smokers want to quit, studies show that only a small percentage of those who try to quit are able to. Many smokers require more than one attempt before they successfully quit smoking; studies show that less than 40 percent of smokers are able to quit on their first attempt.

Methods of quitting fall into three broad categories: a gradual reduction in the number of cigarettes used each day, an immediate and complete cessation of smoking ("cold turkey"), and use of nicotine replacement products. There are several types of nicotine replacement products on the market including gum, skin patches, nasal spray, lozenges, and inhalers. Although nicotine replacement products ease the physical withdrawal symptoms, they do not ease emotional difficulty of giving up smoking.

Each method of quitting has some advantages and disadvantages. Consulting with a doctor or health professional is useful for those considering quitting, to help them determine with which method they might have the greatest chance of success.

No matter what method of quitting is chosen, counseling and the support of family and friends are important for success. The American Cancer Society offers many print and online resources for those attempting to quit smoking.

Reading Support   **Health Online**   **Academic Integration** For additional academic integration strategies, visit the Teacher Center at **health.glencoe.com**.

Reading Preview

Activating Background Vocabulary Prompt students to recall everything they can think of that relates to the use of tobacco. Record responses on the board. Guide students to sort the information into categories, such as: chemicals in tobacco, the dangers of tobacco, types of tobacco, etc. As students read the lesson, encourage them to add to the list.

FOLDABLES Study Organizer *Dinah Zike's Reading and Study Skills for Teen Health* provides interactive graphic organizers that help students comprehend and retain health concepts as they read. Use the Foldable™ on page 221 or find more Foldables™ activities for the chapter on **Tobacco** in the separate booklet, available in the TCR.

Lesson 1   Tobacco: A Harmful Drug

Pairs Reading Assign one student as the coach and the other as the reader. Have the reader read the section **What's in Tobacco** aloud. Have the coach summarize the main idea and supporting details of the section, then ask the reader to clarify any questions. Have the students reverse roles and direct the new reader to begin reading the next section.

Lesson 2   Teens and Tobacco

Thinking Aloud 1) Ask students to predict what **Resisting Negative Influences** will be about. 2) Model the images you form while reading—"I see teens urging other teens to try smoking so they will look cool." 3) Relate the reading to your own experience—"This reminds me of a movie I saw." 4) Note points that need clarification—"I don't understand this part…" and model strategies to clarify—"I think I'll reread this page to make this more clear." Have students practice this strategy aloud with a partner.

Lesson 3   Staying Tobacco Free

Review and Recall Have students stop reading and ask them to recall what they have learned so far. Ask them to review the key terms. In a class discussion, ask students to tell what they remember about the definition of secondhand smoke. Is it dangerous? Can it harm people who don't smoke? Have students go back to review what they have read for additional facts. Encourage students to ask questions.

Post Reading

Dramatic Presentations Guide student groups to create a role play of teens using refusal skills to say no to tobacco use. Encourage students to incorporate the main concepts and supporting details of this lesson while organizing and planning their dramatic presentations.

Key for Using the Teacher Wraparound Edition

Use this key to help you identify the different types of prompts found in the Teacher Wraparound Edition.

R **Reading Strategies** activities help you teach reading skills and vocabulary.

C **Critical Thinking** strategies help students apply and extend what they have learned.

U **Universal Access** activities provide differentiated instruction for students learning to speak English, along with suggestions for teaching various types of learners.

HS **Health Skills Practice** activities reinforce Health Skills concepts and help students apply these skills in their everyday lives.

W **Writing Support** activities provide writing opportunities to help students comprehend the text.

AL **Active Learning** strategies provide a variety of activities for presenting lesson content, including Quick Demos and engaging classroom projects that get students actively involved.

Key to Ability Levels

Teaching Strategies and activities have been coded for ability level and appropriateness

AL Activities for students working above grade level

OL Activities for students working on grade level

BL Activities for students working below grade level

EL Activities for English Learners

Symbols

 Transparencies

CD-ROM

 health.glencoe.com

 Print Resources

Tobacco

Chapter at a Glance

Lesson 1 identifies how tobacco damages your health, explains how tobacco leads to addiction, and explains how to communicate the dangers of tobacco use to others.

Lesson 2 identifies factors that influence teens to try tobacco, identifies negative influences on teens to use tobacco, and explains how to gather reliable information on teens and tobacco use.

Lesson 3 demonstrates ways to say no to tobacco use, explains how someone can kick the tobacco habit, and explains the rights of nonsmokers.

R Reading Strategy

Interpreting the Photo
Have students examine the photo. Ask: How is this teen being a health advocate? *Sample answer: He is encouraging others to avoid tobacco.* **Ask: What are some other ways** that teens can communicate health information to others? *Sample answer: Teens can talk to others about ways to stay healthy.* **OL**

Chapter Preview

Lesson 1 Tobacco:
         A Harmful Drug............... 222

Lesson 2 Teens and Tobacco 227

Lesson 3 Staying Tobacco Free...... 230

Building Health Skills...................... 234

TIME Health News 236

Chapter Reading Review.................. 237

Chapter Assessment 238

▲ **Working With the Photo**

R This teen has become an advocate for a smoke-free **environment. What are some ways you can encourage others to say no to tobacco.**

220

Universal Access

Differentiated Learning Glencoe provides teacher support and student materials for all learners in the health classroom.
- Spanish Glosario and chapter summaries for the English Language Learners.
- *Reading Tutor* and related worksheets support reluctant readers.

- *Universal Access* strategies throughout the Teacher Wraparound Edition and Fast Files help you present materials for gifted students, at-risk students, physically impaired students, and those with behavior disorders or learning disabilities.

Start-Up Activities

Before You Read How much do you know about tobacco? Take the short quiz below to find out.

HEALTH QUIZ Answer *true* or *false* for each of the following questions. Keep a record of your answers.

1. Tobacco contains a number of harmful chemicals.
2. One form of tobacco that is perfectly safe and harmless is smokeless tobacco.
3. Smokers who make up their mind to quit can easily break the tobacco habit.

ANSWERS: 1. true; 2. false; 3. false

FOLDABLES™ Study Organizer

As You Read Make this Foldable™ to help you organize information in Lesson 1 on the harmful effects of tobacco. Begin with a plain sheet of 8½" × 11" paper.

1 Fold a sheet of paper in half along the short axis.

2 Open and fold the bottom edge up to form a pocket. Glue the edges.

3 Label the cover as shown. Label the pockets "Causes" and "Effects." Place an index card or quarter sheet of notebook paper into each pocket.

Tobacco Addiction

List and describe the causes and effects of tobacco addiction on the index cards or sheets of notebook paper cut into quarter sections. Store these cards in the appropriate pockets of your Foldable™.

Health Online Visit health.glencoe.com and complete the Chapter 9 crossword puzzle.

221

FOCUS

Activating Prior Knowledge

What I Know Ask volunteers to name one of the harmful effects of using tobacco.

 Guide to Reading

BUILDING VOCABULARY

- Have students skim the lesson to find definitions for each of the vocabulary terms. Then call on volunteers to give definitions for the terms.
- Use Vocabulary PuzzleMaker to reinforce vocabulary terms.

READING STRATEGY

 Have students use their Foldables™ as they read Lesson 1.

- **Finding the Main Idea** As students read the lesson, have them record the main idea of each section. Call on students to read aloud their main ideas after they have completed the entire lesson.

 Quick Write

To help students get started on their Quick Writes, have them brainstorm negative effects of using tobacco products.

 Reading Check

Answer nicotine, carbon monoxide

Lesson 1

Tobacco: A Harmful Drug

 Guide to Reading

● Building Vocabulary
Explain how each vocabulary word below is related to tobacco.

- nicotine (p. 222)
- carbon monoxide (p. 222)
- tar (p. 222)
- addiction (p. 223)
- emphysema (p. 223)
- snuff (p. 226)

● Focusing on the Main Ideas
In this lesson, you will be able to

- **identify** how tobacco damages your health.
- **explain** how tobacco leads to addiction.
- **practice** the skill of advocacy to inform others about the dangers of tobacco use.

● Reading Strategy
Finding the Main Idea Copy the headings from the lesson onto a sheet of paper. After each heading, write a sentence that describes the main idea of each section.

FOLDABLES Study Organizer Use the Foldable™ on p. 221 as you read this lesson.

Quick Write

Write a paragraph about the reasons many people choose to remain tobacco free.

▲ More and more locations are displaying this sign. **Why do you think this is happening?**

What's in Tobacco

Tobacco contains a number of harmful chemicals. One of these, **nicotine** (NIH·kuh·teen), is *a drug found in tobacco that speeds up the heartbeat and affects the central nervous system*. It narrows blood vessels to and from the heart. Nicotine is also found in garden insect sprays.

Tobacco also contains **carbon monoxide** (KAR·buhn·muh·NAHK·syd). This is *a poisonous, odorless gas produced when tobacco burns*. It attaches to red blood cells, preventing them from carrying a full load of oxygen. Carbon monoxide is also an ingredient in car and truck exhaust. Breathing carbon monoxide can lead to death by suffocation.

A third substance, **tar,** is *a thick, oily, dark liquid that forms when tobacco burns*. Tar deposits cover the linings of the lungs. If tar is allowed to build up, breathing problems and lung disease can result.

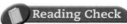 **Reading Check** **Identify** What are two harmful chemicals found in tobacco?

Lesson 1 Resources

📁 **Chapter FAST FILE Resources**
Guided Reading and Writing 9-1
Concept Mapping Activity 9-1
Cross-Curriculum Activity 9-1
Reteaching Activity 9-1
Enrichment Activity 9-1
Lesson Quiz 9-1

Technology
🔦 Transparency 9-1
🎧 Audio Summaries
💿 *ExamView*
🎧 Vocabulary PuzzleMaker
💿 StudentWorks™ Plus

How Tobacco Harms the Body

"How much harm can one cigarette do?" People who ask that question might be surprised by the answer. Just one puff releases harmful chemicals into the mouth, throat, and lungs. It can cause feelings of dizziness and light-headedness.

Over time, the effects of tobacco build. Long-term nicotine use is linked to heart and lung disease. The tar from tobacco coats the inside of the lungs. It greatly increases the smoker's risks of lung cancer and emphysema (em·fuh·SEE·muh). **Emphysema** is *a disease that occurs when the tiny air sacs in the lungs lose their elasticity, or ability to stretch.* This reduces the amount of oxygen passing from the lungs into the blood. Breathing becomes more difficult for the smoker. Teens who smoke may find it harder to play sports and stay physically active. **Figure 9.1** on pages 224–225 shows other harmful effects of tobacco use.

Nicotine and Addiction

Another serious problem related to tobacco use is that nicotine is a powerfully addictive drug. **Addiction** is *the body's physical or mental need for a drug or other substance.* Addiction causes users to depend on the substance in order to feel good. They begin to need the substance just to function normally. Once addicted, quitting becomes extremely difficult. People who try to break their addiction may experience unpleasant symptoms. These include shakiness, headache, nervousness, and sleeping problems. Once a person has overcome his or her addiction, these symptoms will go away and the person will feel much better.

Reading Check

Define What does *addiction* mean? Use it in a sentence.

 Tobacco effects the body in many ways. **What affect can tobacco have on a person's appearance?**

Lesson 1: Tobacco: A Harmful Drug   **223**

Connect To...
Math

Just Do the Math

Using tobacco is an expensive habit. A single pack of cigarettes costs approximately $3.81. If a person smokes one pack of cigarettes each day, calculate the following:

- Approximately how much would a smoker spend on cigarettes in one month?

- How much would he or she spend in one year?

Imagine you had that much money to spend. What are some other ways you would choose to spend the money?

TEACH

Connect To...
Math

Just Do the Math
Tell students to use 30 days as the length of one month for their calculations. Cigarettes for one month cost $114.30. The cost for a full year is $1,371.60. **OL**

AL Active Learning

Advertisements Divide the class into small groups. Have each group develop a print, radio, or television advertisement that clearly describes how tobacco can harm the body. Have groups share their advertisement. **OL**

Academic Vocabulary

Linked Students learn that long-term nicotine use is *linked* to heart and lung disease. Tell students that the word *link* refers to a connecting factor. Ask: How is this definition related to other meanings of the word *link*? Sample answer: *A link in a chain is connected to other links.* **OL**

Reading Check

Answer Addiction is the body's need for a drug or other substance.

Caption Answers

Photo Caption, p. 220 As teens realize the dangers of smoking, they take a stand against tobacco.
Photo Caption Wrinkles, stained teeth, yellowed fingers.

✖ Promoting Coordinated School Health

Preventing Teen Smoking Schools can help teens avoid using tobacco products through education. According to the Centers for Disease Control and Prevention, some of the components of an effective school tobacco use prevention program are:

- a school-wide ban on the use of tobacco products at all functions
- a clear anti-tobacco message delivered in all subject areas and at all grade levels
- smoking cessation assistance for students and staff who currently use tobacco

R Reading Strategy

Analyzing a Graphic Have students examine Figure 9.1 and consider the harmful effects of tobacco. Ask: Name three body systems that are harmed by tobacco use. *Sample answers: respiratory system, cardiovascular system, digestive system, excretory system* Ask: Name two ways that using tobacco can affect a person's appearance. *Sample answers: It stains skin and teeth; it turns fingernails yellow.* **OL**

AL Active Learning

Small Group Presentations Have students work in small groups. Ask each group to present information about the harmful effects of smoking from the point of view of one of the body parts mentioned in Figure 9.1. Allow students 10 minutes to work in their groups to develop their presentations. Have each group share its presentation with the class. **OL**

Health *Online*

Allow time for students to research online resources. Have students work in pairs and have partners proofread one another's letters and make corrections before turning them in.

Caption Answer

Photo Caption Smoking reduces the amount of oxygen carried in the blood.

▶ **FIGURE 9.1**

R THE HARMFUL EFFECTS OF TOBACCO

The chemicals in tobacco harm many parts of the body. What is the harmful effect on the blood vessels?

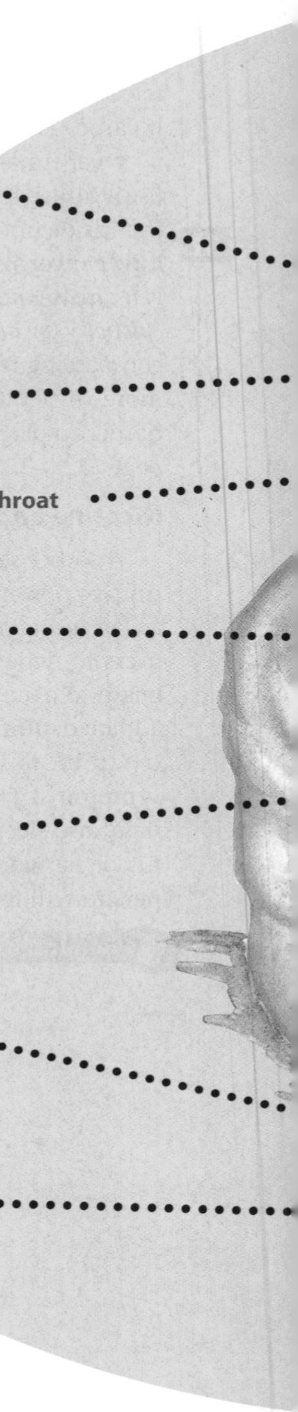

Health *Online*

Topic: Avoiding the Harmful Effects of Tobacco

Visit health.glencoe.com for Student Web Activities to learn more about what cigarette smoke does to the body and how to help smokers quit.

Activity: Using the information provided at the link above, write a letter to the editor of your local paper talking about what you feel should be done to help make your community smoke free.

Skin
Smoking ages the skin, causing it to wrinkle earlier than a nonsmoker's skin.

Mouth, Teeth, and Throat
Cigarette smoke and smokeless tobacco lead to bad breath and stained teeth. Chemicals in tobacco cause mouth and throat cancers. Smokeless tobacco can cause leukoplakia—white sores in the mouth that can lead to cancer—as well as bone loss around the teeth. It also wears away tooth enamel.

Throat

Lungs
The tar in cigarette smoke coats the inside of the lungs. This prevents them from working efficiently. Chemicals in tobacco smoke can also contribute to lung cancer.

Heart
Nicotine increases the heart rate and causes blood vessels to become narrower. Narrow vessels make the heart pump harder to move blood through the body. This extra effort raises blood pressure and can result in heart attack or stroke.

Fingers
Over time, tobacco use can cause fingers to yellow and stain.

Stomach, Bladder, and Colon
Harmful substances in tobacco smoke can lead to stomach ulcers and bladder and colon cancers. Compared to nonsmokers, smokers are more than twice as likely to get bladder cancer.

Cultural Perspectives

Cultural Background and Teen Smoking
Studies have shown that teens from different cultural backgrounds have different rates of tobacco use. It has also been shown that cultural background plays a role in the particular influences that can lead a teen to smoke. A study at the University of Southern California School of Medicine found that some groups were less likely to succumb to pressure from peers than others. Cultural influence seems to be a factor on whether some teens are influenced by their parents to avoid tobacco use.

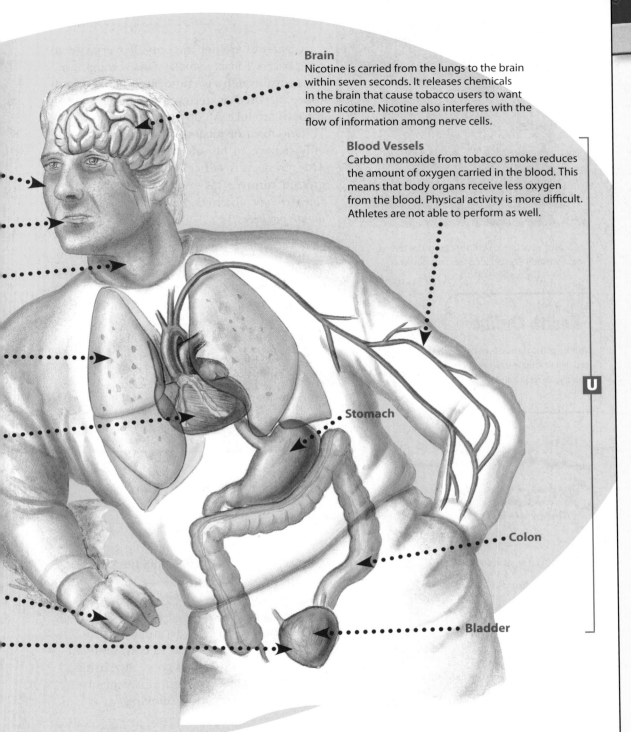

Brain
Nicotine is carried from the lungs to the brain within seven seconds. It releases chemicals in the brain that cause tobacco users to want more nicotine. Nicotine also interferes with the flow of information among nerve cells.

Blood Vessels
Carbon monoxide from tobacco smoke reduces the amount of oxygen carried in the blood. This means that body organs receive less oxygen from the blood. Physical activity is more difficult. Athletes are not able to perform as well.

Stomach

Colon

Bladder

Lesson 1: Tobacco: A Harmful Drug **225**

U Universal Access

English Learners Pair English learners with English-proficient students to review the content of these two pages in Figure 9.1. Have pairs read aloud the callouts on the skin, mouth, teeth, and throat, the brain, and so on. Encourage students to review the Glossary/Glosario for definitions and vocabulary terms Have students practice the vocabulary terms orally in order to practice pronunciation. Then allow time for volunteers to describe the effects of tobacco on each of the parts of the body. **EL**

What Teens Want to Know

Are bidis and kreteks safe? According to studies by the Centers for Disease Control and Prevention (CDC), 2.4 percent of middle school students have smoked bidis. Bidis are sweet-flavored, imported cigarettes. Bidis are attractive because of their flavors and their availability. Kreteks are reportedly used by 2 percent of middle school students. Kreteks contain cloves and tobacco. Bidis and kreteks are dangerous because they have more nicotine and tar than regular cigarettes. Have students use online resources to learn more about the dangers of bidis and kreteks.

Caption Answer

Photo Caption, p. 226 Fans may respect the choice of sports figures. They are sending the message that using tobacco is not a healthy habit.

225

ASSESS

 Reading Check

Answer Smokeless tobacco is addictive, can cause cancer, and damages teeth and gums.

Assessment Resources

Lesson Review Quiz
 ExamView
📁 Fast Files Activities
Online Quizzes and Activities

Reteaching

- Assign Concept Map 9-1 or Reteaching Activity 9-1 in the Fast Files. 📁
- Have students write a short paragraph explaining three ways that tobacco can harm the body.

Enrichment

- Assign Enrichment Activity 9-1 in the Fast Files. 📁
- Have students develop a 5-question quiz that could be used to assess understanding of Lesson 1. Then have students trade their quiz with a classmate.

CLOSE

Have students identify harmful effects of using smokeless tobacco.

▲ Major sports are discouraging the use of smokeless tobacco among players. **How might this influence fans?**

Health *Online*

Visit **health.glencoe.com** and complete the Interactive Study Guide for Lesson 1.

Other Forms of Tobacco

Cigarettes are not the only delivery system for tobacco. Tobacco smoke is also brought into the body through cigars and pipes. Bidis—hand-rolled, flavored cigarettes—are another smoked tobacco product. All do harm to the body.

One form of tobacco some people mistakenly believe to be safe is smokeless tobacco. This product is either chewed in a coarsely ground form or taken in as snuff. **Snuff** is *finely ground tobacco that is inhaled or held in the mouth or cheeks.*

Just like cigarettes, smokeless tobacco products can become habit-forming. In addition, harmful substances in smokeless tobacco can form white spots on your gums and inside your cheeks. These can eventually turn into cancer. Smokeless tobacco also causes bad breath and stains the teeth. Grit and sugar in tobacco can cause cavities and gum disease.

 Reading Check **Explain** What are some of the dangers of smokeless tobacco?

Lesson 1 Review

 **After You Read**

Review this lesson for new terms, major headings, and Reading Checks.

What I Learned

1. *List* How does nicotine affect the body?

2. *Vocabulary* What is *emphysema*?

3. *Identify* Name two forms of smokeless tobacco.

Thinking Critically

4. *Analyze* Anne was pressured by a girl at school to try tobacco. "You can always quit any time you want," the girl said. How might Anne reply?

5. *Apply* What advice would you give someone who asks you about smokeless tobacco?

Applying Health Skills

6. *Advocacy* Conveying accurate health information and ideas to both individuals and groups shows good citizenship. Create a poster that informs students about the dangers of smoking.

Health *Online* For more review questions for Lesson 1, go to **health.glencoe.com**.

Lesson 1 Review Answers

1. Nicotine is an addictive drug that affects the central nervous system.
2. It is a disease in which tiny air sacs in the lungs are damaged. Tar is an ingredient in smoke that leads to emphysema.

3. It is chewed in a coarsely ground form and used as snuff, finely ground tobacco.
4. She might reply by saying that tobacco is addictive, and that breaking an addiction is a difficult process.

5. Smokeless tobacco is associated with many health risks and should be avoided.
6. Posters should accurately reflect the lesson content.

Teens and Tobacco

Guide to Reading

● **Building Vocabulary**
Read the terms below. If you have come across these in earlier chapters, review your notebook definitions. If you have not, copy their meanings as they appear in this lesson.

- negative peer pressure (p. 228)
- media (p. 228)

● **Focusing on the Main Ideas**
In this lesson, you will be able to

- **identify** factors that influence teens to try tobacco.
- **recognize** negative influences on teens to use tobacco.
- **access** reliable information on teens and tobacco use.

● **Reading Strategy**
Organizing Information Using information from the lesson, create a graphic organizer showing beliefs and facts about tobacco use.

Facts about Teens and Tobacco

Some teens mistakenly believe tobacco helps them fit in better among their peers. If anything, the *opposite* is true. The Centers for Disease Control and Prevention (CDC) and other organizations report a steady drop in teen tobacco use over the past decade.

Yet despite this positive trend, some teens continue to become first-time smokers. According to the same sources, every day 4,000 young people try their first cigarette. Why do some teens start smoking? **Figure 9.2** summarizes reasons teens give for trying tobacco. It also shows why their beliefs about tobacco use may not be accurate.

Quick Write

Think about influences that might lead some teens to try tobacco. Write a paragraph explaining how a teen can resist these influences.

▶ Friends can influence the choices you make. **Why is it important to choose friends who don't smoke?**

FOCUS

Activating Prior Knowledge

What I Know Have students list ways that they are positively or negatively influenced about tobacco use.

Guide to Reading

BUILDING VOCABULARY
- Explain that *media* refers to ways of communicating information, such as newspapers and television. Ask students to name some ways they can be influenced by the media.
- Use Vocabulary PuzzleMaker to reinforce vocabulary terms.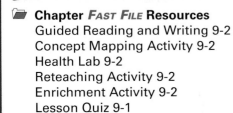

READING STRATEGY
Organizing Information
Instruct students to make a graphic organizer that can show two categories of information. Have students include the labels "Myths" and "Facts" in their graphic organizer.

Quick Write

To introduce the Quick Write, have students brainstorm ways to resist negative influences.

Caption Answer

Photo Caption You should choose friends who don't smoke because of the health benefits of avoiding tobacco use.

TEACH

R Reading Strategy

Analyzing a Graphic After students have examined Figure 9.2, have them write a paragraph that uses at least one of the "Realities" from the infographic to explain why teens should not start smoking. **OL**

MediaWatch

The Truth About Tobacco

Have students read the feature. Allow time for discussion of the anti-tobacco campaign. Ask students who might have seen these ads share their reactions.

Encourage a discussion of other similarly effective ways to reach teens about the dangers of smoking.

Reading Check

Answer Negative peer pressure is pressure to go along with the harmful behaviors or beliefs of your peers. Negative peer pressure is often what causes teens to try tobacco.

Caption Answer

Figure Caption *Sample answer:* My parents smoke, so it cannot be too harmful.

228

▼ **FIGURE 9.2**

R REASONS FOR TEEN TOBACCO USE AND THE REALITIES

These are some of the reasons teens give for using tobacco. Are there other reasons or realities you can add to either list?

Some Teens Believe	In Reality
Smoking makes a person look cool.	Tobacco stains teeth, leads to bad breath, and causes wrinkled skin.
Tobacco makes teens more accepted among their peers.	Between 70 and 80 percent of teens have never tried tobacco. Teens who use tobacco are also more likely to get in fights, carry weapons, and use alcohol and other drugs.
Using tobacco makes teens seem more grown-up.	The number of adult tobacco users is also on the decline.
Tobacco won't hurt your health for many years.	Some of tobacco's effects begin with the first use. Tobacco use is habit-forming. Once a person starts using tobacco, it can be very difficult to quit.

Resisting Negative Influences

Many teens decide to try tobacco because they are influenced by others around them. One such influence is **negative peer pressure.** This is *pressure you feel to go along with harmful behaviors or beliefs of your peers.* A teen whose friends use tobacco is more likely to try it as well.

The same is true of teens with family members who use tobacco. Studies show that teens from homes where tobacco is used are far more likely to start smoking.

Yet another negative influence is the media. The **media** include *the various methods of communicating information, including newspapers, magazines, radio, television, and the Internet.* Several years ago, two government agencies researched the media's influence on teen tobacco use. The study examined 200 popular films and 1,000 popular songs. The findings showed that tobacco was used in more than three-fourths of movies intended for young viewers. The study also showed that nearly a third of pop songs glamorize tobacco use.

Reading Check

Define What is *negative peer pressure*? What part does it play in tobacco use among teens?

MediaWatch

The Truth about Tobacco

The truth® Campaign was the largest anti-tobacco campaign ever targeted at teens. Using TV ads, print ads, and the Internet, the Campaign educated teens on the dangers of smoking. How effective was the truth® Campaign? Between 2000 and 2002, 85 percent of teens said that the ad they saw gave them good reasons not to smoke.

What are some other ways to inform teens about the dangers of smoking?

Cultural Perspectives

American Media and Tobacco A study of movies found that more than 80 percent of PG-13 rated movies contained incidents of tobacco use or references to tobacco products. In a separate study, teens who were allowed to see R-rated films were found to be more likely to start smoking than teens who were not allowed to see R-rated movies. Have students discuss the impact of the media on their decisions. Then, have students write a persuasive paragraph expressing their opinion of the portrayal of smoking in movies aimed at children and young teens. **OL**

Tobacco Advertising

One especially powerful influence is advertising. Estimates show that the tobacco industry spends $10 billion a year advertising its products. Some of these ads have been proven effective at reaching young people. Another effective method of advertising is "point-of-sale" promotions. These include giveaways and catchy displays near cash registers at stores that sell cigarettes. Recently, cigarette advertisers have even begun to place ads targeted at teens on the Internet.

▶ Signs like this are used to help prevent teens from smoking. **Can you think of some other ways to help teens avoid tobacco use?**

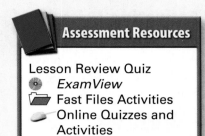

Health *Online*

Visit **health.glencoe.com** and complete the Interactive Study Guide for Lesson 2.

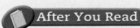

Lesson 2 Review

After You Read

Review this lesson for new terms, major headings, and Reading Checks.

What I Learned

1. *Give Examples* Name two factors that might influence teens to try tobacco.

2. *Vocabulary* Define *media*.

3. *Recall* What are two negative pressures teens might face when it comes to tobacco use?

Thinking Critically

4. *Apply* Identify an example of negative peer pressure to use tobacco. Tell what could do or say to resist this pressure.

5. *Hypothesize* Tobacco advertising on TV was outlawed some years ago. Why do you think this law was passed?

Applying Health Skills

6. *Accessing Information* The lesson mentioned several reliable sources of health information. Gather additional facts or statistics from these or other reliable sources on teen tobacco use. Share your findings with classmates.

Health *Online* For more review questions for Lesson 2, go to **health.glencoe.com**.

Lesson 2: Teens and Tobacco **229**

ASSESS

Assessment Resources

Lesson Review Quiz
- *ExamView*
- Fast Files Activities
- Online Quizzes and Activities

Reteaching

- Assign Concept Map 9-2 or Reteaching Activity 9-2 in the Fast Files. 📁
- Have students write down three factors that influence teens to try tobacco and explain why teens are influenced by these factors.

Enrichment

- Assign Enrichment Activity 9-2 in the Fast Files. 📁
- Challenge students to develop a survey that could be used to determine the average number of cigarette advertisements their classmates see or hear each day.

CLOSE

Have students work in small groups to list three myths and three facts about tobacco use.

Caption Answer

Photo Caption Keep tobacco use out of the media.

Lesson 2 Review Answers

1. *Sample answer:* Advertising and peer pressure are factors that influence teens to try tobacco.
2. The media include methods of communicating information, including newspapers, television, and the Internet.

3. *Sample answers:* negative peer pressure, imitating family members, and media messages
4. Answers should include saying no, offering alternatives, and walking away.

5. *Sample answer:* Tobacco is harmful, and TV advertising is one of the more powerful forms of reaching consumers.
6. Students should explain how they know their sources are reliable.

Lesson 3

FOCUS

Activating Prior Knowledge

What I Know Ask students to recall methods for saying no to unhealthy behaviors.

Guide to Reading

BUILDING VOCABULARY
- After students have located the definitions of the vocabulary terms in the lesson, have them write a sentence explaining how the two terms are related.
- Use Vocabulary PuzzleMaker to reinforce vocabulary terms.

READING STRATEGY
- **Identifying Problems and Solutions** Have students read the Reading Strategy. Tell students to note ideas in Lesson 3 that will help them complete this activity.

Quick Write

Remind students to use descriptive language when they write their poems or stories. Have volunteers share their completed Quick Writes with the class.

Academic Vocabulary

Domestic Explain that *domestic* can mean "within a country's borders," or "pertaining to the home or household." Have students write a sentence that correctly uses the word *domestic*. **OL**

Lesson 3

Staying Tobacco Free

Guide to Reading

Building Vocabulary
Copy the terms below in your notebook. As you read the lesson, write the definitions for each term.
- secondhand smoke (p. 232)
- passive smokers (p. 232)

Focusing on the Main Ideas
In this lesson, you will be able to
- **demonstrate** ways to say no to tobacco use.
- **explain** how someone can quit using tobacco.
- **understand** the rights of nonsmokers.

Reading Strategy
Identifying Problems and Solution After reading this lesson, state the problem with secondhand smoke. Then think of a solution for how to build a tobacco-free environment.

Quick Write

Write a poem or story about a planet that is smoke-free.

▲ Nicotine patches can help a person quit smoking. **What other sources of help are available to those who want to quit smoking?**

Using Refusal Skills

Saying no to tobacco is important, but it is not always easy. Some teens feel pressure from peers to use tobacco. Others see family members smoking and are curious about what it's like.

When faced with real-life pressures, refusal skills can help you say no effectively. Be prepared with some reasons for saying no to tobacco. You can find some examples in **Figure 9.3.** You may be offered tobacco when you least expect it, so it is best to be prepared. Practice saying no in an assertive style, one that shows you are serious but respectful to others. Speak in a firm voice with your head and shoulders up. This will tell others that you mean what you say.

Kicking the Tobacco Habit

The human body was not designed to inhale smoke of any kind. Some of the damage done by smoking can never be reversed. Once the small airways inside your lungs have been damaged, they cannot repair themselves. Quitting tobacco, however, prevents further damage to the body and will improve a person's overall health.

Lesson 3 Resources

📁 **Chapter *Fast File* Resources**
Guided Reading and Writing 9-3
Concept Mapping Activity 9-3
Decision-Making Activity 9-3
Reteaching Activity 9-3
Enrichment Activity 9-3
Lesson Quiz 9-3

Technology
🔋 Transparency 9-3
💿 Audio Summaries
💿 *ExamView*
💾 Vocabulary PuzzleMaker
💿 StudentWorks™ Plus

▼ FIGURE 9.3

R SAYING NO TO TOBACCO

If someone offers you tobacco, here are some ways to say no.
What are some other ways of refusing tobacco?

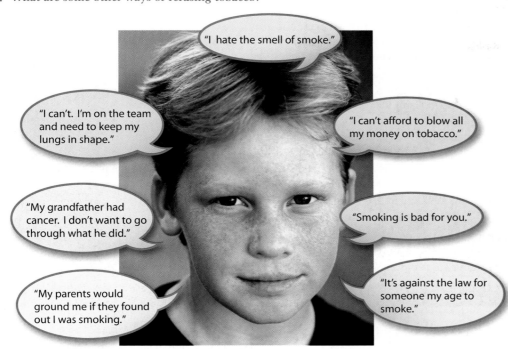

"I hate the smell of smoke."

"I can't. I'm on the team and need to keep my lungs in shape."

"I can't afford to blow all my money on tobacco."

"My grandfather had cancer. I don't want to go through what he did."

"Smoking is bad for you."

"My parents would ground me if they found out I was smoking."

"It's against the law for someone my age to smoke."

W One way to quit tobacco use is the cold turkey method. In this method, the user simply stops all use of the tobacco product. This method can be difficult for many people. They need help breaking an addiction to nicotine. One source of help is nicotine replacement therapies (NRT). These are products to assist a person in breaking a tobacco habit. They include nicotine gums, lozenges, and patches worn on the skin.

Community support groups are another option. Local chapters of the American Cancer Society sponsor programs to help users quit. The American Lung Association and American Heart Association have similar programs. Some schools also now have programs to help teens who want to quit using tobacco.

 **Reading Check**   **Give Examples** Identify three ways of saying no to tobacco.

DEVELOPING Good Character

Good Citizenship

One important character trait is citizenship. Good citizens look out for the welfare of the community. The term *community* means more than just your neighborhood. It also includes the environment, the air we breathe. Obeying laws that regulate smoking is one way of showing good citizenship. **What are some other ways of showing good citizenship when it comes to tobacco?**

Lesson 1: Tobacco: A Harmful Drug   **231**

TEACH

DEVELOPING Good Character

Good Citizenship
Have students work in pairs to read the feature. Ask each pair to brainstorm ways to show good citizenship when it comes to tobacco. Develop a class list of ideas by having each pair of students state one of their ideas. **OL**

R Reading Strategy

Analyzing a Graphic Have students discuss the reasons for not smoking that are shown in Figure 9.3. Challenge students to identify other reasons for not smoking. List students' responses on the board. **OL**

W Writing Support

Persuasive Writing Have students write a persuasive paragraph explaining the benefits of quitting tobacco. The paragraph should mention some of the resources available to those who are trying to quit. Have students self-edit and revise their work before they turn it in. **OL**

Caption Answers

Photo Caption, p. 230 community support, nicotine gum
Figure Caption *Sample answer:* I will not sing well in choir if I smoke.

Dealing with Sensitive Issues

Family Privacy and Tobacco Use
Information about the damaging effects of tobacco and secondhand smoke can be challenging for students who would like their parents to quit smoking. Without singling out individual students, provide pamphlets and handouts listing community resources available to those who are trying to quit smoking. Explain that nicotine is highly addictive, and many people have difficulty overcoming this addiction. Be certain to respect family privacy during class discussions of secondhand smoke.

Health Skills Activity

Advocacy

Spreading the Word About Tobacco

Use the following strategies to help students complete the activity:

- Provide materials for students to use as they complete their posters, brochures, or signs.
- Guide students as they develop a plan for asking retailers to display signs. Have students role-play appropriate interaction with a store owner or manager.
- Have students work as a class to brainstorm other ways of encouraging students and adults to avoid tobacco use. Have students follow up on one or more of the ideas. **OL**

Reading Check

Answer, p. 231 *Sample answers:* Three ways to say no to tobacco are: I hate the smell of smoke. Smoking is bad for you. It is illegal for teens to smoke.

Answer, p. 233 Secondhand smoke can cause breathing problems, heart disease, and lung cancer.

Health Skills Activity

Advocacy

Spreading the Word about Tobacco

You can do your part to help other teens avoid smoking. Here are steps you can take to help your peers help themselves.

- Make colorful posters encouraging teens to avoid using tobacco. Include information on the health dangers of tobacco. With permission from school administrators, hang your posters on hallways at school.
- Create a brochure telling what harmful ingredients are contained in tobacco products and how they damage the body. Distribute your brochure to students and adults in your community.
- Offer to make signs for local retailers where teens frequent, urging teens to say no to smoking. Ask retailers to place these signs in a location where they will be seen.

With a Group

Brainstorm other ways of encouraging students and adults in your community to avoid the risks of tobacco use.

Tobacco and the Nonsmoker

The dangers of tobacco exist not only for the smoker but for the nonsmoker as well. Tobacco use affects the health of the people around you and in the community.

When a smoker lights up, she or he releases **secondhand smoke.** This is *a mixture of the smoke given off by the burning end of tobacco products and the smoke exhaled by smokers.* Secondhand smoke pollutes the air around the smoker. *Nonsmokers who breathe in secondhand smoke* are called **passive smokers.** Passive smokers develop some of the same health problems as smokers. They may develop coughs, breathing problems, heart disease, and lung cancer. About 3,000 nonsmokers die of lung cancer each year.

Secondhand smoke causes other health problems. Children with respiratory infections may not recover as quickly when exposed to secondhand smoke. Children with asthma may also have more frequent and severe attacks.

Health Online

Visit **health.glencoe.com** and complete the Interactive Study Guide for Lesson 3.

TECHNOLOGY AND HEALTH

Technology Can Help Smokers Quit A controlled study found that young smokers who received encouraging text messages throughout the day were more than twice as likely to be successful at quitting smoking as were those who did not receive the messages. Have students discuss ways in which they could use technology to encourage others not to smoke. For example, computers can be used to access information about the dangers of tobacco use and e-mail can be used to discuss the dangers of smoking with a friend. **OL**

Rights of the Nonsmoker

As a nonsmoker, you have the right to breathe air free of tobacco smoke. You have the right to ask people not to smoke around you. For this reason, the federal government has passed laws protecting nonsmokers' rights. Since 1989, it has been illegal to smoke on domestic airplane flights. *Domestic* means "within the country's borders." Many restaurants have set aside specific areas for smokers or banned smoking altogether. The same is true of many offices and factories. Some towns and cities have even banned smoking in certain outdoor locations. These include beaches, children's play areas, and public gardens.

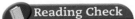 **Reading Check** **Explain** In what way is tobacco use harmful to nonsmokers?

▶ You can help make your community smoke-free. **How can you go about achieving the goal represented by the signs in this picture?**

Lesson 3 Review

 After You Read

Review this lesson for new terms, major headings, and Reading Checks.

What I Learned

1. **Vocabulary** Define *secondhand smoke*. Use it in a sentence.

2. **List** What are two reasons for refusing to use tobacco?

3. **Recall** What have some communities done to protect the rights of nonsmokers?

Thinking Critically

4. **Evaluate** Why do you think it is important to practice refusal skills in advance?

5. **Apply** Tina would like to get her grandfather to stop smoking. When she asked him to stop, he said it was too difficult. What might Tina suggest?

Applying Health Skills

6. **Communication Skills** With classmates, develop a skit showing polite ways to ask a smoker to put out a cigarette. The skit should illustrate ways of asking that are assertive.

Health Online For more review questions for Lesson 3, go to **health.glencoe.com**.

Lesson 3: Staying Tobacco Free **233**

ASSESS

 Assessment Resources

Lesson Review Quiz
ExamView
Fast Files Activities
Online Quizzes and Activities

Reteaching

- Assign Concept Map 9-3 or Reteaching Activity 9-3 in the Fast Files.
- Ask volunteers to describe or demonstrate ways to say no to tobacco.

Enrichment

- Assign Enrichment Activity 9-3 in the Fast Files.
- Have students research the rates of lung cancer for smokers and nonsmokers in the United States. Ask students to prepare a short report to present to the class.

CLOSE

Randomly call on students to describe strategies, resources, and technology that can be used to help smokers quit.

Caption Answer

Photo Caption Avoid tobacco use and tell others about the health risks of tobacco.

Lesson 3 Review Answers

1. The term means environmental smoke. Sentences will vary.

2. *Sample answers:* Tobacco use damages many body systems; tobacco use increases the risk of cancer; tobacco use is illegal for teens.

3. *Sample answer:* Some communities have banned smoking in public locations.

4. *Sample answer:* Practicing refusal skills helps you feel confident when you say no.

5. *Sample answer:* Tina might suggest community resources such as support groups.

6. Skits will vary. Remind students of the way to make an assertive request.

Building Health Skills

Taking a Stand Against Tobacco

SKILL
Refusal Skills

Activating Prior Knowledge

Ask students to give reasons for why they should avoid using tobacco. List their responses on the board.

- **Objective** After completing the activity, students will be able to use refusal skills to resist pressure to use tobacco.
- **Time** 45 minutes
- **Materials** paper, pencil

Teacher Classroom Resources
- Building Health Skills
- Transparency 3-4

Model

- Have students read about Claire and Elise. Ask: Which teen is resisting negative peer pressure? *Claire* Name one of the things Claire does to resist the pressure from Elise. Sample answers: *She clearly says no; she walks away.*

National Health Standards Addressed

4.6, 7.1, 7.4, 7.6

234

Taking a Stand Against Tobacco

DIRECTIONS

Refusal Skills involve saying no to behavior that is unhealthy or unsafe. This activity will give you the opportunity to develop and master this important health skill. Here's a guide to the different parts of this activity:

① In the **Model** section, you will read about a teen who performs the health skill successfully. This "model" scenario will show you how the skill is done.

② The **Practice** section will help guide you in practicing the skill.

③ In the **Apply** section, you will have a chance to perform the skill on your own. You can use the Self-Check to check your work.

To complete this activity, first read the scenario presented in the Model. Then move on to the Practice. Finally, go ahead and try the Apply.

① Model

Refusal skills can help you say no to negative peer pressure. Read about how a teen named Claire handled peer pressure to use tobacco.

During the baseball game, Elise showed Claire a cigarette she found on the grass near the center field bleachers. She said someone in the stands must have dropped it.

Elise asked Claire to try the cigarette with her after the game. Claire said no in a firm voice. She told Elise that she would rather go to the batting cage after the game. When Elise started making chicken noises, Claire decided the conversation was over. She walked away to watch another teammate hit the ball.

Teaching Tips

Learning New Skills Ask students how it felt to ride a bike, in-line skate, use a new computer program, or skateboard for the first time. (Students will probably say it felt awkward, not natural, etc) Explain that it is normal not to feel comfortable doing a new skill the first few times. Emphasize that with practice, however, using health skills such as refusal skills begins to feel more natural. Encourage students to stand in front of a mirror or use a tape player at home to practice refusal skills in a strong, confident voice.

❷ Practice

Claire uses refusal skills again when she is offered tobacco by a classmate, Jennifer. Read the following conversation, then answer the questions at the end.

Jennifer: Try one of these special flavored cigarettes.

Claire: No thanks. From what I've read, all cigarettes can affect your health.

Jennifer: You can't believe everything you read.

Claire: I still don't want one. Let's go play my new computer game instead.

Jennifer: Ok, let's go.

1. Which refusal skills did Claire use?

2. What words would you use if you were in a similar situation?

Skill Summary
REFUSAL SKILLS

When you're pressured to do something you know is unhealthy, remember the word *S.T.O.P.*:

- <u>S</u>ay no in a firm voice..
- <u>T</u>ell why.
- <u>O</u>ffer other options.
- <u>P</u>romptly leave the situation.

❸ Apply

With a classmate, develop a situation where a teen feels pressure to use tobacco. Choose another form of tobacco, such as smokeless tobacco. Write a conversation between two or more teens. Use all the skills you have learned to refuse tobacco. In your refusal, include reasons why tobacco is an unhealthy choice.

Self-Check

- Did we use all of the refusal skills?
- Did we include reasons why tobacco is unhealthy?

Practice

- Divide the class into small groups to read the Practice paragraph.
- Then, have students work in their groups to answer the questions.
- Call on different groups to share answers to each question.

Apply/Assess

- Check that each pair of students has chosen a form of tobacco other than cigarettes.
- Remind each pair of students to incorporate the refusal skills in the conversation it develops.
- Have each pair of students share its conversation with the class.
- You may wish to distribute the Building Health Skills Activity in the Fast Files.

ASSESSMENT SCORING

Student work should meet all criteria to achieve the highest score.

Skills Student work demonstrates:
- the word no.
- a reason.
- another option.
- evidence of leaving if necessary.

Concepts Student work includes:
- accurate information about danger of tobacco.
- relationships between tobacco use and health.

Kick Butts

Objectives

Students will be able to
- identify ways that health advocates share information
- describe ways that students can be health advocates

Motivator

Ask students to think about how they react to advice given by adults. Then ask students to think about how they react to advice given by students their age. Which advice are they more likely to tune out? Which advice are they more likely to listen to?

Teaching the Activity

- Have students read the feature to find KBD's motto. (Stand out, speak up, and seize control). Ask: Which part of the motto promotes advocacy? *speak up* **BL**
- Have students recall their responses to the Motivator activity. Then, have them create a bulleted list of reasons why students can be effective health advocates. Ask volunteers to share their lists with the class. **OL**

TIME *health news*

Across the country, more and more teens are working together to stamp out smoking. They say it's time to...

KICK BUTTS

Did you know that with every puff of a cigarette, a smoker inhales more than 4,000 chemicals? These dangerous substances include ammonia—an ingredient in toilet cleaner, and arsenic—a powerful rat poison.

Scary facts like these have inspired teens all across the United States to take part in Kick Butts Day (KBD), an annual event sponsored by the Campaign for Tobacco-Free Kids. The day, which is run by teens for teens, is about giving young people information to make the right decision about smoking.

A DAY TO TAKE ACTION (AND HAVE FUN!)

"When I found out that tobacco kills 13,400 people every day," says Megan Shaheen, 13, from Washington, D.C., "I knew I had to do something."

Megan heard about KBD from a friend and decided to get involved. Megan especially liked KBD's motto, which is "Stand out, speak up, and seize control."

What does the motto mean to Megan? "It means I can make my opinions known about smoking," she says. "Now I'm going to speak out to tell my friends and other kids about the dangers of smoking."

Megan's not alone in getting her message heard. For over ten years, thousands of teens have used KBD as a chance to speak up. They get their anti-tobacco messages across through fun activities, such as school and neighborhood carnivals, track meets, and battles of the bands.

SURGEON GENERAL'S WARNING: Smoking Causes Lung Cancer, Heart Disease, Emphysema, and May Complicate Pregnancy

TEENS REACHING TEENS

The good news is youth movements like KBD seem to be working. According to the Campaign for Tobacco-Free Kids, smoking among high school students decreased from 36.4 percent in 1997 to 21.9 percent in 2003.

"Kids talking to kids sometimes works better than adults talking to kids," says Josh Parker, 15, from East Lansing, MI. "The numbers show when we put our minds to something, teens can make a change."

Activity **Media, Technology, and Culture**

Technology Have students use the Internet to find information about the Campaign for Tobacco-Free Kids and Kick Butts Day. The Web site offers activities that can be used throughout the year to help teens advocate against tobacco. Have students select one activity to carry out as a class, or have them develop their own health advocacy activity. After students have completed the project, have each student write an explanation of how the activity was an effective way to be a health advocate. Have students make suggestions for ways they could increase their effectiveness as a health advocate in the future.

Reading Review

Foldables™ and Other Study Aids Take out the Foldable that you created for Lesson 1 and any graphic organizers that you created for Lessons 1–3. Find a partner, and quiz each other using these study aids.

Lesson 1 | Tobacco: A Harmful Drug

Key Ideas

- Tobacco increases your risk of cancer and other serious diseases. It also stains your teeth, causes bad breath, and ages the skin.
- The nicotine in tobacco leads to addiction. Smokers begin to depend on nicotine to feel good and function normally.
- The chemicals in tobacco harm many parts of the body. Tobacco damges the lungs, heart, fingers, brain, and blood vessels.
- Smokeless tobacco is also addictive. It can form spots in the mouth that can turn to cancer and cause sores in the mouth, throat, and stomach.

Vocabulary

- nicotine (p. 222)
- carbon monoxide (p. 222)
- tar (p. 222)
- addiction (p. 223)
- emphysema (p. 223)
- snuff (p. 226)

Lesson 2 | Teens and Tobacco

Key Ideas

- Teens use tobacco for many reasons. They believe that tobacco makes them feel grown-up, helps them fit in better, and has no short-term health risks.
- Negative influences that can lead teens to try tobacco include media messages, negative peer pressure, and family members who use tobacco.
- Tobacco advertising can be a powerful influence on teens.

Vocabulary

- negative peer pressure (p. 228)
- media (p. 228)

Lesson 3 | Staying Tobacco Free

Key Ideas

- Refusal skills can help you say no effectively. Be prepared with some reasons to say no to tobacco.
- Ways of kicking the tobacco habit include going "cold turkey," using aids such as nicotine gums or patches, and getting support from a community group.
- Passive smokers can develop some of the same health problems as smokers.
- Nonsmokers have the right to breathe air free of tobacco smoke and to ask others not smoke around them.

Vocabulary

- secondhand smoke (p. 232)
- passive smokers (p. 232)

Assessment Resources

- 📁 Chapter 9 Summary and Activity
- Audio Summaries
- 📁 Reading Tutor
- 📁 Performance Assessment
- 📁 Chapter 9 Test
- ⊙ *ExamView*
- Vocabulary PuzzleMaker
- Online Learning Center

Reading Review

Use of Study Aids

- **Using the Dinah Zike Foldable™ Study Organizer** Have students use the **FOLDABLES™** Study Organizer Foldable™ to review the harmful effects of tobacco.

Key Ideas

- **Use the Headings** Have students skim through the lesson. As they locate each bold-face head, have them stop to be sure they remember the main idea of the text under that head.

Vocabulary Review

- **Vocabulary Sentences** Have students write a sentence that correctly incorporates two or more vocabulary words. (For example, The *nicotine* in cigarettes causes *addiction*.)

Teaching Tips

Reading in Health Class When a writing assignment is part of the health lesson, distribute and explain the grading rubric before students begin the assignment. Remind students that content is only one component of a writing assignment. The rubric will remind students of other aspects of writing, such as spelling and grammar, which can also affect their score. Explain that referring to the rubric after they write allows them to self-edit their work to achieve their best possible grade.

Assessment

Reviewing Vocabulary and Main Ideas

1. Emphysema
2. Addiction
3. Tar
4. negative peer pressure
5. media
6. b
7. c
8. c
9. b
10. a

Thinking Critically

11. *Sample answer:* People become addicted to the nicotine. Addiction causes users to depend on the substance in order to feel good and function normally. People who try to break their addiction experience unpleasant symptoms so they may start smoking again to feel better.

12. *Sample answer:* Teens often learn their behaviors from their families, so teens with parents who smoke might learn this behavior from their parents.

 After You Read

HEALTH QUIZ

Now that you have read the chapter, look back at your answers to the Health Quiz on the chapter opener. Have your ideas changed? What would your answers be now?

Reviewing Vocabulary and Main Ideas

On a sheet of paper, write the numbers 1–5. After each number, write the term from the list that best completes each sentence.

- carbon monoxide
- tar
- addiction
- emphysema
- media
- negative peer pressure
- secondhand smoke
- passive smokers

Lesson 1 Tobacco: A Harmful Drug

1. _____ is a disease in which tiny air sacs in the lungs are damaged and lose their elasticity.

2. _____ is the body's physical or mental need for a drug or other substance.

3. _____ is a thick, oily, dark liquid that forms when tobacco burns.

Lesson 2 Teens and Tobacco

4. Pressure you feel to go along with harmful behaviors or beliefs of your peers is known as _____.

5. Newspapers, radio, television, and the Internet are examples of the _____.

Lesson 3 Staying Tobacco Free

On a sheet of paper, write the numbers 6–10. Choose the letter of the word or phrase that best completes each statement or question.

6. It is illegal in many states for teens to
   a. listen to tobacco advertisements.
   b. use tobacco products.
   c. advocate for a smoke-free environment.

7. *Cold turkey* is
   a. a type of cigarette product in which the tobacco is flavored.
   b. a type of tobacco product that is held in the mouth rather than smoked.
   c. a method of quitting tobacco in which the user simply stops using all such products.

8. Each of the following is a nicotine replacement therapy *except*
   a. nicotine gum.
   b. patches worn on the skin.
   c. group counseling

9. All of the following statements are true about passive smokers *except*
   a. They are nonsmokers.
   b. They are smokers who are unaware of the dangers of smoking.
   c. They develop some of the same health problems as smokers.

10. Since 1989, it has been illegal to
    a. smoke on domestic airplane flights.
    b. be a passive smoker.
    c. release secondhand smoke into the environment.

Health *Online* Visit health.glencoe.com and take the Online Quiz for Chapter 9.

Health *Online*

Have students visit **health.glencoe.com** to take the Chapter 9 Quiz.

HEALTH QUIZ Wrap-Up

Tobacco Ask students to review their answers to the chapter opener Health Quiz. Ask volunteers to identify any answers they would change based on what they learned while reading the chapter. If students have not changed their answers, ask volunteers to state one new fact they learned while reading the chapter.

Thinking Critically

Using complete sentences, answer the following questions on a sheet of paper.

11. **Evaluate** Why do you think it is difficult for smokers to quit smoking?

12. **Analyze** Explain why a teen whose parents use tobacco might be more likely to do the same.

Write About It

13. Imagine getting a letter from a friend living in another city. In the letter, your friend tells you about a new group of friends that smoke. Your friend is thinking of trying a cigarette too. Write a letter to your friend giving advice on the dangers of smoking.

 Career Corner

Anesthesiologist People undergoing surgery or certain medical treatments need drugs so they don't feel any pain. These drugs are called anesthetics. The physician who gives anesthetics is called an *anesthesiologist*. Like other doctors, anesthesiologists need at least four years of medical school and advanced training. Find out more about this and other health careers by clicking on *Career Corner* at **health.glencoe.com**.

14. Write a paragraph explaining how a smoke-free environment would benefit both smokers and nonsmokers.

Write About It

13. **Personal Writing** Students' letters should mention the dangers of smoking and ways to resist negative peer pressure.

14. **Expository Writing** Expository writing informs, explains, defines, or gives directions. Students' expository paragraphs should include facts stating how a smoke-free environment benefits both smokers and nonsmokers. Students should mention the health benefits of breathing smoke-free air.

Standardized Test Practice

1. C
2. A

 Career Corner

Anesthesiologist Have students visit the Career Corner at **health.glencoe .com** to gather more information about a career as an anesthesiologist. Students interested in a career in anesthesiology should be interested in math and science and enjoy working in a hospital setting.

Standardized Test Practice

Math

Trends in Smoking Among Americans
Use the table to answer the questions.

Year	Smokers per 100 Americans
1965	41.9
1974	37.0
1979	33.3
1985	29.9
1990	25.3
1995	24.6
2000	23.1
2002	22.4

TEST-TAKING TIP

When questions involve graphs or tables, study the data carefully. Make sure you understand the information being presented.

1. In which year shown did the number of smokers per hundred Americans drop below 25?
   A. 1985   **C.** 1995
   B. 1990   **D.** 1994

2. Which of the following does the table show?
   A. The percentage of American smokers has steadily declined.
   B. The percentage of American smokers has steadily risen.
   C. The number of smokers over age 41 has declined.
   D. The percentage of smokers below age 23 has risen.

Test-Taking Tips

Interpreting a Graph or Chart Tell students that some test questions will require reading and interpreting a table, graph, or chart. Students should be reminded to pay particular attention to the title and axis labels or column heads. Have students note any units used. After students have examined the graphic, they should read the questions and then return to the graphic to find the correct answers.

CHAPTER 10 pp. 240–265	Standards		Skills and Activities
	National	State/Local	
	National Health Education Standards 5.1, 5.2, 5.3		**IM EXPRESS,** *p. 241* **HANDS-ON HEALTH** "Say No to Drugs" Skit, *p. 262* **BUILDING HEALTH SKILLS** *Decision Making* Avoiding Drug Abuse, *pp. 260–261*
LESSON 1 **The Dangers of Alcohol Use** pp. 242–245	National Health Education Standards 1.4, 1.8, 5.3, 6.2, 8.2		**DEVELOPING GOOD CHARACTER** *Being a Responsible Friend, p. 243*
LESSON 2 **Alcoholism and Addiction** pp. 246–248	National Health Education Standards 1.4, 1.5, 1.6, 1.8, 3.2, 3.4, 4.2, 4.4, 5.2, 5.3, 7.7, 8.2, 8.3		
LESSON 3 **What Are Illegal Drugs?** pp. 249–252	National Health Education Standards 1.1, 1.3, 1.4, 1.6, 1.7, 1.8, 3.1, 4.3, 5.3, 7.4, 8.2		**DEVELOPING GOOD CHARACTER** *Fairness, p. 251*
LESSON 4 **Drug Abuse** pp. 253–255	National Health Education Standards 1.1, 1.2, 1.3, 1.6, 1.7, 1.8, 3.2, 5.2, 7.4, 8.2, 8.3		
LESSON 5 **Avoiding Alcohol and Drugs** pp. 256–259	National Health Education Standards 1.1, 1.4, 1.6, 2.4, 3.1, 3.2, 3.4, 4.2, 4.3, 4.4, 4.6, 5.3, 6.1, 7.4, 7.6, 8.2		**HEALTH SKILLS ACTIVITY** *Advocacy* Getting SADD About Substance Abuse, *p. 257*

PACING THE CHAPTER

Lesson 1	45 min	**Lesson 4**	30 min	**Chapter Review**	45 min
Lesson 2	30 min	**Lesson 5**	45 min	**Hands-on Health**	30 min
Lesson 3	45 min	**Building Health Skills**	45 min		

BLOCK SCHEDULING

For block scheduling, assign students Building Health Skills feature *Avoiding Drug Abuse*, pages 260–261, and Guided Reading and Writing. 📁

Reproducible Resources	Assessment	Media and Technology
Chapter *FAST FILE* Resources Chapter Summaries and Activities `REVIEW` Building Health Skills Activity `TEACH` Performance Assessment Activity `EXTEND` Universal Access Activities `TEACH` Parent Letter and Activities **Student Activities Workbook** `TEACH` **Reading Tutor** `TEACH`	Building Health Skills Activity, *pp. 260–261* Chapter 10 Assessment, *pp. 264–265* **Chapter *FAST FILE* Resources** Performance Assessment Activity, *p. 4* Chapter 10 Test, *p. 7* *ExamView® Test Generator*	**TeacherWorks**™ includes: • Interactive Teacher Edition • Lesson Planner with Calendar • Access to all blackline masters • Correlations to standards StudentWorks™ Plus Online Student Edition Dinah Zike's Teaching Health with Foldables™
Chapter *FAST FILE* Resources Concept Mapping Activity 10-1 `REVIEW` Cross-Curriculum Activity 10-1 `EXTEND` Enrichment Activity 10-1 `EXTEND` Lesson Plan 10-1 Guided Reading and Writing 10-1 `TEACH` Reteaching Activity 10-1 `REVIEW`	Lesson 1 Review, *p. 245* Vocabulary PuzzleMaker *ExamView® Test Generator*	Vocabulary PuzzleMaker *ExamView® Test Generator* StudentWorks™ Plus Transparency 10-1 **Health** *Online*
Chapter *FAST FILE* Resources Concept Mapping Activity 10-2 `REVIEW` Health Lab 10–2 `EXTEND` Enrichment Activity 10-2 `EXTEND` Lesson Plan 10-2 Guided Reading and Writing 10-2 `TEACH` Reteaching Activity 10-2 `REVIEW`	Lesson 2 Review, *p. 248* Vocabulary PuzzleMaker *ExamView® Test Generator*	Vocabulary PuzzleMaker *ExamView® Test Generator* StudentWorks™ Plus Transparency 10-2 **Health** *Online*
Chapter *FAST FILE* Resources Concept Mapping Activity 10-3 `REVIEW` Cross-Curriculum Activity 10-3 `EXTEND` Enrichment Activity 10-3 `EXTEND` Lesson Plan 10-3 Guided Reading and Writing 10-3 `TEACH` Reteaching Activity 10-3 `REVIEW`	Lesson 3 Review, *p. 252* Vocabulary PuzzleMaker *ExamView® Test Generator*	Vocabulary PuzzleMaker *ExamView® Test Generator* StudentWorks™ Plus Transparency 10-3 **Health** *Online*
Chapter *FAST FILE* Resources Concept Mapping Activity 10-4 `REVIEW` Decision-Making Activity 10-4 `EXTEND` Enrichment Activity 10-4 `EXTEND` Lesson Plan 10-4 Guided Reading and Writing 10-4 `TEACH` Reteaching Activity 10-4 `REVIEW`	Lesson 4 Review, *p. 255* Vocabulary PuzzleMaker *ExamView® Test Generator*	Vocabulary PuzzleMaker *ExamView® Test Generator* StudentWorks™ Plus Transparency 10-4 **Health** *Online*
Chapter *FAST FILE* Resources Concept Mapping Activity 10-5 `REVIEW` Decision-Making Activity 10-5 `EXTEND` Enrichment Activity 10-5 `EXTEND` Lesson Plan 10-5 Guided Reading and Writing 10-5 `TEACH` Reteaching Activity 10-5 `REVIEW`	Lesson 5 Review, *p. 259* Vocabulary PuzzleMaker *ExamView® Test Generator*	Vocabulary PuzzleMaker *ExamView® Test Generator* StudentWorks™ Plus Transparency 10-4 **Health** *Online*

Chapter and Lesson Resources

The *Teen Health* resources are designed for **differentiated learning abilities. You may want to use the coded items in this way:**

`REVIEW` —activities to review or reinforce content

`TEACH` —activities to teach basic concepts

`EXTEND` —activities to extend or enrich lesson content

 OUT OF TIME?

Use Health Skills Activities *Getting SADD About Substance Abuse,* page 257, or Developing Good Character, page 251.

Risk Factors for Teen Drug Use

The material in this chapter will help students identify some of the factors that can lead to substance abuse, consequences of substance abuse, and strategies for refusing drugs and alcohol.

Understanding the risk factors that make teens vulnerable to drug and alcohol abuse can help in the identification of high-risk students. Although teens who abuse drugs or alcohol do not fit a single profile, the following are common risk factors that have been shown to increase a teen's likelihood of substance abuse:

- A family member who has drug or alcohol problems—Not only do some people have a genetic predisposition to substance abuse, but a substance abuser in the family can mean ready access to drugs or alcohol.

- Lack of parental supervision or a poor relationship with parents or guardians

- Poor self-esteem or impulsiveness

- Access to drugs or alcohol though friends or in the community

- Hostile and rebellious behavior or attention deficit hyperactivity disorder

- Friends who use drugs or alcohol—A study found that more than half of sixth graders have experienced peer pressure to use alcohol.

Help students understand that having one or more of these risk factors does not necessarily mean that a person will become a substance abuser. Instead, recognizing risk factors helps people take actions that can protect their health. By understanding ways in which they may be vulnerable to substance abuse, students can develop strategies to address those factors. Explain that positive personal choices, community resources, and school services can all help individuals avoid substance abuse.

Cirrhosis and Liver Damage

One of the ways that alcohol damages physical health is by causing cirrhosis of the liver. Cirrhosis is a condition in which liver tissue becomes scarred and blood is no longer able to flow easily through the scarred liver. Cirrhosis damages the liver's ability to remove toxins from the blood, produce bile, and perform its other functions.

Alcohol causes liver damage because the liver is the organ that filters alcohol from the blood and breaks it down. The results of this process are chemicals that cause damage to the liver cells. Repeated exposure to these chemicals causes the scarring associated with cirrhosis.

Cirrhosis causes a wide variety of symptoms, and in some cases it causes no symptoms at all. Some signs of cirrhosis are fatigue, weight loss, weakness, itching, dark urine, and yellowing of the skin.

At this time, there is no medical treatment that can reverse the damage caused by cirrhosis. People can, however, take steps to limit further damage to their liver after they are diagnosed with cirrhosis. For example, avoiding alcohol, reducing salt intake, and eating healthful foods are all steps that can slow the progress of the disease. In some cases, the liver becomes severely damaged and a liver transplant is the only option for survival.

The liver is important for the body's immune response. Cirrhosis impairs the liver's ability to respond to infection. For this reason, people with cirrhosis need to be careful to avoid others who are ill.

Students should be reminded that there are several causes of cirrhosis—having cirrhosis does not necessarily indicate that a person abuses alcohol or did so in the past. Hepatitis B and hepatitis C, exposure to certain drugs or toxins, and some inherited diseases also cause cirrhosis.

GOVERNMENT WARNING:
(1) ACCORDING TO THE SURGEON GENERAL, WOMEN SHOULD NOT DRINK ALCOHOLIC BEVERAGES DURING PREGNANCY BECAUSE OF THE RISK OF BIRTH DEFECTS.
(2) CONSUMPTION OF ALCOHOLIC BEVERAGES IMPAIRS YOUR ABILITY TO DRIVE A CAR OR OPERATE MACHINERY, AND MAY CAUSE HEALTH PROBLEMS.

Support for Teaching Reading

Reading Preview

Activating Background Vocabulary Ask students what comes to mind when they think of the terms "alcoholism" and "drug abuse." Write their responses on the board. Direct students to sort their responses into categories such as health risks and legal consequences. Guide students in a discussion of remaining alcohol and drug-free.

FOLDABLES Study Organizer *Dinah Zike's Reading and Study Skills for Teen Health* provides interactive graphic organizers that help students comprehend and retain health concepts as they read. Use the Foldable™ on page 241 or find more Foldables™ activities for the chapter on **Alcohol and Other Drugs** in the separate booklet, available in the TCR.

Lesson 1   The Dangers of Alcohol Use

Determining Main Ideas Have students consider the question in the first heading in the lesson. "What Is Alcohol?" Guide students to find the main idea of the paragraph: Alcohol is a drug that affects the way the mind and body function." Show students how to find supporting details about the effects of alcohol on the body.

Lesson 2   Alcoholism and Addiction

Monitoring Comprehension Show students how to ask and answer their own questions during independent reading, such as: "What is my purpose in reading this? The title of the section is **Alcoholism and Addiction.** My purpose must be to recognize the problems caused by alcohol use." Have students write the answers to their questions as they read and to reread a section if they can't find the answer.

Lesson 3   What are Illegal Drugs?

Listen-Read-Discuss Present the lesson in a brief lecture to give students background information. Next, have students read silently, making a list of questions for clarification. Finally, stop students during reading and ask: "What do you understand most from what you have read so far? What do you understand least? What questions do you still have?"

Lesson 4   Drug Abuse

Compare and Contrast Illustrate a three-column chart on the board. Direct students to read independently to find out about the effects of drug use on the three sides of the health triangle. Have students record facts about drug effects on physical, mental/emotional, and social health.

Lesson 5   Avoiding Alcohol and Drugs

3-2-1 Strategy Ask students to write a brief summary identifying **three** key points they found while reading the lesson (avoiding substance abuse, ways to stay substance-free, alternatives to drug and alcohol use). Next, have students list **two** things in the lesson they thought were interesting. Finally, ask students to write **one** question they still have. Have student pairs reread to find the answers.

Post Reading

Informational Presentations Direct students to gather more information on the dangers of alcohol and drug use. Guide students to use speaking strategies effectively to convey meaning to the audience during an informational presentation.

Key for Using the Teacher Wraparound Edition

Use this key to help you identify the different types of prompts found in the Teacher Wraparound Edition.

R **Reading Strategies** activities help you teach reading skills and vocabulary.

C **Critical Thinking** strategies help students apply and extend what they have learned.

U **Universal Access** activities provide differentiated instruction for students learning to speak English, along with suggestions for teaching various types of learners.

HS **Health Skills Practice** activities reinforce Health Skills concepts and help students apply these skills in their everyday lives.

W **Writing Support** activities provide writing opportunities to help students comprehend the text.

AL **Active Learning** strategies provide a variety of activities for presenting lesson content, including Quick Demos and engaging classroom projects that get students actively involved.

Key to Ability Levels

Teaching Strategies and activities have been coded for ability level and appropriateness

AL Activities for students working above grade level

OL Activities for students working on grade level

BL Activities for students working below grade level

EL Activities for English Learners

Symbols

Transparencies

CD-ROM

health.glencoe.com

Print Resources

CHAPTER 10

Alcohol and Other Drugs

Chapter at a Glance

Lesson 1 identifies how alcohol affects the body and mind, explains why some teens use alcohol, and presents skills teens can use to help a friend avoid alcohol.

Lesson 2 describes the cycle of addiction to alcohol, identifies the health risks of drinking during pregnancy, and communicates ways that teens can reduce stress without using alcohol.

Lesson 3 identifies the dangers of illegal drugs, explains the risks of using marijuana and inhalants, and identifies the risks of using stimulants, narcotics, anabolic steroids, and hallucinogens.

Lesson 4 identifies the harmful effects of drug abuse, explains recovery and withdrawal, and describes treatments for drug addicts.

Lesson 5 explains why it is important to avoid illegal drugs, and identifies alternatives to substance abuse.

R Reading Strategy

Interpreting the Photo Have students examine the photo. Ask: How are these teens practicing the health skill of advocacy? *They are informing others about an issue that can affect health.* What are some other ways these teens could share information about the dangers of drug and alcohol use? Sample answer: *They could make pamphlets.* **OL**

240

CHAPTER 10
Alcohol and Other Drugs

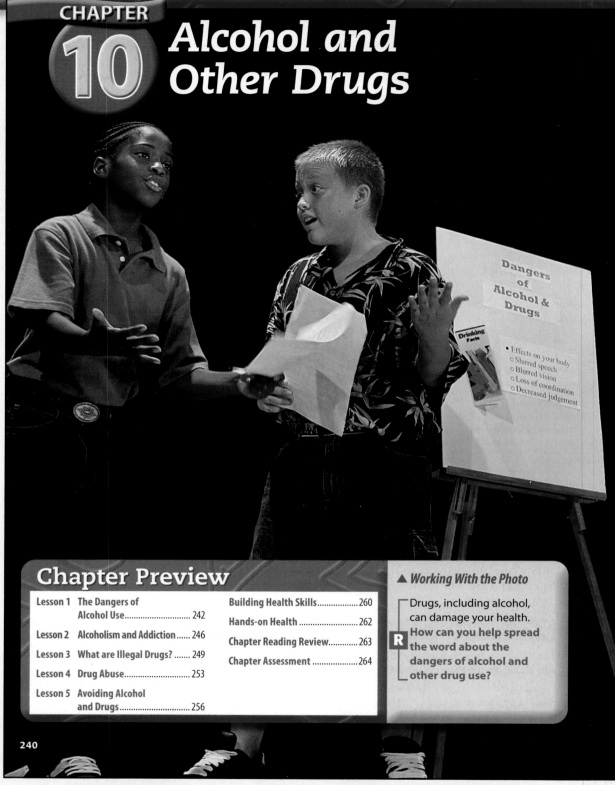

240

Chapter Preview

Lesson 1	The Dangers of Alcohol Use	242
Lesson 2	Alcoholism and Addiction	246
Lesson 3	What are Illegal Drugs?	249
Lesson 4	Drug Abuse	253
Lesson 5	Avoiding Alcohol and Drugs	256

Building Health Skills	260
Hands-on Health	262
Chapter Reading Review	263
Chapter Assessment	264

▲ Working With the Photo

R Drugs, including alcohol, can damage your health. How can you help spread the word about the dangers of alcohol and other drug use?

Universal Access

Differentiated Learning Glencoe provides teacher support and student materials for all learners in the health classroom.

- Spanish Glosario and chapter summaries for the English Language Learners.
- *Reading Tutor* and related worksheets support reluctant readers.

- Universal Access strategies throughout the Teacher Wraparound Edition and Fast Files help you present materials for gifted students, at-risk students, physically impaired students, and those with behavior disorders or learning disabilities.

Start-Up Activities

Before You Read Read the Instant Message below. Imagine you are mona_k15. How would you respond to carrie_64's offer? Keep a record of your answer.

IM Express

mona_k15: i want to go to nikki's party but my cold is worse. i'll have to wait till saturday to see. ☹

carrie_64: i have some medicine i got from my doctor last time i was sick. i'll give it to you when i see you in english class.

FOLDABLES™ Study Organizer

As You Read Make this Foldable™ to record information on alcohol and its harmful effects, presented in Lesson 1. Begin with two sheets of notebook paper.

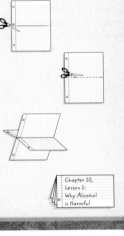

1 Fold one sheet in half from top to bottom. Cut about 1" along the fold at both ends, stopping at the margin lines.

2 Fold the second sheet in half from top to bottom. Cut the fold between the margin lines.

3 Insert the first sheet through the second sheet and align folds.

4 Fold the bound pages in half to make a booklet, and label the cover as shown. Then label each page as instructed by your teacher.

Take notes on alcohol's harmful effects on the appropriate page of your booklet.

> Chapter 10,
> Lesson 1:
> Why Alcohol
> is Harmful

Health Online Visit **health.glencoe.com** and complete the Health Inventory for Chapter 10.

241

IM Express

Drug Safety Have students write down their response to carrie_64's offer. Ask volunteers to share their answers with the class. Tell students that they will have a chance to change their responses after they have read the chapter.

No Child Left Behind

Safe School
The importance of a drug-free environment for learning is recognized in the No Child Left Behind Act. The Safe and Drug Free School and Communities program distributes funds for programs that discourage drug use.

FOLDABLES™
Study Organizer Dinah Zike Foldables™

Organizing Information Model the steps at the front of the class as students make their Foldables™. Have students use the Foldable™ as they read Lesson 1. Explain that the Foldable™ can be used to organize information about the dangerous effects of alcohol. It can also be used to record notes and the lesson vocabulary terms. After the students have finished the chapter, remind them to use their completed Foldables™ to review the content of Lesson 1. **BL**

Health Online

Have students visit **health.glencoe.com** and complete the Health Inventory for Chapter 10.

FOCUS

Activating Prior Knowledge

What I Know Have students describe negative effects of alcohol use with which they are familiar.

Guide to Reading

BUILDING VOCABULARY

- Ask students to preview the lesson to find the definitions of the vocabulary terms. Then have students write sentences describing how two of the terms are related.
- Use Vocabulary PuzzleMaker to reinforce vocabulary terms.

READING STRATEGY

 Have students use their Foldables™ as they read Lesson 1.

- **Sequencing** Students' flowcharts should include effects on the stomach, the blood-stream, and the liver.

uick Write

Have students discuss the ways alcohol use is portrayed in their chosen story.

Academic Vocabulary

Expand Students learn that alcohol causes blood vessels to expand. Explain that *expand* means "to increase in size." Ask students to name antonyms of the word *expand*. Sample answers: *shrink, contract* **OL**

242

The Dangers of Alcohol Use

Guide to Reading

● Building Vocabulary
In your notebook, write definitions of what you think the terms below mean. Make corrections as needed when you come upon the definitions in the lesson.

- alcohol (p. 242)
- drug (p. 242)
- cirrhosis (p. 243)
- blood alcohol content (BAC) (p. 243)

● Focusing on the Main Ideas
In this lesson, you will be able to

- **identify** how alcohol affects the body and mind.
- **explain** why some teens use alcohol.
- **recognize** factors that influence alcohol's effects.

● Reading Strategy
Sequencing Make a flow chart that shows where alcohol travels in the body once it is swallowed. Describe what the drug does to each body part it passes through.

FOLDABLES Study Organizer Use the Foldable™ on p. 241 as you read this lesson.

uick Write

Write about a story you have read or heard involving the dangers of alcohol use.

What Is Alcohol?

Have you ever seen food that is spoiled and has mold on it? This change is caused by a chemical reaction. A similar change leads to the creation of alcohol. **Alcohol** (AL·kuh·hawl) is *a substance produced by a chemical reaction in carbohydrates*. Alcohol is a drug. A **drug** is *a substance that changes the structure or function of the body or mind*. Like other drugs, alcohol can cloud judgment, making it difficult to think and act responsibly. Over time, alcohol can also cause disease and damage body organs. One of the greatest dangers of using alcohol is that its effects are unpredictable. There is no telling how a person's mind or body might react when he or she has been drinking.

Alcohol's Effects on the Body

Alcohol begins to affect the body systems soon after it is consumed. In the stomach, it increases the flow of acid used for digestion. Over time, the extra acid can cause sores to develop in the stomach lining. These sores are called *ulcers*.

From the stomach, alcohol moves into the bloodstream and causes the blood vessels to expand. More blood passes through

242 Chapter 10: Alcohol and Other Drugs

 Chapter *FAST FILE* Resources
Guided Reading and Writing 10-1
Concept Mapping Activity 10-1
Cross-Curriculum Activity 10-1
Reteaching Activity 10-1
Enrichment Activity 10-1
Lesson Quiz 10-1

Technology
- Transparency 10-1
- Audio Summaries
- *ExamView*
- Vocabulary PuzzleMaker
- StudentWorks™ Plus

the blood vessels making the body feel warm. As blood flows close to the surface of the skin, the body loses heat. In cold weather, this can cause the body temperature to drop dangerously low before the drinker feels cold.

Consuming alcohol regularly over a long period of time puts a strain on the liver. Heavy drinkers are particularly at risk of developing **cirrhosis** (suh·ROH·sis). This is *destruction and scarring of the liver tissue*. Cirrhosis can lead to death.

Drinking large amounts of alcohol in a short time can lead to alcohol poisoning. The drinker may vomit, become unconscious, or have trouble breathing. If this occurs, the user may be at risk of serious harm or even death.

Alcohol's Effects on the Brain

When alcohol reaches the brain, it slows the body's functions and reaction time. Reaction time is how long it takes a person to respond to a situation. People whose reaction time has been slowed by alcohol are dangerous behind the wheel of a car. They cannot react quickly enough to avoid other vehicles or pedestrians.

Drinking alcohol makes it hard for people to think and speak clearly. They may say or do things they would not normally say or do. A person under the influence of alcohol is also more likely to engage in high-risk behaviors.

Reading Check **Define** How does alcohol affect the brain?

Factors that Influence Alcohol's Effects

Different people react to alcohol in different ways. How a person reacts depends on several factors, including his or her **blood alcohol content (BAC).** This is *a measure of the amount of alcohol present in a person's blood*. It is expressed as a percentage. A BAC of 0.02% will cause most people to feel lightheaded. A BAC of 0.08% interferes with a person's ability to drive a car safely. Police officers use this percentage to determine if a driver is legally drunk. A BAC of 0.40% can lead to coma and death.

▼ Drunk driving is a major cause of traffic accidents. **Explain how alcohol contributes to auto accidents.**

DEVELOPING
Good Character

Being a Responsible Friend

One way of showing you are a responsible person is by looking out for the well-being of others. Don't let a friend get in a car with a driver who has been drinking. If your friend is using alcohol, urge him or her to get help. Don't hesitate to talk to an adult yourself if your friend is unwilling to reach out. This is not breaking your friend's trust. It is taking the first step in getting your friend the help he or she needs. What are some other ways you can show you are responsible and care about a friend's health?

TEACH

DEVELOPING
Good Character

Being a Responsible Friend
Have students work in small groups to read the feature. Then have each group write and practice a role-play that demonstrates another way to show responsibility by caring about a friend's health. After each group has performed, ask the class to evaluate the role-play.
OL

AL Active Learning

Group Project Divide the class into two groups. Have one group make a list of ten questions about ways that alcohol affects the brain. Have the other group develop a list of ten questions about ways that alcohol affects the body. Explain that each group will use its questions to try to "stump" the other group. Have each group ask its questions of the other group.
OL

Reading Check

Answer Alcohol slows response time and affects the ability to reason.

Caption Answer

Photo Caption Alcohol impairs a driver's reaction time and ability to drive.

HEALTH LITERACY

Binge Drinking Consuming five or more alcoholic beverages in a row is considered binge drinking. Media attention often focuses on binge drinking by college students. However, binge drinking is also practiced by students in middle school and high school. A recent study by a researcher at Columbia University found that 9 percent of seventh graders had taken part in binge drinking. By eighth grade, 19 percent of students reported taking part in binge drinking. Explain that alcohol poisoning is one serious risk of binge drinking.

W Writing Support

Descriptive Writing Have students review the ways in which alcohol affects the body and the list of factors that influence the effects of alcohol. Then have students write a descriptive paragraph from the point of view of a specific tissue, organ, or organ system describing the negative effects alcohol has on its functioning. **AL**

R Reading Strategy

Analyzing a Graphic Have students examine Figure 10.1. Remind them that one myth about alcohol use is that drinking beer or wine will not lead to drunkenness or addiction. Teens might be encouraged to drink by others who claim "It's only wine (or beer)." Challenge students to explain how the information in the infographic could be used to counteract this peer pressure. **OL**

Reading Check

Answer, p. 245 Some teens drink because they think alcohol will help them relax.

Health Online

Visit **health.glencoe.com** and complete the Interactive Study Guide for Lesson 1.

A number of other factors can influence how alcohol affects an individual. These factors include the following.

W

- **The person's body weight.** The less a person weighs, the greater the effect the alcohol will have.
- **The person's rate of consumption.** Drinking quickly can overload the liver. When this happens, alcohol builds up in the body and continues to affect the brain and blood vessels.
- **The amount the person consumes.** The size of a drink and the alcohol content will influence its effects. **Figure 10.1** compares the alcohol content of different alcoholic beverages.
- **The amount the person has eaten.** Food slows the absorption of alcohol into the bloodstream. When the stomach is empty, alcohol enters the bloodstream and affects the body much quicker.
- **The presence of other drugs in the person's system.** When you combine alcohol with other drugs, including medicines, they react with each other. This can cause serious harm or even death.

▼ **FIGURE 10.1**

R **ALCOHOL CONTENT IN DIFFERENT DRINKS**

The three drinks here are different sizes. Yet all contain the same amount of alcohol. All have the same effect on the brain and body. **How many ounces of beer would produce the same effect as 6 ounces of wine?**

Mixed drink 1.5 ounces of liquor

Beer 12 ounces

BEER

Wine 4 ounces

Caption Answers

Photo Caption Six ounces of wine is equal to 18 ounces of beer.
Photo Caption, p. 245 Answers should include a variety of healthful activities.

What Teens Want to Know

What is alcopop? The term *alcopop* is used to describe malt-based drinks that have a sweet or fruity flavor. These alcoholic beverages can be advertised on television because they are malt-based. According to the American Medical Association, these drinks have become especially popular with teen girls. In fact, a study showed that more than 30 percent of teen girls have tried alcopop. Have students research the dangers of alcopop. Then have students make a poster explaining why teens should avoid these beverages. **OL**

Teens Who Drink

In the United States, drinking alcohol is illegal for anyone under the age of 21. Therefore, teens caught drinking can be arrested. They may also be suspended or expelled from school. Teens who use alcohol risk developing health problems as well. Research has shown that the brains of teenagers continue to develop until the age of 20. Alcohol can affect this development by interfering with the brain's learning and memory functions. When the brain doesn't function properly, it is difficult to do well in school.

In spite of the health and safety risks, some teens still choose to drink. Why? Some believe that alcohol helps them relax, fit in, and be accepted by their peers. Others feel that drinking helps them escape their problems. In reality, alcohol usually makes problems worse. If you have a problem, talk to a friend or trusted adult.

▲ Finding healthy activities to do with your friends will help you avoid alcohol. **What are some other healthy activities you can enjoy with your friends?**

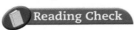 **Reading Check** **Identify** What reasons do teens give for drinking?

Lesson 1 Review

 After You Read

Review this lesson for new terms, major headings, and Reading Checks.

What I Learned

1. **Vocabulary** Define *alcohol*, and use it in an original sentence.

2. **Recall** Give two examples of how alcohol affects the body.

3. **Identify** What do the letters *BAC* stand for? What does BAC measure?

Thinking Critically

4. **Evaluate** Which of alcohol's effects do you think is the most harmful?

5. **Analyze** Why is a person under the influence of alcohol more likely to engage in other high-risk behaviors?

Applying Health Skills

6. **Goal Setting** Identify some goals you have set for yourself, such as college or playing on a sports team. Explain the effects alcohol use could have on these plans.

Health Online For more review questions for Lesson 1, go to **health.glencoe.com**.

ASSESS

Assessment Resources

Lesson Review Quiz
- *ExamView*
- Fast Files Activities
- Online Quizzes and Activities

Reteaching

- Assign Concept Map 10-1 or Reteaching Activity 10-1 in the Fast Files.
- Have students create a diagram or poster that shows three ways that alcohol affects the body and three ways that alcohol affects the brain.

Enrichment

- Assign Enrichment Activity 10-1 in the Fast Files.
- Have students use print or online resources to research alcohol poisoning. Ask students to prepare a presentation of their findings to share with the class.

CLOSE

Have volunteers name reasons that teens should not drink alcohol.

Lesson 1 Review Answers

1. Alcohol is a substance produced by a chemical reaction in carbohydrates. Sentences will vary.

2. *Sample answers:* stomach ulcers, strain on the liver, cirrhosis

3. BAC stands for "blood alcohol content," the alcohol present in blood expressed as a percentage.

4. *Sample answer:* I think impaired reasoning is alcohol's most harmful effect, because it leads to other risk behaviors.

5. Alcohol impairs judgment and affects a person's ability to make good decisions.

6. Student goals will vary, but should include a description of harmful effects of alcohol that could prevent them from reaching the goal.

245

FOCUS

Activating Prior Knowledge

What I Know Ask students to recall the definition of *addiction*, which was taught in Chapter 9. Write the word on the board and develop a class definition of the term. Then have students brainstorm words they associate with *addiction*.

Guide to Reading

BUILDING VOCABULARY
- Explain that a *syndrome* is a group of symptoms that occur together in a disorder. Challenge students to relate this to the meaning of the term *fetal alcohol syndrome.*
- Use Vocabulary PuzzleMaker to reinforce vocabulary terms.

READING STRATEGY
Predicting Have students work in small groups to share their predictions. After students have completed the lesson, have them look back to see if their predictions were correct.

Quick Write

Before students write their paragraphs, have them recall the negative effects of alcohol use that were discussed in Lesson 1.

Alcoholism and Addiction

Guide to Reading

● **Building Vocabulary**
Copy the terms below into your notebook. Define each as you come across them in your reading.
- tolerance (p. 247)
- alcoholism (p. 247)
- fetal alcohol syndrome (FAS) (p. 248)

● **Focusing on the Main Ideas**
In this lesson, you will be able to
- **describe** the cycle of addiction to alcohol.
- **identify** the health risks of drinking during pregnancy.
- **communicate** ways that teens can reduce stress without using alcohol.

● **Reading Strategy**
Predicting Quickly look at the main headings, figures, and captions. Predict the kinds of information that will be covered.

Quick Write

Write a paragraph describing how you think alcoholism might affect a person's life.

Why You Should Avoid Alcohol

Using alcohol carries a number of short- and long-term consequences. People who have been drinking alcohol may do or say things they will regret later. Teens whose judgment has been clouded by alcohol may take part in high-risk behaviors. These include using other drugs, engaging in sexual activity, or riding in a car driven by another drinker.

When used over time, alcohol can damage a person's health. For teens, it also can negatively affect relationships with parents and other family members. It also can affect performance in school and have a lasting effect on a teen's future.

Addiction and Alcoholism

People who use alcohol regularly over a long period of time risk becoming addicted to alcohol. As noted in Chapter 9, addiction is a physical or mental need for a drug. The cycle of addiction is sometimes represented by a downward spiral, as shown in **Figure 10.2.** The spiral shows how addiction to alcohol starts off by having an occasional drink. Soon, drinking becomes a habit. He or she begins drinking larger amounts of alcohol. As time goes on, the person develops a tolerance. **Tolerance** is *a need for increasing amounts of a substance to achieve the same effect.*

Lesson 2 Resources

📁 **Chapter *FAST FILE* Resources**
Guided Reading and Writing 10-2
Concept-Mapping Activity 10-2
Health Lab 10-2
Reteaching Activity 10-2
Enrichment Activity 10-2
Lesson Quiz 10-2

Technology
🖐 Transparency 10-2
⊙ Audio Summaries
⊙ *ExamView*
🖱 Vocabulary PuzzleMaker
⊙ StudentWorks™ Plus

If this cycle isn't interrupted, the person develops an addiction to alcohol. A person who is addicted to alcohol suffers from **alcoholism.** This is *a disease in which a person has a physical and mental need for alcohol.* A person with this disease is called an *alcoholic.*

Help for Alcoholics and Their Families

Alcoholism cannot be cured, but it can be treated. Treatment includes cleansing all alcohol from the body. An alcoholic also needs help dealing with the physical and emotional desire to have a drink.

Alcoholism is a problem that affects more than the alcoholic. It can be a painful experience for family members as well. Children of alcoholics sometimes blame themselves. They believe something they did drove a parent to drink. This is not the case. A child is never to blame for a parent's alcoholism.

When a family member suffers from alcoholism, other family members can try to help. There are community support groups that can help the alcoholic and his or her family. Alcoholics Anonymous (AA) helps people with alcoholism. Al-Anon provides support for family members living with an alcoholic. Alateen, a group within Al-Anon, helps teenage children of alcoholic parents learn to cope with problems at home. Listings for these organizations can be found in phone directories and on the Internet.

Reading Check Identify What are two steps in the cycle of addiction?

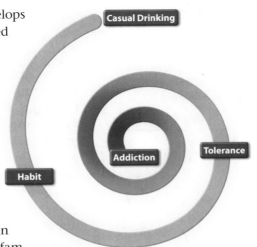

Casual Drinking

Tolerance

Addiction

Habit

▲ **FIGURE 10.2**

SPIRAL OF ADDICTION

R

The spiral of addiction begins with casual drinking. Where does the spiral end?

▶ Help is available for alcoholics and their families. **Name two organizations that can help.**

Lesson 2: Alcoholism and Addiction **247**

Dealing with Sensitive Issues

Alcohol Use Students may have difficulty with this lesson if a member of their family suffers from alcohol addiction. Emphasize the fact that children are never to blame for a family member's alcoholism. Have students work as a class to develop a list of resources, including phone numbers or Web addresses, for teens dealing with a family member's alcoholism. After students have completed the list, have them create a pamphlet listing the resources. Ask the school nurse to display or distribute the pamphlets. **OL**

Reading Check

Answer FAS stands for fetal alcohol syndrome problems caused by alcohol use during pregnancy.

ASSESS

Assessment Resources

Lesson Review Quiz
- *ExamView*
- Fast Files Activities
- Online Quizzes and Activities

Reteaching

- Assign Concept Map 10-2 or Reteaching Activity 10-2 in the Fast Files.
- Have students write a short paragraph that defines the term *alcoholism* and identifies two organizations that can help alcoholics and their families.

Enrichment

- Assign Enrichment Activity 10-2 in the Fast Files.
- Have students create a graphic showing the steps in the cycle of addiction.

CLOSE

Have students name ways that teens can reduce stress without using alcohol.

Health *Online*

Visit health.glencoe.com and complete the Interactive Study Guide for Lesson 2.

Pregnancy and Alcohol

Have you seen warning labels like the one shown on this page? They warn women not to drink alcohol during pregnancy. Alcohol consumed during pregnancy passes from the mother into the developing baby's bloodstream. This places the baby at risk of developing **fetal** (FEE·tuhl) **alcohol syndrome,** or **FAS.** This is *a group of permanent physical and mental problems caused by alcohol use during pregnancy.* Babies with FAS often weigh less than average. They may suffer from birth defects, mental retardation, or learning disabilities that may go unnoticed until they are in school. To protect the health of their babies, pregnant women should completely avoid consuming alcohol.

AL

GOVERNMENT WARNING:
(1) ACCORDING TO THE SURGEON GENERAL, WOMEN SHOULD NOT DRINK ALCOHOLIC BEVERAGES DURING PREGNANCY BECAUSE OF THE RISK OF BIRTH DEFECTS.
(2) CONSUMPTION OF ALCOHOLIC BEVERAGES IMPAIRS YOUR ABILITY TO DRIVE A CAR OR OPERATE MACHINERY, AND MAY CAUSE HEALTH PROBLEMS.

Reading Check

Define What do the letters *FAS* stand for? What is FAS?

◀ All alcoholic beverages are required by law to carry the warning label shown here. **What two uses of alcohol does this label warn against?**

Lesson 2 Review

After You Read

Review this lesson for new terms, major headings, and Reading Checks.

What I Learned

1. *Vocabulary* Explain the connection between *tolerance* and *alcoholism*.

2. *Compare* How are Alateen and Al-Anon similar? How are they different?

3. *Explain* Who is at risk when a pregnant woman drinks? Explain.

Thinking Critically

4. *Analyze* In what ways can alcoholism affect a family?

5. *Evaluate* Sid was at a party where teens were talking about drinking. He was told that trying alcohol once won't hurt him. Explain whether this statement is accurate.

Applying Health Skills

6. *Stress Management* Some people use alcohol to reduce stress. As a class, brainstorm ways that teens can reduce stress without the use of alcohol.

Health *Online* For more review questions for Lesson 2, go to **health.glencoe.com**.

Lesson 2 Review Answers

1. Tolerance is the need for increasing amounts of a substance. Tolerance to alcohol can lead to alcoholism.

2. Both groups help family members of alcoholics; Alateen is geared for teens.

3. The developing baby can suffer low birth weight and mental retardation.

4. *Sample answer:* Family members can feel that they are to blame for the alcoholic's drinking.

5. Using alcohol even once can lead to other risk behaviors and arrest.

6. *Sample answers:* physical activity, talking with a friend, listening to music

Lesson 3

What Are Illegal Drugs?

Guide to Reading

● **Building Vocabulary**
Review the terms below. Write each, along with its definition, in your notebook.

■ illegal drugs (p. 249)
■ marijuana (p. 249)
■ inhalants (p. 250)
■ stimulants (p. 250)
■ anabolic steroids (p. 251)
■ narcotics (p. 251)
■ hallucinogens (p. 252)

● **Focusing on the Main Ideas**
In this lesson, you will be able to

■ **identify** the dangers of illegal drugs.
■ **explain** the risks of using marijuana and inhalants.
■ **identify** the risks of using stimulants, narcotics, anabolic steroids, and hallucinogens

● **Reading Strategy**
Identifying Cause-and-Effect Make a two-column chart. In the first column, write the names of the drugs you learned about. In the second, list the effects of these drugs.

Illegal Drugs

Drugs that are made and sold without getting approval from the government are illegal. **Illegal drugs** are *drugs that are made and used purely for their effects.* Anyone who is caught making, selling, or using illegal drugs can be arrested. Punishment can include stiff fines and lengthy jail sentences. Using illegal drugs can damage your health and can even cause death. In this lesson, you will learn about several types of illegal drugs and how they can affect your health.

Marijuana

Marijuana (mar·uh·WAHN·uh) is *an illegal drug that comes from the hemp plant.* Marijuana, also known as *pot* or *weed,* is usually smoked. Using marijuana can increase your heart rate and decrease your energy level. It can also interfere with memory and concentration. Users may also experience hallucinations and panic attacks. They may see or hear things that aren't real and feel terrified for no reason. Over time, marijuana can cause brain damage. People who use marijuana are more likely to try other dangerous drugs.

 Quick Write

Write a list of problems that people might develop from using illegal drugs.

▼ Knowing the facts about illegal drugs can help you avoid using drugs. **What are some ways to get information about illegal drugs?**

249

Lesson 3 Resources

 Chapter *FAST FILE* Resources
Guided Reading and Writing 10-3
Concept Mapping Activity 10-3
Cross-Curriculum Activity 10-3
Reteaching Activity 10-3
Enrichment Activity 10-3
Lesson Quiz 10-3

Technology
⚓ Transparency 10-3
◉ Audio Summaries
◉ *ExamView*
✏ Vocabulary PuzzleMaker
◉ StudentWorks™ Plus

FOCUS

Activating Prior Knowledge

What I Know Have students write a list of negative effects of illegal drug use on physical, mental/emotional, and social health. Have volunteers share one of the effects from their lists with the class.

Guide to Reading

BUILDING VOCABULARY
■ Ask students to explain the relationship between the first vocabulary term, *illegal drugs,* and the other terms (they are all categories, or kinds, of illegal drugs).
■ Use Vocabulary PuzzleMaker to reinforce vocabulary terms.

READING STRATEGY
Classifying Have students prepare a page in their notebook by writing the names of the categories across the top. Then, as students read the lesson, have them write examples under the headings.

Quick Write

To help students get started with their Quick Write, lead a class discussion of problems associated with illegal drug use.

Caption Answer

Photo Caption pamphlets, reliable Web sites

TEACH

HS Health Skills Practice

Advocacy Have students discuss the dangers of inhalant use. If possible, provide for students additional print resources about the dangers of inhalants. Have students prepare a public service announcement that could be used to discourage inhalant use. Ask students to share their public service announcements with the class, and if possible, with other classes at the same grade level. **OL**

U Universal Access

Reluctant Readers and Writers Have students work in small groups to prepare a concept map that organizes the information about marijuana, inhalants, and stimulants. Circulate among the groups to be sure that each group has identified an appropriate format for its concept map. **OL**

Reading Check

Answer Marijuana and inhalants are similar in that they can both affect brain function; they are different because marijuana is illegal to buy, while inhalants are legal, but are used illegally.

Caption Answer

Photo Caption parents, guardians, teachers, counselors, or a doctor

▶ Talking to a trusted adult can help teens cope with problems without using drugs. **Who are some adults you could turn to for help?**

Inhalants

Inhalants (in·HAY·luhnts) are *substances whose fumes or vapors are inhaled, or breathed in.* Most toxic or poisonous inhalants are common household products like adhesives, lighter fluids, cleaning solvents, and paint. Breathing in these fumes or vapors can cause hallucinations. They can also damage brain cells. Damaging brain cells can make a person lose consciousness and go into a coma. A coma is a deep state of unconsciousness. If the brain has been permanently damaged, a person can die or never wake up.

 **Reading Check** **Compare** Compare and contrast marijuana and inhalants.

Stimulants

Stimulants (STIM·yuh·luhnts) are *drugs that speed up the body's functions.* They cause increases in the heart and breathing rates. They can also cause loss of coordination, physical collapse, heart failure, and brain damage. Illegal stimulants include cocaine and methamphetamines.

Cocaine and Crack

One highly addictive illegal stimulant is cocaine (koh·KAYN). Cocaine's effects are unpredictable and very dangerous. Using cocaine even once can cause the user's blood pressure and heart rate to rise to dangerous levels. Cocaine use can also cause feelings of restlessness, anxiety, and loss of appetite. Cocaine is inhaled or injected with a needle. Crack cocaine, or *rock,* is an especially pure

Promoting Coordinated School Health

Helping Teens Avoid Drugs A coordinated school health program has several components that help teens avoid drugs. Health instruction that teaches the hazards of drug use and refusal skills is one component. Other components of a coordinated school health plan that can discourage drug use are counseling and health services. Referrals to community services when appropriate are also a part of coordinated school health. Ask the school nurse and the guidance counselor to provide you with a list of these resources.

and powerful form that is heated and smoked. It has been linked to many deaths. People who use crack cocaine often engage in other high-risk behaviors such as sexual activity.

Methamphetamine

Another dangerous stimulant whose use has increased in recent years is methamphetamine (meth·uhm·FEH·tuh·meen). Nicknamed *meth* or *crank,* methamphetamine is very addictive. It is available as pills, capsules, powder, and chunks. Effects of the drug include an abnormal or exaggerated level of activity and decreased appetite. Long-term use can damage brain cells, cause breathing problems, and even cause a stroke.

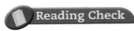 **Reading Check** **Give Examples** How do stimulants harm the body?

Anabolic Steroids

Some drugs mimic the behavior of chemicals made by the body. One example is **anabolic steroids** (a·nuh·BAH·lik STEHR·oydz), *synthetic drugs based on a male hormone.* Doctors sometimes prescribe steroids to treat certain medical conditions. Some athletes use steroids to increase their body weight and strength. Steroids should never be used for this purpose. Users may become violent and deeply depressed. Steroids can also cause problems in sexual development, liver and brain cancer, and heart attacks.

AL

Narcotics

Narcotics (nar·KAH·tics) are *strong drugs that relieve pain.* Some narcotics are medicines prescribed by doctors. For example, a patient may be given a narcotic after surgery to relieve pain. Some narcotics, however, are illegal.

▶ Responsible teens strengthen their muscles in healthy ways. They steer clear of anabolic steroids. **What are some other physical activities that will build muscle strength?**

Lesson 3: What are Illegal Drugs? **251**

HEALTH LITERACY

Prescription Narcotics Certain prescription narcotics are widely abused. A study by the Department of Health and Human Services found that 2.5 percent of eighth graders had illegally used prescription pain medication and 1.7 percent had illegally used oxycodone. Students may have the misconception that prescription drugs are not dangerous. Explain to students that these drugs are highly addictive. Tell students that using these drugs, even for the first time, can result in a fatal overdose.

ASSESS

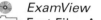

Assessment Resources

Lesson Review Quiz
- *ExamView*
- Fast Files Activities
- Online Quizzes and Activities

Reteaching

- Assign Concept Map 10-3 or Reteaching Activity 10-3 in the Fast Files.
- Ask students to write a paragraph that describes the dangers of illegal drug use that incorporates lesson vocabulary terms.

Enrichment

- Assign Enrichment Activity 10-3 in the Fast Files.
- Have students develop a list of health problems that result from using a specific illegal drug. Then have students write a newspaper article warning teens to avoid that particular drug.

CLOSE

Have students identify a risk associated with drug use.

The most commonly used illegal narcotic is heroin. Heroin comes from a substance taken from the Asian poppy plant. It usually appears as a white or brown powder. Its street names include *smack*, *H*, *skag*, and *junk*. People who use heroin risk unconsciousness and death. Since it is usually injected, heroin users can also become infected with HIV and hepatitis from shared needles.

Hallucinogens

Hallucinogens (huh·LOO·suhn·uh·jenz) are *illegal drugs that cause the user's brain to create or distort images and to see and hear things that aren't real.* As the name suggests, users experience hallucinations. PCP (*angel dust*) and LSD (*acid*) are two very dangerous hallucinogens. Another hallucinogen, called MDMA or Ecstasy, is also a stimulant. Use of these drugs can lead to strange and/or violent behaviors. Users may also become confused or depressed. Long-term use can lead to brain damage.

Health Online

Visit **health.glencoe.com** and complete the Interactive Study Guide for Lesson 3.

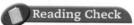

Reading Check **Identify** What are some risks of using hallucinogens?

Lesson 3 Review

After You Read

Review this lesson for new terms, major headings, and Reading Checks.

What I Learned

1. *Vocabulary* Define *inhalant*. Use the word in a sentence.

2. *Recall* What is a street name for crack cocaine? Describe this illegal drug.

3. *List* What are some of the health risks associated with heroin use?

Thinking Critically

4. *Apply* Suppose a friend told you steroids were safe because they are sometimes used as a medicine. How would you respond? Is this valid health information?

5. *Analyze* One day, as Wesley is leaving baseball practice, an older teen offers him some pills. "These will help you hit the ball a mile," the teen says. What advice would you give Wesley?

Applying Health Skills

6. *Practicing Healthful Behaviors* Make a list of ways you can have fun and stay active without using drugs. Share your list with classmates.

Health Online For more review questions for Lesson 3, go to **health.glencoe.com**.

Lesson 3 Review Answers

1. Inhalants are substances whose fumes or vapors are inhaled. Sentences will vary.

2. "Rock" is a street name of crack cocaine. It is a pure and powerful form of cocaine.

3. *Sample answers:* unconsciousness, hepatitis, risk of HIV, and death

4. No, steroids are only safe if used under a doctor's care. Steroids can cause health problems, and this is not from a reliable source, such as a parent or guardian, school nurse, doctor, or other health professional.

5. Wesley should refuse the offered pills, these are probably anabolic steroids.

6. After students have shared their lists, develop a list containing all of their ideas and post it in the classroom.

Lesson 4

Drug Abuse

Guide to Reading

● Building Vocabulary
Copy the terms below into your notebook. Put a checkmark next to the terms you know. Put an *X* next to those you don't know.

- drug abuse (p. 253)
- overdose (p. 253)
- recovery (p. 254)
- withdrawal (p. 254)
- drug rehabilitation (p. 255)

● Focusing on the Main Ideas
In this lesson, you will be able to

- **identify** the harmful effects of drug abuse.
- **explain** recovery and withdrawal.
- **describe** treatments for drug addicts.

● Reading Strategy
Drawing Conclusions Based on this lesson, list three different ways drug abuse affects your health. Give one example for each of the three sides of your health triangle.

What is Drug Abuse?

Drug abuse is *the use of any drug in a way that is unhealthy or illegal.* Using illegal drugs is a form of drug abuse. Purposely using medicines in ways they were not intended to be used is another form of drug abuse. One medicine that is sometimes abused by teens is a stimulant drug prescribed to treat attention deficit/hyperactivity disorder, or ADHD. Using this drug for any other reason than to treat ADHD is illegal and dangerous. Abuse of this medicine can lead to increased heart rate, high blood pressure, and nervousness. Other possible effects include stroke and seizure.

Harmful Effects of Drug Abuse

People who abuse drugs risk damaging their health and their relationships. Drug abuse can affect all three sides of your health triangle in the following ways.

- **Physical health:** The physical effects of drug abuse can range from sleeplessness and irritability to damage to the body organs. Drug abuse can also cause heart failure and stroke. An **overdose** of drugs—*taking a fatal amount of a drug*—can cause death. It is impossible to tell how much is too much for any given user.

Quick Write

Write about an experience you have had recovering from something, such as a bad cold.

Lesson 4: Drug Abuse **253**

Lesson 4 Resources

 Chapter *FAST FILE* Resources
Guided Reading and Writing 10-4
Concept Mapping Activity 10-4
Decision-Making Activity 10-4
Reteaching Activity 10-4
Enrichment Activity 10-4
Lesson Quiz 10-4

Technology
- Transparency 10-4
- Audio Summaries
- *ExamView*
- Vocabulary PuzzleMaker
- StudentWorks™ Plus

Lesson 4

FOCUS

Activating Prior Knowledge

What I Know Have students make a list of five harmful effects of drug abuse. Ask volunteers to share entries from their lists with the class.

Guide to Reading

BUILDING VOCABULARY
- Explain that the term *rehabilitation* means "to restore to a condition of health." Tell students that drug rehabilitation involves restoring all three sides of the health triangle.
- Use Vocabulary PuzzleMaker to reinforce vocabulary terms.

READING STRATEGY
Drawing Conclusions Remind students that drugs have multiple effects. Have them record multiple effects and examples of each drug in a chart.

Quick Write

To help students get started on the Quick Write, have them work as a class to brainstorm a list of items that would require recovery.

Academic Vocabulary

Function On page 254, the text explains that people with an addiction can not function without drugs. Explain that, in this case, the word *function* is used as a verb. *Example: The function of my pen is to write.* **OL**

TEACH

Active Learning

Lessons for Younger Students Have students work in small groups to develop lessons that could be used to teach younger students about the ways drugs harm physical, mental/emotional, and social health. Have each group present its lesson to the class. Have students choose two lessons that best convey the information. If possible, arrange for students to actually teach the lessons to younger students. **OL**

Reading Check

Answer A mental effect of using drugs is damage to brain cells; a social effect is withdrawing from family and friends.

C Critical Thinking

Analyze Ask: How does the process of recovery and drug rehabilitation address each part of the health triangle? *Sample answer: Care from a medical doctor deals with the physical symptoms of withdrawal; mental/ emotional and social health is addressed with counseling or support from the community.* **OL**

Reading Check

Answer, p. 255 Recovery means to overcome an addiction and return to a mostly normal life.

Caption Answer

Photo Caption Using drugs even once can cause permanent damage.

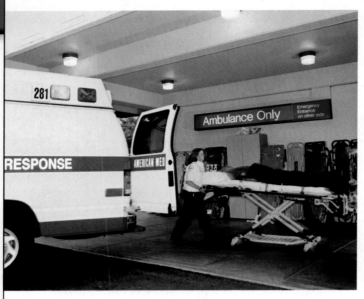

▲ Drug use of any kind is very dangerous. **Why is it risky to try illegal drugs even once?**

• **Mental/emotional health:** Stimulant drugs kill brain cells. These cells continue to die off even after the abuse stops. The brain damage that results can interfere with the user's ability to think. Other drugs cause depression. For teens with low self-esteem, drug-related depression can cause them to think about or commit suicide. **AL**

• **Social health:** Teens who abuse drugs may lose interest in school. They may also withdraw from family and friends. Some teens who abuse drugs fall in with a rough crowd. They become members of gangs, which puts them at risk of being injured in gang-related violence.

Reading Check

List Name a mental/emotional and a social effect of drug abuse.

Addiction

People who abuse drugs are also at risk of developing an addiction. As noted earlier, addiction is a physical and/or mental need for a drug. There is no telling how many times a person can use a drug before becoming addicted. People with an addiction to a drug can no longer function without it. The drug becomes central to their day-to-day life. The addict needs more and more of the drug to feel better.

The Road to Recovery

Recovery begins when a person stops using a drug so the body can cleanse and repair itself. **Recovery** means *to overcome an addiction and return to a mostly normal life.* At the beginning of recovery, the addict may go through withdrawal. **Withdrawal** is *a series of physical and mental symptoms that occur when a person stops using an addictive substance.* Vomiting, hallucinations, and severe anxiety are common withdrawal symptoms. Anyone going through withdrawal needs help from a doctor.

254 Chapter 10: Alcohol and Other Drugs

HEALTH LITERACY

DXM Dextromethorphan is an ingredient in many over-the-counter cough and cold medicines. Pure DXM powder is also available on the Internet. When used in larger than recommended doses, DXM acts as a depressant and produces hallucinogenic effects. This drug is easily available to young teens. Help students recognize the danger of misusing cold medications. Explain that these medications are sometimes called skittles, triple-C, dex, or tussin. Remind students that overdoses of these drugs can be fatal.

Help for Drug Abusers and Their Families

Drug addiction is a disease much like diabetes or heart disease. Like these diseases, treatment for drug addiction requires that sufferers make permanent changes to their behavior. They may also have to change the kinds of medications they take.

Treatment usually includes counseling to help addicts deal with their mental and emotional dependency on drugs. In some cases, **drug rehabilitation** is needed. This is *a process in which a person relearns how to live without the abused drug.* The person is sent to live at a facility for recovering addicts and usually stays from 6 to 12 months.

Because an abuser's family is affected by his or her addiction, they need help, too. Community organizations exist to help families of drug abusers. You will learn more about these in the next lesson.

 Reading Check　**Define** What is recovery?

 **Health Online**

Visit **health.glencoe.com** and complete the Interactive Study Guide for Lesson 4.

ASSESS

Assessment Resources

Lesson Review Quiz
ⓒ *ExamView*
📁 Fast Files Activities
🖱 Online Quizzes and Activities

Reteaching
● Assign Concept Map 10-4 or Reteaching Activity 10-4 in the Fast Files. 📁
● Have students work in pairs to discuss ways that drug abuse harms the three sides of the health triangle. Ask pairs to write a summary of their findings.

Enrichment
● Assign Enrichment Activity 10-4 in the Fast Files. 📁
● Have students prepare a multimedia presentation or video that could be used to discourage others from trying drugs. Remind students to include the harmful effects of drug abuse and addiction and the process of withdrawal. Have students share their videos with the class.

CLOSE

Ask volunteers to describe negative effects of drug use.

Lesson 4 Review

 After You Read

Review this lesson for new terms, major headings, and Reading Checks.

What I Learned

1. *Describe* Discuss two forms of drug abuse.

2. *Vocabulary* What is an *overdose*? Why are overdoses dangerous?

3. *Explain* What is one form of treatment for drug abuse?

Thinking Critically

4. *Predict* How could drug abuse affect a teen's future?

5. *Analyze* When Alan broke his arm, the doctor prescribed a painkiller. Even after the pain stopped, Alan continued to take the medication. Is he abusing the drug? Why or why not?

Applying Health Skills

6. *Communication Skills* Create a poster that communicates the dangers of drug abuse. You may refer to any of the health problems or other difficulties mentioned in the lesson.

Health Online For more review questions for Lesson 4, go to **health.glencoe.com**.　　Lesson 4: Drug Abuse **255**

Lesson 4 Review Answers

1. Using illegal drugs and purposely using a medicine in a way other than intended are two forms of drug abuse.
2. An overdose is taking a fatal amount of a drug. Overdosing can cause permanent damage or death.

3. Answers may include ridding the body of the drug, counseling, and drug rehabilitation.
4. Legal consequences and harmful physical effects could prevent a teen from accomplishing his or her goals.

5. Yes, he is taking a medication for reasons other than the one for which it was prescribed—as a pain killer.
6. Students' posters should include some of the dangers of drug abuse mentioned in the lesson.

FOCUS

Activating Prior Knowledge

What I Know Challenge students to work as a class to generate a list of ten reasons why it is important to avoid illegal drugs.

 Guide to Reading

BUILDING VOCABULARY

■ Remind students that the term *substance abuse* refers not just to illegal drugs, but also to misuse of legal drugs and consumption of alcohol by those under the age of 21.
■ Use Vocabulary PuzzleMaker to reinforce vocabulary terms.

READING STRATEGY

Finding the Main Idea Model the Reading Strategy activity for students by writing the first major heading and main idea on the board in outline format. Encourage students to phrase the main ideas in their own words rather than copying from the text.

uick Write

Remind students that long-term goals are those that take many months or years to reach. After students have competed their writing, have volunteers share the impact drugs could have on meeting their goals.

256

Lesson 5

Avoiding Alcohol and Drugs

 Guide to Reading

● **Building Vocabulary**
Write the definition of the terms below in your notebook.

■ substance abuse (p. 256)
■ alternative (p. 258)

● **Focusing on the Main Ideas**
In this lesson, you will be able to

■ **demonstrate** the skill of advocacy to explore ways to communicate the dangers of substance abuse.
■ **explain** ways to stay substance-free.
■ **identify** alternatives to substance abuse.

● **Reading Strategy**
Finding the Main Idea Copy the major and minor headings onto a sheet of paper. Leave a space after each heading. Write a sentence after each heading that summarizes its main idea.

uick Write

Write a brief statement of your long-term goals. Then add another sentence or two explaining how drug use could affect those goals.

▶ Positive peer pressure can help you avoid substance abuse. **What are some other examples of positive peer pressure?**

Avoiding Substance Abuse

Positive health behaviors include saying no to **substance abuse.** This is *using illegal or harmful drugs, including any use of alcohol while under the legal drinking age.* Being substance-free shows self-control. It means you have taken charge of your life and your health. In this lesson, you will learn healthy ways to avoid using alcohol or other illegal drugs.

256 Chapter 10: Alcohol and Other Drugs

Lesson 5 Resources

📁 **Chapter *FAST FILE* Resources**
Guided Reading and Writing 10-5
Concept Mapping Activity 10-5
Decision-Making Activity 10-5
Reteaching Activity 10-5
Enrichment Activity 10-5
Lesson Quiz 10-5

Technology
⬇ Transparency 10-5
💿 Audio Summaries
💿 *ExamView*
💿 Vocabulary PuzzleMaker
💿 StudentWorks™ Plus

Health Skills Activity

Advocacy

Getting SADD About Substance Abuse

Spreading the word about the dangers of substance abuse can save lives. That is why Students Against Destructive Decisions (SADD) was created. SADD is a worldwide organization. It helps students make positive decisions about challenges in their lives.

Members of SADD speak out against the use of alcohol, drugs, or other harmful substances. You can take a stand against substance abuse, too.

With a Group
Explore ways of communicating the dangers of abusing substances. What are some of the different methods organizations such as SADD use to communicate their information to students?

Ways to Stay Substance-Free

Teens can be influenced to use alcohol and drugs in several ways. The media often show people enjoying alcohol. You may also see adults around you using alcohol. Your friends or peers may pressure you to use alcohol or other illegal substances.

The best way to avoid being pressured to use illegal substances is to use refusal skills. State your decision clearly and assertively. When you speak assertively, you are letting people know you are serious. If outside pressure is strong, walk away. If it continues, seek help from a parent or other trusted adult. Making friends with people who have also chosen not to use drugs will help. They will support your decision and help you avoid situations where drugs and alcohol may be present.

Some teens choose to use alcohol or other drugs to cope with problems. However, alcohol and other drugs will often make problems worse. Instead, talk to a parent, guardian, or other trusted adult. They can help you find positive ways to deal with problems.

 **Reading Check** **Check** What are two ways teens can be influenced to use alcohol or other drugs?

TEACH

Health Skills Activity

Advocacy

Getting SADD about Substance Abuse

Use the following strategies to help students complete the activity:

- Have students work in small groups to generate a list of ways to advocate against substance abuse.
- Then ask students to identify how groups such as SADD can help teens be effective health advocates.

U Universal Access

Students with Different Learning Styles Divide the class into small groups and challenge them to create board games that demonstrate the positive effects of staying substance-free, avoiding drugs and alcohol and the negative effects of drug and alcohol use. Then have groups trade games. After each group has played another group's game, discuss how the games effectively communicated the dangers of drug and alcohol use. **OL**

Reading Check

Answers Media or negative peer pressure can influence teens.

Caption Answer

Photo Caption, p. 256 Peers can positively influence you to engage in healthful activities.

Home, School, and Community

Community Invite a local police officer or drug counselor to visit the class to discuss the legal consequences of drug use. Have students prepare questions in advance for the speaker. After the speaker's visit, have students discuss the ways in which an arrest for drug use could affect their futures. Have students write a persuasive paragraph encouraging teens to avoid drugs that includes information provided by the guest speaker. **OL**

AL Active Learning

Role-Play Have students work in pairs to develop short role-plays showing how teens can exert positive peer pressure to help others avoid drug use and offer alternatives. Have each pair of students practice its role-play, and then perform it for the class. After all role-plays have been performed, lead a class discussion of ways in which teens can be positive role models. OL

Reading Check

Answer Alternative is another way of thinking or acting.
Answer, p. 259 Nar-Anon

R Reading Strategy

Analyzing a Graphic After students have examined Figure 10.3, have them work as a class to develop a list of more alternatives to substance abuse. Encourage students to think beyond the examples in the figure to develop ideas specific to their own interests. Write the following on the board: "I say no to drugs, I say yes to _____." Have each student complete the sentence with a positive alternative to substance abuse that reflects their interests and abilities. OL

Health Online

Topic: Avoiding Alcohol

Visit health.glencoe.com for Student Web Activities to learn ways to say no to peers who want you to drink.

Activity: Using the information provided at the link above, create an alcohol fact sheet that includes tips for saying no to peer pressure.

▶ **FIGURE 10.3**

R ALTERNATIVES TO SUBSTANCE ABUSE

These are some activities you can enjoy without using alcohol or other drugs. Can you think of any other positive alternatives to substance abuse?

Alternatives to Drug and Alcohol Use

When someone offers you drugs or alcohol and you refuse, it is a good idea to suggest a positive alternative. An **alternative** (ahl·TER·nuh·tihv) is *another way of thinking or acting*. Offering a positive alternative allows you to change the subject, redirecting the conversation to another topic. This can help relieve some of the pressure you may be feeling. It also gives you the opportunity to be a positive influence on your friends or other peers. If you are with someone who suggests drinking alcohol, think of something else you both can do. You might suggest getting something to eat or playing a video game instead. **Figure 10.3** shows some other healthful alternatives. **AL**

Reading Check

Define What is an alternative?

- **Have fun at drug-free and alcohol-free events.** Avoid environments where alcohol or other drugs are present. Use positive peer pressure to help others avoid these environments.

- **Improve your talents or skills.** Choose an activity you like, and practice it until you become an expert. Become a great skateboarder, a computer whiz, or the best artist at school.

- **Be part of a group.** Join a sports team, a club, or a community group.

- **Start your own business.** Make yourself available for babysitting, yard work, or other odd jobs. Let friends and neighbors know.

Caption Answer

Figure Caption *Sample answer:* Volunteering in my community is another alternative to substance abuse.

What Teens Want to Know

How can I avoid negative peer pressure? Peer pressure is one of the main reasons teens start using drugs. Help students understand that they are more likely to be offered drugs by a friend in a social setting than by a drug dealer on the street. Being able to say no to friends is a key skill for avoiding drug use. Review refusal skills and have students discuss ways to say no to a friend who has offered drugs or alcohol. Remind students that practicing refusal skills in advance can help them make healthy decisions in a confident way. **OL**

Help for Families of Substance Abusers

In Lesson 2, you learned about the kinds of support that are available for alcoholics and their families. Similar community resources exist for people with substance abuse problems. They are designed to help a person get his or her life back on track. One organization for families of drug addicts is Nar-Anon. Like Al-Anon, Nar-Anon holds meetings that teach family members how to handle the problems associated with living with an addict.

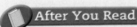 **Reading Check**

Give Examples Name one organization that helps families affected by substance abuse.

Health Online

Visit health.glencoe.com and complete the Interactive Study Guide for Lesson 5.

▶ Support from friends can help you stay substance-free. **What resources are available in your community for teens with substance abuse problems?**

Lesson 5 Review

After You Read

Review this lesson for new terms, major headings, and Reading Checks.

What I Learned

1. *Vocabulary* Define *substance abuse*. Use it in a sentence.

2. *Identify* Name two alternatives to drug abuse.

3. *Recall* What are two ways to stay substance-free?

Thinking Critically

4. *Apply* Tell how choosing to be substance-free can build character.

5. *Evaluate* How can suggesting a positive alternative to alcohol or drug use help you stay substance-free?

Applying Health Skills

6. *Refusal Skills* Think about ways to say no to harmful behaviors. Team up with a classmate. Role-play a situation where you use these strategies to say no to illegal drugs.

Health Online For more review questions for Lesson 5, go to **health.glencoe.com**.

Lesson 5: Avoiding Alcohol and Drugs **259**

ASSESS

Assessment Resources

Lesson Review Quiz
- *ExamView*
- Fast Files Activities
- Online Quizzes and Activities

Reteaching

- Assign Concept Map 10-5 or Reteaching Activity 10-5 in the Fast Files. 📁
- Have students work in small groups to generate a list of ways to avoid substance abuse.

Enrichment

- Assign Enrichment Activity 10-5 in the Fast Files. 📁
- Challenge students to create a photo essay that shows alternatives to drug and alcohol use for youth in their community. Have students present their photo essays to the class.

CLOSE

Have students work as a class to develop a list of ways to communicate the dangers of drug use to others.

Caption Answer

Photo Caption Students should identify local groups.

Lesson 5 Review Answers

1. Substance abuse is using illegal or harmful drugs, including using alcohol while under the legal drinking age. Sentences will vary.

2. *Sample answers:* suggest alternatives, such as playing videos, going out for a bite to eat

3. Stay substance-free by using refusal skills and choosing friends who avoid substance abuse.

4. *Sample answer:* Being substance-free shows responsibility, a trait of good character.

5. You can use positive peer pressure to plan drug-free activities with friends.

6. Role-plays should include reasons for saying no to drugs found in the lesson.

Building Health Skills

DECISION MAKING

Avoiding Drug Abuse

DIRECTIONS

Decision making involves taking steps to make healthy and responsible choices. This activity will give you the opportunity to develop and master this important health skill. Here's a guide to the different parts of this activity:

❶ In the **Model** section, you will read about a teen who performs the health skill successfully. This "model" scenario will show you how the skill is done.

❷ The **Practice** section will help guide you in practicing the skill.

❸ In the **Apply** section, you will have a chance to perform the skill on your own. You can use the Self-Check to check your work.

To complete this activity, first read the scenario presented in the Model. Then move on to the Practice. Finally, go ahead and try the Apply.

260 Chapter 10: Alcohol and Other Drugs

❶ Model

Jason was at his friend Ryan's house where several teens were gathering to watch a movie. One of the teens suggested that everyone go to his house to drink some beer.

Jason did not feel good about the situation. He knew if he went with his friends, he would feel pressured to try the beer. Jason used the decision-making process to help him decide what to do.

1. **State the situation.** I am being pressured to drink beer. I really don't want to do that.

2. **List the options.** I could go ahead and try the beer this one time. I could just leave. I could also say that I would rather stay and watch the movie.

3. **Weigh the possible outcomes.** I would be breaking my promise to myself that I wouldn't experiment with alcohol or other drugs. Also, we could get caught drinking, which would upset my parents. If I just go home, I'll feel left out. If I say I don't want to drink beer, maybe Ryan will back me up.

4. **Consider your values.** Keeping my promise to myself is important. I also don't want to upset my parents.

5. **Make a decision and act.** Jason decided to stay and watch the movie. Ryan decided to stay as well.

❷ Practice

The decision-making process worked well for Jason. He used it again to help him decide whether to go to a party at another teen's house. A friend told Jason that someone was bringing marijuana to the party and they could try it.

On your own paper, show the steps Jason should use to make a decision about whether or not to go to the party. If Jason wanted to spend time with his friends, what are some positive alternatives he could suggest?

Skill Summary
DECISION MAKING

- State the situation.
- List the options.
- Weigh the possible outcomes.
- Consider your values.
- Make a decision and act.

❸ Apply

With a small group, brainstorm ways a teen might be affected by someone else's use of drugs. Choose one of these ideas and write a short story about a teen who is in this situation. Show how the teen uses the decision-making process to make a healthy choice.

Self-Check

- Did our story tell how a teen might be affected by someone else's drug use?
- Did the teen use all the decision-making steps?
- Did we show a healthy choice?

Practice

- Have students work in pairs to complete the Practice activity.
- Lead a class discussion of the options Jason should consider when making his decision. Have students volunteer creative options for dealing with the described situation.

Apply/Assess

- Have students work in small groups to complete the Apply activity.
- Allow 10 minutes for groups to write the story and practice acting it out.
- After each group performs, have audience members identify how the steps of decision making were portrayed in the skit.
- You may wish to distribute the Building Health Skills Activity in the Fast Files.

ASSESSMENT SCORING

Student work should meet all criteria to achieve the highest score:

Skills Student work demonstrates:
- a statement of the situation.
- a list of options.
- consideration of outcomes.
- consideration of values.
- identification of an action.
- an evaluation of the decision.

Concepts Student work includes:
- identification of ways teens are affected by another's drug abuse.
- a health-enhancing choice.

"Say No to Drugs" Skit

Time: 30 minutes
Materials: pencil or pen, paper

Introducing Hands-on Health

- Have students review the refusal skills that were discussed in Chapter 3. Ask students to describe some ways to say no to unhealthy choices.

Teaching the Activity

- Have students work in small groups to complete the activity.
- Have students spend five minutes constructing their two-column lists. Then allow 10 minutes for students to write and rehearse their skits.
- After students have performed their skits and received the completed questionnaires, have each group work to answer the Wrapping It Up questions.

HANDS-ON HEALTH

"Say No to Drugs" Skit

Refusal skills are useful for keeping drugs out of your life. It takes good communication skills to say no in a firm way without offending others. In the activity below, you and your classmates will have a chance to practice refusal skills by creating and acting out a skit.

What You Will Need

- pencil and paper

What You Will Do

1. Work with a group of classmates. Think of one-liners teens might use to try to persuade their peers to use drugs. For example, "Just give it a try," or "One time won't hurt."

2. Fold a sheet of paper in half lengthwise to form two columns. In the first column, write your one-liners. Now try to think of ways teens could respond that would allow them to refuse the drug. Write these in the second column.

3. Review your lists. Select the three most persuasive one-liners and the three best refusals. Use these to create a skit to perform for your classmates.

4. After you have finished your performance, pass around a short questionnaire. The questionnaire should ask classmates to tell you what they felt was good and what they thought could be improved in your skit. The questionnaire should conclude by asking them for suggestions on how to improve your refusal strategies.

Wrapping It Up

1. Did your classmates find your refusal statements convincing?

2. If not, what suggestions did they offer for strengthening them?

HANDS-ON HEALTH Assessment

Discussion Ask students: What are some verbal and nonverbal ways to make refusal statements convincing? Sample answers: *verbal: saying no clearly, using a firm tone of voice; nonverbal: standing up straight, looking the other person in the eye*

Why is it important to avoid hostility when refusing an unhealthy behavior?

Sample answer: *Avoiding hostility helps you to refuse a bad choice without starting an argument or physical fight.*

Reading Review

FOLDABLES Study Organizer

Foldables™ and Other Study Aids After You Read Take out the Foldable™ that you created for Lesson 1 and any graphic organizers that you created for Lessons 1–5. Find a partner, and quiz each other using these study aids.

Lesson 1 The Dangers of Alcohol

Key Ideas

• Alcohol use speeds the heart rate, harms the liver, and slows the body's functions and reaction time.

• Among reasons teens give for drinking are fitting in with friends or family members who drink, feeling more grown-up, or escaping problems.

Vocabulary

• alcohol (p. 242)
• drug (p. 242)
• cirrhosis (p. 243)
• blood alcohol content (BAC) (p. 243)

Lesson 2 Alcoholism and Addiction

Key Ideas

• The cycle of addiction to alcohol starts with an occasional drink, then becomes a habit, then he or she develops a tolerance, followed finally by an addiction.

• Drinking during pregnancy places the developing baby at risk for fetal alcohol syndrome, or FAS.

Vocabulary

• tolerance (p. 247)
• alcoholism (p. 247)
• fetal alcohol syndrome (FAS) (p. 248)

Lesson 3 What Are Illegal Drugs?

Key Ideas

• The risks of marijuana use include hallucinations and panic attacks. Inhalants can damage brain cells.

• Stimulants can cause accelerated heart and breathing rates. Narcotics can lead to unconsciousness and death. Anabolic steroids can cause depression. Hallucinogens can lead to violent behavior.

Vocabulary

• illegal drugs (p. 249)
• marijuana (p. 249)
• inhalants (p. 250)
• stimulants (p. 250)
• anabolic steroids (p. 251)
• narcotics (p. 251)
• hallucinogens (p. 252)

Lesson 4 Drug Abuse

Key Ideas

• Drug abuse affects your physical, mental/emotional, and social health.

• People who are recovering from a drug addiction may go through withdrawal.

Vocabulary

• drug abuse (p. 253)
• overdose (p. 253)
• recovery (p. 254)
• withdrawal (p. 254)
• drug rehabilitation (p. 255)

Lesson 5 Staying Alcohol- and Drug-Free

Key Ideas

• Use refusal skills to help you stay substance-free.

• When someone offers you drugs or alcohol, offer a positive alternative.

Vocabulary

• substance abuse (p. 256)
• alternative (p. 258)

Chapter 10 Reading Review **263**

Assessment Resources

📁 Chapter 10 Summary and Activity
💊 Audio Summaries
📁 Reading Tutor
📁 Performance Assessment
📁 Chapter 10 Test
💿 *ExamView*
💊 Vocabulary PuzzleMaker
💊 Online Learning Center

Reading Review

Study Aids

● **Using the Dinah Zike Foldable™ Study Organizer** Have students use the 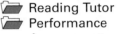 Foldable™ to review alcohol's harmful effects.

Key Ideas

● **Use the Main Ideas** Have students rephrase each main idea in the form of a question. Then have students work in pairs to review the main ideas using these questions.

Vocabulary Review

● **Vocabulary Flashcards** Have students use index cards to make flashcards for the vocabulary terms in the chapter. Have students work in pairs to review the chapter vocabulary using their completed flashcards.

Teaching Tips

KWL Have students use the Know-Want-to-Know-Learned strategy to link prior knowledge to new information. Before students read each lesson, have them prepare a three-column table with the headings "Know," "Want to Know," and "Learned." Have them record what they already know about the topic in the far left column. Then have students write two or more questions in the "Want to Know" column. Have students record answers to their questions and other information they learned while reading the lesson in the "Learned" column.

Reviewing Vocabulary and Main Ideas

1. Cirrhosis
2. alcohol
3. drug
4. tolerance
5. Alcoholism
6. True
7. False, stimulants
8. False, narcotic
9. False, hallucinogen
10. True
11. False, recovery
12. True
13. an alternative
14. Nar-Anon

Thinking Critically

15. Answers will vary. Possible responses might include the danger that drunk drivers pose to others on the road and the health risks faced by babies born to mothers who drink.
16. Answers will vary. Possibilities might include the observation that this is a myth or that because a dangerous practice is widespread does not justify trying it.

 **After You Read**

IM *Express*

Now that you have read the chapter, review your answer to the I.M. Express on the chapter opener. Have your ideas changed? What would your answer be now?

Reviewing Vocabulary and Main Ideas

On a sheet of paper, write the numbers 1–5. After each number, write the term from the list that best completes each sentence.

- alcohol
- alcoholism
- blood alcohol content (BAC)
- cirrhosis
- drug
- fetal alcohol syndrome (FAS)
- inhalants
- tolerance

Lesson 1 **The Dangers of Alcohol Abuse**

1. _____, destruction and scarring of the liver tissue, is a disease that can lead to death.
2. A substance produced by a chemical reaction in carbohydrates is called _____.
3. A(n) _____ is a substance that affects the structure or function of the body or mind.

Lesson 2 **Alcoholism and Addiction**

4. A need for increasing amounts of a substance to achieve the same effect is called _____.
5. _____ is a disease in which alcohol becomes a force in the drinker's life.

*On a sheet of paper, write the numbers 6–14. Write **True** or **False** for each statement. If the statement is false, change the underlined word or phrase to make it true.*

Lesson 3 **What Are Illegal Drugs?**

6. Many toxic <u>inhalants</u> are household products.
7. Cocaine and crack are two examples of <u>hallucinogens</u>.
8. Heroin is a commonly used illegal <u>anabolic steroid</u>.
9. People who use <u>inhalants</u> such as PCP or LSD often show strange and/or violent behavior.

Lesson 4 **Drug Abuse**

10. The use of any drug in a way that is unhealthy or illegal is an example of <u>drug abuse</u>.
11. Overcoming an addiction and returning to a mostly normal life is called <u>withdrawal</u>.
12. People who need <u>drug rehabilitation</u> are often sent to live at a special facility for recovering addicts.

Lesson 5 **Avoiding Alcohol and Drugs**

13. Another way of thinking or acting that takes the place of substance abuse is known as <u>tolerance</u>.
14. <u>Al-Anon</u> is an organization that helps families of drug addicts.

Health *Online* Visit health.glencoe.com and take the Online Quiz for Chapter 10.

Health *Online*

Have students visit **health.glencoe.com** to take the Chapter 10 Quiz.

IM *Express Wrap-Up*

Drug Safety Have students look back at their response to carrie_64. Ask students to use information from the chapter to identify why mona_k15's offer should be refused.

Even though this is medication from a doctor, if it is being used for something other than what it was prescribed for, it is drug abuse.

Thinking Critically

Using complete sentences, answer the following questions on a sheet of paper.

15. Apply How might a person under the influence of drugs or alcohol put other people at risk?

16. Synthesize A friend tells you he plans to use an illegal substance. When you warn him of the dangers, the friend replies, "Lots of kids our age do it." How do you respond?

Write About It

17. Accessing Information Write a paragraph describing why you think it is important for family members of alcoholics to attend support groups such as Al-Anon and Alateen.

Career Corner

Substance Abuse Counselor Do you have a desire to help people? Are you a good listener? If you are, you might consider a career as a substance abuse counselor. People in this profession help those who are addicted to alcohol and other drugs cope with their problems. Most substance counselors have four-year college degrees. Their specialty may be in counseling, psychology, or social work. To learn more about the requirements for a career as an alcohol abuse counselor, visit *Career Corner* at **health.glencoe.com**.

18. Refusal Skills Write a short story about a teen who is being pressured to use drugs or alcohol. Identify the skills the teen uses to say no.

Write About It

17. Descriptive Writing Explain to students that descriptive writing presents a clear picture, attracts the reader, and presents broad views or focuses on details. Students' paragraphs will vary but should include views on why family members of alcoholics would benefit from support groups.

18. Narrative Writing Explain to students that narrative writing tells a clear story arranged in a logical order. This type of writing presents interesting characters, a plot, a setting, and dialog. Students' stories will vary, but should include a teen using refusal skills to avoid drugs and alcohol.

Standardized Test Practice

1. B
2. C

Career Corner

Substance Abuse Counselor Have students visit the Career Corner at **health.glencoe.com** to gather more information about a career as an alcohol abuse counselor. Alcohol abuse counselors should have a strong desire to help others and enjoy working with individuals and families.

Standardized Test Practice

Math

Use the graph to answer the questions.

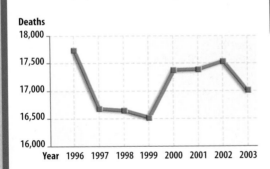

Deaths

| Year | 1996 | 1997 | 1998 | 1999 | 2000 | 2001 | 2002 | 2003 |

TEST-TAKING TIP

Estimation will help you eliminate choices in a math problem that are clearly wrong. This will give you more time to find the true answer.

1. Rounding to the nearest thousand, for which 3-year period did deaths total about 50,000?

   A. 1996-1998   **C.** 1998-2000

   B. 1997-1999   **D.** None of the above.

2. In 2003, there were a total 42,643 traffic deaths from all causes. Estimate what percentage of these deaths resulted from drunk driving?

   A. 30   **C.** 40

   B. 35   **D.** 45

Test-Taking Tips

Estimating in Math Advise students that using estimation when answering math questions is a useful strategy for eliminating wrong answers. By estimating, a student should be able eliminate one or more answer choice. Remind students that exact computations might be required to find the correct answer among the remaining choices.

CHAPTER 11 pp. 266–293	Standards		Skills and Activities
	National	**State/Local**	**HEALTH QUIZ**, *p. 267* TIME HEALTH NEWS Don't Panic, *p. 290* **BUILDING HEALTH SKILLS** *Goal Setting* Protecting Your Health, *pp. 288–289*
	National Health Education Standards 6.1, 6.2, 6.3		
LESSON 1 **What Causes Disease?** pp. 268–271	National Health Education Standards 1.1, 1.5, 1.6, 1.8, 5.1, 6.1, 8.2		**Connect To... SCIENCE** Helpful Bacteria, *p. 270*
LESSON 2 **Communicable Diseases** pp. 272–276	National Health Education Standards 1.1, 1.3, 1.5, 1.6, 1.8, 5.3, 7.4, 8.1		**DEVELOPING GOOD CHARACTER** Keep It to Yourself, *p. 273* **HEALTH SKILLS ACTIVITY** *Practicing Healthful Behaviors* Handwashing for Health, *p. 276*
LESSON 3 **Understanding STDs** pp. 277–281	National Health Education Standards 1.1, 1.6, 1.7, 1.8, 3.2, 3.4, 3.6, 4.6, 5.1, 5.2, 5.3, 6.1, 7.1, 7.3		**Connect To... SCIENCE** New Strains of HIV, *p. 280* **HEALTH SKILLS ACTIVITY** *Accessing Information* Accurate Information on HIV and AIDS, *p. 281*
LESSON 4 **Noncommunicable and Hereditary Diseases** pp. 282–287	National Health Education Standards 1.1, 1.3, 1.5, 1.6, 1.7, 1.8, 5.3, 7.1, 7.4, 8.2		

PACING THE CHAPTER

Lesson 1	45 min	Lesson 4	90 min	Chapter Review	45 min
Lesson 2	45 min	TIME Health News	20 min		
Lesson 3	90 min	Building Health Skills	45 min		

BLOCK SCHEDULING

For block scheduling, assign students Building Health Skills feature *Protecting Your Health*, pages 288–289, and Guided Reading and Writing.

Planning Guide

Reproducible Resources	Assessment	Media and Technology
Chapter *FAST FILE* Resources Chapter Summaries and Activities **REVIEW** Building Health Skills Activity **TEACH** Performance Assessment Activity **EXTEND** Universal Access Activities **TEACH** Parent Letter and Activities **Student Activities Workbook** **TEACH** **Reading Tutor** **TEACH**	Building Health Skills Activity, *pp. 288–289* Chapter 11 Assessment, *pp. 292–293* **Chapter *FAST FILE* Resources** Performance Assessment Activity, *p. 4* Chapter 11 Test, *p. 7* ⊙ *ExamView® Test Generator*	**Teacher Works™ includes:** • Interactive Teacher Edition • Lesson Planner with Calendar • Access to all blackline masters • Correlations to standards ⊙ StudentWorks™ Plus Online Student Edition Dinah Zike's Teaching Health with Foldables™
Chapter *FAST FILE* Resources Concept Mapping Activity 11-1 **REVIEW** Decision-Making Activity 11-1 **EXTEND** Enrichment Activity 11-1 **EXTEND** Lesson Plan 11-1 Guided Reading and Writing 11-1 **TEACH** Reteaching Activity 11-1 **REVIEW**	Lesson 1 Review, *p. 271* Vocabulary PuzzleMaker ⊙ *ExamView® Test Generator*	Vocabulary PuzzleMaker ⊙ *ExamView® Test Generator* ⊙ StudentWorks™ Plus Transparency 11-1 **Health *Online***
Chapter *FAST FILE* Resources Concept Mapping Activity 11-2 **REVIEW** Cross-Curriculum Activity 11–2 **EXTEND** Enrichment Activity 11-2 **EXTEND** Lesson Plan 11-2 Guided Reading and Writing 11-2 **TEACH** Reteaching Activity 11-2 **REVIEW**	Lesson 2 Review, *p. 276* Vocabulary PuzzleMaker ⊙ *ExamView® Test Generator*	Vocabulary PuzzleMaker ⊙ *ExamView® Test Generator* ⊙ StudentWorks™ Plus Transparency 11-2 **Health *Online***
Chapter *FAST FILE* Resources Concept Mapping Activity 11-3 **REVIEW** Cross-Curriculum Activity 11–3 **EXTEND** Enrichment Activity 11-3 **EXTEND** Lesson Plan 11-3 Guided Reading and Writing 11-3 **TEACH** Reteaching Activity 11-3 **REVIEW**	Lesson 3 Review, *p. 281* Vocabulary PuzzleMaker ⊙ *ExamView® Test Generator*	Vocabulary PuzzleMaker ⊙ *ExamView® Test Generator* ⊙ StudentWorks™ Plus Transparency 11-3 **Health *Online***
Chapter *FAST FILE* Resources Concept Mapping Activity 11-4 **REVIEW** Health Lab 11–4 **EXTEND** Enrichment Activity 11-4 **EXTEND** Lesson Plan 11-4 Guided Reading and Writing 11-4 **TEACH** Reteaching Activity 11-4 **REVIEW**	Lesson 4 Review, *p. 287* Vocabulary PuzzleMaker ⊙ *ExamView® Test Generator*	Vocabulary PuzzleMaker ⊙ *ExamView® Test Generator* ⊙ StudentWorks™ Plus Transparency 11-4 **Health *Online***

Chapter and Lesson Resources

The *Teen Health* resources are designed for differentiated learning abilities. You may want to use the coded items in this way:

REVIEW —activities to review or reinforce content

TEACH —activities to teach basic concepts

EXTEND —activities to extend or enrich lesson content

 OUT OF TIME?

Use Health Skills Activities *Handwashing for Health,* page 276, or *Developing Good Character,* page 273.

Maintaining a Healthy School Environment

Illnesses and school absences make it difficult for students to do their best. Each year in the United States students are absent from school for a total of 164 million days. As students study communicable diseases in this chapter, stress the positive steps that can be taken in the school environment to maintain health and prevent the spread of germs.

Handwashing is one of the best ways to keep germs from spreading. Techniques for effective handwashing are described in this chapter. Remind students that they should wash their hands before and after they eat, after using the restroom, and after using a tissue or coughing into their hands. The Centers for Disease Control and Prevention (CDC) offers resources on its Web site that can be used to educate students about the importance of good hand hygiene to help prevent the spread of germs.

Studies have shown that the use of instant hand sanitizers in conjunction with handwashing is an effective way to reduce student absences. These sanitizers, which do not require water, paper towels, or a trip to the restroom, can be an effective way to improve hand hygiene in students.

Encourage students to carry tissues, and if possible, provide tissues in the classroom. Remind students to use a tissue when they sneeze and to cough into the crook of their elbow, not into their hands.

Explain to students that staying home when they are ill shows good character by respecting others. With the class, discuss the school's guidelines for when students who are ill should remain at home. These guidelines, which should be available from the school nurse, should also be observed by the school's faculty and staff.

Heart Disease in Young People

Heart disease is the leading cause of death of adult Americans. The vast majority of those who die of heart disease are middle-aged or older adults. This leads many young people to the misconception that heart disease is something they do not need to be concerned about.

According to the American Heart Association, about one million teens have a set of risk factors that increase their chances of developing heart disease. This condition, called metabolic syndrome, is characterized by high blood sugar levels, high blood pressure, obesity, and elevated cholesterol levels. Metabolic syndrome is also associated with an increased risk for type 2 diabetes.

When students learn about heart disease as a part of the lesson on noncommunicable diseases, explain that heart disease is something that develops over many years. Tell students that their habits now can affect their risk of developing heart disease later in life. Some of the risk factors for heart disease that young people have control over are:

- smoking
- sedentary lifestyle
- obesity

By avoiding tobacco, getting regular physical activity, and maintaining a healthy body weight, teens can reduce their risk of developing heart disease later in life.

Support for Teaching Reading

 Reading Support **Health Online** **Academic Integration** For additional academic integration strategies, visit the Teacher Center at **health.glencoe.com**.

Reading Preview

Activating Background Vocabulary Have students copy the key chapter terms onto index cards. Direct students to arrange the cards into categories, such as: pathogens, the immune system, STDs, and so on. Have students rearrange the cards several times into different categories to build comprehension and classification skills.

FOLDABLES Study Organizer *Dinah Zike's Reading and Study Skills for Teen Health* provides interactive graphic organizers that help students comprehend and retain health concepts as they read. Use the Foldable™ on page 267 or find more Foldables™ activities for the chapter on **Preventing Disease** in the separate booklet, available in the TCR.

Lesson 1 What Causes Disease?

Preview and Predict Show students how to skim the lesson title, headings, and captions. Have students write a sentence for each subheading, predicting what they will learn when they read that section. Encourage students pairs to share their predictions after reading the lesson and revise as necessary.

Lesson 2 Communicable Diseases

Compare and Contrast Illustrate a two-column chart on the board. Ask students to read silently about communicable diseases. As they read, have students record facts about colds on one side of the chart and the flu on the other. Encourage students to compare their charts with a partner.

Lesson 3 Understanding STDs

Active Silent Reading Have students stop reading and close their books. Ask students what they have just read about STDs and/or Abstinence. Write responses on the board. Guide students in a discussion about the main topics. Refer students back to the text to reread and clarify questions.

Lesson 4 Noncommunicable and Hereditary Diseases

Paraphrasing Have student pairs close their books after reading and take turns describing what they have read about **Noncommunicable Diseases**. Determine if students are identifying the main ideas of the lesson. If students are unable to explain the information clearly, have them reread the text.

Post Reading

Technology-Based Presentations Guide students in a discussion about ways to prevent sexually transmitted diseases. Have students work in pairs to develop a presentation that incorporates audiovisual aids and technology.

Key for Using the Teacher Wraparound Edition

Use this key to help you identify the different types of prompts found in the Teacher Wraparound Edition.

R **Reading Strategies** activities help you teach reading skills and vocabulary.

C **Critical Thinking** strategies help students apply and extend what they have learned.

U **Universal Access** activities provide differentiated instruction for students learning to speak English, along with suggestions for teaching various types of learners.

HS **Health Skills Practice** activities reinforce Health Skills concepts and help students apply these skills in their everyday lives.

W **Writing Support** activities provide writing opportunities to help students comprehend the text.

AL **Active Learning** strategies provide a variety of activities for presenting lesson content, including Quick Demos and engaging classroom projects that get students actively involved.

Key to Ability Levels

Teaching Strategies and activities have been coded for ability level and appropriateness

AL Activities for students working above grade level

OL Activities for students working on grade level

BL Activities for students working below grade level

EL Activities for English Learners

Symbols

Transparencies

CD-ROM

health.glencoe.com

Print Resources

Preventing Diseases

Chapter at a Glance

Lesson 1 identifies the two main types of disease and describes four common disease-causing pathogens.

Lesson 2 describes ways that pathogens are spread, identifies common communicable diseases, and explains how to demonstrate healthful behaviors that limit the spread of pathogens.

Lesson 3 identifies common STDs, describes how HIV and other STDs are spread, explains how to access current information on HIV and AIDS, and explains how students can protect themselves from STDs.

Lesson 4 identifies causes of various noncommunicable diseases, explains how to develop behaviors to maintain heart health, and identifies ways to help prevent diseases such as cancer and diabetes.

R Reading Strategy

Interpreting the Photo
Have students to examine the photo. Ask: These students are teaching others about staying healthy and preventing disease. What are some benefits of sharing this information?

Sample answers: fewer communicable diseases being passed around school; fewer students missing school due to illness

Chapter Preview

Lesson 1   What Causes Disease? 268

Lesson 2   Communicable Diseases ..272

Lesson 3   Understanding STDs 277

Lesson 4   Noncommunicable and
Hereditary Diseases 282

Building Health Skills 288

TIME Health News 290

Chapter Reading Review 291

Chapter Assessment 292

▲ *Working With the Photo*

R Disease-causing germs are so tiny they require an electron microscope to be seen. **Why is it important for scientists to identify germs that cause disease?**

🏃 Universal Access

Differentiated Learning Glencoe provides teacher support and student materials for all learners in the health classroom.

- Spanish *Glosario* and chapter summaries for the English Language Learners.
- *Reading Tutor* and related worksheets support reluctant readers.

- Universal Access strategies throughout the Teacher Wraparound Edition and Fast Files help you present materials for gifted students, at-risk students, physically impaired students, and those with behavior disorders or learning disabilities.

Start-Up Activities

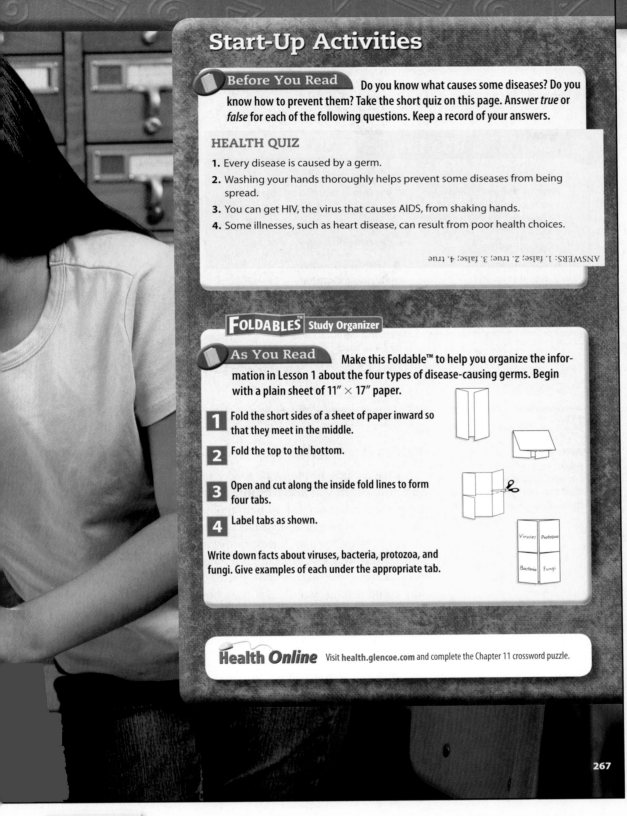

Before You Read
Do you know what causes some diseases? Do you know how to prevent them? Take the short quiz on this page. Answer *true* or *false* for each of the following questions. Keep a record of your answers.

HEALTH QUIZ

1. Every disease is caused by a germ.
2. Washing your hands thoroughly helps prevent some diseases from being spread.
3. You can get HIV, the virus that causes AIDS, from shaking hands.
4. Some illnesses, such as heart disease, can result from poor health choices.

ANSWERS: 1. false; 2. true; 3. false; 4. true

FOLDABLES Study Organizer

As You Read
Make this Foldable™ to help you organize the information in Lesson 1 about the four types of disease-causing germs. Begin with a plain sheet of 11″ × 17″ paper.

1 Fold the short sides of a sheet of paper inward so that they meet in the middle.

2 Fold the top to the bottom.

3 Open and cut along the inside fold lines to form four tabs.

4 Label tabs as shown.

Write down facts about viruses, bacteria, protozoa, and fungi. Give examples of each under the appropriate tab.

Health Online Visit **health.glencoe.com** and complete the Chapter 11 crossword puzzle.

267

HEALTH QUIZ

Preventing Disease Have students record their responses to the Health Quiz in their notebooks. Remind students to watch for the answers to these questions as they read the chapter. Tell students that they will have a chance to review and correct their answers to the Health Quiz after they have completed the chapter.

No Child Left Behind

English Learners
Use some of the following strategies to accommodate English Learners in the health classroom:

- Use visual models, pictures, and figures in the text to illustrate the chapter's main ideas.
- Allow students to work with a peer to complete written work.
- Have English Learners practice pronouncing the vocabulary terms aloud.
- Have students use the reading checks to measure reading comprehension throughout the lessons.
- Students who speak Spanish can utilize the Spanish Glosario and chapter summaries.

FOLDABLES Study Organizer
Dinah Zike Foldables™

Organizing Information If students are having difficulty making the Foldable™, have them work with partners. Have students record information about bacteria, viruses, protozoa, and fungi and examples of diseases caused by each of these pathogens as they read Lesson 1. Encourage students to identify the main idea about each pathogen to record in their Foldable™. Remind students to use their Foldable™ for review before they complete the chapter assessment. **BL**

Health Online

Have students visit **health.glencoe.com** and complete the Health Inventory for Chapter 11.

FOCUS

Activating Prior Knowledge

What I Know Ask students to recall the last time a cold or upset stomach "went around" school. Ask students to identify other types of diseases that get passed from person to person. Tell students that in this lesson they will learn about the causes of these diseases.

Guide to Reading

BUILDING VOCABULARY

■ Explain that *communicable diseases* can be passed from person to person. Have students use this information to determine the meaning of the term *noncommunicable diseases.* (diseases that do not spread)

■ Use Vocabulary PuzzleMaker to reinforce vocabulary terms.

READING STRATEGY

 Have students use their Foldables™ as they read Lesson 1.

■ **Graphic Organizers** Students' concept maps should identify bacteria, viruses, protozoa, and fungi as four causes of communicable disease.

Quick Write

Challenge students to identify at least two ways to avoid spreading germs. Have volunteers share their completed letters with the class.

268

What Causes Disease?

Guide to Reading

● **Building Vocabulary**
Arrange the terms below into two lists. One list should be labeled *Causes,* the other *Effects.*

■ disease (p. 268)
■ communicable diseases (p. 268)
■ noncommunicable diseases (p. 269)
■ pathogen (p. 269)
■ viruses (p. 269)
■ bacteria (p. 270)
■ protozoa (p. 270)
■ fungi (p. 270)

● **Focusing on the Main Ideas**
In this lesson, you will be able to

■ **identify** the two main types of disease.
■ **recognize** four common disease-causing organisms.
■ **describe** how germs are spread.

● **Reading Strategy**
Analyzing a Graphic
Create a concept map that shows causes of communicable diseases. Use the diagram to the right as a guide.

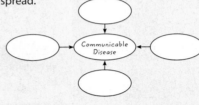

FOLDABLES Study Organizer Use the Foldable™ on p. 267 as you read this lesson.

Quick Write

Write a letter to the editor of a school paper. Discuss ways students can avoid spreading germs.

What Is a Disease?

Angela came home from soccer practice with a cough and sore throat. She was also running a slight fever. Angela's mother gave her some medicine to help relieve her symptoms and told her to rest. A couple of days later, Angela was back on her feet.

Recovering from an illness or disease has not always been so simple. A **disease** (dih·ZEEZ) is *a condition that affects the proper functioning of the body or mind.* The science of fighting disease has come a long way in the past hundred years. Science has made important strides in treating some diseases and preventing others. In this chapter, you'll learn about common diseases and ways to prevent them.

Types of Diseases

There are two basic categories of disease. **Communicable** (kuh·MYOO·nih·kuh·buhl) **diseases** are *diseases that can be spread,* such as colds. You can get a communicable disease

268 Chapter 11: Preventing Diseases

Lesson 1 Resources

📁 **Chapter *FAST FILE* Resources**
Guided Reading and Writing 11-1
Concept Mapping Activity 11-1
Decision-Making Activity 11-1
Reteaching Activity 11-1
Enrichment Activity 11-1
Lesson Quiz 11-1

Technology
🔦 Transparency 11-1
🔊 Audio Summaries
🔊 *ExamView*
💿 Vocabulary PuzzleMaker
🔊 StudentWorks™ Plus

from another person, an animal, or an object. In contrast, **noncommunicable diseases** are *diseases that do not spread.* Diabetes and cancer are two noncommunicable diseases. You can't catch these diseases from another person.

▲ Taking care of your body can help you recover from a cold quickly. **Which of the two major types of disease is a cold?**

Reading Check **Define** What is a noncommunicable disease? What is an example?

Germs That Cause Disease

Where do communicable diseases come from in the first place? They start with organisms so tiny they can only be seen with a microscope. The popular name for these organisms is *germs*. The scientific name is *pathogens*. A **pathogen** is *a microscopic organism that causes communicable diseases.* Pathogens can be grouped into four main classes: bacteria, viruses, fungi, and protozoa. Within each class are many different *strains*, or subtypes.

Viruses

Viruses (VY·ruh·suhz) are *tiny, nonliving particles that invade and take over healthy cells.* Viruses are so tiny they require a special microscope to be seen. Like bacteria, some strains of viruses are harmless. Some, however, cause serious diseases. For example, AIDS—an immune disorder and hepatitis—a serious disease of the liver—are caused by viruses. So are the common cold, the flu, and measles.

Lesson 1: What Causes Disease? **269**

TECHNOLOGY AND HEALTH

Technology for Fighting Disease Edward Jenner's development of the first vaccine in 1749 was a huge step forward in preventing disease. Today, DNA technology plays a role in the development of new drugs and vaccines. Recombinant DNA technology has been used since the 1980s to produce insulin to treat diabetes. Pharmacogenomics is the relatively new science of relating the response to medication to genetics. The goal of pharmacogenomics is to improve the drug safety, determine the best dosage for drugs, and create improved vaccines.

AL Active Learning

Game Show Divide the class into small groups. Have each group develop five game-show style questions about pathogens including bacteria, protozoa, fungi, and viruses. Then have each group use its questions to quiz the class. **OL**

Connect To...
Science

Helpful Bacteria

After students have read the feature, have them use print and online resources to research helpful bacteria, including those in and on the human body, those used in food production, and those used in the production of medications. Ask: What is one specific way that bacteria are important to humans? *Sample answer: Bacteria are used to produce foods used by humans.* **OL**

Reading Check

Answer Two similarities of bacteria and viruses are that both can cause disease and both require a microscope to be seen. One difference between bacteria and viruses are that viruses are nonliving while bacteria are living. Bacteria and viruses also differ in the specific diseases they cause.

Caption Answer

Photo Caption common cold, strep throat, Lyme disease, malaria

Connect To...
Science

Helpful Bacteria

Some bacteria are essential to good health. One helpful strain of bacteria lives inside your body, in your intestines. These bacteria play an important role in breaking down food during digestion. Other helpful bacteria live on your skin and eat dead skin cells.

How can you help maintain the health of your skin and digestive system?

▶ These are close-ups of four common pathogens. **What are some examples of diseases caused by these organisms?**

Bacteria

Bacteria (bak·TIR·ee·uh) are *extremely small single-celled organisms with no cell nucleus.* A nucleus is a cell's control center. Bacteria are everywhere. Some of the diseases they can cause include strep throat and Lyme disease. They can also cause tooth decay. It is important to note that not all bacteria are harmful to humans. Some are even helpful. In fact, we could not live without bacteria.

Protozoa

Protozoa (proh·tuh·ZOH·uh) are *single-celled organisms that have a nucleus.* Some protozoa, called *parasites,* attach themselves to healthy cells. They rob the cell of its nutrients without killing it. Although most protozoa are harmless to humans, some strains can cause disease. One of the most famous and deadliest diseases caused by a protozoan is malaria. Malaria is found in tropical regions and spread by a certain kind of mosquito. **AL**

Fungi

Fungi (FUHN·jy) are *primitive single- or many-celled organisms that cannot make their own food.* Fungi survive by breaking down other living organisms and absorbing their nutrients. Most fungi are harmless to humans. For example, mushrooms are a fungus and certain kinds are safe to eat. Some strains of fungi such as molds and yeasts cause disease, including athlete's foot and ringworm.

 **Reading Check** **Compare** Identify two similarities and two differences between bacteria and viruses.

🏠 Home, School, and Community

At School As students study germs and disease transmission in this chapter, have them note ways in which a healthy school environment can be maintained. Challenge students to consider steps that individuals can take to improve their own health and the health of others. Have students contribute to a class list of strategies for maintaining a healthy school. Then have students create a poster encouraging one of the habits from the list. With permission, have students place their posters in hallways, the cafeteria, or other common areas of the school. **OL**

How Germs Are Spread

Because germs are so tiny, they can easily be spread. There are four common ways germs are spread. One is by *direct* physical contact with others. Simply shaking hands with someone can pass along germs that are on the skin. Another way is through *indirect* contact. You can pick up germs that travel through the air when people sneeze or cough. Germs can also be spread indirectly by sharing cups, utensils, or other personal items.

A third way germs are spread is by eating or drinking contaminated food or water. Bacteria that cause food poisoning are spread this way. The fourth most common way germs are spread is through contact with animals or insects. Germs can enter your body if you are bitten by a sick animal or disease-carrying insect.

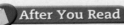

Reading Check **List** Name four ways germs are spread.

The West Nile virus is spread by infected mosquitoes. **What are some ways you can protect yourself against mosquito bites?**

Health Online

Visit **health.glencoe.com** and complete the Interactive Study Guide for Lesson 1.

 Reading Check

Answer Germs are spread by direct physical contact, indirect contact, contaminated food or water, and contact with infected animals or insects.

ASSESS

Assessment Resources

Lesson Review Quiz
- *ExamView*
- Fast Files Activities
- Online Quizzes and Activities

Reteaching

- Assign Concept Map 11-1 or Reteaching Activity 11-1 in the Fast Files.
- Have students name the two main categories of disease and describe one example of each.

Enrichment

- Assign Enrichment Activity 11-1 in the Fast Files.
- Have students create crossword puzzles that include some or all of the lesson vocabulary terms.

CLOSE

Ask students to name a disease and identify the kind of pathogen that causes the disease.

Lesson 1 Review

After You Read

Review this lesson for new terms, major headings, and Reading Checks.

What I Learned

1. *Vocabulary* Define *pathogen*. Use the word in a sentence.

2. *Recall* Name a disease caused by a fungus.

3. *Identify* Name four common disease-causing organisms.

Thinking Critically

4. *Explain* What is the difference between a communicable disease and a non-communicable disease?

5. *Apply* At lunchtime, Maria offers Victoria a bite of her sandwich. Victoria remembers that Maria was coughing and sneezing earlier in class. Should Victoria accept the bite of sandwich? Explain your answer.

Applying Health Skills

6. *Decision Making* Imagine you are in school when you begin to feel like you are coming down with a cold. What are your options? What healthy decisions could you make?

Health Online For more review questions for Lesson 1, go to **health.glencoe.com**.

Lesson 1: What Causes Disease? **271**

Lesson 1 Review Answers

1. A pathogen is a microscopic organism or virus that causes disease.
2. *Sample answers:* athlete's foot, ringworm
3. Four common pathogens are bacteria, viruses, fungi, and protozoa.

4. Communicable diseases can be spread; noncommunicable diseases cannot be spread.
5. *Sample answer:* No, Victoria should not accept the bite of sandwich because Maria might have a cold.

6. I would take precautions to avoid spreading the cold to others in my school.

FOCUS

Activating Prior Knowledge

What I Know Have students name four types of disease-causing pathogens. List their responses on the board. Tell students that this lesson explains what happens when a pathogen enters their body.

 Guide to Reading

BUILDING VOCABULARY
- Have students write a sentence that shows the relationship between two of the lesson vocabulary terms.
- Use Vocabulary PuzzleMaker to reinforce vocabulary terms.

READING STRATEGY
Sequencing Have students make notes while reading the lesson. Students' responses should describe the immune response that occurs when a pathogen enters the body.

Q uick Write

After students have completed the Quick Write, have each student describe one of the steps that he or she took to get better.

Communicable Diseases

📖 Guide to Reading

● Building Vocabulary
List the terms below in your notebook. Put an *X* next to those terms that can cause you harm. Put a checkmark next to those that help you.
- contagious (p. 272)
- infection (p. 274)
- immune system (p. 274)
- lymphocyte (p. 274)
- antibodies (p. 274)
- immunity (p. 274)
- vaccine (p. 275)

● Focusing on the Main Ideas
In this lesson, you will be able to
- **recognize** ways pathogens are spread.
- **identify** common communicable diseases.
- **demonstrate** healthful behaviors that limit the spread of pathogens.

● Reading Strategy
Sequencing Describe the sequence of events that occur when a pathogen enters the body.

Q uick Write

Think about the last time you missed school because of an illness. Describe the illness and the steps you took to get better.

Common Communicable Diseases

Can you guess the name of the most common communicable disease? You've probably had it several times. It is the common cold. Colds are responsible for more school absences than any other illness. There are more than 200 different viruses that cause colds. Symptoms include runny nose, sneezing, coughing, sore throat, headache, and mild fever. When these symptoms first appear, you are contagious (kuhn·TA·juhs). **Contagious** means *you can spread the virus to others by direct or indirect contact*. To help prevent this from happening, be sure to cover your mouth and nose when you sneeze or cough.

◀ Sneezing without covering your mouth and nose spreads thousands of pathogens. **What are some other ways pathogens are spread?**

Caption Answer

Photo Caption Direct contact such as sharing utensils can spread pathogens.

Lesson 2 Resources

📁 **Chapter *FAST FILE* Resources**
Guided Reading and Writing 11-2
Concept Mapping Activity 11-2
Cross-Curriculum Activity 11-2
Reteaching Activity 11-2
Enrichment Activity 11-2
Lesson Quiz 11-2

Technology
👆 Transparency 11-2
🔊 Audio Summaries
🔊 *ExamView*
 Vocabulary PuzzleMaker
🔊 StudentWorks™ Plus

There is no cure for the common cold. To help your body recover, you should rest in bed and drink plenty of fluids. Your parent or guardian may also give you over-the-counter (OTC) medicines that will help with the symptoms. If you have a sore throat for several days, you should see a doctor.

Another communicable disease you are familiar with is influenza (in·floo·EN·zuh). You probably know it as "the flu." Flu symptoms include high fever and joint and muscle aches. Resting and drinking fluids can help you recover faster. Some strains of the flu are serious and can require a doctor's care.

Some other common communicable diseases are listed in **Figure 11.1.** All except hepatitis A are spread through direct or indirect contact. A person gets hepatitis A from food or water containing the virus.

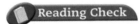

Reading Check **Define** What does *contagious* mean? Use the word in a sentence.

DEVELOPING Good Character

Keep It to Yourself

When you have a cold, take action to prevent spreading your cold to others. Be careful to cover your mouth and nose when you cough or sneeze. Keep as much distance between yourself and others as you can. Avoid sharing cups, utensils, or other personal items. What character traits are you demonstrating when you take steps to prevent spreading communicable diseases?

Your Body's Defenses

AL In a typical day, your body is exposed to millions of germs, so why aren't you sick all the time? The answer is that your body is protected by its own defense system. This system is like a well-designed fort. It actively protects your health around the clock.

R **FIGURE 11.1**

COMMON COMMUNICABLE DISEASES

This table lists several common communicable diseases. What are the symptoms of strep throat?

Disease	Symptoms	Treatment
Mononucleosis	Swollen lymph glands (in neck, underarms, groin), headaches, sore muscles, sore throat, fever, fatigue	Pain relievers, rest, liquids
Hepatitis A, B, and C	Weakness, fatigue, nausea, vomiting, fever, yellowing of eyes, abdominal pain, dark urine	Rest, healthful food choices (medication for Types B and C)
Tuberculosis (TB)	Cough, fatigue, persistent fever, night sweats, weight loss	Antibiotics taken over a long period of time
Strep throat	Sore throat, fever, chills, body aches, loss of appetite, nausea, vomiting, swollen tonsils or glands	Antibiotics, soft food, liquids, gargling with salt water

HEALTH LITERACY

The Flu Influenza, or the flu, is a contagious disease caused by a virus. There are actually several different strains, or types, of influenza. The viruses that cause influenza mutate constantly. When a new strain develops for which people have no immunity and there is no vaccine, it can cause an epidemic. In 1918, for example, a flu epidemic killed approximately 40 million people worldwide. New flu strains appear about every 10 to 15 years. Have students research flu epidemics and ways that modern medical technology is used to fight influenza. OL

TEACH

DEVELOPING Good Character

Keep It to Yourself Have students work individually to read the feature. Then ask: What traits of good character are demonstrated by an individual who takes steps to keep his or her cold from spreading? Sample answers: *citizenship, caring, responsibility, respect*

AL Active Learning

Lessons for Younger Students Have students write and illustrate a picture book that could be used to teach younger students about germs, disease, and the body's defenses. Have students share their books with the class, and if possible, with younger students. AL

R Reading Strategy

Analyzing a Chart Have students read the information in Figure 11.1. Ask: What symptom do all of these illnesses have in common? *fever* Tell students that they will learn why fever is a common symptom of illnesses as they read the next section of text, which describes the immune response. OL

Reading Check

Answer *Contagious* means that an illness can be spread to others by direct or indirect contact.

AL Active Learning

Video Game Have students prepare a detailed plan in storyboard format for a video game based on the immune system's response to pathogens. Tell students that the game should somehow use the following vocabulary words: infection, immune system, lymphocytes, antibodies, and immunity. Have students present their plans to the class. **AL**

Academic Vocabulary

Despite On this page, students learn that sometimes germs find a way into the body despite barriers. Explain that the word *despite* means "in spite of." Have volunteers use the word *despite* in a spoken sentence. **OL**

 Reading Check

Answer Skin and the mucous membranes are two barriers that protect your body against germs.

▲ To prevent the spread of germs, stay home and rest when you are sick. **What are some other ways to prevent the spread of communicable diseases?**

Your Body's First Line of Defense

Your body's defense system has several barriers that work to prevent germs from entering your body. One of these barriers is your skin. The skin, your body's largest organ, acts like a wall around the inner organs. Another barrier is formed by body fluids such as tears and saliva. These contain chemicals that kill certain organisms. Your *mucous membranes* also act as barriers. These are tissues that line the insides of your mouth, throat, nose, and eyes. They are coated with a sticky fluid that traps and destroys germs.

Sometimes, despite these barriers, germs find a way into your body. They might reach your bloodstream, for example, through a cut or scrape. When this happens, you can develop an **infection.** This is *the result of pathogens or germs invading the body, multiplying, and harming some of your body's cells.* Fortunately, your body is equipped with agents that can fight infection. Among them is a chemical called *pyrogen* (PY·ruh·juhn). The release of this chemical triggers a rise in body temperature, or *fever.* The increase in body temperature makes it hard for germs to survive.

AL

Your Immune System

Most of the time, the body's first line of defense is successful in fighting off infections. When it is not, your second line of defense swings into action. This is your **immune** (ih·MYOON) **system,** *a group of cells, tissues, and organs that fight disease.* One key part of the immune system is lymphocytes (LIM·fuh·syts). **AL** A **lymphocyte** is *a white blood cell that attacks pathogens or harmful germs.* Some lymphocytes attack pathogens directly. Others produce **antibodies.** These are *chemicals produced specifically to fight a particular invading substance.* Antibodies recognize germs that reenter the body and will attack and destroy them. This *resistance to infection* is called **immunity.**

 **Reading Check**

Identify Identify two barriers that protect your body against germs.

Caption Answer

Photo Caption Stay away from people who are sick, wash hands regularly.

What Teens Want to Know

Is it harmful to take antibiotics when you don't really need them? Students (and their parents) may expect a prescription for an antibiotic every time they have a minor illness. Remind students that antibiotics are useful for bacterial illness, not viral illness like colds, coughs, or influenza. Explain that using antibiotics when they are not needed can contribute to the development of antibiotic resistant infections. Have students research the problems related to the overuse of antibiotics and prepare a short oral report to share with the class. **OL**

Preventing Communicable Diseases

You can help your body prevent disease by avoiding germs. First, steer clear of people who you know are sick. Second, get in the habit of washing your hands regularly. Your hands are constantly picking up germs from objects in your environment. When you put your hands to your mouth or nose, these germs can enter your body. Keep a supply of pre-moistened wipes handy for when you need to wash your hands but soap and water are not available. You can also help your body fight germs by practicing healthy behaviors. Get enough rest, eat healthy foods, and exercise regularly.

Some communicable diseases can be prevented with vaccines. A **vaccine** (vak·SEEN) is *a dead or weakened pathogen introduced into your body.* This triggers the immune system to make antibodies to fight the pathogen. However, because the pathogen is dead or weakened, you don't become ill. **Figure 11.2** lists some common vaccines and when they should be taken.

 **Reading Check**   **List** Name two actions you can take to help your body's defenses.

> **Health *Online***
>
> Visit **health.glencoe.com** and complete the Interactive Study Guide for Lesson 2.

▼ FIGURE 11.2

R VACCINES GIVEN AT DIFFERENT AGES

This table lists the vaccines that help protect against developing certain diseases. At what ages is the vaccine for measles given?

Vaccine and the Diseases It Protects Against	Typical Vaccination Schedule
Hep B: hepatitis B	Birth, 2 months, 15–18 months
DTaP: diphtheria, tetanus, pertussis (whooping cough)	2, 4, 6, and 15–18 months; 4–6 years; Td (tetanus and diphtheria toxoid) boosters at 11–12 years; and every 10 years thereafter
Hib: diseases caused by *Hemophilus influenza* type B (Hib) bacteria	2, 4, 6, and 12–15 months
IPV: poliomyelitis	2, 4, and 12–15 months; 4–6 years
PCV: diseases caused by *Streptococcus pneumoniae* bacteria	2, 4, 6, and 12–15 months
MMR: measles, mumps, rubella	12–15 months; 4–6 years
Varicella: chicken pox	15 months; can be given any time after 12 months
Hep A: hepatitis A	2 doses at least 6 months apart, anytime between 2 and 18 years; used only in high-risk areas or for high-risk groups

Source: Table based on immunization schedule recommended by the Centers for Disease Control and Prevention, the American Academy of Pediatrics, and the American Academy of Family Physicians

---

🏠 Home, School, and Community

At Home Healthy behaviors, including getting enough rest, eating foods rich in vitamins, exercising regularly, and practicing regular handwashing are mentioned as ways to help maintain health. Have students work individually to set a health goal to improve one of these habits. Have students write down their goal and record their progress toward the goal daily for one week. Have students write a sentence evaluating their progress at the end of the week. **OL**

R Reading Strategy

Analyzing a Chart Have students examine Figure 11.2. Ask: In what stage of life are most vaccines administered? *infancy* What vaccines are required for students in your age group? *DTaP. The measles vaccine is given at 12–15 months.* **OL**

HS Health Skills Practice

Practicing Healthful Behaviors Have students make a list of ways to prevent communicable diseases, such as regular handwashing and avoiding those who are ill. Have students write a slogan promoting proper handwashing techniques. Then have students share their slogans with the class. Have the class brainstorm ways to share their slogans with other students in the school, for example, by using them as a part of a school newsletter or in the daily announcements. **OL**

U Universal Access

English Learners Develop a modified *CLOZE* paragraph to assess students' understanding of the lesson vocabulary terms. Have English learners complete the modified *CLOZE* paragraph. Then have students practice pronunciation by saying aloud individual vocabulary terms or full sentences. **EL**

Reading Check

Answer Getting enough rest and eating foods rich in vitamins can help your immune system stay healthy.

Health Skills Activity

Practicing Healthful Behaviors

Handwashing for Health

One behavior that can help limit the spread of germs is washing your hands thoroughly. Thorough handwashing includes rubbing your hands together for at least 15 seconds using soap and warm water. Be sure to wash the creases in your skin and fingernails where germs can collect. Rinse and dry your hands completely since germs can thrive in moist environments.

Wash your hands after using the restroom and before eating or handling food. Also avoid touching your mouth and eyes with your hands. This can allow germs to enter your body and make you sick.

On Your Own

Practice this handwashing technique. In the future, remember to use this technique to help your body stay healthy.

Health Skills Activity

Practicing Healthful Behaviors

Handwashing for Health

Remind students to think about these hand-washing tips the next time they wash their hands.

ASSESS

Assessment Resources

Lesson Review Quiz
 ExamView
Fast Files Activities
Online Quizzes

Reteaching

- Assign Concept Map 11-2 or Reteaching Activity 11-2 in the Fast Files.
- Have students work with partners to outline the facts about the immune system covered in this lesson.

Enrichment

- Assign Enrichment Activity 11-2 in the Fast Files.
- Have students research autoimmune disorders and report their findings.

CLOSE

Ask students to identify healthful behaviors that can limit the spread of pathogens.

Lesson 2 Review

After You Read

Review this lesson for new terms, major headings, and Reading Checks.

What I Learned

1. **Describe** What is the most common communicable disease? Name other common communicable diseases.

2. **Vocabulary** Define *antibodies*, and use it in a sentence.

3. **List** Name a disease that can be prevented with a vaccine.

Thinking Critically

4. **Apply** Why should you avoid sharing an ice cream cone with a friend who has a cold?

5. **Analyze** How does handwashing help protect the health of your school and community?

Applying Health Skills

6. **Advocacy** As a group, create a brochure or flyer informing students of ways they can protect themselves against the spread of communicable diseases. Include a list of common communicable diseases.

Health Online For more review questions for Lesson 2, go to **health.glencoe.com**.

Lesson 2 Review Answers

1. The most common communicable disease is the common cold. Other communicable diseases are influenza; mononucleosis; hepatitis A, B, and C; tuberculosis; and strep throat.

2. An antibody is a chemical that fights a specific pathogen.

3. Students may list any disease noted in Figure 11.2.

4. Sharing food is one way that colds are spread.

5. By washing away the germs on your hands, you keep them from spreading to others, which protects the health of the community.

6. Students' brochures or fliers should contain information from the chapter.

Understanding STDs

Guide to Reading

● **Building Vocabulary**
Copy the terms below into your notebook. As you come across them in your reading, write the definition for each term beside it.

■ sexually transmitted diseases (STDs) (p. 277)
■ HIV (p. 278)
■ AIDS (p. 278)
■ abstinence (p. 280)

● **Focusing on the Main Ideas**
In this lesson, you will be able to

■ **identify** common STDs.
■ **describe** how HIV and other STDs are spread.
■ **access** current information on HIV and AIDS.
■ **explain** how to protect yourself from STDs.

● **Reading Strategy**
Organizing Information There are many myths and facts about the spread of HIV. As you read, keep a list of both in your notebook.

Sexually Transmitted Diseases

Sexually transmitted diseases (STDs) are *communicable diseases spread from one person to another through sexual activity.* They are also known as *sexually transmitted infections (STIs).* Anyone who is sexually active can get an STD.

You can't tell if someone has an STD just by looking at him or her. It is possible to have an STD but have no visible symptoms or symptoms that come and go. Whether or not symptoms are visible, the person is still contagious and could spread the STD to another person.

STDs can cause serious health problems. They can affect menstrual health and damage the reproductive system. If left untreated, some STDs can prevent a person from being able to have children. Some can even cause death. A person with an STD needs to see a doctor for treatment right away.

▶ Knowing how HIV is and is *not* spread is important. **Why is it important to recognize myths about the spread of this illness?**

 Quick Write

You probably know that HIV, the virus that causes AIDS, is contagious. Make a list of ways you think HIV is spread.

Lesson 3 Resources

 Chapter *Fast File* Resources
Guided Reading and Writing 11-3
Concept Mapping Activity 11-3
Cross-Curriculum Activity 11-3
Reteaching Activity 11-3
Enrichment Activity 11-3
Lesson Quiz 11-3

Technology
Transparency 11-3
Audio Summaries
ExamView
Vocabulary PuzzleMaker
StudentWorks™ Plus

FOCUS
Activating Prior Knowledge

What I Know Ask students to name the four ways in which communicable diseases are spread (direct contact, indirect contact, contaminated food or water, animals and insects). Write their answers on the board. Circle the phrase "direct contact." Explain that Lesson 3 discusses diseases that are spread by direct contact.

Guide to Reading

BUILDING VOCABULARY
■ Ask students to identify what the abbreviations *STDs, HIV,* and *AIDS* stand for.
■ Use Vocabulary PuzzleMaker to reinforce vocabulary terms.

READING STRATEGY
Organizing Information Have students prepare a T-diagram in their notebooks. One side of the diagram should be labeled "Myths," and the other side should be labeled "Facts." Have students add to both sides of the T-diagram as they read the lesson.

Quick Write

Use students' responses to the Quick Write to identify misconceptions students may have about HIV transmission.

277

TEACH

 Writing Support

Persuasive Writing Have students use the information in Figure 11.3 as supporting details in a persuasive paragraph encouraging students to practice abstinence from risky behaviors. Remind students that persuasive writing uses facts to support a position. Have students proofread their work and correct any errors they find before turning it in. **OL**

Reading Check

Answer STDs can cause serious, permanent damage if they are not treated by a doctor.

R **Reading Strategy**

Analyzing a Chart After students have examined the information in Figure 11.3, have them recall the definition of the term *antibiotic,* which is found in Chapter 6. Give students a clue by asking for the meaning of the prefix *anti-.* Then have students use this information to determine which of the STDs listed in the chart are caused by a bacteria (chlamydia, gonorrhea, syphilis). **OL**

Caption Answers

Photo Caption, p. 277 Accurate information can help prevent illness.
Figure Caption genital warts, genital herpes, hepatitis B

Figure 11.3 lists five common STDs. Be aware that getting one of these diseases does not make a person immune to it. Any time there is contact with a pathogen that causes an STD, the disease can return. It is also important to note that most of these diseases have no vaccines. The only one that does is Hepatitis B.

 **Explain** Why does a person with an STD need to see a doctor?

HIV and AIDS

HIV, which stands for *human immunodeficiency virus,* is *the virus that causes AIDS.* HIV attacks a specific type of lymphocyte called a *T-cell.* (See **Figure 11.4.**) The virus replaces the cell's genetic information with its own and then multiplies. The more T-cells that are taken over by HIV, the harder it becomes for the body to fight pathogens.

Eventually, the T-cell count drops so low that the immune system can no longer protect the body. When this happens, AIDS, or *acquired immunodeficiency syndrome* develops. **AIDS** is *a condition characterized by life-ending infections and a T-cell count under 200.*

▼ **FIGURE 11.3**

COMMON STDs

R This table identifies common sexually-transmitted diseases. Which STDs cannot be cured with antibiotics?

STD	Common Symptoms	Treatment
Chlamydia (kluh·MIH·dee·uh)	Pain or burning feeling during urination; unusual discharge from penis or vagina; often has no symptoms (especially in females) but can still be spread	Cured with antibiotics
Gonorrhea (gah·nuh·REE·uh)	Pain or burning during urination; unusual discharge from penis or vagina; abdominal pain; sometimes has no symptoms (especially in females) but can still be spread	Cured with antibiotics
Syphilis (SI·fuh·lis)	Red, wet, painless sores at place where virus enters body, followed by rash and flu-like symptoms; can lead to brain damage and other serious health problems, especially in infants	Cured with antibiotics
Genital warts	Small pink or red bumps in genital area; can increase risk of certain cancers in women	Warts can be removed by a doctor but may return because virus remains in body
Genital herpes (HER·peez)	Itching or pain followed by painful, itchy sores in genital area; symptoms come and go, but virus is still present and able to be spread	Antiviral medication relieves symptoms when sores appear; no cure
Hepatitis B	Weakness, fatigue, nausea, vomiting, fever, yellowing of eyes, abdominal pain, dark urine	Rest, healthful food choices, antiviral medication

278 Chapter 11: Preventing Diseases

HEALTH LITERACY

Opportunistic Infections An HIV infection becomes AIDS when the immune system's ability to fight off infections is impaired. *Opportunistic infections* is the term used to describe the illnesses that people with AIDS experience as a result of their weakened immune systems. Common opportunistic illnesses include a variety of pneumonia called Pneumocystis carinii pneumonia, various fungal diseases, and hepatitis C. A type of cancer called Kaposi's sarcoma also occurs in AIDS patients. AIDS is a fatal illness, but it is opportunistic infections that cause death, not HIV itself.

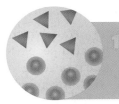
1 HIV enters the bloodstream.

2 The virus attacks and damages T-cell lymphocytes. These cells are an important part of the immune system.

3 As the virus multiplies, more and more lymphocytes are destroyed. The immune system gets weaker and weaker.

4 Death occurs when the immune system is too weak to fight off infections that a healthy immune system could easily resist.

 HIV   T-cell   Dead T-cell   Pathogen

R Reading Strategy

Analyzing a Graphic After students have examined Figure 11.4, have them use four index cards to organize the information they have learned. Have students use one index card for each stage shown in the infographic. On each index card, have students summarize in their own words how HIV affects the immune system. **OL**

C Critical Thinking

Integrating Concepts Explain that HIV is spread through sexual contact and sharing needles during drug use. Have students recall what they learned in Chapter 10 to explain how alcohol use could lead to exposure to STDs, including HIV. (Alcohol use interferes with decision making, which can lead to high-risk behaviors such as drug use and sexual activity.) **OL**

When AIDS weakens the immune system, the body cannot fight off other infections or diseases. Symptoms can include fatigue, frequent long-lasting fevers or cough, and sweating heavily at night. Drugs can delay the onset of AIDS, but there is no cure. People with AIDS will eventually die from diseases that a healthy immune system could have resisted.

How HIV Spreads

HIV is spread through specific body fluids. These include semen, fluid from the vagina, blood, and breast milk. Semen is the fluid that carries sperm.

There are several ways these fluids spread from one person to another. One is by sexual contact. Another is by sharing needles. Drug users can get HIV from a needle already used by an infected person. A pregnant woman with HIV can pass the virus to her developing baby. An infected mother can also spread HIV to her baby when breast-feeding.

HIV spreads *only* through contact with infected body fluids. You cannot get the virus from the air or from mosquito bites. It is not carried in sweat or tears or passed by touching objects such as toilet seats. You will not get HIV by shaking hands or hugging a person with the virus. At one time, the virus was spread when blood donated by people infected with HIV was used for transfusions. Since 1985, all donated blood in the United States is tested for HIV. Therefore, the risk of getting the virus from a blood transfusion is extremely low.

▲ **FIGURE 11.4**

HIV IN THE IMMUNE SYSTEM **R**

HIV prevents the immune system from doing its job. What is the function of the immune system?

Lesson 3: Understanding STDs   **279**

What Teens Want to Know

How do I act around a person with AIDS? Always respect students' privacy and keep any personal information confidential. Remind the class that believing rumors about HIV and AIDS is harmful, and that they should know the facts. Explain to students that those with HIV and AIDS should be treated no differently than any other person. Remind students that they cannot get HIV by simply being near a person with the virus and that sharing a school bus, classroom, computer keyboard, or restroom with an infected person does not pose a risk of infection.

Caption Answer

Photo Caption The immune system fights off pathogens that enter the body.

Connect To...
Science

New Strains of HIV
Use print resources for this activity, or have students access Internet resources at **health .glencoe.com**. Have students work in small groups to perform the research. Then have groups prepare and present a short report explaining their findings. **OL**

Reading Check

Answer HIV is spread by sexual contact and shared needles. It is not spread by shaking hands or hugging.

Health Skills Activity

Accessing Information

Accurate Information on HIV and AIDS

Divide the class into three groups. Have each group contact one of the listed organizations and identify HIV and AIDS resources offered for teens. Then have the groups work together to form a comprehensive list. Have students share the list with the school nurse as a resource for students who have questions about HIV and AIDS. **OL**

Academic Vocabulary

Accurate Sources of accurate information about HIV and AIDS are described. Ask a student to define the word *accurate*. Then ask other students to name synonyms of the word *accurate* (true, reliable, correct). **OL**

280

Connect To...
Science

New Strains of HIV

Since HIV first appeared, medical researchers have been developing medications to fight it. At the same time, the virus has been *mutating*. This means it changes itself in ways that make these medications powerless against it. Researchers continue to try to keep up with these new strains of the virus.

Using the Internet or print resources, learn about what steps are currently being taken to fight HIV.

Health *Online*

Visit **health.glencoe.com** and complete the Interactive Study Guide for Lesson 3.

Treatment for People with HIV and AIDS

In recent years, medical technology has slowed down the effects of HIV. New medicines are allowing infected people to live longer. A search for an effective HIV vaccine is ongoing. At present, however, there is no cure for HIV or AIDS. Anyone who becomes infected with HIV is at risk of developing AIDS.

Detecting HIV

People infected with HIV often show no symptoms for a long time. On the outside, they may look perfectly healthy. However, they can still pass on the virus. Laboratory tests are the only way of knowing if a person has HIV. These tests show whether antibodies to the virus are present. If a test shows no antibodies, it should be repeated in six months. A person recently infected may not have had time to develop antibodies.

Reading Check

List Name two ways HIV is spread and two ways it is *not* spread.

Preventing HIV and STDs

HIV infection, AIDS, and other STDS can be prevented. The following are some ways to avoid getting these diseases.

- Choose abstinence. **Abstinence** *is not participating in high-risk behaviors*. These include avoiding sexual contact with another person.
- Avoid sharing needles. This includes the kind of needles used for body piercing. These needles can carry infection into your bloodstream.
- Say no to alcohol and drugs. People who use alcohol or drugs often lose the ability to make wise decisions. They are more likely to engage in risky behaviors.

Getting Help

Teens who think they may have an STD need to take action. They must find out if they are infected. If they are, they need to be treated. The first step in getting help is to talk to a parent or trusted adult. This step is difficult for many teens. They may feel embarrassed or worry that a parent will be angry or disappointed. However, if left untreated, STDs can permanently damage the reproductive system and cause other serious health problems.

Reading Check

Define What is abstinence?

TECHNOLOGY AND HEALTH

Medications for HIV and AIDS Scientists continue to work on new technologies that will combat HIV and AIDS. HIV infection is currently being treated with a variety of drugs. These drugs function in several ways. Two of the types of drugs stop the HIV from replicating itself. Another type keeps cells infected with HIV from releasing more virus into the body. A newer class of drugs, called fusion or entry inhibitors, stops the HIV from entering uninfected cells. Although there is no cure for HIV, currently available drug therapies can slow the progression of HIV to AIDS.

Health Skills Activity

Accessing Information

Accurate Information on HIV and AIDS

Research on HIV and AIDS is ongoing. New information is being discovered all the time. Knowing where to find it is important. Everyone needs to have up-to-date information on how to prevent an HIV infection. Here are some sources you can trust for accurate information.

- **The Center for Disease Control and Prevention (CDC).** The CDC is the leading federal health information agency.
- **The National Institutes of Health (NIH).** Like the CDC, the NIH is part of the U.S. Department of Health and Human Services. The NIH awards research grants to hospitals and health professionals.
- **National Health Council.** Based in Washington, D.C., this organization is a leader in health advocacy.

With a Group
Locate and contact one of these organizations. Find out what kinds of HIV and AIDS information it offers to teens.

Lesson 3 Review

After You Read
Review this lesson for new terms, major headings, and Reading Checks.

What I Learned

1. *Vocabulary* What do the letters *STD* stand for?

2. *List* What are some ways in which HIV and other STDs are spread?

3. *Recall* Explain the relationship between HIV and AIDS.

Thinking Critically

4. *Evaluate* Why might drinking alcohol increase your risk of getting an STD?

5. *Apply* A teen fears he or she has an STD. Why is it important for this teen to see a health care provider?

Applying Health Skills

6. *Communication Skills* Review the steps in the S.T.O.P. strategy discussed in Chapter 3. Then develop a list of responses to peer pressure to engage in sexual activity.

Health Online For more review questions for Lesson 3, go to **health.glencoe.com**.　　Lesson 3: Understanding STDs　**281**

Lesson 3 Review Answers

1. STD stands for "sexually transmitted disease," a communicable disease spread by sexual contact.
2. HIV and other STDs are spread through sexual contact and shared needles.
3. HIV is a virus that harms the immune system, causing a disease called AIDS.
4. Alcohol interferes with decision making and can lead to high-risk behaviors.
5. Some STDs can damage the reproductive system, others can be deadly, and therefore treatment is essential.
6. Have students list reasons to avoid sexual contact. Their lists can be used for the "Tell why not" step of the S.T.O.P. strategy.

CHAPTER 11
Lesson 3

 Reading Check

Answer, p. 280 Abstinence is choosing not to take part in high-risk behaviors.

ASSESS

Assessment Resources

Lesson Review Quiz
- *ExamView*
- Fast Files Activities
- Online Quizzes and Activities

Reteaching

- Assign Concept Map 11-3 or Reteaching Activity 11-3 in the Fast Files.
- Have students describe three ways to avoid getting STDs and AIDS. (Avoid sexual contact with others; avoid sharing needles; do not use drugs or alcohol.)

Enrichment

- Assign Enrichment Activity 11-3 in the Fast Files.
- Have students make a pamphlet describing how and where to obtain reliable information about STDs.

CLOSE

Go around the room and have students identify myths and facts about HIV transmission.

281

FOCUS

Activating Prior Knowledge

What I Know Have students identify diseases that are not passed from person to person. Ask students if they can identify the cause of any diseases they name.

Guide to Reading

BUILDING VOCABULARY

■ Ask students to explain how the following terms are related to one another: *chronic, diabetes, insulin.* (*Diabetes* is a *chronic* disease in which the body does not make or cannot properly use *insulin*.)

■ Use Vocabulary PuzzleMaker to reinforce vocabulary terms.

READING STRATEGY

Comparing and Contrasting Have students create a four-column chart in their notebooks. The columns should be labeled, from left to right, "Disease," "Cause," "Symptoms," and "Treatment." As students read the lesson, have them fill in their charts.

Quick Write

Have students share their completed Quick Write with the class. Develop a list of noncommunicable diseases based on students' work. Have students add to the list as they read the lesson.

282

Noncommunicable and Hereditary Diseases

Guide to Reading

● Building Vocabulary
Explain how the terms below are related. Write the definitions as you come across the terms in the lesson.

■ chronic (p. 283)
■ cancer (p. 284)
■ tumor (p. 284)
■ allergy (p. 285)
■ asthma (p. 285)
■ diabetes (p. 286)
■ insulin (p. 286)

● Focusing on the Main Ideas
In this lesson, you will be able to

■ **identify** causes of various noncommunicable diseases.
■ **develop** behaviors to keep your heart healthy.
■ **identify** ways to help prevent diseases like cancer and diabetes.

● Reading Strategy
Comparing and Contrasting Create a chart that shows the cause, symptoms, and treatment of four noncommunicable diseases.

Quick Write

Some diseases are not spread from person to person. Name some diseases you know about that you don't catch from someone else. List some reasons why these diseases might develop.

What Causes Noncommunicable Diseases?

Noncommunicable diseases are caused by several different things. One cause is poor health habits. For example, lack of physical activity, being overweight, or eating foods high in fat can lead to heart disease and diabetes. Another cause of noncommunicable disease is a person's environment. Living in a city with heavy smog, for example, can lead to lung disease. A third cause is heredity. Diseases, such as allergies or muscular dystrophy can be passed from a parent to a child. Sometimes noncommunicable diseases result from harm done by a communicable disease. An infection from measles, for example, can spread to the brain and cause brain damage.

Some noncommunicable diseases are present at birth. Others develop later in life. One disease that shows up at birth is Down syndrome. This is a disease caused by an abnormal arrangement of chromosomes. Another noncommunicable disease a person is born with is congenital heart disease. This is a defect in a heart valve or one of the big blood vessels leading out of the heart.

Reading Check

Give Examples Identify two noncommunicable diseases that can be present at birth.

Lesson 4 Resources

📁 **Chapter *FAST FILE* Resources**
Guided Reading and Writing 11-4
Concept Mapping Activity 11-4
Health Lab 11-4
Reteaching Activity 11-4
Enrichment Activity 11-4
Lesson Quiz 11-4

Technology
🔋 Transparency 11-4
🔊 Audio Summaries
🔊 *ExamView*
✏️ Vocabulary PuzzleMaker
🔊 StudentWorks™ Plus

Heart Disease

Heart disease is the number one cause of death in the United States. Heart disease and many other non-communicable diseases are **chronic** (KRAH·nik), or *long-lasting*. A common cause of heart disease is the narrowing or blockage of blood vessels. When this happens, the heart has a hard time doing its job and becomes weak. The result can be a heart attack or stroke. Stroke is a destruction of brain tissue caused when the heart can't pump enough blood to the brain.

Heart disease is also caused by high blood pressure. This is a condition in which the heart is forced to work unusually hard. High blood pressure can be inherited. It can also be caused by stress, kidney problems, or eating too many foods high in fat or cholesterol.

▲ Some noncommunicable diseases are passed on through heredity. **What are some other causes of noncommunicable diseases?**

Heart-Healthy Habits

You can lessen the risk of developing heart disease by practicing some of the following positive health behaviors:

- Stay physically active. Aerobic activity can strengthen your heart and blood vessels. It can also lower blood pressure.

- Maintain a healthy weight. Having less body fat reduces the strain on the heart and blood vessels.

- Eat foods high in fiber and low in salt, fat, and cholesterol.

- Learn to manage stress. Reducing or managing stress can help lower blood pressure.

- Avoid tobacco products. This can lower your risk of stroke, heart attack, and other diseases.

Treating Heart Disease

Heart disease can be treated with medication. There are medicines that widen blood vessels, lower blood pressure, and control a person's heartbeat. When the problem is too serious to be corrected by medication, surgery is recommended. Operations can be done to open blocked arteries or insert devices that regulate the heartbeat. In severe cases, a heart transplant may be considered.

 **Reading Check**

List Name two positive health behaviors that can reduce the risk of heart disease.

Health *Online*

Topic: Keeping Your Heart Healthy

Visit health.glencoe.com for Student Web Activities to learn more about how you can keep your heart strong and healthy.

Activity: Using the information provided at the link above, create a heart health quiz that will help other teens figure out if they are at risk for heart problems.

TEACH

R Reading Strategy

Identifying Cause and Effect Have students work as a class to list causes and effects of heart disease. Record their responses on the board. Have students use a similar strategy for organizing information about cancer, allergies, asthma, and diabetes. **BL**

HS Health Skills Practice

Accessing Information Have students work in small groups to use reliable sources to find out more about a heart-healthy diet. Have students use the information they find to make a heart-healthy menu for one day. Have each group share its menu with the class and give an explanation for each of the selected foods. **OL**

Health *Online*

After students have completed the activity, check over quizzes for accurate information. Then allow students to administer their quizzes to the class.

Reading Check

Answer Reducing stress and eating a healthy diet can reduce the risk of heart disease.

Caption Answer

Photo Caption Causes include poor health habits, environment, or heredity.

Cultural Perspectives

Hereditary Diseases A person's racial and ethnic background has a large effect on the risk of developing certain hereditary disorders. For example, the genetic disorder that occurs most commonly in Caucasians is cystic fibrosis. Tay-Sachs disease, a fatal genetic disorder that affects the nervous system, is found predominantly among those with ancestors from Eastern Europe. The most common genetic disorder among African Americans is sickle-cell disease. Have students research genetic disorders. Have them develop a list of facts about one specific genetic disorder. **OL**

283

AL Active Learning

Poster Have students make a poster that describes one of the seven warning signs of cancer. The poster should include information encouraging anyone experiencing this symptom to see a medical professional. Display the completed posters in the classroom. **OL**

U Universal Access

Reluctant Readers and Writers Read aloud to students the information about the four main ways that cancer is treated. Then ask: What are some similarities and differences of the four main types of cancer treatment? *Sample answer: The treatments are similar in that all work to destroy cancer cells. The treatments are different in that some, like surgery and radiation, work at a specific location in the body, while chemotherapy and biologic treatments work throughout the body.* **OL**

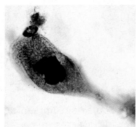

▲ As old cells die, new ones take over. **What happens in the case of cancer?**

Cancer

Sometimes a healthy cell in your body is replaced with one or more abnormal cells. When these cells multiply and destroy the healthy tissue around them, the result is cancer. **Cancer** is *a disease caused by abnormal cells that grow out of control.* Cancer is the second leading cause of death in the United States.

Many cancers start out as a **tumor.** This is *a mass of abnormal cells.* Some tumors are noncancerous, or benign (bih·NYN). This means they do not spread. Tumors that are cancerous, or malignant (muh·LIG·nuhnt), spread to surrounding tissue. Eventually, cancerous cells from the tumor may spread throughout the body.

Cancer is caused by heredity, exposure to cancer-causing substances, or poor health choices. For example, the chemicals found in tobacco have been proven to cause cancer. In fact, cigarette smoking accounts for at least 30% of all cancer deaths.

You can lower your risk of getting cancer by taking care of your body. Eat well, stay active, protect your skin with sunscreen, and avoid exposing your body to dangerous substances like tobacco and drugs.

Treating Cancer

When cancer is discovered early, there is a greater chance that the person can be treated successfully. There are seven cancer warning signs. People who notice any of these should see a doctor right away.

AL

- **C**hanges in bowel or bladder habits
- **A** sore that does not heal
- **U**nusual bleeding or discharge
- **T**hickening or lump in the breast or elsewhere
- **I**ndigestion or difficulty swallowing
- **O**bvious changes in a wart or mole
- **N**agging cough or hoarseness

U There are four main ways cancer is usually treated: surgery, radiation, chemotherapy, and biologic therapies. Surgery is used to remove tumors. Radiation (ray·dee·AY·shuhn) is used to destroy cancer cells in a specific location. Both of these treatments are most effective when the cancer has not spread. If the cancer has spread, chemotherapy (kee·moh·THEHR·uh·pee) is

---

Caption Answer

Photo Caption Cancer occurs when an abnormal cell replaces a cell that has died.

What Teens Want to Know

Is tanning ever safe? Some teens have misconceptions about tanning. Some believe that indoor tanning is safe. Others think that tanning is not harmful unless they get a sunburn. As students read the information about cancer prevention, stress that using sunscreen, avoiding the sun during peak hours, and avoiding indoor tanning are healthy habits that will reduce their risk of getting skin cancer. Have students use online or print resources to research the hazards of tanning. Ask students to share a short report of their findings with the class. **OL**

often used because it travels throughout the body to destroy cancer cells wherever they occur. Biologic treatments work with the body's immune system, stimulating it to fight cancer.

Allergies

When Mike is around cats, he sneezes and his eyes itch. Mike is allergic to cats. An **allergy** is *the body's sensitivity to certain substances*. A substance that causes an allergic reaction is called an *allergen* (AL·er·juhn). Common allergens include the dander in animal hair or fur, dust, pollen, grass, and some molds. People can also have allergies to certain foods, such as peanuts.

Allergies are caused by an overreaction of the immune system. The system reacts to allergens as if they were pathogens entering your body.

Simple medical tests can determine if a person has allergies and what he or she is allergic to. Although there is no cure for an allergy, certain medicines can ease the symptoms and even prevent allergic reactions. You can also try to avoid the allergen.

 **Reading Check** **Recall** What seven-letter word forms the warning signs for cancer?

Asthma

A health problem related to allergies is **asthma** (AZ·muh). This is *a chronic disease in which the airways become irritated and swollen*. During an asthma attack, the small airways of the lungs become coated with a thick mucous. It becomes difficult to breathe. If the attack is severe, the person may experience a feeling of suffocation and begin to panic.

Asthma attacks can be triggered by a number of factors. These include allergens, physical activity, and cold or damp air. Smoke from cigarettes and other forms of air pollution can also cause asthma attacks.

Treatment for minor asthma attacks includes inhaling medication that relaxes the airways, making it easier to breathe. Severe attacks may require a visit to the hospital for additional treatment. Most asthmatics regularly take medicine that helps prevent attacks. Avoiding known triggers can also help prevent attacks. Untreated, asthma can lead to permanent lung damage or in some cases death.

▼ Animal dander can sometimes trigger an asthma attack. **What other factors can trigger an asthma attack?**

R Reading Strategy

Comparing and Contrasting Have students work for 5 minutes in small groups to compare and contrast allergies and asthma. Then go around the room and have each group name one way allergies and asthma are similar and one way they are different. OL

Reading Check

Answer The word *CAUTION* can be used to remember the warning signs of cancer.

AL Active Learning

Quick Demo Roll a piece of notebook paper into a tube with a diameter of approximately 1 inch. Explain that this tube represents a normal airway. Then roll the paper much more tightly, so that the resulting tube has a smaller diameter. Explain that this tube represents a person's airways during an asthma attack. Have students imagine how much more difficult it would be to get air through the constricted airways represented by the narrow roll of paper. OL

◆ Promoting Coordinated School Health

Asthma Each year, asthma causes approximately 14 million days of school absence. The Centers for Disease Control and Prevention (CDC) have developed six strategies for including asthma management as a part of a coordinated school health program. These strategies, which can be found on the CDC's Web site, provide guidelines for coordinating services for students with asthma, including asthma education, heath services, and safe physical education. The strategies also outline recommendations for coordinating school, family, and community involvement.

Caption Answer

Photo Caption *Sample answer:* Physical activity and cigarette smoke can also trigger asthma.

285

Advocacy Explain to students that some of the risk factors for type 2 diabetes, such as genetics, cannot be controlled by the individual. However, maintaining a healthy weight and engaging in adequate amounts of physical activity are ways that the risk of type 2 diabetes can be decreased. Have students work in small groups to create public service announcements that can be used to encourage other students to decrease their risk of diabetes by practicing healthful behaviors. **OL**

R **Reading Strategy**

Inferring Direct students' attention to the section on Type 2 Diabetes in Young People and Figure 11.5. Ask volunteers to summarize the data in the paragraph. Then ask: What factors do you think have contributed to the increase in the percentage of young people who are overweight? Sample answers: *poor diet, fast food, sedentary lifestyle* Discuss ways to combat obesity in young people. One step that could help to correct this problem is increased participation in sports and physical activities. **OL**

Reading Check

Answer, p. 287 Type 1 diabetes and type 2 diabetes have similar symptoms.

Diabetes

Diabetes (dy·uh·BEE·teez) is *a disease that prevents the body from using the sugars and starches in food for energy.* Diabetes is caused when the body doesn't make or can't use insulin. **Insulin** is *a hormone produced by the pancreas,* that normally moves sugars into cells.

Depending on the specific problem, diabetes is categorized as type 1 or type 2. In type 1 diabetes, the body does not produce insulin at all. In type 2, the body makes insulin but is unable to use it efficiently.

Some symptoms of diabetes are increased thirst, frequent urine production, lack of energy, and blurred vision.

Type 2 Diabetes in Young People

HS At one time, type 2 diabetes occurred mainly in adults. That has changed. Today, half of all new cases of type 2 diabetes involve young people. This increase is related to the increase in obesity among children and teens. The bar graph in **Figure 11.5** shows a steady increase over a forty-year period. How many percentage points has the obesity rate risen among people your age?

R ▼ **FIGURE 11.5**

PERCENTAGE OF OBESE CHILDREN AND TEENS OVER A 40-YEAR TIME PERIOD

The number of obese young people is rising. What steps can be taken to correct this problem?

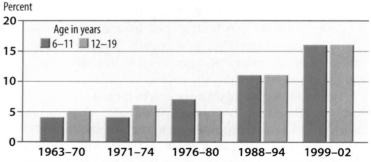

NOTE: Excludes pregnant women starting with 1971–74. Pregnancy status not available for 1963–65 and 1966–70. Data for 1963–65 are for children 6–11 years of age; data for 1966–70 are for adolescents 12–17 years of age, not 12–19 years. SOURCE: CDC/NCHS, NHES and NHANES

Dealing with Sensitive Issues

Diabetes Students may have the misconception that all cases of diabetes are caused by unhealthy lifestyle choices such as a lack of physical activity or obesity. Some of the risk factors for diabetes, such as a genetic predisposition for the disease, cannot be controlled. Remind students that type 1 diabetes is caused when the body's immune system destroys cells in the pancreas that produce insulin. This type of diabetes is usually diagnosed in young people and is not brought on by lifestyle choices.

Treatment for Diabetes

People who have diabetes must be careful to monitor the amount of sugar in their blood. They also need to follow a treatment plan that helps their bodies cope with the disease. Taking insulin, exercising regularly, and watching their weight are all part of a successful treatment plan. Eating foods that help keep an even level of sugar in the blood is also important. Physical exercise lowers blood sugar and pressure, improves the body's ability to use insulin, and helps prevent complications like heart disease. Staying at a healthy weight makes it easier for the body to use the food it takes in.

Developing a good meal plan can help a diabetic decide how much and what kinds of foods to eat. There are several meal plans that have been used successfully to help diabetics manage their blood sugar. They include the Diabetes Food Pyramid, Rate Your Plate, Exchange Lists, and Carbohydrate Counting. Each diabetic must decide which is best with the help of his or her doctor or dietician.

 **Reading Check** **Compare** How are type 1 and type 2 diabetes similar?

Health *Online*

Visit **health.glencoe.com** and complete the Interactive Study Guide for Lesson 4.

Lesson 4 Review

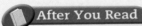 **After You Read**

Review this lesson for new terms, major headings, and Reading Checks.

What I Learned

1. *Vocabulary* What is a *chronic* disease?

2. *Identify* Name a noncommunicable disease triggered by an allergen.

3. *Describe* What are some ways of preventing cancer?

Thinking Critically

4. *Synthesize* Name some ways to keep your heart healthy and lessen the risks of heart disease.

5. *Compare* How are allergies and asthma similar? How are they different?

Applying Health Skills

6. *Communication Skills* Some diseases have similar symptoms. How can good communication skills help someone get the right treatment? Make a list of information you think is important to communicate to the doctor when you are sick.

Health *Online* For more review questions for Lesson 4, go to **health.glencoe.com**.

Lesson 4: Noncommunicable and Hereditary Diseases **287**

ASSESS

Assessment Resources

- Lesson Review Quiz
- *ExamView*
- Fast Files Activities
- Online Quizzes and Activities

Reteaching

- Assign Concept Map 11-4 or Reteaching Activity 11-4 in the Fast Files.
- Have students develop three questions about what they learned in the lesson and provide answers.

Enrichment

- Assign Enrichment Activity 11-4 in the Fast Files.
- Have students research ways that teens can change their lifestyles now to prevent heart disease later in life. Have students develop a lesson that could be used to teach students at their own grade level this information. Then have students share their lesson with the class and, if possible, with other classes at the same grade level.

CLOSE

Ask volunteers to name healthful behaviors that can help reduce the risk of developing cancer.

Lesson 4 Review Answers

1. A chronic disease is one that continues for a long time.
2. Allergies and asthma are diseases triggered by allergens.
3. Avoiding tobacco, the sun's UV rays, and cancer-causing substances are ways to reduce the risk of cancer.
4. Answers include getting regular physical activity; maintaining a healthy weight; eating foods high in fiber and low in salt, fat, and cholesterol; learning to manage stress; and avoiding tobacco products.
5. Allergies and asthma have some of the same triggers. They have different symptoms.
6. *Sample answers:* You should tell your doctor what activity caused the symptoms to start and how frequently the symptoms occur.

Building Health Skills

GOAL SETTING

Protecting Your Health

Protecting Your Health

SKILL
Goal Setting

Activating Prior Knowledge

Have students identify ways that an illness can change their daily routine.

- **Objective** After completing the activity, students will be able to use the steps of goal setting to manage an illness.
- **Time** 45 minutes
- **Materials** paper, pencil

Teacher Classroom Resources

📁 Building Health Skills
⬇ Transparency 1-5

Model

- Have students work individually to read about how Carly managed her illness and met her goal of trying out for the softball team. Ask: How did goal setting help Carly manage her illness? Sample answer: *Goal setting allowed Carly to continue an activity she enjoyed, despite her illness.*

DIRECTIONS

Goal Setting involves setting positive goals and taking steps to achieve them. This activity will give you the opportunity to develop and master this important health skill. Here's a guide to the different parts of this activity:

❶ In the **Model** section, you will read about a teen who performs the health skill successfully. This "model" scenario will show you how the skill is done.

❷ The **Practice** section will help guide you in practicing the skill.

❸ In the **Apply** section, you will have a chance to perform the skill on your own. You can use the Self-Check to check your work.

To complete this activity, first read the scenario presented in the Model. Then move on to the Practice. Finally, go ahead and try the Apply.

❶ Model

Carly set a goal to try out for the school softball team. By increasing her physical activity, Carly hopes to build up her lung endurance to help her better manage her asthma. Here are the steps Carly is taking to reach her goal.

1. **Set a specific goal.**

   I plan to try out for the school softball team.

2. **List the steps to reach your goal.**

   I will start practicing for 30 minutes at a time. Then gradually build up to 60 minutes as my lungs get stronger.

3. **Get help from others.**

   I will see my doctor to keep my asthma under control. I will ask a friend to practice with me after school.

4. **Evaluate your progress.**

   I will create an activity calendar to keep track of how often I am practicing.

288

National Health Standards Addressed
6.1, 6.2, 6.3

Teaching Tips

Setting Goals Successfully Discuss how following the goal-setting steps increases the likelihood of success. Link goal setting to both short-term and long-term goals, e,g. making a good grade on a test (short term) or doing well enough in school to be on the Honor Roll (long term).

Encouraging Students to Set Goals Explain to students that, as they get older, increasing interests and responsibilities means they will need to plan how to use their time wisely. Goal setting will help them stay focused on what really is important for them.

❷ Practice

Carly and Megan get hungry while doing homework at Carly's house after school. Read their conversation. Use what you know about disease prevention to answer the questions below.

Megan: I'm starving! Do you have any potato chips to snack on?

Carly: I do, but I would rather eat some fruit. I'm trying to develop good habits to help my body stay healthy.

Megan: That makes sense. What kind of fruit do you have?

1. What is Carly's new goal?
2. What is one step she is taking to reach this goal?
3. How does Megan's support help Carly with her goal?

Skill Summary
GOAL SETTING

- Set a specific goal.
- List the steps to reach your goal.
- Get help from others.
- Evaluate your progress.
- Reward yourself.

❸ Apply

Choose one of the diseases discussed in this chapter. Write a short story about a teen who sets a goal to prevent or manage the disease. Include details about the disease. List the steps the teen will take to reach the goal. Share your story with other classmates.

Self-Check

- Did the teen in my story set a clear, realistic goal?
- Does my story include details about my chosen disease?
- Does my story show how the teen will reach his or her goal?

Practice

- Have students work in pairs to complete the Practice activity.
- Go around the room and call on pairs of students to share their answers to the Practice questions.
- Lead a class discussion of the importance of a reward in celebrating the achievement of a goal.

Apply/Assess

- Have students work in pairs to complete the Apply activity.
- Allow 15 minutes for students to write their stories.
- After each pair of students shares its story with the class, lead a class discussion of other health skills that are useful in managing illness, for example, accessing information, stress management, and practicing healthful behaviors.
- You may wish to distribute the Building Health Skills Activity in the Fast Files. 📁

ASSESSMENT SCORING

Student work should meet all criteria to achieve the highest score:

Skills Student work identifies:
- a realistic fitness goal.
- steps to reach that goal.
- resources for help and support.

- checkpoints to evaluate progress.
- potential obstacles and ways to overcome them.
- a reward.

Concepts Student work includes:
- accurate health information.

TIME *health news*

Don't Panic!

Objectives

Students will be able to
- identify probable causes of some common symptoms.
- recognize warning signs of potentially serious medical problems.
- describe ways that emotions can affect physical health.

Motivator

Ask students to recall the symptoms they experienced the last time they were ill.

Teaching the Feature

- The article points out that stress and worry can be both the cause and the result of physical symptoms. Have students read the article. Ask for volunteers to read aloud sections of the article that show examples of each. **OL**
- Make a T-chart on the board. Label one side "Reliable" and the other side "Not Reliable." Ask: If you were experiencing the symptoms described in the reading, where could you get reliable information? Sample answers: *doctor, nurse, friends, Internet* As students supply answers, write them in the T-chart. Medical professionals should be placed under the heading "Reliable." Friends and the Internet should be placed under the heading "Not Reliable." **OL**

Don't PANIC!

Ever get a splitting headache or super-bad stomachache and feel convinced you have a deadly disease? Chances are those symptoms aren't life-threatening! So don't worry for no reason. Read this so you don't panic.

POUNDING HEADACHE

WORST NIGHTMARE
Brain tumor!

MORE LIKELY STORY
A migraine or a tension headache—up to 20 percent of all teens experience them regularly.

WHAT TO DO Take acetaminophen or ibuprofen. If headaches occur frequently (once a week), see your doctor, who can evaluate you. Your doctor might prescribe medicine or suggest relaxation methods.

WHEN TO WORRY Get to the emergency room if your headache is severe or accompanied by vomiting, vision changes, high fever, or numbness or tingling in your arms or legs.

HEART FLUTTERS

WORST NIGHTMARE
Heart attack!

MORE LIKELY STORY
Anxiety. When you're tense, stress hormones rise, which may cause your heart to race.

WHAT TO DO If it happens once or twice, don't worry. If it occurs more regularly, get it checked out. The cause could be anything from cold medicine to a thyroid problem.

WHEN TO WORRY See a doctor as soon as possible if your symptoms include shortness of breath or dizziness—that may mean a heart condition.

BELLY PAIN

WORST NIGHTMARE
Appendicitis!

MORE LIKELY STORY
Constipation. This can cause some teens to double over in pain.

WHAT TO DO Drink water (eight glasses a day) and eat fiber-rich foods, such as whole wheat bread.

WHEN TO WORRY Call your doctor right away if the pain is severe or accompanied by fever or vomiting. It could signal anything from food poisoning or a urinary-tract infection to—yes—appendicitis.

290

Activity | *Media, Technology, and Culture*

Media Read aloud the poem "Sick," by Shel Silverstein. Use the poem to start a discussion about the relationship between emotions and physical symptoms. Ask: What can you infer is causing the girl's symptoms? Sample answer: *dreading school* How do you know? Sample answer: *Her symptoms disappear when she realizes it is Saturday.* Have each student write a poem in any style that conveys the information in the article, including the symptoms, their likely causes, and warning signs of serious problems. Have students proofread and revise their poems.

Reading Review

FOLDABLES Study Organizer

Foldables™ and Other Study Aids Take out the Foldable™ that you created for Lesson 1 and any graphic organizers that you created for Lessons 1–4. Find a partner, and quiz each other using these study aids.

Lesson 1 What Causes Disease?

Key Ideas
- The two main types of disease are communicable and noncommunicable.
- The four common disease-causing organism groups are bacteria, viruses, protozoa, and fungi.

Vocabulary
- disease (p. 268)
- communicable diseases (p. 268)
- noncommunicable diseases (p. 269)
- pathogen (p. 269)
- viruses (p. 269)
- bacteria (p. 270)
- protozoa (p. 270)
- fungi (p. 270)

Lesson 2 Communicable Diseases

Key Ideas
- Pathogens are spread through direct contact, indirect contact, through impure food or unclean water, and contact with animals or insects.
- Barriers, such as the skin, tears, and the immune system help prevent your body from getting sick.

Vocabulary
- contagious (p. 272)
- infection (p. 274)
- immune system (p. 274)
- lymphocyte (p. 274)
- antibody (p. 274)
- immunity (p. 274)
- vaccine (p. 275)

Lesson 3 Understanding STDs

Key Ideas
- Sexually transmitted diseases are communicable diseases spread by sexual contact.
- HIV infection is spread through specific body fluids, including semen, fluid from the vagina, blood, and breast milk.
- You can protect yourself from STDs by choosing abstinence from high-risk behaviors.

Vocabulary
- sexually transmitted diseases (STDs) (p. 277)
- HIV (p. 278)
- AIDS (p. 278)
- abstinence (p. 280)

Lesson 4 Noncommunicable and Hereditary Diseases

Key Ideas
- Causes of various noncommunicable diseases include poor health habits, environment, heredity, and harm done by a communicable disease.
- You can keep your heart healthy by being physically active, maintaining a healthy weight, and managing stress.
- To avoid diseases like cancer and diabetes, you should avoid tobacco, protect yourself from the sun's UV rays, and maintain an active, healthful lifestyle.

Vocabulary
- chronic (p. 283)
- cancer (p. 284)
- tumor (p. 284)
- allergy (p. 285)
- asthma (p. 285)
- diabetes (p. 286)
- insulin (p. 286)

Assessment Resources

- 📁 Chapter 11 Summary and Activity
- 💿 Audio Summaries
- 📁 Reading Tutor
- 📁 Performance Assessment
- 📁 Chapter 11 Test
- 💿 *ExamView*
- 💿 Vocabulary PuzzleMaker
- 💿 Online Learning Center

Reading Review

Study Aids

- **Using the Dinah Zike Foldable™ Study Organizer** Have students use the Foldable™ to review the four main types of pathogens.

  FOLDABLES Study Organizer

Key Ideas

- **Use the Reading Checks** Have students work with a partner to review the answer to each of the Reading Checks found throughout the chapter.

Vocabulary Review

- **Vocabulary Notebook** Have students use a section of their notebooks to record the meaning of each chapter vocabulary term in their own words. At the conclusion of the chapter, have students review their vocabulary notebook entries.

Teaching Tips

Reviewing Main Ideas At the conclusion of each lesson, have students assess their comprehension of the material by reviewing the Focusing on the Main Ideas section found on the lesson opener page. For example, after reading Lesson 1, *What Causes Disease?*, students should be able to identify the two main categories of disease and recognize four common types of disease-causing organisms. At the conclusion of the chapter, students should review all of the Main Ideas in preparation for completing the Chapter Assessment.

Reviewing Vocabulary and Main Ideas

1. Communicable diseases
2. bacteria
3. viruses
4. infection
5. immune system
6. antibodies
7. True
8. False, reproductive system
9. False, AIDS
10. True
11. False, tumors
12. True

Thinking Critically

13. Both communicable and noncommunicable diseases are avoidable to a degree by adopting healthful behaviors. The causes of the two types of disease are different; communicable diseases are caused by pathogens and noncommunicable diseases are caused by heredity, environment, or lifestyle.

14. Answers will vary. Examples include living in areas of heavy smog causes lung cancer, sun exposure causes skin cancer, disease-carrying insects can cause illness.

Health *Online*

Have students visit **health.glencoe.com** to take the Chapter 11 Quiz.

292

After You Read

HEALTH QUIZ

Now that you have read the chapter, look back at your answers to the Health Quiz in the chapter opener. Would you change any of them? What would your answers be now?

Reviewing Vocabulary and Main Ideas

On a sheet of paper, write the numbers 1–7. After each number, write the term from the list that best completes each sentence.

- antibodies
- bacteria
- communicable diseases
- contagious
- immune system
- infection
- noncommunicable diseases
- vaccine
- viruses

Lesson 1 What Causes Disease?

1. _____ are diseases that can be spread, such as colds.
2. Extremely small single-celled organisms with no cell nucleus are called _____.
3. Tiny, nonliving particles that invade and take over healthy cells are known as _____.

Lesson 2 Communicable Diseases

4. A condition in which pathogens invade the body, multiply, and harm some of your body's cells is known as _____.
5. Your _____ is a group of cells and organs that fight disease.

6. Chemicals designed to fight a specific invading substance are called _____.

*On a sheet of paper, write the numbers 7–12. Write **True** or **False** for each statement. If the statement is false, change the underlined word or phrase to make it true.*

Lesson 3 Understanding STDs

7. Another name for STDs is <u>STIs</u>.
8. STDs can damage the <u>circulatory system</u>, making it impossible ever to have children.
9. When a person's T-cell count drops below 200, she or he likely has <u>hepatitis B</u>.

Lesson 4 Noncommunicable and Hereditary Diseases

10. A disease that is <u>chronic</u> continues for a long time.
11. Many cancers start out as masses of abnormal cells called <u>allergens</u>.
12. People with diabetes sometimes need shots of <u>insulin</u>, a hormone produced by the pancreas.

Thinking Critically

Using complete sentences, answer the following questions on a sheet of paper.

13. **Compare and Contrast** In what way are communicable and noncommunicable diseases alike? How are they different?

Health *Online* Visit health.glencoe.com and take the Online Quiz for Chapter 11.

HEALTH QUIZ Wrap-Up

Preventing Disease Have students look back at their responses to the Health Quiz. For each quiz question, have volunteers explain whether or not they would change their answer. Have the volunteers use information from the chapter to explain why their original answers were correct or incorrect.

14. **Evaluate** Explain how a person's environment can contribute to disease.

Write About It

15. **Practicing Healthful Behaviors** Write a journal entry describing the last time you were sick with a cold or flu. List some positive health behaviors you can practice to help prevent illness in the future.

16. **Analyzing Influences** Imagine that you are writing an article about a noncommunicable disease. Identify different factors that can cause this disease. Explain how to reduce the risk of developing a noncommunicable disease.

Career Corner

Medical Technologist Do you like looking at things under a microscope? Do you enjoy doing science experiments? If so, you might think about a career as a medical technologist. These professionals work in hospitals and laboratories. Their job is to test patients' blood and other tissues. This helps doctors diagnose and treat diseases. To do this job, you will need a four-year degree in medical technology or life sciences. Visit *Career Corner* at **health.glencoe.com** to learn more about this and other careers.

Standardized Test Practice

Reading

Read the passage and then answer the questions.

Edward Jenner (1749–1823)

Edward Jenner was a keen observer of nature from an early age. This would come in handy in guiding his life's work.

Jenner was born in England in 1749. He studied medicine and became a respected surgeon. During Jenner's time, a disease called smallpox was a leading cause of death. Scientists understood this was caused by a virus; however, no one knew how to prevent it from spreading.

Jenner noticed a similarity between symptoms of smallpox and another disease called cowpox. However, cowpox did not hurt humans. Jenner gave his gardener's son a shot containing a small amount of cowpox virus. Six weeks later, he gave the same person a shot containing smallpox virus. The person did not become sick. The first vaccine had been discovered!

1. The main idea of this passage is that
   A. Diseases can be deadly.
   B. Smallpox and cowpox are related.
   C. Edward Jenner discovered the first vaccine.
   D. Even the deadliest disease is eventually cured.

2. What trait helped Edward Jenner succeed in his most important life's work?
   A. His refusal to quit when the going got rough
   B. His stubbornness
   C. His powers of observation
   D. His dedication to his wife and family

Chapter 11 Assessment **293**

Write About It

15. **Personal or Descriptive Writing** Student journal entries will vary but should describe their last illness and explain prevention strategies, which may include avoiding close contact with people who are sick, washing hands often, eating healthful foods, and being physically active.

16. **Expository Writing** Explain to students that expository writing shares knowledge to help others understand. Student articles will vary, but should demonstrate an understanding of factors that influence noncommunicable diseases and ways to reduce the risk of developing a noncommunicable disease.

Standardized Test Practice

1. C
2. C

Career Corner

Medical Technologist Have students visit the Career Corner at **health.glencoe.com** to gather more information about a career as a medical technologist. Explain that students interested in a career as a medical technologist should enjoy working in a laboratory setting, keeping accurate and detailed records, and being part of a team.

Test-Taking Tips

Comprehending Concepts Explain to students that some questions based on a reading passage might require them to sum up the main idea of the entire passage. Remind students that finding the main idea of a passage requires reading and understanding the entire passage.

Question 1 of the Standardized Test Practice is an example of this type of question. Other questions ask students to look back to find a specific detail from the passage. Question 2 of the Standardized Test Practice is an example of this type of question.

CHAPTER 12 pp. 294–325	Standards		Skills and Activities
	National	State/Local	**HEALTH INVENTORY** *p. 295* **HANDS-ON HEALTH** Are You Earth Friedly? *p. 324* **BUILDING HEALTH SKILLS** *Advocacy* Reduce Waste, *pp. 322–323*
	National Health Education Standards 8.2, 8.4, 8.5		
Lesson 1 **Personal Safety Habits** pp. 296–299	National Health Education Standards 1.1, 1.4, 1.5, 1.6, 1.8, 5.2, 5.3, 7.1, 7.4, 7.5, 7.6, 8.2		**HEALTH SKILLS ACTIVITY** *Practicing Healthful Behaviors* Building Safe Habits, *p. 299*
Lesson 2 **Safety at Home and Away** pp. 300–304	National Health Education Standards 1.1, 1.4, 1.5, 1.6, 3.2, 3.4, 4.8, 5.1, 5.2, 5.3, 7.1, 7.4, 7.5, 7.6, 8.2, 8.4, 8.5		**DEVELOPING GOOD CHARACTER** Safety and Personal Responsibility, *p. 301* **HEALTH SKILLS ACTIVITY** *Advocacy* Fire Escape Plan, *p. 302*
Lesson 3 **Safety Outdoors** pp. 305–307	National Health Education Standards 1.1, 1.5, 1.6, 1.8, 5.3, 7.1, 7.4, 7.5, 7.6		
Lesson 4 **Safety in Severe Weather** pp. 308–311	National Health Education Standards 1.1, 1.5, 2.2, 3.2, 3.3, 7.1, 7.4, 7.5, 7.6		
Lesson 5 **First Aid for Emergencies** pp. 312–317	National Health Education Standards 1.1, 1.5, 1.6, 1.7, 3.2, 3.4, 3.6, 4.4, 5.1, 7.1, 7.4, 7.5, 7.6, 7.7, 8.4		
Lesson 6 **Protecting Your Environment** pp. 318–321	National Health Education Standards 1.1, 1.5, 1.6, 5.2, 5.3, 7.4, 7.6, 8.2, 8.4		**Connect To... SCIENCE** Alternate Energy Sources, *p. 319*

Planning Guide

StudentWorks™ Plus

Glencoe Exclusive!
TeacherWorks™
All-In-One Planner and Resource Center

Reproducible Resources	Assessment	Media and Technology
Chapter *FAST FILE* Resources Chapter Summaries and Activities REVIEW Building Health Skills Activity TEACH Performance Assessment Activity EXTEND Universal Access Activities TEACH Parent Letter and Activities **Student Activities Workbook** TEACH **Reading Tutor** TEACH	Building Health Skills Activity, *pp. 322–323* Chapter 12 Assessment, *pp. 326–327* **Chapter *FAST FILE* Resources** Performance Assessment Activity, *p. 4* Chapter 12 Test, *p. 7* 💿 *ExamView® Test Generator*	TeacherWorks™ includes: • Interactive Teacher Edition • Lesson Planner with Calendar • Access to all blackline masters • Correlations to standards 💿 StudentWorks™ Plus 📀 Online Student Edition Dinah Zike's Teaching Health with Foldables™
Chapter *FAST FILE* Resources Concept Mapping Activity 12–1 REVIEW Decision-Making Activity 12–1 EXTEND Enrichment Activity 12–1 EXTEND Lesson Plan 12–1 Guided Reading and Writing 12–1 TEACH Reteaching Activity 12–1 REVIEW	Lesson 1 Review, *p. 299* 📀 Vocabulary PuzzleMaker 💿 *ExamView® Test Generator*	📀 Vocabulary PuzzleMaker 💿 *ExamView® Test Generator* 💿 StudentWorks™ Plus 🔦 Transparency 12-1 📀 Health *Online*
Chapter *FAST FILE* Resources Concept Mapping Activity 12–2 REVIEW Cross-Curriculum Activity 12–2 TEACH Enrichment Activity 12–2 EXTEND Lesson Plan 12–2 Guided Reading and Writing 12–2 TEACH Reteaching Activity 2–2 REVIEW	Lesson 2 Review, *p. 304* 📀 Vocabulary PuzzleMaker 💿 *ExamView® Test Generator*	📀 Vocabulary PuzzleMaker 💿 *ExamView® Test Generator* 💿 StudentWorks™ Plus 🔦 Transparency 12-2 📀 Health *Online*
Chapter *FAST FILE* Resources Concept Mapping Activity 12–3 REVIEW Decision-Making Activity 12–3 TEACH Enrichment Activity 12–3 EXTEND Lesson Plan 12–3 Guided Reading and Writing 12–3 TEACH Reteaching Activity 2–3 REVIEW	Lesson 3 Review, *p. 307* 📀 Vocabulary PuzzleMaker 💿 *ExamView® Test Generator*	📀 Vocabulary PuzzleMaker 💿 *ExamView® Test Generator* 💿 StudentWorks™ Plus 🔦 Transparency 12-3 📀 Health *Online*
Chapter *FAST FILE* Resources Concept Mapping Activity 12–4 REVIEW Cross-Curriculum Activity 12–4 EXTEND Enrichment Activity 12–4 EXTEND Lesson Plan 12–4 Guided Reading and Writing 12–4 TEACH Reteaching Activity 12–4 REVIEW	Lesson 4 Review, *p. 311* 📀 Vocabulary PuzzleMaker 💿 *ExamView® Test Generator*	📀 Vocabulary PuzzleMaker 💿 *ExamView® Test Generator* 💿 StudentWorks™ Plus 🔦 Transparency 12-4 📀 Health *Online*
Chapter *FAST FILE* Resources Concept Mapping Activity 12–5 REVIEW Decision-Making Activity 12–5 TEACH Enrichment Activity 12–5 EXTEND Lesson Plan 12–5 Guided Reading and Writing 12–5 TEACH Reteaching Activity 12–5 REVIEW	Lesson 5 Review, *p. 317* 📀 Vocabulary PuzzleMaker 💿 *ExamView® Test Generator*	📀 Vocabulary PuzzleMaker 💿 *ExamView® Test Generator* 💿 StudentWorks™ Plus 🔦 Transparency 12-5 📀 Health *Online*
Chapter *FAST FILE* Resources Concept Mapping Activity 12–6 REVIEW Health Lab 12–6 EXTEND Enrichment Activity 12–6 EXTEND Lesson Plan 12–6 Guided Reading and Writing 12–6 TEACH Reteaching Activity 12–6 REVIEW	Lesson 6 Review, *p. 321* 📀 Vocabulary PuzzleMaker 💿 *ExamView® Test Generator*	📀 Vocabulary PuzzleMaker 💿 *ExamView® Test Generator* 💿 StudentWorks™ Plus 🔦 Transparency 12-6 📀 Health *Online*

First Aid and Babysitter Training

The American Red Cross is an excellent resource for those who are interested in learning more about first aid and community safety. Contact your local chapter of the American Red Cross to check the availability of the following classes, which may be of interest to your students:

- **Babysitter Training** This class is appropriate for young teens who care for younger siblings or work as babysitters. The curriculum includes information about first aid, safety, and dealing with emergencies.

- **Basic Aid Training** This class introduces young people to the basics of first aid and explains how to deal with emergency situations. The CHECK-CALL-CARE strategy is a part of this class.

- **Community First Aid and Safety** This class is a more in-depth look at responding to medical emergencies and performing basic first aid on infants, children, and adults. It is offered to older teens and adults.

Additional courses in CPR, automated external defibrillator use, sports safety, and pet first aid are available for adults and may be of interest to faculty and staff.

School Recycling Program

Use the information in this chapter as a springboard for students and staff to begin or expand your school's recycling program.

School recycling programs vary in scope. If your school does not currently recycle wastes, have a brainstorming session with students about the best way to begin. Develop a list of ideas, and arrange for a meeting with building administrators to get approval to implement the ideas. Consider the logistics of collecting and storing recyclables. Discuss recycling plans with the school custodians before starting a collection program.

Before beginning a recycling program, it is a good idea to determine which types of waste make up the bulk of the school's trash. Paper, glass, and aluminum are usually found in sufficient quantities to warrant collection and recycling.

If your school already has a recycling program in place, consider ways that it can be expanded. Consider adding items, for example, printer cartridges or plastics. Have students research composting to reduce school wastes. Although composting is not truly recycling, it reduces the amount of waste taken to the landfill, and may tie in with the science curriculum.

To maintain student motivation, consider holding grade-level competitions involving amounts of recycling. Contact the local media to see if they would consider writing an article about students' recycling efforts. Ask local businesses for incentives or rewards that can be used to encourage student participation in the recycling program.

Support for Teaching Reading

Reading Preview

Activating Background Vocabulary Ask students what comes to mind when they think of the words "accident," or "emergency". Write their responses on the board. Discuss appropriate responses to emergencies.

FOLDABLES | **Study Organizer** *Dinah Zike's Reading and Study Skills for Teen Health* provides interactive graphic organizers that help students comprehend and retain health concepts as they read. Use the Foldable™ on page 295 or find more Foldables™ activities for the chapter on **Safety and the Environment** the separate booklet, available in the TCR.

Lesson 1   Personal Safety Habits

Determining Main Ideas Have students restate the first heading in the lesson as a question, i.e. "What is important for **Staying Safe**?" Guide students to find the main idea of the first section: reducing your risk of accidental injury.

Lesson 2   Safety at Home and Away

Monitoring Comprehension Show students how to ask: "What is my purpose in reading this? The title of the section is **Safety at Home and Away**. My purpose must be to find out how to stay safe.

Lesson 3   Safety Outdoors

Listen-Read-Discuss Present the lesson in a brief lecture. Have students read silently. Stop students during reading and ask: "What do you understand most from what you have read so far?

Lesson 4   Safety in Severe Weather

Compare and Contrast Direct students to read about natural disasters and weather emergencies. Have students record facts about natural disasters in one column of their charts and weather emergencies in the other. Encourage students to compare their charts with a partner.

Lesson 5   First Aid for Emergencies

3-2-1 Strategy Ask students to write a brief summary identifying **three** key points they found while reading the lesson (what is CPR, first aid for bleeding, first aid for choking). Next, have students list **two** things in the lesson they thought were interesting. Finally, ask students to write **one** question they still have, and then find answers.

Lesson 6   Protecting Your Environment

Self-Questioning Model self questioning: "What is my purpose for reading this? The title of the section is **Air Pollution**. My purpose is to understand the dangers of polluted air." Have students write answers to their questions as they reread the section.

Post Reading

Informational Presentations Direct students togather more information on safety and environmental issues. Guide students to use speaking strategies effectively to convey meaning to the audience during an informational presentation.

Key for Using the Teacher Wraparound Edition

Use this key to help you identify the different types of prompts found in the **Teacher Wraparound Edition**.

R **Reading Strategies** activities help you teach reading skills and vocabulary.

C **Critical Thinking** strategies help students apply and extend what they have learned.

U **Universal Access** activities provide differentiated instruction for students learning to speak English, along with suggestions for teaching various types of learners.

HS **Health Skills Practice** activities reinforce Health Skills concepts and help students apply these skills in their everyday lives.

W **Writing Support** activities provide writing opportunities to help students comprehend the text.

AL **Active Learning** strategies provide a variety of activities for presenting lesson content, including Quick Demos and engaging classroom projects that get students actively involved.

Key to Ability Levels

Teaching Strategies and activities have been coded for ability level and appropriateness

AL Activities for students working above grade level

OL Activities for students working on grade level

BL Activities for students working below grade level

EL Activities for English Learners

Symbols

📠 Transparencies

💿 CD-ROM

🖱 health.glencoe.com

📁 Print Resources

Chapter at a Glance

Lesson 1 identifies the parts of the accident chain, describes ways of preventing accidental injuries, and explains good safety habits.

Lesson 2 explains how to prevent accidental injuries in the home, emphasizes advocacy for family fire escape plans, safety tips and rules of the road, and describes school and community safety.

Lesson 3 describes water safety, explains safety when hiking or camping, and describes safe decision-making skills.

Lesson 4 identifies types of weather emergencies, natural disasters, and explains how to prepare for these events.

Lesson 5 identifies strategies for responding to injuries, describes first aid measures.

Lesson 6 identifies the causes of air, water, and land pollution, and explains ways to protect the environment.

R Reading Strategy

Interpreting the Photo
Have students examine the photo. What health skills could these teens use to let others know the rules of water safety?
Sample answers: *advocacy, communication* OL

294

Chapter Preview

Lesson 1 **Personal Safety Habits** 296

Lesson 2 **Safety at Home and Away** 300

Lesson 3 **Safety Outdoors** 305

Lesson 4 **Safety in Severe Weather** 308

Lesson 5 **First Aid for Emergencies** 312

Lesson 6 **Protecting Your Environment** 318

Building Health Skills 322

Hands-on Health 324

Chapter Reading Review 325

Chapter Assessment 326

▲ *Working With the Photo*

R Observing rules of safety is important. **What is the role of a lifeguard?**

294

Universal Access

Differentiated Learning Glencoe provides teacher support and student materials for all learners in the health classroom.

● Spanish Glosario and chapter summaries for the English Language Learners.

● *Reading Tutor* and related worksheets support reluctant readers.

● Universal Access strategies throughout the Teacher Wraparound Edition and Fast Files help you present materials for gifted students, at-risk students, physically impaired students, and those with behavior disorders or learning disabilities.

Start-Up Activities

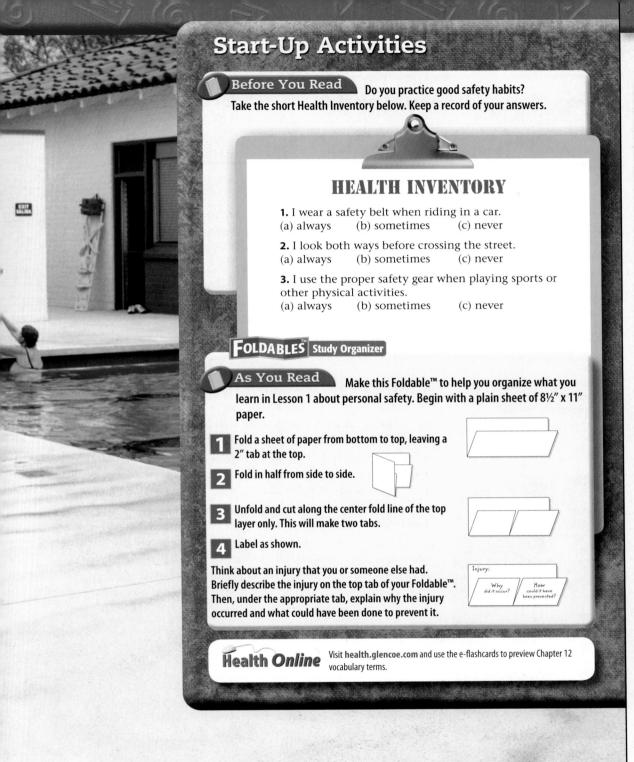

Before You Read Do you practice good safety habits? Take the short Health Inventory below. Keep a record of your answers.

HEALTH INVENTORY

1. I wear a safety belt when riding in a car.
(a) always   (b) sometimes   (c) never

2. I look both ways before crossing the street.
(a) always   (b) sometimes   (c) never

3. I use the proper safety gear when playing sports or other physical activities.
(a) always   (b) sometimes   (c) never

FOLDABLES Study Organizer

As You Read Make this Foldable™ to help you organize what you learn in Lesson 1 about personal safety. Begin with a plain sheet of 8½" x 11" paper.

1 Fold a sheet of paper from bottom to top, leaving a 2" tab at the top.

2 Fold in half from side to side.

3 Unfold and cut along the center fold line of the top layer only. This will make two tabs.

4 Label as shown.

Think about an injury that you or someone else had. Briefly describe the injury on the top tab of your Foldable™. Then, under the appropriate tab, explain why the injury occurred and what could have been done to prevent it.

Injury:
| Why did it occur? | How could it have been prevented? |

Health Online Visit **health.glencoe.com** and use the e-flashcards to preview Chapter 12 vocabulary terms.

295

HEALTH INVENTORY

Safety Habits This Health Inventory asks about the students' personal safety habits. Encourage students to honestly answer each of the questions. Assure students that they can keep their answers confidential. Tell students that they will have another chance to discuss the importance of each of the safety habits addressed in the Health Inventory after reading the chapter.

No Child Left Behind

Using Assessment Effectively

Have students look back over some of the projects they have completed throughout the year as a part of the health curriculum. Ask students to write a brief reflection on three of their favorite projects. Have students include the concepts they learned while working on the project, ways that those concepts could apply to their everyday life, and details they would like to learn about this topic in the future.

Health Online

Have students visit **health.glencoe.com** and complete the Health Inventory for Chapter 12.

FOLDABLES
Study Organizer **Dinah Zike Foldables™**

Organizing Information After students have completed the folding steps described in the student text, have them think of an injury they or someone they know has had. Have students record a brief description of the injury on the top tab of the Foldable™.

As students learn about the accident chain in Lesson 1, have them record information on why the injury occurred and ways that the injury could have been prevented. Have students record notes about Lesson 1 on the back of the Foldable™, including definitions of the lesson vocabulary terms. **BL**

FOCUS

Activating Prior Knowledge

What I Know Have students describe the steps of decision making. Tell students that Lesson 1 describes how good decision making can help them prevent accidents.

 Guide to Reading

BUILDING VOCABULARY

- Explain to students that the word *accidental* is an adjective, a word that can be used to modify or describe a noun. Have students relate this to the meaning of the term *accidental injuries*.
- Use Vocabulary PuzzleMaker to reinforce vocabulary terms.

READING STRATEGY

 Have students use their Foldables™ as they read Lesson 1.

- **Identifying Cause and Effect** As students read the lesson, remind them to make their lists of three events, or causes, of accidental injury.

uick Write

Before students begin writing, have them discuss healthy habits that can help them avoid injury. List the students' responses on the board. Have students refer to the list for ideas as they prepare their Quick Writes.

296

Personal Safety Habits

 Guide to Reading

● **Building Vocabulary**
Describe how the terms below are related. Write the correct definitions as you read them in the lesson.

- accident (p. 296)
- accidental injuries (p. 296)
- accident chain (p. 297)

● **Focusing on the Main Ideas**
In this lesson, you will be able to:

- **identify** the parts of the accident chain.
- **describe** ways of preventing accidental injuries.
- **practice** healthful behaviors to develop good safety habits.

● **Reading Strategy**
Identifying Cause-and-Effect List three events that can result in your accidental injury.

FOLDABLES Study Organizer Use the Foldable™ on p. 295 as you read the lesson.

Quick Write

Describe some good safety habits you practice at home.

◀ Some safety information is learned at an early age. **Why is it important to keep safety in mind as we grow older?**

Staying Safe

We all begin learning about safety when we are very young. A toddler who goes near a stove will be warned, "Don't touch! Hot!" Older children are told to look both ways before crossing the street. Learning about safety and practicing behaviors that will keep you safe can help prevent accidents from occurring. An **accident** is *an unexpected event that results in damage or harm.* Every day, thousands of people suffer **accidental injuries.** These are *injuries caused by unexpected events.*

Many accidents happen at or near home. Many involve ordinary, everyday activities, such as riding a bike. Why do accidents happen? How can you reduce your risk of accidental injury? How can you help others stay safe? In the pages ahead, you will find answers to these questions.

 **Reading Check** **Define** What are accidents?

Lesson 1 Resources

📁 **Chapter *FAST FILE* Resources**
Guided Reading and Writing 12-1
Concept Mapping Activity 12-1
Decision-Making Activity 12-1
Reteaching Activity 12-1
Enrichment Activity 12-1
Lesson Quiz 12-1

Technology
🔦 Transparency 12-1
💿 Audio Summaries
💿 *ExamView*
🖱 Vocabulary PuzzleMaker
💿 StudentWorks™ Plus

The Accident Chain

Many accidents can be prevented. They often occur because of an **accident chain,** *a sequence of events that often leads to an accidental injury.* **Figure 12.1** illustrates the links in the accident chain. For any accident to occur, three elements must be present. These are *the situation, the unsafe habit, and the unsafe act.* To understand the role each of these elements plays, consider Greg's accident:

- **The Situation.** Greg and Maria are throwing a football in their driveway. The ball lands on the garage roof.

AL

- **The Unsafe Habit.** Maria suggests getting a ladder. Greg says he will save time by climbing the tree next to the garage.

- **The Unsafe Act.** To reach the ball, Greg must lean out on a high, narrow branch. The branch snaps under Greg's weight and he falls.

The three elements leading to Greg's fall and the resulting injury form the accident chain.

▼ **FIGURE 12.1**

THE ACCIDENT CHAIN

R

Unsafe habits and acts can lead to accidental injury.
How could Greg have avoided getting hurt?

TEACH

AL Active Learning

Newspaper Story Have students write a newspaper story about a fictional accident. Students' articles should identify the three parts of the accident chain that led up to the accident. Have students proofread and correct their articles before turning them in. **OL**

R Reading Strategy

Analyzing a Graphic As students examine Figure 12.1, ask: How could Greg use decision making to avoid this accident? Sample answer: *By following the steps of the decision-making process, Greg may avoid an accident.* **OL**

Academic Vocabulary

Occur On this page, students learn reasons accidents occur. Tell students that *occur* is another word for *happen.* Have volunteers use the word *occur* in a sentence. **OL**

 Reading Check

Answer, p. 296 Accidents are unexpected events that result in damage or harm.

Caption Answers

Photo Caption, p. 296 Teens have increased responsibility for taking care of themselves and others.

Figure Caption Greg could have waited for his brother to get the ladder.

297

HEALTH LITERACY

The Toll of Accidental Injuries Students might not realize how common accidental injuries are among people in their age group in the United States. According to the Centers for Disease Control and Prevention (CDC), accidents cause more deaths of Americans under 35 than any other single cause. The number one cause of these injuries is automobile accidents. Students should be aware of the risks of riding with impaired or inexperienced drivers and the importance of always wearing a safety belt. Other injuries result from bicycle accidents, drowning, and sports injuries.

Health Skills Activity

Practicing Healthful Behaviors

Building Safe Habits

Have students read the feature on the next page. Then divide the class into four groups. Assign each group one of the bulleted safety tips. In their groups, have students use print and online resources to find out more about how that particular habit can help teens stay safe. Have each group prepare a short presentation to share its findings with the class. Then have each group make a list of other safety habits, as directed in the On Your Own activity. Have each group share its list with the class.

AL Active Learning

Role-Plays Have students work in pairs to write and rehearse a role-play that demonstrates a teen saying no to a risky behavior that could cause an accident. The script should identify reasons for saying no to the behavior. Have volunteers perform their role-plays for the class. **OL**

 Reading Check

Answer *Sample answer:* I could break the accident chain by wearing a helmet when bicycling.

Caption Answer

Photo Caption *Sample answer:* I play football, which requires a helmet, pads, and a mouth guard.

298

▶ Wearing the right gear can prevent accidental injury. **What sport or activity do you like? What kind of protective gear is worn in this sport or activity?**

How to Prevent Accidental Injuries

AL You can reduce the risk of accidental injury by practicing positive health behaviors. Many accidents can be prevented by simply breaking the accident chain. By removing or changing any one link, you can stop an accident from happening. Look back at Greg's accident chain.

Greg could have changed the situation. He and his brother could have played ball in a more open area. Greg could have also broken the second link—the unsafe habit. Instead of climbing the tree, he should have waited for the ladder. Finally, Greg could have changed the unsafe action. When he saw he could not reach the ball, he should have stopped trying. He should have climbed back down and gone for the ladder or asked an adult for help.

Health Online

Visit **health.glencoe.com** and complete the Interactive Study Guide for Lesson 1.

 **Reading Check** **Give Examples** Give an example of how to prevent an injury by breaking the accident chain.

298 Chapter 12: Safety and the Environment

What Teens Want to Know

Do I really need a helmet? According to the Youth Risk Behavior Survey carried out by the CDC, between 80 and 90 percent of teens rarely or never wear bicycle helmets when riding a bike. However, bicycle helmets have been shown to reduce the risk of brain injury during a cycling accident. In fact, some studies predict that more than 85 percent of the brain injuries suffered by cyclists could be prevented by helmets. Have students discuss reasons why teens are reluctant to wear bicycle helmets. Then have students research and report on the serious effects of brain injury. **OL**

Health Skills Activity

Practicing Healthful Behaviors

Building Safe Habits

As teens become more independent, it is important to develop good safety habits. This includes being careful, thinking ahead, and taking precautions. The following are some additional good safety habits.

- Stay away from risky behaviors. Choose not to participate in unsafe activities.
- Resist negative peer pressure. Do not give in to friends who want you to take careless chances.
- Know your limits. Do not attempt to do more than you can do safely. If you just learned how to snowboard, for example, don't go down a hill more difficult than you can handle.
- Wear proper protective gear when playing sports or other physical activities. Before beginning a new sport or activity, find out what protective gear you will need.

On Your Own

Make a list of other safety habits. Explain how these safety habits can prevent accidental injury. Share your list with the class.

ASSESS

Assessment Resources

Lesson Review Quiz
- *ExamView*
- Fast Files Activities
- Online Quizzes and Activities

Reteaching

- Assign Concept Map 12-1 or Reteaching Activity 12-1 in the Fast Files.
- Have students work in pairs to review the steps of the accident chain. Then ask random pairs of students to name the three elements of the accident chain that lead up to common accidents.

Enrichment

- Assign Enrichment Activity 12-1 in the Fast Files.
- Have each student write a paragraph identifying one specific risk behavior that can cause teens to have accidents, and describing, in detail, health skills that can help teens avoid that particular risk behavior.

CLOSE

Call on students to name healthful habits that can help prevent accidents.

Lesson 1 Review

 After You Read

Review this lesson for new terms, major headings, and Reading Checks.

What I Learned

1. *Vocabulary* What are *accidental injuries*?

2. *List* What three elements must be present for an accident to occur?

3. *Recall* How can many accidents be prevented?

Thinking Critically

4. *Apply* Grant's friend dared him to walk across a narrow 12-foot-high fence. What should Grant do, and why?

5. *Evaluate* Why is it important to know your limitations?

Applying Health Skills

6. *Decision Making* Tina wants to go bike riding with a friend, but she left her helmet in her Dad's truck. What are Tina's options? Use the decision-making process to help Tina make a safe decision.

Health Online For more review questions for Lesson 1, go to **health.glencoe.com**.

Lesson 1: Personal Safety Habits **299**

Lesson 1 Review Answers

1. Accidental injuries are injuries caused by unexpected events.
2. the situation, the unsafe habit, the unsafe act
3. Many accidents can be prevented by simply breaking the accident chain.

4. Answers should include advising Grant to resist because accepting the dare could lead to personal injury.
5. *Sample answer:* Knowing your limits helps you avoid taking risks or trying activities beyond your skill level.

6. Students should apply the steps of decision making to come to the conclusion that Tina should not ride her bike without her helmet.

FOCUS

Activating Prior Knowledge

What I Know Ask students to identify hazards in their home, school, and community. Tell students that this lesson will help them identify additional hazards and will describe safety rules to help them avoid these hazards.

Guide to Reading

BUILDING VOCABULARY

- Tell students that the word part *ped-* means "foot." Have students use this information to infer the meaning of the word *pedestrian* (someone traveling on foot, someone walking).
- Use Vocabulary PuzzleMaker to reinforce vocabulary terms.

READING STRATEGY

Compare Ask students to review the chapter and note a similarity and a difference in the described safety procedures. Then go around the room and ask students to share their answers.

Quick Write

After students have completed their Quick Writes, have volunteers share their writing with the class. Have students note different safety rules associated with different ways of getting to school.

Safety at Home and Away

Guide to Reading

● Building Vocabulary
Copy the terms below into your notebook. Circle those terms that help you maintain personal safety.

- hazards (p. 300)
- smoke alarm (p. 302)
- fire extinguisher (p. 302)
- pedestrians (p. 303)
- Neighborhood Watch program (p. 304)

● Focusing on the Main Ideas
In this lesson, you will be able to:

- **explain** how to prevent accidental injuries in your home.
- **practice** the skill of advocacy to help family members develop a fire escape plan.
- **identify** safety tips and rules of the road.
- **describe** how to be safe in your school and community.

● Reading Strategy
Compare Preview the lesson. Explain ways in which the various safety procedures described are similar. How are they different?

Quick Write

List two or three safety rules you follow on your way to and from school.

Safety at Home

Home is a place where everyone should feel safe and comfortable. Yet, homes can contain **hazards,** *possible sources of harm.* Stairways, for example, can lead to falls. Appliances can cause shocks. Following safety rules can reduce the risks of home hazards.

▶ Use a step ladder to reach an item on a high shelf. **How does this safety habit help prevent injury?**

Lesson 2 Resources

📁 **Chapter *FAST FILE* Resources**
Guided Reading and Writing 12-2
Concept Mapping Activity 12-2
Cross-Curriculum Activity 12-2
Reteaching Activity 12-2
Enrichment Activity 12-2
Lesson Quiz 12-2

Technology
⚓ Transparency 12-2
 Audio Summaries
💿 *ExamView*
 Vocabulary PuzzleMaker
💿 StudentWorks™ Plus

▶ Picking up toys that are left on the stairs can help prevent falls. **What other ways can you help prevent accidents in the home?**

Kitchen Safety

More accidents happen in the kitchen than any other room in the house. Here are some ways to reduce the risk of injury. To avoid cutting yourself, learn to handle knives correctly. Keep your fingers clear of the blade. Don't leave food cooking on the stove unattended. Turn pot handles inward, away from the edge. Keep small children away from the stove. Wipe up any spills right away.

Preventing Falls

To prevent falls, keep stairways well lighted and free of clutter. Keep loose objects off the floor, where they might be tripped over. Rugs should be fastened down firmly. When reaching for items on high shelves, use a sturdy ladder or step stool. Never stand on a chair. Avoid running on wet or waxed floors.

AL

Electrical Safety

In order to avoid electrical hazards, always pull plugs out by the plug itself. Never tug on the cord, which can damage it. If a cord does become frayed, don't use the appliance until it is repaired. Unused outlets should be covered in homes where there are small children. Keep electrical appliances away from water, and never use them if your skin is wet or if you are in a bathtub.

Gun Safety

If guns are kept in the home, they should always be stored in locked cabinets. Store ammunition separately. Never handle a gun without an adult present. Never point a gun at a live target.

DEVELOPING Good Character

Safety and Personal Responsibility

Being responsible includes looking out for the well-being of others. You can start doing this at home right now. Pick up an object you see lying on the floor where someone might trip over it. This can prevent someone you care about from being injured. **What other actions can you take to show responsibility for your safety or the safety of others?**

Lesson 2: Safety at Home and Away **301**

🏘 Home, School, and Community

At Home Access to guns by children and teens is a risk factor for both intentional and unintentional injury. Guns are found in 30 to 40 percent of American homes. A study in the *Journal of the American Medical Association* found that when guns kept in the home were stored unloaded, in a locked container, and away from ammunition, the risk of injury to children and teens in the home was reduced by 70 percent. Students should be familiar with guidelines for gun safety, including never handling a gun without an adult present and never aiming a gun at anyone. **OL**

Health Skills Activity

Advocacy

Fire Escape Plan

Have students read the information about creating a fire escape plan for their family. Have each student prepare a written plan specific to their home and family. To respect students' privacy, do not ask students to share their plans with the class. Remind students to share their plan with their family and to practice the plan so each family member knows what to do in case of fire. **OL**

U Universal Access

Learning Disabled Review with students the "stop, drop, and roll" strategy. If possible, find a poster that shows this technique so that students can visualize each step. **BL**

> **Reading Check**
>
> **Answer** Clutter on the floor and frayed electrical cords are two hazards in the home.

Academic Vocabulary

Disposing On this page, a safe way of disposing of matches is described. Ask a volunteer to define the term *dispose* (to get rid of). Then have students use the term *dispose* in a written sentence. **OL**

Health Skills Activity

Advocacy

Fire Escape Plan

Having an escape plan can help your family prevent injuries or death in the event of a fire. Choose the nearest exit from your home. This may be a first-floor window, as well as a door. Have a back-up exit in case the first is blocked. All family members should know the route to exits from their bedroom. Make to sure to have an outdoor meeting place. This is where everyone is to gather upon getting out safely. That way, you will know if a member is trapped inside. If this is the case, let the fire department rescue the person. Never go back inside a burning building for any reason.

On Your Own

With your family, create an escape plan for your home. Practice your escape plan until every family member knows what to do in the event of a fire.

Fire Safety

To prevent fires, always make sure matches are out before disposing of them. Keep these and cigarette lighters out of reach of small children. Never leave candles burning unattended. In addition, each level of your house should have a **smoke alarm,** *a device that makes a warning noise when it senses smoke.* Replace the batteries in your smoke alarms twice a year to keep them working properly.

It is also a good idea to keep a **fire extinguisher** in the kitchen. This is *a device which releases chemicals that smother flames.* Smother grease fires with a pot lid or baking soda if there is no fire extinguisher. Never use water. Water will cause the burning grease to explode, creating more fire or burning you.

In the event of a major fire, leave the building immediately. Never try to put it out yourself or stop to gather possessions. **U** Every second counts. Make sure your family has an escape route. If your clothes catch fire, remember to *stop, drop, and roll.* First, *stop* moving. If you run, the rush of air will fan the flames. Then *drop* to the floor and *roll* to smother the flames.

> **Reading Check** 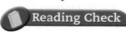 **Give Examples** Give two examples of hazards in the home.

✷ Promoting Coordinated School Health

Fire Safety Education Regular fire drills are one important aspect of school fire safety. Education about fire safety as a part of the curriculum is an important component of coordinated school health. The student text provides information about safety during a fire in the home. Extend the content by reviewing school fire safety. Have students review the school's fire safety policies. Then have students develop a skit to demostrate fire safety in the school building that they could perform for the school or for younger students. **OL**

▼ FIGURE 12.2

R

RULES OF ROAD SAFETY

Eighty-three percent of all traffic accidents occur within 20 miles of home. How can you help prevent accidents while riding your bike on the road?

Rules of the Road

- Ride your bike with the traffic flow, and obey traffic rules and signals.
- Never weave in and out of traffic.
- When riding with a friend, ride in single file, not abreast.
- Be aware of others. Always watch for cars and pedestrians.
- Be visible to others. Wear bright, reflective clothes. Make sure your bike has lights and reflectors.

Tips for Personal Safety

- When riding in a motor vehicle, use your safety belt.
- When riding a bike, skating, or riding a scooter, use safety gear. These include a helmet, pads, and gloves.
- Don't skate or ride a scooter after dark.
- Avoid riding or skating on wet, dirty, or uneven surfaces.
- Wear pants that won't catch in a bicycle chain.
- Keep your speed under control. When skating, know how to stop and fall properly.

Safety on the Road

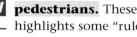

Safety on the road applies to drivers, passengers, and **pedestrians.** These are *people traveling on foot.* **Figure 12.2** highlights some "rules of the road" and other safety practices.

Reading Check **Give Examples** Name one *do* and one *don't* safety road tip.

Safety at School

Schools should be places for students to learn and develop physical, mental/emotional, and social skills. Sometimes, though, violence can occur at school. Knowing strategies to prevent violence can help you maintain your personal health and stay safe in school.

Preventing School Violence

Many schools are taking action to prevent violence. Some are using peer mediation and crisis prevention programs. Others are conducting programs that teach students to respect others. Health education classes that teach conflict resolution are helping curb school violence. Many schools

▼ Some schools now have metal detectors to make sure weapons are not brought in. **Does your school have these safety procedures? Do you agree that they should be in place?**

R Reading Strategy

Analyzing a Chart Direct students' attention to Figure 12.2, which lists rules for road safety. Ask: What additional tips for road safety would you add to these lists? Sample answer: *Passengers in a motor vehicle should take care not to distract the driver.* OL

W Writing Support

Persuasive Writing Have students write a persuasive paragraph explaining to other teens why following safety rules when bicycling is important. Remind students that persuasive writing involves stating a position on a topic and using facts to support the position. Remind students to proofread their work before turning it in. OL

Reading Check

Answer *Sample answers:* Do wear reflective clothing. Don't weave in and out of traffic.
Answer, p. 304 One way that both schools and communities increase safety is by increasing the presence of police or security officers.

Caption Answers

Figure Caption Obeying local traffic rules and riding with traffic can help prevent accidents when riding a bike on the road.
Photo Caption *Sample answer:* Yes, my school has metal detectors. I agree with this policy.
Photo Caption, p. 304 Curfews are another measure taken to increase safety.

Dealing with Sensitive Issues

Weapons at School School safety is a concern for students, parents, and teachers. According to the CDC, more than 6 percent of high school students have carried a weapon to school. It is important to review with students the appropriate actions to take if they find out that a friend or acquaintance has a weapon at school. Remind students that they should always contact a teacher or staff member immediately if they learn of a weapon in the school. Tell students that being a good friend does not mean keeping a secret about a weapon. OL

303

ASSESS

Reteaching

- Assign Concept Map 12-2 or Reteaching Activity 12-2 in the Fast Files.
- Have students make a written list of tips for safety at home. Go around the room and have students describe ways to implement one of the tips.

Enrichment

- Assign Enrichment Activity 12-2 in the Fast Files.
- Have students do further research about preventing school violence. Then have each student prepare a short written report summarizing their findings.

CLOSE

Ask for volunteers to describe one aspect of an effective fire escape plan.

▲ Neighborhood Watch programs are one measure for keeping communities safe. **What are some other anti-crime measures?**

Health *Online*

Visit **health.glencoe.com** and complete the Interactive Study Guide for Lesson 2.

---

now have police or security officers present. Some schools have metal detectors, to detect weapons brought to school. You can help too. One way is by never carrying a weapon. Alert school officials if you know, or suspect, someone has a weapon.

Safety in the Community

Schools are not alone in facing crime and violence. Many communities are struggling with the same problems. Some have passed laws against guns. They have also made the punishments for violent crimes stricter. In many areas, people have formed **Neighborhood Watch programs.** These are *programs in which residents are trained to identify and report suspicious activity.* Communities may also try to protect teens by setting curfews. Drug-free zones and after-school and summer programs have also been enacted.

You can help protect yourself against dangerous situations. Walk with purpose to and from your home. Travel with another person or in a group, whenever possible. Avoid taking shortcuts through unfamiliar or unsafe areas.

 **Reading Check**

Compare How are the actions being taken to make schools safer similar to those that make communities safer.

Lesson 2 Review

 After You Read

Review this lesson for new terms, major headings, and Reading Checks.

What I Learned

1. *Recall* Where should smoke alarms be placed in the home?

2. *Describe* What are two ways of making yourself safe when riding your bike?

3. *Vocabulary* What is a *Neighborhood Watch program?*

Thinking Critically

4. *Explain* In what ways is a cluttered room a hazard?

5. *Analyze* Why do you think there is debate on whether metal detectors should be in schools?

Applying Health Skills

6. *Conflict Resolution* Using the T.A.L.K. strategy, write a dialogue between two teens who are trying to resolve a conflict without using violence.

Health *Online* For more review questions for Lesson 2, go to **health.glencoe.com**.

Lesson 2 Review Answers

1. There should be one smoke detector on every level of the home.
2. Answers include any two of the following: wearing a helmet; avoiding wet, dirty, or uneven surfaces; wearing pants that will not catch in the chain; and keeping your speed under control.
3. Resident volunteers undergo training to identify and report suspicious activity.
4. *Sample answer:* It could cause falls and injuries.
5. Answers will vary, but should mention school safety vs. personal rights and freedoms.
6. Answers should include the steps of the T.A.L.K. strategy and a peaceful resolution.

Safety Outdoors

 Guide to Reading

● **Building Vocabulary**
In your notebook, write the term below. See if you can guess its meaning based on the root *therm-*, which means temperature.
■ hypothermia (p. 306)

● **Focusing on the Main Ideas**
In this lesson, you will be able to:
■ **describe** what you need to know for water safety.
■ **explain** safety when hiking or camping.
■ **practice** decision-making skills to make safe choices.

● **Reading Strategy**
Finding the Main Idea For each main heading in this lesson, write one sentence that states the main idea.

Staying Safe Outdoors

Do you enjoy swimming or boating? How about hiking or camping? These and other outdoor activities are more fun when you "play it safe."

Factors in your environment can affect your personal health. Before scheduling any outing, plan ahead. Check the weather forecast and make sure you have the proper safety gear for each activity. Be aware of your skills and abilities. Remember to wear sunscreen and bug protection.

Water Safety

Water activities can be a lot of fun. To avoid injury, you should learn and follow water safety rules. Know how to swim well. Good swimmers are less likely to panic in an emergency. Even good swimmers, however, should never swim alone. They should always use the "buddy system." Agree with one or more people to know each other's whereabouts. Go to beaches or pools that have lifeguards. Always know the water depth before entering—especially diving. Never dive into shallow water.

 **uick Write**

Write a short paragraph about your favorite outdoor activity. Include two or three sentences on how to be safe when doing this activity.

▼ Water activities and sports can be fun. **What can you do to make them safe as well?**

 Lesson 3 Resources

Chapter *FAST FILE* Resources
Guided Reading and Writing 12-3
Concept Mapping Activity 12-3
Decision-Making Activity 12-3
Reteaching Activity 12-3
Enrichment Activity 12-3
Lesson Quiz 12-3

Technology
Transparency 12-3
Audio Summaries
ExamView
Vocabulary PuzzleMaker
StudentWorks™ Plus

FOCUS

Activating Prior Knowledge

What I Know Ask students to identify outdoor activities that they enjoy. List their responses on the board. Then ask volunteers to describe safety tips for these activities.

 Guide to Reading

BUILDING VOCABULARY
■ Have students review the lesson for the meaning of the word *hypothermia*. Then have students name other weather-related hazards (frostbite, heat exhaustion).
■ Use Vocabulary PuzzleMaker to reinforce vocabulary terms.

READING STRATEGY
Finding the Main Idea Encourage students to write the main idea of each section in their own words.

uick Write

Have students use the list of activities and safety tips that were generated in the Activating Prior Knowledge activity as ideas for their Quick Writes.

Academic Vocabulary

Appropriate Page 306 mentions the importance of wearing clothing appropriate for the weather. Tell students that *appropriate* means "suitable." Have students make a list of clothing that is appropriate for a variety of weather conditions. **OL**

TEACH

Reading Strategy

Analyzing a Graphic Have students examine the steps for drowning prevention shown in Figure 12.3. Ask: Why is this technique recommended only for warm water? *In cold water, this technique causes the body to lose heat too quickly.* Note that conserving energy allows you to stay afloat until help arrives. **OL**

AL Active Learning

Game Show Have students work in small groups to develop a list of 10 game-show style questions about water safety or safety on the trail. Then have each group ask its questions for the remainder of the class to answer. **OL**

Reading Check

Answer *Sample answer:* Using the buddy system and going to beaches with lifeguards are two ways to stay safe in the water.

Caption Answers

Photo Caption, p. 305
Wearing a life jacket can help you stay safe during water sports.
Figure Caption, p. 306
Conserving energy allows you to stay afloat until help arrives.
Photo Caption, p. 307 The right equipment, including extra socks, food, and water can make a trip safer.

306

▼ FIGURE 12.3

R **DROWNING PREVENTION**

The technique shown here can help you stay afloat in warm water. In cold water, tread water slowly or float on your back to save energy. **Why is it important to conserve energy while waiting for help?**

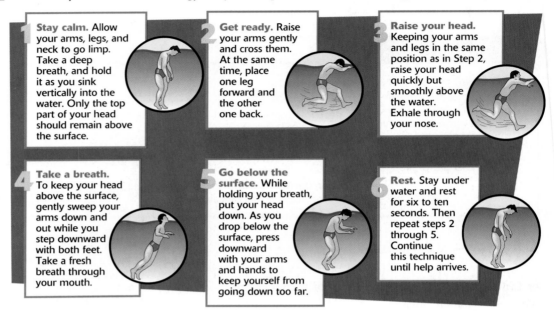

1 **Stay calm.** Allow your arms, legs, and neck to go limp. Take a deep breath, and hold it as you sink vertically into the water. Only the top part of your head should remain above the surface.

2 **Get ready.** Raise your arms gently and cross them. At the same time, place one leg forward and the other one back.

3 **Raise your head.** Keeping your arms and legs in the same position as in Step 2, raise your head quickly but smoothly above the water. Exhale through your nose.

4 **Take a breath.** To keep your head above the surface, gently sweep your arms down and out while you step downward with both feet. Take a fresh breath through your mouth.

5 **Go below the surface.** While holding your breath, put your head down. As you drop below the surface, press downward with your arms and hands to keep yourself from going down too far.

6 **Rest.** Stay under water and rest for six to ten seconds. Then repeat steps 2 through 5. Continue this technique until help arrives.

When boating or waterskiing, wear a life jacket at all times. If the water is cold, wear a wetsuit. This will protect you against developing **hypothermia** (hy·poh·THER·mee·uh). This is *a sudden and dangerous drop in body temperature.* If you ever feel you are in danger of drowning, stay calm. Call for help and use the technique shown in **Figure 12.3.**

Reading Check  **Explain** What are some ways to stay safe in the water?

AL Safety on the Trail

Whether you hike or camp, having the right gear and equipment will help you prevent illness or injury. For hiking, gear should include sturdy, well-cushioned shoes. If shoes are new, break them in a few days before using them to hike. Wearing two pairs of socks can help prevent blisters. Bring enough fresh water and food to last through your trip. Be sure to bring food that won't spoil. You should also wear clothing appropriate for the weather and the season.

🏠 Home, School, and Community

In the Community Knowing how to swim is one of the best ways to stay safe near water. Provide students with information about resources in the community for those who would like to learn how to swim. Lessons may be available at a community center or other exercise facility. The American Red Cross sponsors swim classes in many communities; information is available from your local Red Cross chapter. The school nurse or physical education teacher may also have resources that you can share with your students.

◀ Planning out your trip can make it safer and more fun. **What are some specific things you should take on a hike?**

Reading Check

Answer flashlight and batteries, a cell phone, a compass, and a first-aid kit

When you go hiking or camping, make sure someone knows your destination and expected date and time of return. Bring a cell phone or walkie-talkie in case of emergency. Other necessary items include a compass and a flashlight to prevent you from getting lost. Bring along extra flashlight batteries too. Also, bring a first-aid kit in case of minor injuries on the trail.

Reading Check

Identify What safety items should you bring with you on a hike or camping trip?

Health Online

Visit **health.glencoe.com** and complete the Interactive Study Guide for Lesson 3.

ASSESS

Assessment Resources

Lesson Review Quiz
● *ExamView*
📁 Fast Files Activities
● Online Quizzes and Activities

Reteaching

● Assign Concept Map 12-3 or Reteaching Activity 12-3 in the Fast Files. 📁
● Have students make a poster with a list that outlines water safety rules.

Enrichment

● Assign Enrichment Activity 12-3 in the Fast Files. 📁
● Have students do further research on safety for hikers and campers. Then have students make a brochure that lists safety tips for these activities.

CLOSE

Ask volunteers to describe how weather can be a hazard for those participating in outdoor activities. Then have students name weather-related safety tips.

Lesson 3 Review

After You Read

Review this lesson for new terms, major headings, and Reading Checks.

What I Learned

1. *Recall* What is the buddy system? Why is it important?

2. *Vocabulary* What is *hypothermia*?

3. *List* Name two ways of staying safe during water activities.

Thinking Critically

4. *Apply* Larissa is going for a short hike by herself. What safety precautions should she take before she leaves?

5. *Analyze* Suppose you are swimming in the ocean when you realize you have gone farther than you should. You don't feel you have enough energy left to swim back. What should you do?

Applying Health Skills

6. *Decision Making* You are looking forward to going out on a friend's boat. The weather forecast is for thunderstorms. Use the decision-making process to help you decide what to do.

Health Online For more review questions for Lesson 3, go to **health.glencoe.com**.

Lesson 3: Safety Outdoors **307**

Lesson 3 Review Answers

1. The buddy system is an agreement that two swimmers will keep track of each other and help if one of the swimmers starts to have problems.

2. Hypothermia is a dangerous drop in body temperature.

3. *Sample answers:* learn to swim, use the buddy system, and never dive in shallow water

4. Larissa should tell someone her plans and bring the following: water, food, a cell phone or walkie-talkie, a compass, a flashlight, and a first-aid kit.

5. You should stay calm, try to get the attention of someone on shore, go into drowning prevention mode.

6. Students' responses should indicate that they would not go.

FOCUS

Activating Prior Knowledge

What I Know Ask students to describe a weather-related hazard they learned about in Lesson 3. Tell students that this lesson will describe ways to stay safe in many weather-related situations.

 Guide to Reading

BUILDING VOCABULARY

■ Have students write a sentence that shows how two of the lesson vocabulary terms are related.
■ Use Vocabulary PuzzleMaker to reinforce vocabulary terms.

READING STRATEGY

Compare and Contrast Have students record differences between weather emergencies and natural disasters as they read the lesson. Then have volunteers describe some of the differences they noted.

Quick Write

Have students share their completed Quick Writes with the class. Start a list on the board of suggestions for emergency preparedness using tips from the students' Quick Writes.

308

Lesson 4

Safety in Severe Weather

Guide to Reading

● **Building Vocabulary**
In your notebook, write what you know about each term below. Correct any definitions as you read the lesson.

■ natural disasters (p. 308)
■ hurricane (p. 309)
■ frostbite (p. 310)
■ tornado (p. 310)
■ earthquake (p. 311)

● **Focusing on the Main Ideas**
In this lesson, you will be able to

■ **identify** types of weather emergencies and natural disasters.
■ **recognize** how to prepare for weather emergencies and natural disasters.

● **Reading Strategy**
Compare and Contrast As you read, keep notes on the differences between weather emergencies and natural disasters.

Quick Write

Name weather emergencies common in your area. List two or three things your family does to prepare for these emergencies.

Weather Emergencies and Natural Disasters

Different parts of the country are more likely to experience different kinds of weather emergencies. These include thunderstorms, flooding from rains, hurricanes, tornadoes, and earthquakes. Some of these weather emergencies can cause **natural disasters.** These are *events caused by nature that result in widespread damage, destruction, and loss.*

Being prepared for either type of event will reduce the risk of injury. Make sure your family has an emergency kit. **Figure 12.4** shows some items that belong in such a kit. There should be enough supplies to last a family three days.

▶ **FIGURE 12.4**

EMERGENCY SUPPLY KIT

R An emergency supply kit should contain the items shown here. Does your family maintain a supply kit?

 Lesson 4 Resources

📁 **Chapter FAST FILE Resources**
Guided Reading and Writing 12-4
Concept Mapping Activity 12-4
Cross-Curriculum Activity 12-4
Reteaching Activity 12-4
Enrichment Activity 12-4
Lesson Quiz 12-4

Technology
🔋 Transparency 12-4
🎧 Audio Summaries
⚙ *ExamView*
🎧 Vocabulary PuzzleMaker
⚙ StudentWorks™ Plus

In some emergencies, you may be instructed to leave your home. If this happens, you should take your supplies with you. You should also bring money and any prescription medicines family members need.

Thunderstorms

Thunderstorms can be frightening sometimes. A *thunderstorm* is a heavy rainstorm accompanied by strong winds, lightning, and thunder. They can occur during any season, though they are more common during warm weather. Lightning is the most dangerous part of a thunderstorm. It is caused by clouds releasing stored-up electrical energy.

Danger from lightning is greatest when you are in or near water. Whenever you see lightning or hear thunder, seek shelter.

If you are indoors, stay there. Do not use the telephone, unless it is a cordless or cell phone. If you are outdoors, look for the nearest building. An alternative is an enclosed metal vehicle with the windows completely shut. If you are in an open field with no shelter nearby, lie down. Wait for the storm to pass. Avoid all metal objects including electric wires, fences, machinery, motors, and power tools. Unsafe places include underneath canopies, small picnic or rain shelters, or near trees.

Reading Check **Explain** What causes lightning?

Hurricanes

A **hurricane** (HER·uh·kayn) is *a strong tropical windstorm with driving rain*. Hurricanes occur in coastal regions. They can cause high waves, which in turn can produce flooding. Wind speeds during a hurricane can reach or exceed 100 miles per hour. Hurricane-force winds can turn over cars and knock down buildings.

When a hurricane is forecast, windows should be boarded. Outdoor objects should be brought in. Staying alert to TV or radio reports is important. Sometimes residents will be instructed to leave their homes and head inland. It is necessary to follow these safety instructions.

Floods

The most common natural disasters are *floods,* the rising of a body of water and its overflowing onto normally dry land. These can occur almost anywhere. As noted previously, hurricanes can cause floods. Another cause of flooding is heavy rainfall.

▲ Lightning carries a deadly electrical charge. **What are some safety rules to follow during an electrical storm?**

TEACH

R Reading Strategy

Analyzing a Graphic Have students examine Figure 12.4 on page 308 that shows suggested items for a home emergency kit. Ask: Why should water be included in an emergency kit? *because water supplies might be disrupted* Why is important to periodically review the supplies in your family's emergency kit? *Food items and batteries have expiration dates; the family's needs might have changed.* **OL**

AL Active Learning

Public Service Announcements Have small groups prepare public service announcements that give information about how to stay safe during a thunderstorm. Students can incorporate the tips from the student text or research other thunderstorm safety tips to use in their announcements. Have each group share its public service announcement with the class. **OL**

Reading Check

Answer Lightning is caused by clouds releasing stored electrical energy.

🏠 Home, School, and Community

At Home Have students use print or online resources to find out more about home emergency kits. Have students take into consideration the types of natural disasters and weather emergencies that occur in their communities when they research emergency kits. After students have completed their research, have them work as a class to make a list of items that should be in an emergency kit appropriate for homes in their communities. Have students prepare a pamphlet that can be used to share their information with others. **OL**

Caption Answer

Photo Caption Two safety tips to follow during electrical storms are to stay inside and do not use the phone.

AL Active Learning

Student-Led Learning Divide the class into six groups. Assign each group one of the weather conditions or natural disasters described in the lesson (thunderstorms, hurricanes, floods, blizzards, tornados, and earthquakes). Have each group develop a lesson and a three-question quiz about its topic. Have each group present its lesson. Then have each group use its quiz to assess the effectiveness of its lesson. **OL**

C Critical Thinking

Analyze Have students discuss ways in which they are safer during blizzards and severe weather than people were in the past (better weather forecasts, better communication, safer homes). Then ask students to consider any ways that people are more vulnerable to severe weather than people were in the past. (Due to technology advances, people are more likely to be caught away from home during an emergency.) Write students' responses in two lists on the board. **OL**

Reading Check

Answer Hurricanes can lead to flooding.

Caption Answers

Photo Caption Drinking bottled water is important in the event of a flood.
Photo Caption, p. 311 A tornado is a whirling, funnel-shaped windstorm. You should go to the basement or storm cellar if a tornado is headed your way.

▲ Lowland areas or regions with rivers often experience floods. **What actions can you take in the event of a flood?**

Flooding can be especially serious in regions near large bodies of water. Stay tuned to local radio or television stations for reports of rising water. Sometimes there is little or no warning. This is called a *flash flood*. Never walk or ride in a car through floodwater. There is a risk of being swept away. Watch out for downed power lines, which can cause deadly shocks. Floodwaters often pollute tap water. Drink bottled water just in case.

Once the flood waters go down, make sure that everything that came in contact with the floodwater is cleaned and disinfected. Wear rubber or latex gloves during the cleanup. Throw out all contaminated food. Make sure the water supply is safe before drinking any.

Reading Check **Identify** What other weather emergencies can lead to flooding?

Blizzards

Do you live in an area hit by snow in the winter? If you do, you may experience blizzards. A *blizzard* is a heavy snowstorm accompanied by strong winds. Blizzards make travel difficult, often shutting down roads. Blizzards also make it hard for food and other daily needs to reach consumers. Be careful of downed power lines, which can be dangerous to people on foot.

Blizzards can also lead to "whiteout" conditions. A whiteout is a state where snow falls so rapidly, visibility is significantly reduced. People can become lost or confused. Health risks from being lost in a blizzard include hypothermia, described in Lesson 3. Another health risk is **frostbite,** *freezing of the skin*. Frostbite can cause severe injury to the skin and sometimes to deeper tissues.

Tornadoes

A **tornado** (tor·NAY·doh) is *a whirling, funnel-shaped windstorm that drops from the sky to the ground*. Most tornadoes occur in the flat central regions of the country. These disasters can strike anywhere if the weather conditions are right. If a tornado warning is issued for your area, head to a storm cellar or basement. If you don't have a basement or storm cellar, go

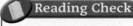

Health Online

Visit health.glencoe.com and complete the Interactive Study Guide for Lesson 4.

TECHNOLOGY AND HEALTH

Weather Forecasting Weather forecasting technology has changed dramatically over the past 100 years. Using accurate forecasting of severe weather, these technologies have contributed to health and safety. With the development of weather satellites and computers, weather forecasts have advanced to the point where 10-day or longer forecasts are common. Have students research technological advances in weather forecasting, including weather satellites and Doppler radar. Have student prepare a multimedia presentation focusing on one of these technologies. **OL**

to a hallway, bathroom, or other inside area without windows. Don't stay in cars or mobile homes. If you are outdoors, look for a ditch and lie down.

 Reading Check **Define** What is a tornado?

Earthquakes

An **earthquake** is *the shaking of the ground as rock below the surface moves.* If you are inside when an earthquake hits, stay there. Brace yourself in a doorway. If there is a piece of sturdy furniture, such as a large desk, crawl under. Move away from objects that could fall or shatter. If you are outside during an earthquake, stand in the open. Keep away from buildings, trees, and power lines. After an earthquake, report any odor of gas. An odor might indicate a leak.

▲ What are tornadoes? What should you do if a tornado is headed your way?

Lesson 4 Review

After You Read

Review this lesson for new terms, major headings, and Reading Checks.

What I Learned

1. **Compare** What is the difference between a weather emergency and natural disaster?

2. **Vocabulary** What is a hurricane? Where do hurricanes occur?

3. **Identify** Which type of weather emergency can lead to whiteout conditions?

Thinking Critically

4. **Evaulate** How does the media influence community health during a natural disaster or weather emergency?

5. **Analyze** Suppose you are swimming when the sky turns dark. You hear a distant rumble. What should you do to take responsibility for your personal health?

Applying Health Skills

6. **Accessing Information** Research online or at the library on how to prepare an emergency supply kit. Write a list of all important supplies that you would need in a severe weather emergency or natural disaster.

Health Online For more review questions for Lesson 4, go to **health.glencoe.com**.

ASSESS

Assessment Resources

Lesson Review Quiz
 ExamView
 Fast Files Activities
Online Quizzes and Activities

Reteaching

● Assign Concept Map 12-4 or Reteaching Activity 12-4 in the Fast Files.

● Have students write a paragraph that summarizes the content of Lesson 4.

Enrichment

● Assign Enrichment Activity 12-4 in the Fast Files.

● Have students identify the education required for a career in meteorology, as well as some of the technologies used by meteorologists. Have students write a report about this career.

CLOSE

Have students make a list of tips for weather-related emergencies. Have students discuss their list with a partner, then revise and add to their list based on feedback from the partner.

Lesson 4 Review Answers

1. Natural disasters tend to cause greater damage and destruction than weather emergencies. Some natural disasters, such as earthquakes, are not weather-related.

2. A hurricane is a strong tropical windstorm with driving rain and high wind that occurs in coastal regions.

3. Blizzards can lead to whiteouts.

4. The media warns the community when a storm is approaching and keeps people informed about road closures and areas to avoid.

5. You should get out of the water and seek shelter.

6. Answers will vary, but should indicate that the student has used a reliable source to develop an emergency supply list.

311

Lesson 5

FOCUS

Activating Prior Knowledge

What I Know Have students recall types of injuries that were discussed in Lesson 1. Then have students describe ways to care for those injuries.

 Guide to Reading

BUILDING VOCABULARY

- Tell students that one meaning of the word degree is "a measure of damage to tissue." Have students relate this to the terms *first-degree burn, second-degree burn, and third degree burn.*
- Use Vocabulary PuzzleMaker to reinforce vocabulary terms.

READING STRATEGY

Sequencing After students have completed their flowcharts, have them review the information in the student text to be sure they included all of the steps in the correct order. Then have students make any necessary revisions.

*Q*uick Write

After students have completed their Quick Writes, ask volunteers to name items they would include in their first-aid kits.

312

First Aid for Emergencies

Guide to Reading

Building Vocabulary

Make two lists. One should be emergency terms, the other first-aid techniques.

- first aid (p. 312)
- rescue breathing (p. 313)
- cardiopulmonary resuscitation (CPR) (p. 314)
- abdominal thrusts (p. 314)
- poison control center (p. 316)
- first-degree burn (p. 316)
- second-degree burn (p. 316)
- third-degree burn (p. 317)

Focusing on the Main Ideas

In this lesson, you will be able to:

- **name** strategies for responding to injuries.
- **describe** how you can help someone who is bleeding.
- **identify** the universal sign for choking.
- **explain** how to help a burn victim.

Reading Strategy

Sequencing Choose two of the emergencies described in the lesson. For each, make a flow chart showing the steps in treating the emergency.

uick Write

List three or four items you would put in a home first-aid kit. Explain why each item is important.

Giving First Aid

Some emergencies are minor. You cut your fingertip and it bleeds. A friend falls while skateboarding and injures his or her knee. Other emergencies can be life-threatening. Taking immediate action can mean the difference between life and death. Often that includes giving **first aid.** This is *the care first given to an injured or ill person until regular medical care can be supplied.*

Helping an injured person can prevent further injury but proper training is needed to give first aid. In an emergency, the American Red Cross suggests the following strategy: CHECK-CALL-CARE.

- **Check the scene and the victim.** Make sure the area is safe for you and the victim. Move the victim only if he or she is in danger.

◀ When reacting to emergencies, first check to see whether you or the victim is in danger. **What should you do next?**

Lesson 5 Resources

📁 **Chapter *FAST FILE* Resources**
Guided Reading and Writing 12-5
Concept Mapping Activity 12-5
Decision-Making Activity 12-5
Reteaching Activity 12-5
Enrichment Activity 12-5
Lesson Quiz 12-5

Technology
⚓ Transparency 12-5
💿 Audio Summaries
💿 *ExamView*
💿 Vocabulary PuzzleMaker
💿 StudentWorks™ Plus

- **Call for help.** Call 911 or the local EMS number. *EMS* stands for "emergency medical service."

- **Care for the person until help arrives.** Use the first-aid techniques discussed in this lesson to treat the victim's injuries until help arrives. **AL**

Life-Threatening Emergencies

How can you tell if an emergency is life-threatening? A victim's life is considered in danger if the person: (1) has stopped breathing, (2) has no heartbeat (3) is bleeding severely, (4) is choking, (5) has swallowed poison, or (6) has been severely burned. People in these situations need help immediately. Call for help and then begin to treat the victim.

Rescue Breathing and CPR

If you suspect a person has stopped breathing, put your ear and cheek close to the victim's nose and mouth. Listen and feel for air exhaled. Look to see if the chest is rising and falling. If the victim is not breathing, perform **rescue breathing.** This is *a substitute for normal breathing in which someone forces air into the victim's lungs.* **Figure 12.5** shows how to perform rescue breathing on an adult or older child. Special rescue breathing techniques are used for infants and children. If you are planning to begin babysitting, contact the American Red Cross for training on infant and child rescue breathing.

▼ FIGURE 12.5

RESCUE BREATHING TECHNIQUE

When a victim is not breathing, first call 911. Then begin rescue breathing if the person has a pulse. **How can you determine if a victim has stopped breathing?** **R**

1 Point the victim's chin upward by gently lifting it up with your fingers and tilting the head back. The airway will now be open.

2 Pinch the victim's nostrils shut. Cover the victim's mouth with your own, forming a tight seal. Give two slow breaths each about two seconds long. Make sure the victim's chest rises during each breath.

3 Watch for the victim's chest to fall, and listen for air flowing from the lungs. If the victim begins breathing normally, stop. Otherwise, give one rescue breath every five seconds until help arrives.

Lesson 5: First Aid for Emergencies **313**

R Reading Strategy

Analyzing a Graphic Direct students' attention to Figure 12.6. Ask: What pressure point would you use to control bleeding from the lower leg? *the pressure point in the upper thigh* Why is it important to elevate the wound above the heart if there are no broken bones? *to slow the flow of blood from the heart to the injured area* OL

U Universal Access

Gifted Students Clotting is an important process to stop severe bleeding. Have students use print or online resources to research the process by which blood clots form. Have students prepare an illustrated report in storyboard format that can be used to explain the process of clotting to the entire class. Have students present their reports. Then have the remainder of the class generate a list of questions about blood clotting. Have students do additional research to find the answers to any questions they cannot answer. AL

Reading Check

Answer CPR is cardiopulmonary respiration—a rescue measure that attempts to restore heartbeat and breathing.

Caption Answer

Figure Caption Knowing the location of pressure points can help you treat someone who is bleeding.

314

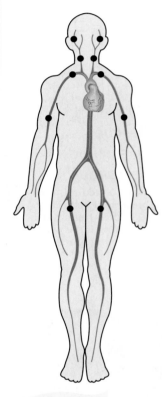

▲ **FIGURE 12.6**

LOCATION OF PRESSURE POINTS

R The dots in this illustration are pressure points. Why is it important to know the location of pressure points on the body?

314   Chapter 12: Safety and the Environment

A life-saving technique for victims whose hearts have stopped beating is **cardiopulmonary resuscitation (CPR).** This is *a rescue measure that attempts to restore heartbeat and breathing.* Only people who have been trained should perform CPR.

Reading Check   **Define** What is CPR?

First Aid for Severe Bleeding

Severe bleeding from an injury can be a serious problem. When treating a victim with severe bleeding, take precautions to limit touching another person's blood. Wear gloves if possible and always wash your hands afterward.

First aid for severe bleeding begins with lying the victim down. Try to elevate his or her legs to reduce the risk of shock. If possible, raise the wounded body part above the victim's heart. Elevating the wound slows the blood coming from the heart to the wound. Do this only if the body part has no broken bones. Apply direct, steady pressure to the wound. Press down firmly with a clean cloth. If necessary, add more cloth without removing the first cloth. At the same time, apply pressure to the main artery supplying blood to the wound. **Figure 12.6** shows several pressure points that can be used to stop bleeding. Push on the pressure point until you feel the bone. Hold the pressure. Do not push so hard that you cut off circulation, however.

Once the bleeding has stopped, cover the wound with a clean cloth. This helps prevent infection. If the victim needs professional medical treatment, leave the bandages in place. Get the person medical help quickly.

First Aid for Choking

Choking is a life-and-death emergency. It is a condition that occurs when a person's airway becomes blocked. A choking victim can die in minutes because air cannot get to the lungs. The universal sign for choking is grabbing the throat between the thumb and forefinger. Knowing this gesture can help you identify a choking victim. It can also help you alert someone in the event you are choking. A person who is choking may gasp for breath. He or she may be unable to speak. The person's face may turn red, then bluish.

For an older child or adult, first aid for choking begins with a question. Ask "Are you choking?" If the victim nods or does not respond, begin using **abdominal thrusts.** These are *quick*

What Teens Want to Know

How much blood is there in a person's body? Students might be curious about the volume of blood in the human body. Explain that an average-sized adult body contains about five liters of blood. It might be helpful for students to think about two-liter beverage containers to help them visualize a volume of five liters. Explain that blood loss can cause death, depending upon the volume of blood lost and other medical problems or injuries that accompany the blood loss. In general, but not always, a sudden loss of two liters or more of blood will cause death.

upward pulls into the diaphragm to force out the object blocking the airway. This technique is illustrated in **Figure 12.7.**

If an infant is choking, position the infant on his or her abdomen along your forearm. Brace your arm against your thigh. Support the infant's head with your hand and point the head down. Using the heel of your hand, give the infant up to five blows between the shoulder blades. If the object is still stuck, turn the victim on his or her back. Support the shoulders and neck with one hand. With the other hand, place two fingers in the middle of the child's breastbone. Press quickly up to five times. Alternate five back blows and five chest thrusts until the object comes out. If the child becomes unconscious, call 911. For more detailed instructions on helping a choking infant, consult a first-aid manual.

Suppose you are choking and no one is around to help. If this happens, don't panic. Instead, make a fist and thrust it quickly into your upper abdomen. This will force out the object blocking your airway. You can also try pushing your abdomen against the back or arm of a chair.

Reading Check **Explain** Describe first aid for a choking infant.

▼ **FIGURE 12.7**

ABDOMINAL THRUSTS

Use these steps to help a victim who is choking. If the person can talk or cough or you can hear breathing, don't do anything. **Why might it be dangerous to perform abdominal thrusts on a person who is not choking?**

1 Stand behind the victim. Wrap your arms around his or her waist, and bend the victim slightly forward. Place your fist slightly above the person's navel.

2 Hold your fist with your other hand, and press it hard into the abdomen with an upward thrust. Repeat until the object is coughed up.

Lesson 5: First Aid for Emergencies **315**

AL Active Learning

Infomercial Have students work in small groups for 15 minutes to write a script for an infomercial describing first aid for choking. Have each group create a video of its infomercial and share it with the class. Evaluate the infomercials based on the accuracy of the content and the creativity with which they are presented. **OL**

R Reading Strategy

Analyzing a Graphic Have students examine Figure 12.7, which shows how to provide first aid for choking. Ask: Why is it important to place your fists below a person's diaphragm when performing abdominal thrusts? Sample answer: *It is the upward pressure on the diaphragm that forces air out of the lungs, expelling the object that is obstructing the airway.* **OL**

Reading Check

Answer First aid for a choking infant consists of supporting the infant's head and body while administering gentle blows to the back alternated with pressure to the breastbone.

Caption Answer

Figure Caption Performing abdominal thrusts on a person who is not choking could cause internal injury.

HEALTH LITERACY

Choking Explain that choking can happen to anyone, but it occurs most frequently in young children. Two-thirds of all fatal choking incidents occur in babies under one year old. Both food and nonfood items can cause choking. In young children, foods such as hot dogs, grapes, popcorn, candy, and chewing gum cause many choking incidents. Coins and balloons are two nonfood items that commonly cause choking in young children. Ask students what precautions they should take to help protect younger siblings, relatives, or friends who visit their home. **OL**

315

AL Active Learning

Real-World Connection Have students locate the phone number for the local poison control center. Then have students make small cards with this information that could be posted by home telephones or carried in a wallet. Provide index cards, scissors, and markers for students to use as they complete this project. **OL**

R Reading Strategy

Organizing Information Have students create a three-column table to organize the information about the three different types of burns. The column heads should be "Type of Burn," "Appearance," and "Treatment." Have students complete the table as they read about burns. **BL**

U Universal Access

English Learners Point out the term *degree* as it is used to describe burns of different severity. Ask students to name other contexts in which they have heard the word *degree*. (In arithmetic, a degree is a portion of a circle or angle, and degrees Celsius and Fahrenheit measure temperature.) Ask: What do all of these have in common? *They all pertain to measurement.* **EL**

First Aid for Poisoning

If you think someone has swallowed poison, get professional help. Call 911, EMS, or your local **poison control center.** This is *a community agency that helps people deal with poisoning emergencies.* The inside cover of your telephone book usually lists the phone number of the center. When you call, you will be given directions on how to treat the victim. **AL**

While waiting for help to arrive, keep the person warm and breathing. Look for extra traces of poison around the victim's mouth. Remove these with a damp, clean cloth wrapped around your finger. Make sure to save the container of poison. Show it to the ambulance team. Tell them all you know about what happened.

Some cases of poisoning are caused by contact with a poisonous plant. Poison ivy, poison oak, and poison sumac are three such plants. Contact with these plants can cause redness, itching, and swelling. Most of these injuries can be easily treated at home using soap and water, rubbing alcohol, and over-the-counter creams. For severe cases, see a doctor for treatment.

 **Reading Check** **List** Give two ways poisons can enter the body.

First Aid for Burns

Different kinds of burns require different treatments. A **U** **first-degree burn** is *a burn in which only the outer part of the skin is burned and turns red.* Cool the burned area with cold water (not ice) for at least 15 minutes. Wrap the burned area loosely in a clean, dry dressing. **R**

Second-degree burns are more serious. A **second-degree burn** is *a serious type of burn in which the damaged area blisters or peels.* Cool the burn in cold water (not ice) and elevate the burned area. Wrap loosely with a clean, dry dressing. Do not pop blisters, or peel loose skin. Call your doctor.

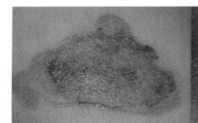 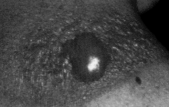 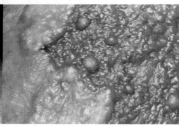

First-degree burn   **Second-degree burn**   **Third-degree burn**

Reading Check

Answer Poisons can enter the body through the mouth or by contact with the skin.

Answer, p. 317 Treat a fracture like a broken bone.

 Home, School, and Community

At Home Many items found in homes can cause poisoning. Medications are one common cause of poisoning. Vitamins with iron cause the greatest number of poisoning deaths in young children. Household chemicals, such as cleansers, detergents, bleaches, and disinfectants also cause poisonings. Drinks and mouthwashes containing alcohol and some kinds of houseplants are also common causes of poisoning. Have students investigate storage recommendation for these items. Then have each student share one fact with the class about safely storing these items. **OL**

A **third-degree burn** is *a very serious burn in which deeper layers of skin and nerve endings are damaged.* Cool the burn with cold water or by applying a wet cloth. Do not apply ice or ointments. Remove clothing that might be stuck to the burned area while you are applying cold water. Wrap the area loosely with a clean, dry dressing and call 911.

First Aid for Breaks and Sprains

A break in a bone is called a *fracture.* If you suspect someone has a fracture, start by asking questions. Ask if the person heard a snap or whether touching the injured area hurts. If you're not sure, treat the person as though they have a broken bone. First, call 911 or EMS. If there is bleeding, apply pressure with a clean cloth. Do not attempt to straighten the injured part. Avoid moving the person.

A sprain occurs when a joint is stretched or twisted or has torn ligaments. Sprains are often sports-related. To treat a sprain use the *PRICE* formula outlined in Chapter 5 (see page 134).

 Reading Check **Explain** How do you treat a fracture?

Health Online

Visit **health.glencoe.com** and complete the Interactive Study Guide for Lesson 5.

ASSESS

Assessment Resources

Lesson Review Quiz
- *ExamView*
- Fast Files Activities
- Online Quizzes and Activities

Reteaching

- Assign Concept Map 12-5 or Reteaching Activity 12-5 in the Fast Files. 📁
- Ask students to write a brief explanation of the CHECK-CALL-CARE strategy in their own words.

Enrichment

- Assign Enrichment Activity 12-5 in the Fast Files. 📁
- Have students do further research on poisoning. Have students create a public service announcement that can be used to promote awareness of poisonous substances commonly found in homes.

CLOSE

Name a variety of injuries described in the lesson. For each injury, ask a student to describe the proper response to that injury.

Lesson 5 Review

 After You Read

Review this lesson for new terms, major headings, and Reading Checks.

What I Learned

1. *Recall* What is the universal sign for choking?

2. *List* Briefly give the steps in controlling severe bleeding.

3. *Vocabulary* What's the difference between a *first-* and *second-degree burn*?

Thinking Critically

4. *Evaluate* What steps can be taken to reduce poisoning risks in homes with small children?

5. *Apply* Ken and Phil see an older adult collapse to the ground. Using the CHECK-CALL-CARE strategy, show how Ken and Phil should respond to this emergency.

Applying Health Skills

6. *Stress Management* Emergency situations are often very stressful. With classmates, discuss strategies for reducing stress while dealing with a medical emergency.

Health Online For more review questions for Lesson 5, go to **health.glencoe.com**.   Lesson 5: First Aid for Emergencies **317**

Lesson 5 Review Answers

1. The universal sign for choking is grabbing the throat between the thumb and forefinger.
2. To control severe bleeding, lay the victim down, elevate the legs, raise the wounded part above the heart if there are no broken bones.

3. A first-degree burn appears as redness, a second-degree burn blisters or peels.
4. *Sample answers:* moving items out of reach; using cabinet locks

5. Ken and Phil should CHECK for danger, CALL for help, and give the victim CARE while they wait for help to arrive.
6. Students may note that role-playing appropriate actions or taking first-aid classes may reduce the stress of these situations.

Lesson 6

FOCUS

Activating Prior Knowledge

What I Know Ask students to name forms of pollution. Record their responses on the board. Tell students that they can add to the list as they read the lesson.

Guide to Reading

BUILDING VOCABULARY
- Tell students that the word part *bio-* means "life." Ask students to use that information to infer the meaning of the term *biodegradable.*
- Use Vocabulary PuzzleMaker to reinforce vocabulary terms. [mouse icon]

READING STRATEGY
Organizing Information Have students prepare their charts before they read the lesson. As they read, they can fill in their charts with the appropriate information.

uick Write

Encourage students to think creatively about ways that a healthy school environment can be maintained. After students have completed their Quick Writes, have them make posters encouraging others to take care of the school environment.

318

Lesson 6

Protecting Your Environment

 Guide to Reading

Building Vocabulary
Write each term in your notebook. Add a definition for each as you come across the term in your reading.
- environment (p. 318)
- pollute (p. 318)
- fossil fuels (p. 319)
- ozone (p. 319)
- smog (p. 319)
- acid rain (p. 319)
- recycling (p. 320)
- conservation (p. 320)
- biodegradable (p. 321)

Focusing on the Main Ideas
In this lesson, you will be able to:
- **identify** the causes of air, water, and land pollution.
- **describe** what happens to garbage after it is thrown away.
- **explain** how you can help protect the environment.

Reading Strategy
Organizing Information Create a chart that shows the causes for the three types of pollution.

uick Write

Your school is part of your environment. Explain how you can help take care of your school environment.

The Health of the Environment

The **environment** is *the sum total of your surroundings.* It includes living things such as people, plants, and animals. It also includes nonliving things such as homes, buildings, cars, and other things we use each day. All living things are affected by the health of the environment.

Unfortunately, the way people live can pollute the environment. **Pollute** (puh·LOOT) means *to make unfit or harmful for living things.* Pollution affects the air we breathe, the water we drink, and the land we live on.

Air Pollution

Some air pollution is caused by natural events. For example, gases and ash from erupting volcanoes pollute the air. The main cause of air pollution, however, is the burning of

◀ People who care about nature want to protect it. **What can you do to help protect nature?**

 Lesson 6 Resources

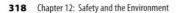

📁 **Chapter FAST FILE Resources**
Guided Reading and Writing 12-6
Concept Mapping Activity 12-6
Health Lab 12-6
Reteaching Activity 12-6
Enrichment Activity 12-6
Lesson Quiz 12-6

Technology
🔋 Transparency 12-6
💿 Audio Summaries
💿 *ExamView*
💿 Vocabulary PuzzleMaker
💿 StudentWorks™ Plus

fossil (FAH·suhl) **fuels.** These are *coal, oil, and natural gas.* They are used to power motor vehicles, run factories, and heat homes and buildings.

Air pollution can cause physical problems such as watery eyes, headaches, dizziness, and breathing difficulties. It also causes other environmental problems. One of these is damage to the ozone (OH·zohn) layer. **Ozone** is *a special form of oxygen.* It naturally occurs in the earth's upper atmosphere. The ozone layer is needed to shield the earth from the sun's harmful rays.

Another problem related to air pollution is **smog.** This is *a yellow-brown haze that forms when sunlight reacts with impurities in car exhaust.* Over long periods, breathing smog can cause serious damage to your lungs. Still another problem is **acid rain.** This is *rainfall that contains air pollution from the burning of fossil fuels.* Over time, acid rain can destroy large forests, wildlife, and plant life.

Reading Check **Identify** Name two environmental problems caused by air pollution.

Water Pollution

Some water pollution is caused directly by the dumping of waste materials. Indirect causes include poisonous wastes buried in landfills and chemical fertilizers used in farming. Harmful substances from both can leak down through the soil and into the *ground water.* This is water that runs deep under the surface. Other causes of water pollution are accidental such as oil spills from tanker ships. This pollution damages beaches and harms wildlife.

No matter what the cause, the cost to the environment is great. Harm to the water supply endangers all living things. People can become sick when they drink polluted water. Eating fish that have absorbed wastes and chemicals can also lead to illness. In some parts of the world, unclean water spreads deadly diseases. Two of these are cholera (KAH·luh·ruh) and typhoid. These illnesses threaten whole communities.

▼ The damage to this sculpture was done by acid rain. **What causes acid rain?**

TECHNOLOGY AND HEALTH

Global Warming The use of technologies for industry and transportation, particularly those that use fossil fuels, has an impact on the composition of the atmosphere. The increase in carbon dioxide and other greenhouse gases affects global climate. There has been a documented increase in the global average surface temperature of between 1 and 2°F in the past 100 years. Global average sea levels have risen due to the warmer temperatures. Have students look for articles about global warming and share their articles with the class. **OL**

AL Active Learning

Real-World Connection Have students compile a list of items found in their homes or in the community that are considered hazardous wastes. Then have students research the procedure for hazardous waste disposal in their community. Have students make posters to inform others about proper disposal of hazardous wastes. **OL**

W Writing Support

Persuasive Writing Have students write a persuasive paragraph encouraging others to conserve natural resources. Tell students that their paragraph must include at least two specific suggestions for actions that reduce the use of resources. Remind students that persuasive writing uses facts to support an opinion. Have students check their work for proper spelling, punctuation, and grammar. **OL**

Health Online

After completing the student Web Activity, display completed brochures in the classroom.

Reading Check

Answer Trash is sent to landfills.

Caption Answer

Photo Caption Beaches become polluted when wastes are dumped into oceans and lakes.

▲ This beach is closed to swimmers due to pollution. **How do our beaches become polluted?**

Health Online

Visit **health.glencoe.com** and complete the Interactive Study Guide for Lesson 6.

Land Pollution

Communities produce large amounts of trash. What do they do with it? Most communities build landfills to bury their wastes. Special linings are designed to prevent pollution from leaking into ground water.

A more serious problem is disposing of hazardous wastes. These include paints, acids, and chemicals used to kill insects. All can cause serious illnesses and environmental damage. Nuclear wastes, the chemicals left over from nuclear power plants, are especially dangerous. They take tens of thousands of years to break down naturally and become harmless. Most communities have approved locations where you can safely dispose of hazardous wastes. **AL**

Reading Check

Explain What happens to trash that is thrown away?

Exhausting Natural Resources

Pollution is not the only environmental problem. Another is overuse of natural resources such as trees. Trees are cut down to make paper and lumber. Removing too many trees upsets the balance of nature. By upsetting this balance, the lives of all living things are endangered.

Another resource we are exhausting is some of our energy sources. The earth's fossil fuel supplies are not endless. Some day they will run out. Current usage rates are making that happen sooner rather than later.

How Can You Help?

"What can one person do?" The answer is *plenty*—especially if you are willing to take positive action.

For starters, you can create less trash. One way is by reusing as many items as possible. Another is by **recycling.** This means *recovering and changing items so they can be used for other purposes*. Find out where there are recycling centers in your community. **W**

Another solution is **conservation,** *the saving of resources*. When you buy new items, look for ones with the least packaging. This will conserve resources. At the same time, it will create

Cultural Perspectives

Ecological Footprints An ecological footprint is a measure of the hectares (one hectare = 2.5 acres) of land required to meet an individual's demands for resources and waste disposal. The United States averages an ecological footprint of 10 hectares per person—the largest in the world. Japan averages approximately 4.5 hectares, and Mexico has an average of about 3 hectares per person. Have students make a bulleted list of five specific ways to reduce their own ecological footprint. **OL**

less trash to throw away. Also, consider whether you need an item at all. Maybe something you already have would do just as well.

Conserve energy at home by turning off electric lights and appliances when not in use. Keep windows closed while the heat or air conditioning is on. Towel dry or air dry dishes instead of heat drying them in a dishwasher.

Conserve water by using less of it. Turn the water off while you brush your teeth. Take shorter showers. Protect our water supply by using cleaning supplies that are biodegradable (by·oh·di·GRAY·duh·buhl). **Biodegradable** means *capable of breaking down naturally without causing pollution*. Don't dump detergents and cleaning supplies down the drain. They only end up in our rivers, lakes, and oceans.

Advocacy

Set a positive example for others. Urge others to carpool to cut down the number of cars on the road. Carpooling means less exhaust in the air from motor vehicles. It also means less fuel consumption.

 **Reading Check** **Give Examples** Name two ways you personally can conserve resources.

Health *Online*

Topic: Protecting the Environment

Visit **health.glencoe.com** for Student Web Activities to learn more about environmental issues and what you can do to help.

Activity: After studying the information provided at the link above, choose an environmental issue that is important to you. Create a brochure that explains the issue and how teens can help.

ASSESS

Assessment Resources

Lesson Review Quiz
ExamView
Fast Files Activities
Online Quizzes and Activities

Reteaching

- Assign Concept Map 12-6 or Reteaching Activity 12-6 in the Fast Files.
- Have students list three types of pollution on a sheet of paper. Then have them identify one cause and one effect of each of the listed types of pollution.

Enrichment

- Assign Enrichment Activity 12-6 in the Fast Files.
- Have students research energy-efficient appliances, compact fluorescent light bulbs, or hybrid automobiles. Have students use a multimedia computer program to prepare a short report of their findings.

CLOSE

Ask students to explain how pollution can affect all three sides of the health triangle.

Lesson 6 Review

 After You Read

Review this lesson for new terms, major headings, and Reading Checks.

What I Learned

1. *Vocabulary* What is *ozone*? Why is it important?

2. *Recall* How does burying wastes in land-fills cause water pollution?

3. *List* What are two ways of conserving water?

Thinking Critically

4. *Analyze* How does properly disposing of hazardous waste affect your environ-ment as well as your personal health?

5. *Synthesize* What role does conservation play in being a good consumer?

Applying Health Skills

6. *Advocacy* One way to help maintain the environment is to become an advo-cate. With a group, brainstorm dif-ferent ways to spread the word about the importance of conserving. Which methods do you think would be most effective?

Health Online For more review questions for Lesson 6, go to **health.glencoe.com**. Lesson 6: Protecting Your Environment **321**

Lesson 6 Review Answers

1. Ozone is a form of oxygen that occurs in Earth's upper atmosphere. It shields Earth from the sun's harmful rays.

2. Harmful substances can leak into soil and reach the water supply.

3. *Sample answers:* turning off the water when you brush your teeth; taking shorter showers.

4. Properly disposing of hazardous waste keeps soil and water from becoming polluted, protecting against the spread of illness.

5. *Sample answer:* A good consumer looks for products with less packaging and reuses bags.

6. Students' responses should show an understanding of the health skill of advocacy and the importance of conservation.

Building Health Skills

Reduce Waste

SKILL
Advocacy

Activating Prior Knowledge

Have students name items that can be reused or recycled. Then have students identify how reusing and recycling benefit the environment.

- **Objective:** After completing the activity, students will be able to apply the skill of advocacy to help protect the environment.
- **Time:** 45 minutes
- **Materials:** paper, pencil

Teacher Classroom Resources

📁 Building Health Skills
🖨 Transparency 12-6

Model

- Have students work individually to read about Justin using advocacy to help his family protect the environment. Ask: What health skills, other than advocacy, does Justin use when he encourages his family to reuse and recycle? *Sample answers: practicing healthful behaviors, communication skills, goal setting*

Reduce Waste

DIRECTIONS

Advocacy involves taking a stand in support of a cause. This activity will give you the opportunity to develop and master this important health skill. Here's a guide to the different parts of this activity:

❶ In the **Model** section, you will read about a teen who performs the health skill successfully. This "model" scenario will show you how the skill is done.

❷ The **Practice** section will help guide you in practicing the skill.

❸ In the **Apply** section, you will have a chance to perform the skill on your own. You can use the Self-Check to check your work.

To complete this activity, first read the scenario presented in the Model. Then move on to the Practice. Finally, go ahead and try the Apply.

❶ Model

As Justin learned about ways to protect the environment, he wanted to take action within his own family. He decided to speak with his mom. Read a part of their conversation below.

Justin: We've been studying the environment in school. I would like our family to do more to protect our world.

Mom: What do you have in mind?

Justin: Well, I've noticed things that could still be useful in our trash. We can look carefully at every item before throwing it away. If it is something that someone else might use, we can give it to charity. We can also do a better job of recycling and using fewer disposable items, like paper plates.

Mom: Those are great ideas! Let's tell the rest of the family.

National Health Standards Addressed

8.2, 8.4, 8.5

▶ **Teaching Tips**

Brainstorming Students can generate several ideas quickly through brainstorming. Allot a brief period (about two minutes) for students to brainstorm in their groups all the ways they could reuse items normally thrown away.

Facilitating Creativity Students may create a product such as an illustrated poster or collage to advocate for reusing items. This will allow students to be creative and also lets them call upon their own personal experiences of trying to persuade their peers.

② Practice

Justin now wants to help his school learn to recycle and reuse items. He made a list of suggestions, which included using both sides of every piece of paper before it is thrown into the recycle bin. He also suggested starting a recycling program for printer cartridges and old computers.

1. With a group, write a letter to the school administrators. In your letter, convince them to adopt Justin's suggestions and two other suggestions from your group.

2. Share your letter with other groups in your class. How is your response similar to or different from theirs?

Skill Summary
ADVOCACY

The skill of advocacy asks you to

- Take a clear stand on an issue.
- Persuade others to make healthy choices.
- Be convincing.

③ Apply

Develop a 30 second public service announcement to persuade other teens to reduce, reuse, or recycle. In your announcement, explain why environmental protection is important. Describe at least three actions students should take to ensure a healthier world.

Self-Check

- Did I explain why environmental protection is important?
- Did I describe three actions students should take?
- Is my announcement persuasive to teens?

Practice

- Have students work in small groups to complete the Practice activity.
- Have each group share its letter. Ask: Which group's suggestions are the most practical for Justin to implement at his school? *Answers will vary; students should support their answers with logical reasoning* Which suggestions do you think would be most effective for motivating other students to participate? Why? *Answers will vary; students should support their answers with logical reasoning.*

Apply/Assess

- Have students work in their groups to complete the Apply activity.
- Discuss ways to persuade others to reuse items in their PSAs. Ask students to consider some of the methods they proposed in the Practice activity.
- You may wish to distribute the Building Health Skills Activity in the Fast Files.

ASSESSMENT SCORING

Student work should meet all criteria to achieve the highest score:

Skill Student work illustrates:
- a clear stand.
- a persuasive message.
- a convincing message.

Concept Student work provides:
- an explanation of the importance of reducing waste.
- several creative ways to reuse common items.

Are You Earth-Friendly?

Time: 30 minutes
Materials: pencil or pen, paper

Introducing Hands-on Health

- Ask students to describe ways to protect the environment. Tell students that this activity will help them identify additional strategies that they could use to protect the environment.

Teaching the Activity

- Have students prepare their papers as directed in the activity.
- Then have students complete the inventory.
- Have students total their score as directed. Use a show of hands to determine the number of students in each of the score ranges. Have students make a bar graph of the class results.

HANDS-ON HEALTH

Are You Earth-Friendly?

How do you rate as a friend of the environment? Take this conservation inventory to find out.

What You Will Need

- pencil or pen
- paper

What You Will Do

1. Write the letters *a.* through *j.* on your paper.
2. Write yes or no for each statement:
   a. I take quick showers.
   b. I turn off lights and appliances that are not in use.
   c. I keep windows closed when the heat or air conditioning is on.
   d. I don't let the water run when I'm brushing my teeth.
   e. I recycle products whenever possible.
   f. I bring my own bags to the store.
   g. I find new ways to use old items.
   h. I put litter in trash containers.
   i. I encourage my family to carpool.
   j. I walk or ride my bicycle whenever possible instead of asking for a ride.

Wrapping It Up

Give yourself 1 point for each yes answer. Add up your score to see how you rate.

3 or fewer:	Energy Eater
4 to 7:	Average Earth Friend
8 or more:	Conservation Star

List ways you can improve your rating.

HANDS-ON HEALTH Assessment

Discussion Ask students:
- How could the health skills of decision making and goal setting help you improve your score on the conservation inventory? Sample answer: *By making a decision and setting a goal to begin one of the practices in the inventory, I can improve my score.*

- Ask: Identify one reason that protecting the environment is an important health skill. Sample answer: *The environment has an impact on personal health, so improving the environment improves personal health.*

Reading Review

FOLDABLES | Study Organizer

Foldables™ and Other Study Aids Take out the Foldable™ that you created for Lesson 1 and any graphic organizers that you created for Lessons 1–6. Find a partner and quiz each other using these study aids.

Lesson 1 Safety and You

Key Ideas

- The parts of the accident chain are the situation, the unsafe habit, the unsafe act, and the resulting injury.

Vocabulary

- accident (p. 296)
- accidental injuries (p. 296)
- accident chain (p. 297)

Lesson 2 Safety at Home and Away

Key Ideas

- Road safety includes obeying local traffic rules, being aware of others, being visible to others, and wearing safety gear.

Vocabulary

- hazards (p. 300)
- smoke alarm (p. 302)
- fire extinguisher (p. 302)
- pedestrians (p. 303)
- Neighborhood Watch program (p. 304)

Lesson 3 Safety Outdoors

Key Ideas

- Water safety includes using the buddy system, knowing the water depth, and wearing a life jacket on a boat.

Vocabulary

- hypothermia (p. 306)

Lesson 4 Safety in Severe Weather

Key Ideas

- Being prepared for weather emergencies and natural disasters includes having an emergency kit.

Vocabulary

- natural disasters (p. 308)
- frostbite (p. 310)
- tornado (p. 310)
- hurricane (p. 309)
- earthquake (p. 311)

Lesson 5 First Aid for Emergencies

Key Ideas

- Strategies for responding to injuries include knowing proper first aid techniques for different types of injuries.

Vocabulary

- first aid (p. 312)
- rescue breathing (p. 313)
- cardiopulmonary resuscitation (CPR) (p. 314)
- abdominal thrusts (p. 314)
- poison control center (p. 316)
- first-degree burn (p. 316)
- second-degree burn (p. 316)
- third-degree burn (p. 317)

Lesson 6 Protecting Your Environment

Key Ideas

- You can help protect the environment by reducing, reusing, and recycling.

Vocabulary

- environment (p. 318)
- pollute (p. 318)
- fossil fuels (p. 319)
- ozone (p. 319)
- smog (p. 319)
- acid rain (p. 319)
- recycling (p. 320)
- conservation (p. 320)
- biodegradable (p. 321)

Assessment Resources

- Chapter 12 Summary and Activity
- Audio Summaries
- Reading Tutor
- Performance Assessment
- Chapter 12 Test
- *ExamView*
- Vocabulary PuzzleMaker
- Online Learning Center

Reading Review

Study Aids

- **Using the Dinah Zike Foldable™ Study Organizer** Have students use the 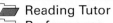 Foldable™ to review injury prevention.

Key Ideas

- **Use the Caption Questions** Have students assess their understanding of the chapter material by reviewing each of the figures and accompanying caption question with a partner.

Vocabulary Review

- **Vocabulary Concept Map** Have students work in small groups to make a concept map that uses some of the chapter vocabulary terms. Provide students with a model of a concept map before they begin. Be available to assist each group with its concept map.

Teaching Tips

Reading in Health Class Use the heads to divide the text into manageable sections for students. Have students read the material under one boldface head. Then assess students' comprehension of the material by using the caption questions and reading checks. Lead a class discussion of the material. Ask students to identify concepts within the reading material that were confusing or difficult. Then spend some time reviewing these concepts before moving on.

Assessment

Reviewing Vocabulary and Main Ideas

1. Accidental injuries
2. accident
3. accident chain
4. hazard
5. Neighborhood Watch program
6. True
7. True
8. False, Floods
9. False, tornados
10. False, CPR
11. False, third-degree
12. False, recycling
13. True

Thinking Critically

14. She might call their attention to the red flag, in case they haven't noticed it. The flag may be an indication that the ice is thin.

15. Advocating for change can improve the streets of a community in two ways. First, it can be used to alert members of the community to dangerous intersections, for example, which may be remedied by the addition of a traffic light or stop sign. Second, it can be used in neighborhoods with crime problems to inspire a Neighborhood Watch program.

After You Read

HEALTH INVENTORY

Now that you have read the chapter, look back at your answer to the Health Inventory on the chapter opener. Have your ideas changed? What would your answer be now?

Reviewing Vocabulary and Main Ideas

On a sheet of paper, write the numbers 1–5. After each number, write the term from the list that best completes each sentence.

- abdominal thrusts
- accident
- accident chain
- accidental injuries
- biodegradable
- hazard
- Neighborhood Watch program
- pedestrians

Lesson 1 Safety and You

1. _____ are injuries caused by unexpected events.
2. A(n) _____ is an unexpected event that results in damage or harm.
3. The situation, the unsafe habit, and the unsafe act are all parts of the _____.

Lesson 2 Safety at Home and Away

4. A loose floor rug that someone might trip on is an example of a _____ in the home.
5. Some communities try to protect teens by developing a _____.

*On a sheet of paper, write the numbers 6–13. Write **True** or **False** for each statement below. If the statement is false, change the underlined word or phrase to make it true.*

Lesson 3 Safety Outdoors

6. Knowing how to <u>swim</u> is an important part of water safety.
7. A <u>first-aid kit</u> comes in handy for treating minor injuries on the trail.

Lesson 4 Safety in Severe Weather

8. <u>Earthquakes</u>, the most common natural disaster, can happen almost anywhere.
9. Whirling, funnel-shaped windstorms, or <u>hurricanes</u>, occur mostly in the flat central regions of the country.

Lesson 5 First Aid for Emergencies

10. A life-saving technique for victims whose hearts have stopped beating is <u>abdominal thrusts</u>.
11. A <u>first-degree</u> burn is very serious because deeper layers of skin and nerve endings are damaged.

Lesson 6 Protecting Your Environment

12. Recovering and changing items so they can be used for other purposes is called <u>pollution</u>.
13. Cleaning supplies that are <u>biodegradable</u> break down naturally without causing pollution.

Health Online Visit health.glencoe.com and take the Online Quiz for Chapter 12.

Health Online

Have students visit **health.glencoe.com** to take the Chapter 12 quiz.

HEALTH INVENTORY WRAP-UP

Safety Habits Have students look back at the Health Inventory in the chapter opener. For each question in the inventory, ask: How can this healthy habit break an accident chain? Sample answer: *Wearing*

a safety belt breaks an accident chain by eliminating an unsafe habit. Then have a class discussion of ways to remember to practice the healthy habits mentioned in the Health Inventory.

Thinking Critically

Using complete sentences, answer the following questions on a sheet of paper.

14. **Analyze** Sara is skating with her friends. They decide to race. Sara notices a red flag on the ice in the distance. What safety tips might she give her friends?

15. **Describe** ways in which the skill of advocacy can make your community safer.

Write About It

16. **Practicing Healthful Behaviors** Write a paragraph discussing some of the positive health behaviors you can practice to help protect the environment.

Career Corner

Occupational Safety and Health Specialist Would you like to help keep people safe while they work? Are you good at solving problems? Then you might want to think about a career in occupational safety and health. In this career, you will look at hazards in the workplace and find ways to prevent or eliminate them. You'll need a four-year degree in occupational safety and health. Visit *Career Corner* at **health.glencoe.com** to learn more about this and other health careers.

17. **Accessing Information** Write a paragraph explaining why reliable information is important to the health of the environment.

Write About It

16. **Descriptive Writing** In descriptive writing, students should present a clear picture and focus on details. Answers will vary, but students could include examples such as conservation, reusing, recycling, picking up litter, or carpooling.

17. **Expository Writing** Expository writing is sharing knowledge to help others understand by informing or explaining. Reliable information can help people dispose of hazardous waste properly. It can also alert people to habits that are harmful to the environment and should be changed.

Standardized Test Practice

1. D
2. B

Career Corner

Occupational Safety and Health Specialist Have students visit the Career Corner at **health.glencoe.com** to gather more information about a career as an occupational safety and health specialist. Have students use print or online resources to find the names of colleges that offer degrees in occupational safety and health.

Standardized Test Practice

Math

Use the following information to answer the questions about safety in the event of lightning.

Earth is struck by lightning approximately 100 times every second. A formula exists for estimating how close a lightning strike is.

1. When you see the flash, begin counting seconds. If no clock is available, count *one-one hundred, two one-hundred,* and so on.

2. When you hear the sound of thunder, stop counting.

3. Each 5 seconds you counted is equal to about 1 mile.

Whenever lightning is within 7 miles of your location, seek shelter. If it is within 10 miles, continue to monitor the track of the storm. To do this, repeat the process for the next lightning flash. If the number is smaller, the storm is headed your way. Take cover.

> **TEST-TAKING TIP**
>
> To solve a math problem, be sure you understand the type of problem. Make sure you understand what you are being asked to do.

1. If you see lightning, count to 22, and then hear thunder,
   A. the lightning is 22 miles away.
   B. the lightning is 2.2 miles away.
   C. the lightning is 5.4 miles away.
   D. the lightning is 4.5 miles away.

2. A camper sees lightning and counts to 41, then hears thunder. Which statement is NOT true?
   A. The lightning is more than 8 miles from the camper's location.
   B. The camper should count again after the next flash.
   C. The camper should seek shelter at once.
   D. The camper is in no immediate danger but is not totally safe.

Test-Taking Tips

Checking Your Work Remind students that when they answer math questions, they should ask themselves the following questions to double check their work:

Did I perform the correct operation? Did I place the decimal point correctly in the answer? Does the answer seem reasonable?

Glossary

The Glossary contains all the important terms used throughout the text. It includes the **boldfaced** terms listed in the "Building Vocabulary" lists at the beginning of each lesson, which also appear in text and art.

The Glossary lists the term, the pronunciation (in the case of difficult terms), the definition, and the page on which the term is defined. The pronunciations here and in the text follow the system outlined below. The column headed "Symbol" shows the spelling used in this book to represent the appropriate method.

Pronunciation Key

Sound	As In	Symbol	Example
ă	hat, map	a	abscess (AB·ses)
ā	age, face	ay	atrium (AY·tree·uhm)
a	care, their	eh	capillaries (KAP·uh·lehr·eez)
ä, ŏ	father, hot	ah	biopsy (BY·ahp·See)
ar	far	ar	cardiac (KAR·dee·ak)
ch	child, much	ch	barbiturate (bar·BI·chuh·ruht)
ĕ	let, best	e	vessel (VE·suhl)
ē	beat, See, city	ee	acne (AK·nee)
er	term, stir, purr	er	nuclear (NOO·klee·er)
g	grow	g	malignant (muh·LIG·nuhnt)
ĭ	it, hymn	i	bacteria (bak·TIR·ee·uh)
ī	ice, five	y	benign (bi·NYN)
		eye	iris (EYE·ris)
j	page, fungi	j	cartilage (KAR·tuhl·ij)
k	coat, look, chorus	k	defect (DEE·fekt)
ō	open, coat, grow	oh	aerobic (ehr·OH·bik)
ô	order	or	organ (OR·guhn)
ȯ	flaw, all	aw	palsy (PAWL·zee)
oi	voice	oy	goiter (GOY·ter)
ou	out	ow	fountain (FOWN·tuhn)
s	say, rice	s	dermis (DER·mis)
sh	she, attention	sh	conservation (kahn·ser·VAY·shuhn)
ŭ	cup, flood	uh	bunion (BUHN·yuhn)
u	put, wood, could	u	pulmonary (PUL·muh·nehr·ee)
ü	rule, move, you	oo	attitudes (AT·i·toodz)
w	win	w	warranty (WAWR·uhn·tee)
y	your	yu	urethra (yu·REE·thruh)
z	says	z	hormones (HOR·mohnz)
zh	pleasure	zh	transfusion (trans·FYOO·zhuhn)
ə	about, collide	uh	addiction (uh·DIK·shuhn)

A

Abdominal thrusts Quick upward pulls into the diaphragm to force out the object blocking the airway. (page 314)

Abstinence (AB·stuh·nuhns) Not participating in high-risk behaviors. (page 44)

Abuse (uh·BYOOS) A pattern of mistreatment of another person. (page 71)

Accident An unexpected event that results in damage or harm. (page 296)

Accident chain A sequence of events that often leads to an accidental injury. (page 297)

Accidental injury An injury caused by an unexpected event. (page 296)

Acid rain Rainfall that contains air pollution from the burning of fossil fuels. (page 319)

Acne (AK·nee) A skin condition caused by overly active oil glands. (page 148)

Addiction The body's physical or mental need for a drug or other substance. (page 223)

Adolescence (a·duhl·EH·suhns) The period between childhood and adulthood. (page 202)

Adrenaline (uh·DRE·nuhl·in) A hormone that prepares the body to respond to stress. (page 47)

Advocacy Taking a stand to make a difference. (page 38)

Advocate Encourage other people to live healthy lives. (page 15)

AIDS A condition characterized by life-ending infections and a T-cell count under 200. (page 278)

Alcohol (AL·kuh·hawl) A substance produced by a chemical reaction in carbohydrates. (page 242)

Alcoholism A disease in which a person has a physical and mental need for alcohol. (page 247)

Allergen A substance that causes an allergic reaction. (page 285)

Allergy The body's sensitivity to certain substances. (page 285)

Alternative (ahl·TER·nuh·tihv) Another way of thinking or acting. (page 258)

Anabolic steroids (a·nuh·BAH·lik·STEHR·oydz) Synthetic drugs based on a male hormone. (page 251)

Antibiotics (an·tih·by·AH·tik) Kill or stop the growth of bacteria and other specific germs. (page 160)

Antibodies Chemicals produced specifically to fight a particular invading substance. (page 274)

Anxiety Feelings of uncertainty or worry over what may happen. (page 46)

Anxiety disorder A serious emotional problem that keeps a person from functioning normally. (page 51)

Assertive Making your wants and needs known in a positive, active manner. (page 66)

Asthma (AZ·muh) A chronic disease in which the airways become irritated and swollen. (page 285)

Astigmatism (ah·STIG·muh·tizm) A misshaped cornea or lens causing objects to look wavy or blurred. (page 152)

Attitude (AT·ih·toodz) What you believe or feel about someone or something. (page 11)

B

Bacteria (bak·TIR·ee·uh) Extremely small single-celled organisms with no cell nucleus. (page 270)

Behavior The way you act in the many different situations and events in your life. (page 11)

Biodegradable (by·oh·di·GRAY·duh·buhl) Capable of breaking down naturally without causing pollution. (page 321)

Blood alcohol content (BAC) A measure of the amount of alcohol present in a person's blood. (page 243)

Blood pressure The force of blood pushing against the blood vessel walls. (page 189)

Body image How you view your body. (page 109)

Body language Facial expressions, eye contact, gestures, and posture. (page 63)

Body system A group of organs that perform a body function. (page 177)

C

Calorie A unit of heat that measures the energy available in foods. (page 100)

Cancer A disease caused by abnormal cells that grow out of control. (page 284)

Carbohydrates (kar·boh·HY·drayts) Sugars and starches contained in foods. (page 95)

Carbon monoxide (KAR·buhn muh·NAHK·syd) A poisonous, odorless gas produced when tobacco burns. (page 222)

Cardiopulmonary resuscitation (CPR) A rescue measure that attempts to restore heartbeat and breathing. (page 314)

Cells The basic building blocks of life. (page 177)

Character The way you think, feel, and act. (page 36)

Cholesterol (kuh·LES·tuh·rawl) A waxy chemical our bodies produce and need in small amounts. (page 106)

Chromosomes (KROH·muh·sohmz) Tiny strands of matter that carry the codes for inherited traits. (page 210)

Chronic (KRAH·nik) Long-lasting. (page 283)

Circulatory system Allows the body to move blood to and from tissues. (page 188)

Cirrhosis (suh·ROH·sis) Destruction and scarring of the liver tissue. (page 243)

Communicable (kuh·MYOO·nih·kuh·buhl) **disease** A disease that can be spread. (page 268)

Communication The clear exchange of ideas and information. (page 15)

Compromise A skill in which each side gives up something in order to reach an agreeable solution. (page 83)

Conflicts Disagreements in ideas, beliefs, or interests. (page 87)

Consequence A result. (page 16)

Conservation The saving of resources. (page 320)

Consumer Someone who buys products or services. (page 155)

Contagious (kuhn·TA·juhs) You can spread the virus to others by direct or indirect contact. (page 272)

Cool-down Gentle activity to slow down after exercise. (page 131)

Cooperation Working together for the common good. (page 75)

Coupons Slips of paper that save you money on certain brands. (page 158)

Culture The collected beliefs, customs, and behaviors of a group. (page 9)

Cumulative (KYOO·myuh·luh·tiv) **risk** The addition of one risk factor to another, increasing the chance of harm or loss. (page 17)

Cuticle (KYOO·ti·kuhl) A nonliving band of outer skin. (page 150)

D

Dandruff Flaking of the outer layer of dead skin cells. (page 149)

Decision A choice that you make. (page 16)

Dehydration A condition caused by too much water loss. (page 134)

Depression An emotional problem marked by long periods of hopelessness and despair. (page 51)

Dermis The thicker inner layer of the skin. (page 147)

Diabetes (dy·uh·BEE·teez) A disease that prevents the body from using the sugars and starches in food for energy. (page 191)

Diaphragm (Dy·uh·fram) A large muscle at the bottom of the chest. (page 185)

Digestion The process by which your body breaks down food into small nutrient particles. (page 185)

Digestive (dy·JES·tiv) **system** The body system that controls the digestion process. (page 185)

Disease (dih·ZEEZ) A condition that affects the proper functioning of the body or mind. (page 268)

Drug A substance that changes the structure or function of the body or mind. (page 242)

Drug abuse The use of any drug in a way that is unhealthy or illegal. (page 253)

Drug misuse Taking medicine in a way that is not intended. (page 162)

Drug rehabilitation A process in which a the person relearns how to live without the abused drug. (page 255)

 E

Earthquake The shaking of the ground as rock below the surface moves. (page 311)

Eating disorder Extreme eating behavior that can seriously damage the body. (page 110)

Egg cell The female reproductive cell. (page 206)

Emotions Feelings such as joy, love, or fear. (page 41)

Empathy The ability to identify and share another person's feelings. (page 74)

Emphysema (em·fuh·*See*·muh) A disease that occurs when tiny air sacs in the lungs lose their elasticity, or ability to stretch. (page 223)

Endocrine (EN·duh·krin) **system** A body system containing glands that regulate growth and other important activities. (page 203)

Endurance (en·DER·uhns) The ability to keep up a physical activity without becoming overly tired. (page 123)

Environment (en·VY·ruhn·muhnt) The sum total of your surroundings. (page 9)

Epidermis The thinner outer layer of the skin. (page 147)

Excretory (EK·skruh·tohr·ee) **system** Gets rid of some of the wastes your body produces and also maintains fluid balance. (page 186)

Exercise Planned, structured, repetitive physical activity that improves or maintains physical fitness. (page 125)

 F

Family The basic unit of society. (page 67)

Farsightedness The ability to see objects at a distance while close objects look blurry. (page 152)

Fats A nutrient found in fatty animal tissue and plant oils. (page 95)

Fertilization The joining of a female egg cell with a male reproductive cell. (page 207)

Fetal (FEE·tuhl) **alcohol syndrome (FAS)** A group of permanent physical and mental problems caused by alcohol use during pregnancy. (page 248)

Fetus A developing, unborn baby from the eighth week until birth. (page 212)

Fiber Tough, stringy part of raw fruits, raw vegetables, whole wheat, and other whole grains. (page 95)

Fire extinguisher A device which releases chemicals that smother flames. (page 302)

First aid The care given to an injured or ill person until regular medical care can be supplied. (page 312)

First-degree burn A burn in which only the outer part of the skin is burned and turns red. (page 316)

FITT principle A method for safely increasing aspects of your workout without injuring yourself. (page 128)

Flexibility The ability to move body joints through a full range of motion. (page 124)

Fluoride A substance that fights tooth decay. (page 146)

Fossil (FAH·suhl) **fuel** Coal, oil, and natural gas. (page 319)

Fraud Deliberately trying to trick consumers into buying a product or service. (page 158)

Friendship A special type of relationship between people who enjoy being together. (page 73)

Frostbite Freezing of the skin. (page 135)

Fungi (FUHN·jy) Primitive single- or many-celled organisms that cannot make their own food. (page 270)

 G

Gang A group whose members often uses violence or takes part in criminal activity. (page 84)

Generic (juh·NEHR·ik) Products that imitate name-brand products but are sold in plain packages. (page 158)

Genes (JEENZ) The basic units of heredity. (page 210)

Goals Something you hope to accomplish. (page 20)

Guarantee A promise to refund your money if the product does not work as claimed. (page 157)

Habit A pattern of behavior that you follow almost without thinking. (page 7)

Hallucinogen (huh·LOO·suhn·uh·jenz) An illegal drug that causes the user's brain to distort images and to see and hear images that are not real. (page 252)

Hazard A possible source of harm. (page 300)

Health A combination of physical, mental/emotional, and social well-being. (page 4)

Health care Any services provided to individuals or communities that promote, maintain, or restore health. (page 163)

Health insurance An insurance policy that covers most health-care costs. (page 166)

Health skills Skills that help you become and stay healthy. (page 12)

Heart The muscle that acts as the pump for the circulatory system. (page 189)

Heat exhaustion An overheating of the body that can result from dehydration. (page 134)

Heredity The process by which biological parents pass traits to their children. (page 8)

HIV The virus that causes AIDS. (page 278)

Hormones (HOR·mohnz) Powerful chemicals, produced by glands, which regulate many body functions. (page 41)

Hurricane (HER·uh·kayn) A strong tropical windstorm with driving rain. (page 309)

Hygiene (HY·jeen) Actions you take to improve or maintain your health. (page 309)

Hypothermia (hy·poh·THER·mee·uh) A sudden and dangerous drop in body temperature. (page 306)

Illegal drugs Drugs that are made and used purely for their effects. (page 249)

Immune (ih·MYOON) **system** A group of cells, tissues and organs that fight disease. (page 274)

Immunity Resistance to infection. (page 274)

Infection The result of pathogens or germs invading the body, multiplying, and harming some of your body's cells. (page 274)

Inhalant (in·HAY·luhnts) A substance whose fumes or vapors are inhaled or breathed in. (page 250)

Insulin A hormone produced by the pancreas. (page 286)

Joints Places where one bone meets another. (page 182)

Lifestyle activities Physical activities that are part of your day-to-day routine or recreation. (page 121)

Long-term goal A goal that you hope to achieve within a period of months or years. (page 21)

Loyal Faithful. (page 74)

Lungs The main organs of the respiratory system. (page 191)

Lymphocyte (LIM·fuh·syt) A white blood cells that attack pathogens or harmful germs. (page 274)

Managed care A health insurance plan that saves money by limiting people's choice of doctors. (page 167)

Marijuana (mar·uh·WAHN·uh) An illegal drug that comes from the hemp plant. (page 249)

Media The various methods of communicating information, including newspapers, magazines, radio, television, and the Internet. (page 10)

Medicines Drugs used to treat, cure, or prevent diseases or other medical conditions. (page 159)

Menstruation (men·stroo·AY·shuhn) Blood, tissue, and the unfertilized egg flow out of the body. (page 207)

Minerals (MIN·uh·ruhls) Elements in foods that help your body work properly. (page 96)

Mood disorder A serious emotional problem where a person's mood goes from one extreme to another. (page 51)

Muscular system All the muscles in your body. (page 183)

MyPyramid food guidance system A system designed to help Americans make healthful food choices. (page 98)

Narcotics (nar·KAH·tics) Strong drugs that relieve pain. (page 251)

Natural disaster An event caused by nature that results in widespread damage, destruction, and loss. (page 308)

Nearsightedness The ability to see objects close to you while distant objects look blurry. (page 152)

Negative peer pressure Pressure you feel to go along with harmful behaviors or beliefs of your peers. (page 228)

Neglect The failure of parents to provide their children with basic physical and emotional care and protection. (page 71)

Negotiation (neh·GOH·shee·AY·shuhn) The process of talking about a conflict and deciding how to reach a compromise. (page 83)

Neighborhood Watch programs Programs in which residents are trained to identify and report suspicious activity. (page 304)

Nervous system The control and communication system of the body. (page 192)

Neuron (NOO·rahnz) A cell that carries electrical messages. (page 192)

Nicotine (NIH·kuh·teen) A drug found in tobacco that speeds up the heartbeat and affects the central nervous system. (page 222)

Noncommunicable diseases Diseases that do not spread. (page 269)

Nurture Fulfill physical, mental/emotional, and social needs. (page 69)

Nutrients (NOO·tree·ents) Substances in food that your body needs to carry out its normal functions. (page 94)

Nutrition (noo·TRIH·shun) The process of taking in food and using it for energy, growth, and good health. (page 94)

Obese Significantly overweight. (page 108)

Organ A structure made up of different types of tissues that all work together. (page 177)

Overdose Taking a fatal amount of a drug. (page 253)

Over-the-counter (OTC) medicine Medicine available without a written order from a doctor. (page 159)

Ozone (OH·zohn) A special form of oxygen. (page 319)

Passive smokers Nonsmokers who breathe in secondhand smoke. (page 232)

Pathogen A microscopic organism that causes communicable diseases. (page 269)

Pedestrian A person traveling on foot. (page 303)

Peer mediation (mee·dee·AY·shuhn) A process in which a specially trained student listens to both sides of an argument to help the people reach a solution (page 83)

Peer pressure The influence that people your age may have on you. (page 76)

Peers Friends and other people in your age group. (page 9)

Physical abuse Involves the use of physical force. (page 71)

Physical activity Any kind of movement that causes your body to use energy. (page 120)

Physical fitness The ability to handle everyday physical work and play without becoming tired. (page 121)

Plaque (PLAK) A soft, colorless, sticky film containing bacteria that grows on your teeth. (page 145)

Poison control center A community agency that helps people deal with poisoning emergencies. (page 316)

Pollute (puh·LOOT) To make unfit or harmful for living things. (page 318)

Prejudice (PREH·juh·dis) An opinion or fear formed without having facts or firsthand knowledge. (page 82)

Prenatal care Special care to ensure that the mother and her baby remain healthy. (page 212)

Prescription (prih·SKRIP·shuhn) **medicine** Medicine sold only with a written order from a doctor. (page 159)

Prevention Practicing health and safety habits to remain free of disease and injury. (page 12)

PRICE Protect, rest, ice, compress, and elevate. (page 134)

Proteins (PROH·teens) Nutrients that provide the building blocks your body needs for growth. (page 95)

Protozoa (proh·tuh·ZOH·uh) Single-celled organisms that have a nucleus. (page 270)

Puberty (PYOO·bur·tee) The time when you start developing physical characteristics of adults of your gender. (page 203.)

R

Recovery To overcome an addiction and return to a mostly normal life. (page 254)

Recovery heart rate How quickly your heart rate returns to normal right after exercise is stopped. (page 130)

Recycling Recovering and changing items so they can be used for other purposes. (page 320)

Refusal skills Ways of saying no. (page 78)

Reinforce Support. (page 33)

Relationship A connection you have with another person or group. (page 62)

Reliable Dependable. (page 74)

Reproductive system The body system that makes it possible to create offspring. (page 206)

Rescue breathing A substitute for normal breathing in which someone forces air into the victim's lungs. (page 313)

Resilience The ability to work through and recover from disappointment. (page 34)

Respiratory system Enables you to breathe. (page 191)

Resting heart rate The number of times your heart beats per minute when you are relaxing. (page 129)

Risk The chance of harm, injury, or loss. (page 16)

Role model A person whose success or behavior serves as a good example for others. (page 39)

S

Saturated (SAT·chur·a·tuhd) **fats** Fats found in many animal products such as butter, meat, and cheese. (page 106)

Second-degree burn A serious type of burn in which the damaged area blisters or peels. (page 316)

Secondhand smoke A mixture of the smoke given off by the burning end of tobacco products and the smoke exhaled by smokers. (page 232)

Self-concept The view you have of yourself. (page 32)

Self-esteem A measure of how much you like and respect yourself. (page 34)

Sexual abuse Any mistreatment of a child or adult involving sexual activity. (page 71)

Sexually transmitted diseases (STDs) Communicable diseases spread from one person to another through sexual activity. (page 277)

Short-term goal A goal that you plan to accomplish in a short time. (page 21)

Side effect Any reaction to a medicine other than the one intended. (page 160)

Skeletal system A body system consisting of bones and the tissues connecting them. (page 181)

Smog A yellow-brown haze that forms when sunlight reacts with impurities in car exhaust. (page 319)

Smoke alarm A device that makes a warning noise when it senses smoke. (page 302)

Snuff Finely ground tobacco that is inhaled or held in the mouth or cheeks. (page 226)

Sodium A mineral that helps control the amount of fluid in your body. (page 106)

Specialist (SPEH·shuh·list) A doctor trained to handle particular health problems. (page 164)

Sperm The male reproductive cells. (page 208)

Spinal cord A tube of neurons that runs along the spine. (page 192)

Sports gear Sports clothing and safety equipment. (page 132)

Stamina (STA·mih·nuh) Your ability to stick with a task or activity for a long period of time. (page 123)

Stimulant (STIM·yuh·luhnts) A drug that speeds up the body's functions. (page 250)

Strength The ability of your muscles to exert a force. (page 123)

Stress Your body's response to changes around you. (page 45)

Substance abuse Using illegal or harmful drugs, including any use of alcohol while under the legal drinking age. (page 256)

Suicide The deliberate act of taking one's own life. (page 51)

Sunscreen A cream or lotion that filters out some UV rays. (page 148)

Tar A thick, oily, dark liquid that forms when tobacco burns. (page 222)

Target heart rate The level at which your heart and lungs receive the most benefit from a workout. (page 130)

Tartar (TAR·tuhr) When plaque hardens into a shell on your teeth and can not be brushed away. (page 145)

Technology The use of scientific ideas to improve the quality of life. (page 10)

Third-degree burn A very serious burn in which deeper layers of skin and nerve endings are damaged. (page 317)

Tissues Groups of similar cells that do the same kind of work. (page 177)

Tolerance (TAHL·er·ence) The ability to accept other people as they are. (page 82)

Tolerance A need for increasing amounts of a substance to achieve the same effect. (page 160)

Tornado (tor·NAY·doh) Whirling, funnel-shaped windstorms that drops from the sky to the ground. (page 310)

Trans fats Fats that start off as oils and are made solid through processing. (page 106)

Tumor A mass of abnormal cells. (page 284)

Unit price Cost per unit of weight or volume. (page 157)

Vaccine (vak·SeeN) A dead or weakened pathogen introduced into your body. (page 275)

Vaccines (vak·SeeN) Medicines that protect you from getting certain diseases. (page 160)

Values Beliefs you feel strongly about that help guide the way you live. (page 18)

Violence The use of physical force to harm someone or something. (page 84)

Viruses (VY·ruh·suhz) Tiny, nonliving particles that invade and take over healthy cells. (page 269)

Vitamins (VY·tuh·muhns) Nutrients that help regulate body functions. (page 96)

Voluntary health agencies Organizations that work to treat and eliminate certain diseases. (page 165)

Warm-up Gentle activity that prepares your body for exercise or sport. (page 130)

Wellness A state of well-being, or total health. (page 7)

Withdrawal A series of physical and mental symptoms that occur when a person stops using an addictive substance. (page 254)

A

Abdominal thrusts/presiones abdominales Movimientos en los que se ejerce una presión hacia arriba sobre el diafragma, para desalojar un objeto que bloquea la vía respiratoria.

Abstinence/abstinencia No participar en conductas de riesgo para la salud.

Abuse/abuso Un patrón de maltrato a otra persona.

Accident/accidente Un evento inesperado que resulta in algún daño.

Accident chain/accidente en cadena Una secuencia de sucesos que muchas veces termina en un daño accidental.

Accidental injury/herida accidental Una herida causada por sucesos inesperados.

Acid rain/lluvia ácida Lluvia contaminada debido a la quema de combustibles fósiles.

Acne/acné Una afección de la piel causada por la actividad excesiva de las glándulas sebáceas.

Addiction/adicción La necesidad física o mental del cuerpo de consumir una droga u otra sustancia.

Adolescence/adolescencia El periodo de vida entre la niñez y la adultez.

Adrenaline/adrenalina Una hormona que prepara el cuerpo para responder el estrés.

Advocacy/defensa Tomar una posición para hacer una diferencia.

AIDS/SIDA Condición caracterizada por infecciones que terminan con la vida y cuenta de células T por debajo de 200.

Alcohol/alcohol Una sustancia producida por una reacción química en carbohidratos.

Alcoholism/alcoholismo Una enfermedad en la cual una persona tiene necesidad física y mental de alcohol.

Allergen/alergeno Una sustancia que causa una reacción alérgica.

Allergy/alergia La sensibilidad del cuerpo a ciertas sustancias.

Alternative/alternativa Un modo distinto de pensar o actuar.

Anabolic steroids/esteroides anabólicos Drogas sintéticas basadas en una hormona masculina.

Antibiotics/antibióticos Medicina que mata o para el crecimiento de bacterias y otros gérmenes específicos.

Antibodies/anticuerpos Sustancias químicas producidas específicamente para combatir a una sustancia invasora determinada.

Anxiety/Ansiedad Sentimiento de incertidumbre o preocupación sobre lo que pueda pasar.

Anxiety disorder/Desorden de ansiedad Un serio problema emocional que mantiene a una persona de funcionar normalmente.

Assertive/firme Dispuesto a defenderte de una manera positiva.

Asthma/asma Enfermedad crónica en la cual las vías respiratorias se irritan e hinchan.

Astigmatism/astigmatismo Una cornea o lente deformado que causa que objetos se vean ondulados o borrosos.

Attitude/actitud Lo que crees o sientes sobre alguien o algo.

 B

Bacteria/bacteria Organismo de una sola célula sin núcleo, extremadamente pequeño.

Behavior/Comportamiento La forma en la cual actúas en diferentes situaciones y eventos en tu vida.

Biodegradable/biodegradable Que se descompone naturalmente, sin causar contaminación.

Blood alcohol content (BAC)/contenido de alcohol en la sangre Una medida de la cantidad de alcohol presente en la sangre de una persona.

Blood pressure/presión sanguínea La
fuerza que ejerce la sangre sobre las paredes
de los vasos sanguíneos.

Body image/imagen corporal Como vez tu
cuerpo.

Body language/lenguaje corporal
Expresiones faciales, contacto visual, gestos
y postura.

Body system/sistema del cuerpo Un grupo
de órganos que ejecuta una función del
cuerpo.

Calorie/caloría Una unidad de calor que
mide la energía disponible en los alimentos.

Cancer/cáncer Una enfermedad causada por
células anormales cuyo crecimiento está
fuera de control.

Carbohydrates/carbohidratos Azucares y
almidones contenidos en las comidas.

Carbon monoxide/monóxido de carbono
Un gas tóxico e inodoro que produce el
tabaco al quemarse.

**Cardiopulmonary resuscitation (CPR)/
resucitación cardiopulmonar** Una
medida de primeros auxilios que intenta
restaurar el ritmo cardiaco y la respiración.

Cells/células Los bloques de estructura básica
de la vida.

Character/carácter La manera en que
piensas, sientes y actúas.

Cholesterol/colesterol Un químico
ceroso que el cuerpo produce y necesita en
pequeñas cantidades.

Chromosomes/cromosomas Filamentos
minúsculos de materia que llevan los
códigos de rasgos heredados.

Chronic/crónico De larga duración.

Circulatory system/sistema circulatorio El
sistema del cuerpo que mueve la sangre
desde y hacia los tejidos.

Cirrhosis/cirrosis La destrucción y
cicatrización del tejido del hígado.

**Communicable disease/enfermedad
contagiosa** Una enfermedad que se puede
propagar.

Communication/comunicación El
intercambio claro de ideas e información.

Compromise/compromiso Una habilidad
en la cual cada lado deja algo para llegar a
una solucion conforme.

Conflicts/conflictos Desentendimientos en
ideas, creencias o intereses.

Consequence/consecuencia Un resultado.

Conservation/conservación La protección
de los recursos naturales.

Consumer/consumidor Una persona que
compra productos o servicios.

Contagious/contagioso Capaz de
propagarse a otros por contacto directo o
indirecto.

Cool-down/enfriamiento Actividad
suave para desacelerarse después de hacer
ejercicios.

Cooperation/cooperación Trabajar juntos
por el bienestar común.

Coupons/cupónes Boletas de papel que te
permite ahorrar dinero en ciertas marcas.

Culture/cultura La colección de creencias,
costumbres y comportamientos de un grupo.

Cumulative risk/riesgo acumulativo La
adición de un riesgo a otro aumentando la
posibilidad de daño o pérdida.

Cuticle/cutícula Una banda de piel externa
sin vida que rodea las unas de las manos y
los pies.

Dandruff/caspa Descamado de la capa
externa de las células muertas de la piel del
cuero cabelludo.

Decision/decisión Las opciones que eliges.

Dehydration/deshidratación Condición
causada por mucha perdida de agua.

Depression/depresión Un problema
emocional marcado por largos periodos de
desesperación.

Dermis/dermis La capa más gruesa y profunda de la piel.

Diabetes/ diabetes Una enfermedad que le impide al cuerpo utilizar los azúcares y almidones de los alimentos para crear energía.

Diaphragm/diafragma Un músculo grande ubicado en la parte inferior del pecho.

Digestion/digestión El proceso por el cual el cuerpo deshace la comida en pequeñas partículas nutrientes.

Digestive system/sistema digestivo El sistema del cuerpo que controla el proceso digestivo.

Disease/enfermedad Condición que afecta el funcionamiento propio del cuerpo o la mente.

Drug/droga Toda sustancia que altera la estructura o el funcionamiento del cuerpo o de la mente.

Drug abuse/abuso de drogas El uso de cualquier droga en una forma no saludable o ilegal.

Drug misuse/uso indebido de las drogas El tomar medicinas sin cumplir con las indicaciones.

Drug rehabilitation/rehabilitacion de las drogas Un proceso por el cual una persona vuelve a aprender como vivir sin el abuso de una droga.

Earthquake/terremoto El sacudimiento de la tierra mientras la capa de roca por debajo de la superficie terrestre se mueve.

Eating disorder/desorden alimenticio Comportamiento alimenticio extremo que puede dañar seriamente el cuerpo.

Egg cell/óvulo La célula reproductora del cuerpo femenino.

Emotions/emociónes Sentimientos.

Empathy/empatía La habilidad de identificar y compartir los sentimientos de otra persona.

Emphysema/enfisema Una enfermedad que ocurre cuando los pequeños sacos de aire en los pulmones pierden la elasticidad o la capacidad de estirarse.

Endocrine system/sistema endocrino Sistema del cuerpo que contiene glándulas que regulan el crecimiento.

Endurance/resistencia Habilidad de mantener una actividad física sin cansarte demasiado.

Environment/ambiente La suma total de tus alrededores.

Epidermis/epidermis La capa externa y más delgada de la piel.

Excretory system/sistema excretor Un sistema del cuerpo que elimina algunos de los desechos producidos en el cuerpo y que mantiene el equilibrio de los líquidos.

Exercise/ejercicio Actividad física planeada, estructurada y repetitiva que mejora o mantiene el buen estado físico.

Family/familia La unidad básica de la familia.

Farsightedness/hipermetropía La capacidad de ver claramente los objetos a la distancia, mientras los objetos cercanos se ven borrosos.

Fats/grasas Un nutriente que se encuentra en tejido animal grasos y como aceites de plantas.

Fertilization/fertilización La unión de una célula reproductiva femenina con una célula reproductiva masculina.

Fetal alcohol syndrome/síndrome de alcoholismo fetal Un conjunto de problemas físicos y mentales permanentes causados por el consumo de alcohol de la madre durante el embarazo.

Fetus/feto El niño en desarrollo desde las ocho semanas hasta el nacimiento.

Fiber/fibra Parte dura y resistente de frutas crudas, vegetales crudos, trigo entero y otros granos.

Fire extinguisher/extintor Un dispositivo que suelta químicos que sofocan llamas de fuego.

First aid/primeros auxilios Los cuidados que se dan a una persona herida o enferma, durante una emergencia hasta que se obtiene asistencia médica regular.

First-degree burn/quemadura de primer grado Una quemadura en que sólo la capa exterior de la piel se quema y enrojece.

FITT principle/principio FITT Un método para aumento seguro de los aspectos de tu entrenamiento sin dañarte a ti mismo.

Flexibility/flexibilidad La habilidad de mover las articulaciones del cuerpo a través del arco completo de movimiento.

Fluoride/fluoruro Una sustancia que combate las caries.

Fossil fuel/combustible fósil Estos son carbón, aceite, y gas natural.

Fraud/fraude Engaño o estafa deliberada.

Friendship/amistad Un tipo especial de relación entre personas que disfrutan el estar juntas.

Frostbite/congelación Congelamiento de la piel.

Fungi/hongos Organismo primitivo de una o mas células que no puede producir su propio alimento.

Gang/cuadrilla Un grupo en el cual los miembros, muchas veces, utilizan violencia para ser parte en actividad criminal.

Generic/genérico Productos que imitan productos de marca pero son vendidos en paquetes simples.

Genes/genes Las unidades básicas de la herencia.

Goal/meta Algo que esperas lograr.

Guarantee/garantía Una promesa de que en caso de que el producto no trabaje como dicho tu dinero será devuelto.

Habit/hábito Un patrón de conducta que sigues casi sin pensarlo.

Hallucinogen/alucinógeno Una droga ilegal que causa que el cerebro de la persona que lo use cree imágenes distorsionadas.

Hazard/peligro Una posible fuente de daño.

Health/salud Una combinación de bienestar físico, mental, emocional y social.

Health care/cuidado medico Cualquier servicio proveído a individuos o comunidades que promueve, mantiene y recobra la salud.

Health insurance/seguro medico Póliza de seguro que cubre la mayor parte de los costos del cuidado de la salud.

Health skills/habilidades de salud Habilidades que ayudan a ser y mantenerte saludable.

Heart/corazón El músculo que funciona como una bomba para el aparato circulatorio.

Heat exhaustion/agotamiento por calor Un recalentamiento de el cuerpo que resulta en deshidratación.

Heredity/herencia Proceso por el cual los padres biológicos pasan rasgos a los hijos.

HIV/VIH El virus que causa el SIDA.

Hormones/hormonas Sustancias químicas potentes producidas por las glándulas que regulan muchas funciones del cuerpo.

Hurricane/huracán Una tormenta tropical fuerte con vientos y lluvia torrencial.

Hygiene/higiene Acciones tomadas para mejorar y mantener tu salud.

Hypothermia/hipotermia Un descenso repentino y peligroso de la temperatura del cuerpo.

Illegal drugs/drogas ilegales Drogas que son hechas y usadas solo por sus efectos.

Immune system/sistema inmunológico Un grupo de células, tejidos y órganos que combaten las enfermedades.

Immunity/inmunidad Una resistencia a un agente infeccioso.

Infection/infección El resultado de la invasión, multiplicación y daño celular de un agente patógeno en tu cuerpo.

Inhalant/inhalante Una sustancia cuyos vapores se inhalan para producir alucinaciones.

Insulin/insulina Una hormona producida por el páncreas.

Joint/articulación Lugars donde hueso se unen con otros huesos.

Lifestyle activities/actividades de vida diaria Actividades físicas que son parte de la rutina diaria o recreación.

Long-term goal/meta a largo plazo Una meta que esperas lograr en un periodo de meses o años.

Loyal/leal Fiel.

Lungs/pulmones Los órganos principales del aparato respiratorio.

Lymphocyte/linfocito Un glóbulo blanco que ataca a los agentes patógenos.

Managed care/asistencia médica regulada Un plan de seguro médico que ahorra dinero al limitar la selección de doctores de las personas.

Marijuana/marihuana Una droga ilegal que proviene de la planta del cáñamo.

Media/medios de difusión Los diversos métodos de comunicación de información que comprenden los periódicos, revistas, radio, televisión e Internet.

Medicine/medicina Una droga que se usa para curar o prevenir enfermedades u otras afecciones.

Menstruation/menstruación Sangre, tejidos y óvulos no fertilizados son expulsados del cuerpo.

Minerals/minerales Elementos en comidas que ayudan al cuerpo a trabajar adecuadamente.

Mood disorder/desorden de humor Un serio problema emocional en el cual el humor de una persona cambia de un extremo al otro.

Muscular system/aparato muscular Todos los músculos de tu cuerpo.

MyPyramid food guidance system/ pirámide alimenticia Un systema diseñada para ayudar a Americanos a tomar decisiones alimenticias saludables.

Narcotics/narcóticos Drogas fuertes que calman el dolor y desaceleran las funciones del cuerpo.

Natural disaster/desastre natural Un evento causado por la naturaleza que resulta en danos extensos, destrucción y perdida.

Nearsightedness/miopía La capacidad de ver claramente los objetos cercanos, mientras los objetos lejanos se ven borrosos.

Negative peer pressure/presión negativa de compañeros Presión que sientes de seguir comportamientos que causen daño o creencia de tus compañeros.

Neglect/negligencia La falla de los padres de proveer a sus niños con protección y cuidado físico y emocional básico.

Negotiation/negociación El proceso de hablar sobre un conflicto y decidir como llegar a un acuerdo.

Neighborhood Watch program/programa de vigilancia vecina Un programa en el cual los residentes están entrenados para identificar y reportar actividades sospechosas.

Nervous system/sistema nervioso El sistema de control y comunicación del cuerpo.

Neuron/neurona Una célula que transporta mensajes eléctricos.

Nicotine/nicotina Una droga que acelera el ritmo cardiaco y afecta al sistema nervioso central.

Noncommunicable disease/enfermedad no contagiosa Una enfermedad que no se propaga.

Nurture/criar Satisfacer las necesidades físicas, emocionales, mentales y sociales de una persona.

Nutrients/nutrientes Substancias en las comidas que tu cuerpo necesita para desarrollar las funciones normales.

Nutrition/nutrición El proceso de consumir comida y utilizarla como energía, crecimiento. Y buena salud.

Obese/obeso(a) Sobrepeso excesivo.

Organ/órgano Una estructura formada por diferentes clases de tejidos que ejecutan una función específica.

Overdose/sobredosis Consumir una cantidad de droga fatal.

Over-the-counter medicine/medicina sin receta Una medicina que se puede adquirir sin receta de un médico.

Ozone/ozono Una forma especial del oxígeno.

Passive smokers/fumador passivo No Fumadores que respiran el humo de segunda mano.

Pathogen/patógeno Un organismo microscópico que causa enfermedades comunicables.

Pedestrian/peatón Una persona que se traslada a pie.

Peer mediation/ meditación de compañeros Un proceso en el cual un estudiante especialmente capacitado escucha los dos lados de un argumento para ayudar a personas a llegar a un acuerdo.

Peer pressure/presión de compañeros La influencia que personas de la misma edad tiene en ti.

Peers/pares Amigos y otras personas de tu grupo de edad.

Physical abuse/abuso físico Implica el uso de fuerza física.

Physical activity/actividad física Cualquier movimiento que cause que el cuerpo use energía.

Physical fitness/buen estado físico La capacidad de llevar a cabo trabajos físicos y juegos cotidianos sin sentirte cansado.

Plaque/placa bacteriana Una película blanda, incolora y pegajosa que contiene bacterias que se reproducen en los dientes.

Poison control center/centro de control de veneno Una agencia de la comunidad que ayuda a personas con emergencias relacionadas con venenos.

Pollute/contaminar Hacer lo impropio o dañoso para cosas vivientes.

Prejudice/prejuicio Una opinión o miedo formada sin tener hechos ni conocimiento de primera mano.

Prenatal care/cuidado pre-natal Cuidado especial para asegurar que el bebe y la madre se mantenga saludables.

Prescription medicine/medicina bajo receta Una medicina que puede venderse sólo con receta escrita por un médico.

Prevention/prevención Mantener hábitos de salud y seguridad para estar libre de enfermedades y lesiones.

PRICE Protege, descansa, hiela, comprime, y eleva.

Proteins/proteínas Nutrientes que proveen los bloques de estructura que el cuerpo necesita para crecer.

Protozoa/protozoos Organismos de una sola célula con núcleo.

Puberty/pubertad El tiempo en el cual comienzas a desarrollar características físicas de adultos de tu genero.

Recovery/recuperación Superar una adicción y regresar a tener una vida mayormente normal.

Recovery heart rate/ritmo cardiaco de recuperación Que tan rápido tu corazón tu corazón regresa a lo normal después de haber parado el ejercicio.

Recycling/reciclaje Recuperar y cambiar un objeto para usarlo con otro propósito.

Refusal skills/habilidades de denegación Formas de decir no.

Reinforce/refuerza Ayuda, soporte.

Relationship/relación Una conexión que tienes con otra persona o grupo.

Reliable/confiable De fiar.

Reproductive system/sistema reproductivo Sistema en el cuerpo que hace posible crear descendientes o bebes.

Rescue breathing/respiración de rescate Un método que reemplaza la respiración normal en el cual otra persona le llena los pulmones de aire a la víctima.

Resilience/resistencia La habilidad de sobrepasar y recuperarte de decepción.

Respiratory system/aparato respiratorio Un aparato del cuerpo que permite la respiración.

Resting heart rate/ritmo cardiaco de descanso Numero de veces que el corazón late por minuto cuando estas relajado.

Risk/riesgo La posibilidad de daño o pérdida.

Role model/modelo ejemplo Una persona que sus éxito o comportamiento sirve de buen ejemplo para otros.

Saturated fats/grasas saturadas Grasas que se encuentran en muchos productos animales como mantequilla, carnes, y queso.

Second-degree burn/quemadura de segundo grado Un tipo de quemadura grave en la que se forman ampollas o se despelleja la piel quemada.

Secondhand smoke/humo de segunda mano Una mezcla del humo producido cuando productos de tabaco son quemados, y el humo exhalado por fumadores.

Self-concept/autoimagen La percepción que tienes de ti mismo.

Self-esteem/autoestima Una medida de cuanto te quieres y te respetas a ti mismo.

Sexual abuse/abuso sexual Cualquier maltrato de un niño o un adulto que implique actividad sexual.

Sexually transmitted diseases (STDs)/ enfermedades transmitidas sexualmente Enfermedades comunicables pasadas de una persona a otra a través de actividad sexual.

Short-term goal/meta a corto plazo Una meta que planeas lograr en un corto periodo de tiempo.

Side effect/efecto colateral Toda reacción a una medicina diferente de la que se procura.

Skeletal system/sistema esquelético Un sistema del cuerpo que consiste de huesos y y los tenjidos que los conectan.

Smog/smog Una neblina de color amarillento-café que se forma cuando la luz solar reacciona con las impurezas en el gas de los escapes de los automóviles.

Snuff/rape Tabaco molido finamente que es inhalado o mantenido en la boca o las mejillas.

Sodium/sodio Un mineral que ayuda a controlar la cantidad de líquido en tu cuerpo.

Specialist/especialista Doctor entrenado para atender problemas de la salud específicos.

Sperm/espermatozoides Células reproductivas masculinas.

Spinal cord/médula espinal Un conducto de neuronas que se encuentra a lo largo de la columna vertebral.

Sports gear/accesorios deportivos Ropa para deportes y equipo de seguridad.

Stamina/stamina La habilidad de poder realizar y mantener una actividad por largos periodos de tiempo.

Stimulant/estimulante Una droga que acelera las funciones del cuerpo.

Strength/fortaleza La capacidad de tus músculos para ejercer una fuerza.

Stress/estrés La respuesta de tu cuerpo a los cambios que ocurren a tu alrededor.

Substance abuse/abuso de sustancias Consumo de drogas ilegales o nocivas, incluso el consumo del alcohol en cualquiera de sus formas antes de la edad legal para beber.

Suicide/suicidio El acto deliberado de quitarse la vida propia.

Sunscreen/bloqueador solar Crema o loción que filtra algunos rayos UV.

Tar/alquitrán Un líquido espeso, aceitoso y oscuro que forma el tabaco al quemarse.

Target heart rate/ritmo cardiaco Deseado el nivel en el cual tu corazón y tus pulmones reciben mayor beneficio de tu entrenamiento.

Tartar/sarro Una materia dura que se forma cuando la placa bacteriana se acumula en los dientes.

Technology/tecnología El uso de ideas científicas para mejor la calidad de vida.

Third-degree burn/quemadura de tercer grado Una quemadura muy grave que daña las capas más profundas de la piel y las terminaciones nerviosas.

Tissues/tejidos Grupos de células similares que tienen la misma función.

Tolerance/tolerancia Un estado por el cual el cuerpo se acostumbra a los efectos de una medicina y necesita mayores dosis para producir el mismo efecto.

Tolerance/tolerancia Necesidad de aumentos de cantidades de una sustancia para conseguir el mismo efecto.

Tornado/tornado Una tormenta en forma de torbellino que gira en grandes círculos y que cae del cielo a la tierra.

Trans fats/grasas de transporte Grasas que empiezan como aceites y se convierten en sólidos a través de procesos.

Tumor/tumor Una masa de células anormales.

Unit price/precio por unidad Costo por unidad de peso o volumen.

Vaccines/vacunas Un patógeno débil o muerto introducido en el cuerpo.

Values/valores Creencias importantes para ti que te ayudan a guiar la forma en que vives.

Violence/violencia El uso de fuerza física para hacer daño a alguien o a algo.

Viruses/virus Pequeñas partículas sin vida que invaden y toman control de células saludables.

Vitamins/vitaminas Nutrientes que ayudan a regular las funciones del cuerpo.

Voluntary health agency/agencia de salud voluntaria Organizaciónes que trabaja para tratar y eliminar algunas enfermedades.

Warm-up/precalentamiento Una actividad moderada que prepara a tu cuerpo para hacer ejercicio.

Wellness/salud Estado de bienestar total.

Withdrawal/síntomas de abstinencia Una serie de síntomas físicos y mentales que ocurren cuando una persona deja de consumir una sustancia adictiva.

Index

A

AA (Alcoholics Anonymous), 247
Abdominal muscles, *184*
Abdominal thrusts, 314–315, *315*
Abstinence, 44
  choosing, 80
  definition of, 44
  and sexually transmitted diseases, 280
Abuse. *See also* Drug abuse
  accessing information on, 72
  definition of, 71
Accessing information
  about HIV and AIDS, *281*
  before buying products, 168–169
  on family abuse, 72
  as health skill, 13, *13*
  and puberty, 214–215
Accident chain, 297, *297*
Accidental injuries, 296, 297
Acid (drug), 252
Acid rain, 319
Acne, 148
Acquired immunodeficiency syndrome. *See* AIDS
Active listening, 65
Addiction
  to alcohol, 246–248, *247*
  definition of, 223
  to drugs, 254–255
  to tobacco, 223
Adolescence, 202–205
  definition of, 202
  emotional changes during, 41
  endocrine system during, 203, *203*
  mental/emotional development during, 204–205
  physical development during, 203–204, *204*
  social development during, 205
Adoptive families, *68*
Adrenal glands, *203*
Adrenaline, *47, 203*
Adulthood, 213, 216

Adults
  choking by, 314–315
  problem-solving help from, 79
  rescue breathing for, 313, *313*
Advertising, 155
  analyzing influences of, *14, 157*
  of athletic shoes, *134*
  communicating messages in, *63*
  consumer skills and, 169
  and healthy choices, 10
  and tobacco, 229, *229*
Advocacy
  and citizenship, 38
  and dangers of smoking, 233
  definition of, 15, 38
  fire escape plan, *302*
  as health skill, 13
  for peace, 84
  for safety and environment, *321*
  and Students Against Destructive Decisions, *257*
  volunteering, *166*
  for waste reduction, 322–323
Aerobic exercise, 125, 138
AIDS (acquired immunodeficiency syndrome), 277, 278, *281*. *See also* HIV
Air, pollution of, 318–319
Airline flights, and smoking, 232
Al-Anon, 247, 258
Alateen, 247
Alcohol
  and addiction, 246–247, 247
  alternatives to using, 258, *258*
  avoiding, 256–259
  and the body system, 180
  chemical dependency on, 246–247
  dangers of, 242–245
  definition of, 242
  in different drinks, *244*
  effects of, 242–244
  and HIV, 280
  and peer pressure, 77
  pregnancy and, 248

  and risk behavior, 246
  and STDs, 280
  and violence, 84
Alcohol poisoning, 243
Alcoholics Anonymous (AA), 247
Alcoholism, 71, 247
Allergens, 285
Allergies, 285
Alternate energy sources, *319*
Alveoli, *191*
American Red Cross, 313
Anabolic steroids, 251
Anaerobic exercise, 125
Analyzing influences
  of advertising, *157*
  on decision making, 24–25
  as health skill, *13, 14, 14*
  and media influence on self-concept, *34*
Anatomy, puberty and changes in, 204, *204*
Anesthesiologists, 239
Angel dust, 252
Anorexia nervosa, 110
Antibiotics, 160
Antibodies, 274
Anxiety, 46
Anxiety disorders, 51
Appendicitis, 290
Appreciation, 68, *69*
Arteries, 189, *189*
Assertiveness, 66, 257
Asthma, 232, 285
Astigmatism, 152
Athletic shoes, *134*
Attitudes (positive), 11
Avoidance
  of alcohol, 256–259
  of conflict, 82
  of drugs, 256–261
  of gangs, 84
  of harmful situations, 84–85
  of harmful substances, 256–259
  of violence, 84–85
  of weapons, 84

B

BAC (Blood alcohol content), 243
Bacteria, 270, *270*
Balance
    and health, 4, 5
    physical activity with eating, 105, 106
Ball-and-socket joints, 182
Beans, 101
Behavior(s). *See also* Practicing healthful behaviors
    assertive, 64, 66, 257
    definition of, 11
    to maintain a healthy body, 194–195
    to reduce risks. *See* Risky behaviors
    self-destructive, 34, 77
    violent, 84
Belly pain, 290
Biceps, *184*
Binge eating, 110
Biodegradable supplies, 321
Biological clock, 196
Bladder, 187, *224*
Bleeding, first aid for, 314
Blended families, 67, *68*
Blizzards, 310
Blood, 188–190, 190, *279*
Blood alcohol content (BAC), 243
Blood cells, 190, *190*
Blood pressure, 189, 283
Blood vessels, 189, *225*
Bodies
    image of, 109
    respect for others', *109*
Body language
    in communication, 65
    definition of, 63
Body systems, 176–180. *See also* specific systems
    caring for, 178–180
    circulatory system, *178, 179,* 188–190
    digestive system, *178, 179,* 185–186
    endocrine system, *178,* 203, *203*
    excretory system, *178, 179,* 186–187
    functions of, *178*

    healthy behaviors related to, 194–195
    immune system, 274, *279*
    interrelationship of, 178, *179*
    joints, 182
    muscular system, 183, *184*
    nervous system, 192, 193
    parts of the body, 176–177
    reproductive system, 206–209, *207, 208, 209*
    respiratory system, *178, 179,* 187, 191
    skeletal system, *178, 179,* 181–182, 182
Bones, 181, *182, 183*
Braces, 147
Brain, 192, *225*
Brain stem, *193*
Brainstorming, 83
Breaks, 317
Breathing, 191, 285, 314
    rescue, 313, *313*
    for stress management, *48*
Bronchi, *191*
Brushing (teeth), 146, *146*
Bulimia, 110
Bullies, 88
Burns, 316–317
Buying skills. *See* Consumer skills

C

Calcium, 181, *183*
Calories
    burned during physical activity, *121*
    and daily values, 104
    definition of, 100
    paying attention to, 103
Camping safety, 306–307
Cancer, 226, 284–285
Capillaries, 189
Carpooling, 21
Carbohydrates, 95
Carbon dioxide, *189, 191*
Carbon monoxide, 221, *225*
Cardiac muscle, 183
Cardiopulmonary resuscitation (CPR), 314
Careers in health
    anesthesiologist, 239
    dental hygienist, 173
    dietetic technician, 117

    family counselor, 91
    health teacher, 29
    medical technologist, 293
    occupational safety and health specialist, 327
    pediatrician, 219
    physicians, 199
    school counselor, 59
    sports medicine, 141
    substance abuse counselor, 265
Caring, 38
CDC (Center for Disease Control and Prevention), *281*
Cells, 177
    blood, 190, *190*
    egg, 206, 207, 209
    healthy vs. abnormal growth of, 284
    neuron, 192
    reproductive, 211
Center for Disease Control and Prevention (CDC), *281*
Central nervous system, 192, *193*
Cerebellum, *193*
Cerebrum, 192, *193*
Cervix, *207*
Chain for goals, *21*
Character, 36–40
    in action, 40
    and caring, 38
    and citizenship, 38, 39, *231, 243*
    and common colds, *273*
    definition of, 36
    developing good, 56
    development of, 38–39
    and fairness, 38, *251*
    and family responsibility, *68*
    and goals, *22*
    and good influences, *9*
    and healthy home environment, 33
    and medicines, *162*
    and prejudice, *82*
    and respect, 37, *109*
    and responsibility, *68, 162, 213*
    and role models, 39
    traits of, 37–38, 56
    in TV programs, *40*
Cheating, *19*

CHECK-CALL-CARE first aid strategy, 312–313
Checkups
    dental, 147
    eye, 152
    health, 164
Chemical dependency
    on alcohol, 247
    on drugs, 254
    on tobacco, 223
Chemotherapy, 284
Childhood, 212
Children
    choking by, 314–315
    rescue breathing for, 313, *313*
Chlamydia, *278*
Choking, 314–315
Cholera, 319
Cholesterol, 106
Chromosomes, 210–211
Chronic diseases, 283
Circulatory system, *178, 179,* 188–190
Cirrhosis, 243
Citizenship, 38, 39, *231, 243*
Cocaine, 250–251
Colds, common, 273, *273*
Colon, *186,* 187, *224*
Color vision, 170
Commercials
    Infomercials, *14*
    messages in, *63*
Communicable diseases, 272–276
    definition of, 268
    prevention of, 275–276
    sexually transmitted diseases, 277–281
Communication. *See also* Messages
    by abstinence, 44
    active listening in, 65
    definition of, 15, 62
    by e-mail, 63, 64
    by empathy, 74
    as health skill, *13*
    and health skills, *13,* 15
    and parents, 68
    skills for, 62–66. *See also* Communication skills
Communication skills, 62–66, 65
    conflict resolution through, 83
    family meetings, *70*

and online safety, *64*
    refusal skills as, 78–80
    styles of, 65, 66
    types of, 63, 64
Communities, safety in, 304
Community health, 163–167
Community support groups, 231
Comparison shopping, 156–157
Complex carbohydrates, 95
Compromise, 83
Conflict resolution, 81–85
    communication in, 83
    as health skill, *13,* 15
    and health skills, *13,* 15
    negotiation for, 83
    T.A.L.K. strategy, 83
    working things out, 86–87
Conflict(s), 81–85
    causes of, 82
    definition of, 81
    prevention of, 82
    violence resulting from, 84
Connecting neurons, 192
Consequences, definition of, 16
Conservation, 320–321, 324
Consumer, definition of, 155
Consumer skills, 155–158, 168–169
Contact lenses, 152
Contagious diseases, 272
Cool-down exercises, 131
Cooperation, 75
Cornea, 152, *152*
Counseling, 72
Couples (family units), *68*
Coupons, 158
CPR (Cardiopulmonary resuscitation), 314
Crack, 250–251
Crank (drug), 251
Crisis centers, 72
Critical thinking, for health/ wellness, 29
Culture, 9
Cumulative risk, 17
Cuticle, 150

D
Daily Value, 104
Dandruff, 149
Deafness, 153, *153*
Death of family member, 70

Decibels, 154
Decision making
    analyzing influences on, 24–25
    and avoiding drug abuse, 260–261
    and choosing healthy foods, 112–113
    and eating disorders, *111*
    as a health skill, *13, 19*
    H.E.L.P. criteria for, 17
    and help for emotional problems, *53*
    and peers, *19*
    process of, 17–19
    steps in, 17–18, *19*
    and television, *18*
Decisions, definition of, 16
Dehydration, 134
Deltoid, *184*
Dental checkups, 147
Dental hygienist, 147, 173
Dental insurance, 167
Dentists, 147
Depression, 51
Dermatologists, 148
Dermis, 147
Development. *See* Growth and development
Diabetes, 109, 286–287
Diaphragm, 191
Diary of foods, 114
Dietary Guidelines for Americans (USDA), 103, 105–107
Dietary practices. *See* Nutrition
Dietetic technicians, 117
Digestion, 95, 185
Digestive system, *178, 179,* 185–186
Direct physical contact, 271
Discount stores, 158
Disease prevention
    for cancer, 284
    for communicable diseases, 275–276
    for diabetes, 287
    for heart disease, 283
    for HIV and STDs, 280
    for noncommunicable and hereditary diseases, 283, 284, 287
    for sexually-transmitted diseases, 280

Disease treatment
    for asthma, 285
    for cancer, 284
    for diabetes, 287
    for heart disease, 283
    for HIV/AIDS, 280
Diseases
    causes of, 268–271
    communicable, 272–276
    defenses against, 274
    definition of, 268
    fetal alcohol syndrome, 248
    germs causing, 271
    hereditary, 282–287
    and immune system, 274
    noncommunicable, 282–287
    from polluted water, 319
    risk of inherited, 8
    sexually transmitted, 277–281
Divorce, 69
Doctors, 162, 163, 219
Domestic airline flights, 232
Drinking. See Alcohol
Driving, 243
Drowning prevention, 306
Drug abuse, 253–255
    and addiction, 254–255
    avoiding, 260–261
    definition of, 253
    help for abusers' families, 258
    and rehabilitation, 255
Drug misuse, 162
Drug rehabilitation, 255
Drug-free zones, 304
Drugs
    abuse of, 253–255
    addiction to, 254–255
    alcohol as a, 242–245, 244
    alternatives to using, 258, 258
    avoiding, 256–261
    and the body system, 180
    chemical dependency on, 254
    definition of, 242
    and help for abusers' families,
        258
    and HIV infection, 280
    illegal, 249–252
    medicines, 159–162
    misuse of, 162
    and peer pressure, 77
    saying no to, 262
    and STDs, 280
    and violence, 84
    withdrawal from, 254–255

E
Early adulthood, 213
Ears, 154–155
Earthquakes, 311
Eating. See Nutrition
Eating disorders, 110–111
Ecstasy, 252
Egg cells, 206, 207, 209, 211
Electrical safety, 301
E-mail, 63, 64
Emergencies
    first aid for, 312–317
    weather, 308–311
Emotional abuse, 71
Emotional health. See Mental/
    emotional health
Emotional neglect, 71
Emotional problems, 50–53
    common types of, 51–52
    help for, 52, 53
Emotional support, 69
Emotions, 41–44
    and abstinence, 44
    during adolescence, 205
    causes of, 41
    dealing with, 54–55
    definition of, 41
    expression of, 43
    managing strong, 43
    problems with, 50–53
    types of, 42
    understanding your, 42
Empathy, 74
Emphysema, 223
Endocrine system, 178, 203, 203
Endurance, 123–124, 138
Energy, redirection of, 49
Environment, 9
Environmental protection,
    318–321
Enzymes, 185
Epidermis, 147
Esophagus, 186
Espelage, Dorothy, 88
Excretory system, 178, 179,
    186–187
Exercise(s)
    aerobic, 125
    anaerobic, 125
    appealing, 130
    cool-down, 131
    definition of, 125
    fitness ratings for, 128

and FITT principle, 128
    for flexibility, 124
    and lifetime fitness, 138
    for strength, 123
    for stress relief, 49
    warm-up, 130
Expiration date, 161
Extended family, 67, 68, 69
Eyeglasses, 152
Eyes, 151–152, 170

F
Facial expressions, 63, 64
Fairness, 38, 251
Fallopian tubes, 207
Falls, preventing, 301
False claims, 158
Family counselors, 91
Family meetings, 70
Family(-ies), 67–72
    changes in, 69, 70
    and character, 38–39, 68
    definition of, 67
    and family meetings, 70
    as health influence, 9
    informing, 85
    roles of members in, 68
    serious problems in, 71
    sources of help for, 72
    strong foundations for, 69
    and tobacco use, 230
    types of, 67, 68
Farsightedness, 152
FAS (fetal alcohol syndrome),
    248
Fats, 95, 101, 106
FDA. See U.S. Food and Drug
    Administration
Feelings. See Emotions
Females
    adolescent changes in, 204
    reproductive system for,
        206–208, 207
Fertilization, 207, 211
Fetal alcohol syndrome (FAS),
    248
Fever, 274
Fiber, 95
Fight-or-flight response, 47
Fingernails, 150, 150
Fingers, 224
Fire extinguisher, 302
Fire safety, 302, 302

First aid, 312–317
　for bleeding, 314
　for breaks, 317
　for burns, 316–317
　CHECK-CALL-CARE strategy
　　for, 312–313
　for choking, 314–315
　definition of, 312
　for poisoning, 316
　and pressure points, *314*
　and rescue breathing, 313,
　　313
　for sprains, 317
First-degree burns, 316, *316*
Fitness. *See* Physical activity and
　fitness
FITT principle for physical
　activity, 128
Flash flood, 310
Flexibility, 124, 138
Floods, 309–310
Flossing (teeth), 146, *146*
Flu, 273
Fluoride, 146
Foldables
　for alcohol and drugs, *241,
　　263*
　for body systems, *175, 197*
　for disease prevention, *267,
　　291*
　for growth and development,
　　201, 217
　for health/wellness, *3, 4, 27*
　for healthy relationships, *61,
　　89*
　for mental/emotional health,
　　31, 57
　for nutrition, *93, 115*
　for personal health, *143, 171*
　for physical activity, *119, 139*
　for safety and environment,
　　295, 325
　for tobacco/smoking, *221, 237*
Food choices, 9
Food labels, 104
Food(s). *See also* Nutrition
　and alcohol, 244
　balancing physical activity
　　with, 105, 106
　and the body system, 179
　choosing, 112–113
　controlling amount of, 103
　and diabetes, 287

　diary for, 114
　eating a variety of, 103
　and food groups, 100–101
　healthy choices of, 102–107
　safety, 105
　temperatures, 105
Fossil fuels, 319
Foster families, 68
Fraud, 158
Frequency of exercise, 128
Friends, 73–77
　health influences of, 9
　pressure from, 76–77, 230
　qualities of good friends, 74
　reasons for choosing, 73
　tips for making, 74
Friendship(s), 205
　being responsible in, *243*
　building strong, 75
　and decision making, *19*
　definition of, 73
Frostbite, 135, 310
Fruits, 100
　dried, 107
　eating more, 105
Fungi, 270

G
Gallbladder, *186*
Gangs, 84
Generic brands, 158
Genes, 210
Genital herpes, *278*
Genital warts, *278*
Germs, 271, 274
Gestures, 63
Glands, *186,* 203, *203*
Goal setting, 20–22
　for fitness, 126–127
　as health skill, *13*
　for increasing activity level,
　　128
　and personal fitness plan,
　　136–137
　and protecting your health,
　　288–289
Goals, 20–23
　chain for, *21*
　definition of, 20
　and good character, 22
　tips for achieving, 22, 23
Gonorrhea, *278*
Good example, setting a, *9*

Government-provided health
　care, 165, 167
Grains, 100, 105
Grief, managing, 70
Ground water, 319
Groups, goal setting for, 22
Growth and development
　during adolescence, 202–205
　of body systems, 176–180
　and heredity, 210–211
　hormones' role in, 203, 205
　and human reproduction,
　　206–209
　and life cycle, 212–213
　prenatal, 211, *211,* 212
Growth pattern, *108*
Guarantee, product, 157
Gums. *See* Teeth and gums
Guns, 301

H
Habit(s)
　creating healthy, 5
　definition of, 7
　eating, 102–103
　safe, *299*
Hair, 149
Hallucinogens, 252
Hand washing, 275, *276*
Hazardous wastes, 320
Hazards, 300
Head lice, 149
Headaches, 290
Health
　definition of, 4
　menstrual, 207–208
Health care services, 163–167
Health fraud, 158
Health influences, 8–11
　behavior as, 11
　culture as a, 9
　environment as a, 9
　family as a, 9
　and good character, *9*
　heredity as a, 8
　of the media, 10
　of peers, 9
　and personal attitudes, 11
　technology as a, 10
Health insurance, 166–167
Health inventories
　for the body system, 175, 198
　for health/wellness, 3, 26, 28

for nutrition, 93, 116
for safety and environment, 295
Health online
  for alcohol and drugs, *241, 244, 248, 252, 255, 258, 264*
  for the body system, *175, 180, 184, 187, 189, 193, 198*
  for disease prevention, *267, 271, 275, 283, 287, 292, 317*
  for emotional/mental health, *44*
  for growth and development, *201, 204, 205, 209, 213, 218*
  for health/wellness, *3, 5, 6, 7, 11, 14, 15, 18, 19, 23, 28*
  for healthy relationships, *61, 66, 69, 72, 77, 80, 85, 90*
  for mental/emotional health, *31, 35, 40, 43, 49, 52, 53, 58*
  for nutrition, *93, 96, 97, 100, 101, 107, 110, 111, 116*
  for personal health, *143, 148, 150, 154, 158, 162, 167, 172*
  for physical activity, *119, 123, 124, 125, 131, 135, 140*
  for safety and environment, *320*
  for safety and the environment, *295, 297, 299, 304, 307, 310, 311, 321, 326*
  for sexually transmitted diseases, *280, 281*
  taking your pulse, *189*
  for tobacco/smoking, *221, 226, 229, 232, 233, 238*
Health quiz
  for disease prevention, 267, 292
  for healthy relationships, 61, 90
  for physical activity, 119, 140
  for tobacco/smoking, 221, 238
Health skills, 12–15. *See also* specific skills
  and accessing information, *13*
  and advocacy, *13*, 15
  analyzing influences as a, *13, 14, 14*
  and communication, *13*, 15

and conflict resolution, *13,* 15
and decision making, *13,* 19
definition of, 12
goal setting, *13*
list of, *13*
practicing healthful behaviors, *13*
prevention as a, 12
refusal skills as a, *13,* 15
and staying informed, 13
and stress management, 13, *13*
Health teachers, 29
Health triangle, 4–6, 5
Hearing, 153, *153,* 154. *See also* Ears
Heart, *184, 189, 189, 224*
Heart and lung endurance, 123
Heart attacks, 283, 290
Heart disease, 109, 283
Heart flutters, 290
Heart rate, *129,* 129–130, *130*
Heat exhaustion, 134
Helmets, 132
H.E.L.P. decision criteria, 17
Hepatitis, 273, *273, 278*
Hereditary diseases
  allergies, 285
  heart disease, 282, 283
  types of, 282
Heredity, 8, *204,* 210–211
Heroin, 252
High blood pressure, 283
Hiking safety, 306–307
Hinge joints, 182
Hitchhiking, 85
HIV (human immunodeficiency virus), 278–280, 280. *See also* AIDS
  accessing information on, *281*
  detection of, 280
  treatment for, 280
Home, safety in, 300–302
Home alone, 84
Home environment, 33
Honesty, 65
Hormones, 203, *203,* 205
  definition of, 41
  in growth and development, 203, 205
Human immunodeficiency virus. *See* HIV
Human reproduction. *See* Reproductive system

Hurricanes, 309
Hygiene
  definition of, 144
  dental, 146, 147
  hand washing and, 275, *276*
  menstrual, 208
Hypertension, 283
Hypothermia, 306

I

"I" messages, 65
Identity. *See* Self-concept
Illegal drugs, 249–252
  anabolic steroids, 251
  definition of, 249
  hallucinogens, 252
  inhalants, 250
  marijuana, 249
  narcotics, 251–252
  stimulants, 250, 253, 254
Illness, 12. *See also* Diseases
IM Express
  for alcohol and drugs, *241, 264*
  for growth and development, *201, 218*
  for mental/emotional health, *31*
  for personal health, *143*
  for safety and environment, *326*
IM (Instant messaging), *64*
Immune system, 274, *279*
Immunity, 274
Immunizations, 164
Indirect contact, 271
Infancy, 212
Infants, choking by, 315
Infections
  definition of, 274
  ear, 153
Influences, analyzing. *See* Analyzing influences
Influenza, 273
Infomercials, *14*
Information, accessing. *See* Accessing information
Inhalants, 250
Injuries. *See also* Safety
  accidental, 296, 297
  definition of, 296
  prevention of, 12, 84, 297
  PRICE formula for, 134
  weather-related, 134–135

Inner ear, *153*
Instant messaging (IM), *64*
Insulin, *203, 286, 287*
Insurance, health, 166, 167
Intensity of exercise, 128
Intestines, *186*
Involuntary muscles, 183
Iris (eye), *152*

J

Joint-custody families, *68*
Joints, 182, *182*

K

Kick Butts Day (KBD), 236
Kidneys, 187
Kitchen safety, 301

L

Labels
 on alcohol, *248*
 medicine, 161, *161*
 on over-the-counter
  medicines, 161, *161*
 product, *156*
Land pollution, 320
Language arts connections
 and character, *39*
 healthy sayings, *13*
 scientific word parts, *179*
Late adulthood, 213
Laxatives, 110
Lens (eye), *152*
Leukoplakia, *224*
Lice, 149
Life cycle, human, 212–213
Lifestyle activities, 121
Listening skills, 83
Liver, *186*
Log for fitness, 129, *129*
Long-term goals, 21
Loudness of sounds, 154
Lower respiratory system, *191*
Loyalty, 74
LSD (drug), 252
Lungs, 123, *189,* 191, *191*
Lymphocytes, 274

M

Males
 adolescent changes in, *204*
 reproductive system in, 208,
  208, 209
Managed care, 167

Managing stress. *See* Stress
  management
Marijuana, 249
Math connections
 finding heart rate, *130*
 smoking costs, *233*
MDMA, 252
Meat, 101
Media, *18*
 and athletic shoes, *134*
 commercials, *63*
 definition of, 10
 influence on self-concept of,
  34
 influences of the, 155
 and role models, *40*
 and tobacco, 228, *228*
Mediation, peer, 83
Medicaid, 167
Medical technologists, 293
Medicare, 167
Medicines, 159–162
 definition of, 159
 effect on body of, 160
 and good character, *162*
 labels on, 161, *161*
 misuse/abuse of, 162
 negative reactions to, 160
 over-the-counter, 159, 161,
  161
 prescription, 159, 162
 responsible use of, 159–162
 safety with, 161
 types of, 159
Melanin, *148*
Menstruation, 207–208
Mental/emotional development,
  204–205
Mental/emotional health, 4–6,
  32–56
 adolescence and emotional
  changes, 41
 benefits of physical activity
  on, 121, 122
 and coping with stress, 45–49
 and drug abuse, 254
 and eating disorders, 110–111
 and emotional problems,
  50–53
 and expression of emotions,
  43
 and grief management, 70
 inventory of, 26

and practice of abstinence, 44
 and self-concept, 32–35
 and types of emotions, 42
Messages
 mixed, 63
 and self-concept, 33
 and tobacco, 228, *228*
Methamphetamine, 251
Middle adulthood, 213
Middle ear, *153*
Migraine headaches, 290
Milk, 101
Minerals, 96
Mirroring of thoughts/feelings,
  65
Misleading claims, 158
Misuse, drug, 162
Mixed messages, 63
Mononucleosis, *273*
Mood disorders, 51
Mood swings, 41, *41,* 205
Motive in advertising, 14
Motor neurons, 192
Mouth, *224*
MRI machines, 10
Mucous membranes, 274
Muscles, 123–125, *179, 184. See
  also* Physical activity and
  fitness
Muscular endurance, 123
Muscular system, *178, 179,* 183,
  184
Music
 hearing and, 154
 and managing emotions, *43*
MyPyramid Food Guidance
  System, 98–101, *99,* 103

N

Nails, *150*
Nar-Anon, 258
Narcotics, 251–252
National Health Council, *281*
National Institutes of Health
  (NIH), *281*
Natural disasters, 308–311
Nearsightedness, 152
Negative messages, 33
Negative peer pressure, 77
 and abstinence, 80
 and conflict, 84
 and tobacco, 228
Negative stress, 47

Neglect, 71
Negotiation, 83
Neighborhood Watch programs,
        304
Nerve cells, *176*, 177
Nervous system, *176, 178, 179,*
        192, *193*
Neurons, 192
Nicotine, 221, 223, *224*, 231
Nicotine patches, 230
NIH (National Institutes of
        Health), *281*
Noise level, hearing and, 154
Noncommunicable diseases,
        282–287
    allergies, 285
    asthma, 285
    cancer, 284–285
    causes of, 282
    definition of, 269
    diabetes, 286–287
    heart disease, 283
Nonsmokers, 232
Nuclear families, *68*
Nuclear wastes, 320
Nurture, definition of, 69
Nutrients, 94–97
    carbohydrates, 95
    definition of, 94
    and digestion, 185
    fats, 95
    minerals, 96
    proteins, 95
    vitamins, 96, *96*
    water, 96, 97, *97*
Nutrition
    choosing healthy foods,
        112–113
    definition of, 94
    and eating disorders, 110–111
    and eating habits, 102–103
    and food choices, 102–107
    and food groups, 100–101
    and food labels, 104
    guidelines for, 103, 105–107
    and keeping a food diary, 114
    and MyPyramid food
        guidance system, 98–101,
        99
    and nutrient needs, 94–97
    and serving sizes, 100–101
Nuts, 107

O

Obesity, 108–109, *286*
Obsessive-compulsive disorder
        (OCD), 51
Occupational safety and health
        specialists, 327
OCD (Obsessive-compulsive
        disorder), 51
Oil glands, *148*
Online information. *See* Health
        online
Open mind (keeping a), 36
Optic nerve, *152*
Organs, *177*
Orthodontists, 147
OTC medicines. *See* Over-the-
        counter medicines
Outcomes, decision, 17
Outdoor safety, 305–307
    for hiking and camping,
        306–307, *307*
    for water and boating,
        305–306
    for weather emergencies,
        308–311
Outer ear, *153*
Ovaries, *203, 206, 207, 207*
Overdose (drug), 254
Over-the-counter (OTC)
        medicines, 159
    safety in using, 161
Oxygen
    in the body system, *178, 179,*
        188, 189, *189*, 191
    ozone as form of, 319
    and smoking, 221, *225*
Ozone, 319

P

Pain, 134, 160, 290
Pancreas, *186*, 203
Parents
    communication with, 68
    and negative peer pressure, 77
    separation of, 69
    supervision by, 88
Passive smokers, 232
Pathogens, 269, 270, 274
PCP (angel dust), 252
Peanuts, 107
Pectoral muscle, *184*
Pedestrians, 303
Pediatrician, 219

Peer mediation, 83
Peer pressure, 76–77, *77*
    negative, 77, 84, 228
    positive, 76, 256
    and refusal skills, 78–80
    and tobacco, 228
Peers
    and decision making, *19*
    definition of, 9, 76
Penis, *208*
Period. *See* Menstruation
Peripheral nerves, *193*
Peripheral nervous system, 192
Personal attitudes, 11
Personal eating plan, 100
Personal fitness plan, 126–131,
        136–137
Personal health
    choosing health products,
        155–158
    and consumer skills, 168–169
    and ears, 151–154
    and eyes, 151–154, 170
    and health care, 163–167
    inventory of, 26
    and medicines, 159–162
    and teeth, skin and hair,
        144–150
Perspiration, 133
Pharmacists, 161, 162, 168
Phobia, 51
Phone, 64
Photographs, working with
    for alcohol and drugs, *240*
    for the body system, *174*
    and disease prevention, *266*
    for growth and development,
        200
    for health/wellness, *2*
    for healthy relationships, *60*
    for mental/emotional health,
        30
    for nutrition, *92*
    for personal health, *142*
    for physical activity, *118*
    for safety and environment,
        294
    for tobacco/smoking, *220*
Physical abuse, 71
Physical activity and fitness,
        122–125, 124–131
    aerobic, 125
    balancing food with, 105

benefits of, 121, 122, 123–125
and the body system, 179
calories burned during, *121*
and cool-down exercises, 130
definition of, 120
and diabetes, 287
and fitness log, 129, *129*
fitness ratings for, *128*
FITT principle, 128
for flexibility, 124
goal setting for, 136–137
and heart rate, *129*, 129–130, *130*
and lifestyle activities, 121
measuring fitness level, *127*
safety in, 132–135, *133*
and staying fit for life, 138
for strength, 123, 125
as stress relief, 49
and warm-up exercises, 130
Physical development, *204*
Physical health, 4–5
benefits of physical activity on, 122
and drug abuse, 253–254
inventory of, 26
Physical neglect, 71
Physicians, 199
Physiology, puberty and changes in, *167*, 204, *204*
Pituitary gland, *203*
Pivot joints, 182
Plaque, 145, 146
Plasma, 190
Platelets, 190
Poison control centers, 316
Poisoning, 243, 316
Poisonous plants, 316
Pollution, 318–321
Portion size, 103
Positive attitudes, 11
Positive messages, 33
Positive peer pressure, 76, 256
Positive stress, 46
Posture, 63
Practicing healthful behaviors
and appealing exercise, *130*
and building strong bones, *183*
and caring for the body system, 194–195
and dealing with feelings, 54–55

and online safety, *64*
for physical activity, *122*
and the reproductive system, *209*
and safe habits, *299*
Pregnancy, 80, 211, 248
Prejudice
definition of, 82
myth of positive, *82*
Prenatal care, 212
Prenatal development, 211, *211*, 212
Prescription medicines, 159, 162
labels for, 161, *161*
Pressure points, *314*
Prevention
of accidental injuries, 297
of cancer, 284
of communicable diseases, 275
of conflicts, 82
definition of, 12
of diabetes, 287
of drowning, 306
of heart disease, 283
of HIV and STDs, 280
of injuries, 12, 84, 297
of noncommunicable and hereditary diseases, 283, 284, 287
of sexually-transmitted diseases, 280
of violence in schools, 303–304
Preventive care, 163
PRICE formula for injuries, 134
Priorities, setting, 48
Product labels, *156*
Products. *See* Consumer skills
Protective gear (for sports), 12
Proteins, 95
Protozoa, 270
Puberty, 203, 204
accessing information about, 214–215
physical changes during, 204, *204*
Public health (government health care), 165, 167
Pulse rate. *See* Heart rate
Pupil (eye), *152*

Q
Quadriceps, *184*
Questions, asking, 83
Quiz. *See* Health quiz

R
Radiation treatments, 284
Reading guides
for alcohol and drugs, *242, 249, 253, 256*
for the body system, *176, 181, 185, 188*
for disease prevention, *272, 277, 282, 286*
for growth and development, *202, 206, 210*
for health/wellness, *4, 8, 12, 16, 20*
for healthy relationships, *62, 67, 73, 78, 81*
for mental/emotional health, *32, 36, 41, 45, 50*
for nutrition, *94, 98, 102, 108*
for personal health, *144, 151, 155, 159, 163*
for physical activity, *120, 126, 132*
for safety and environment, *296, 300, 305, 308, 318*
for sexually transmitted diseases, *277*
for tobacco/smoking, *222, 227, 230*
Reading skills
for alcohol and drugs, *245, 247, 248, 250, 251, 252, 254, 255, 257, 258*
for the body system, *178, 180, 182, 183, 187, 190, 191, 192*
for disease prevention, *269, 270, 271, 273, 275, 278, 280, 282, 283, 285, 287*
for growth and development, *178, 205, 208, 209, 212*
for health/wellness, *3, 6, 10, 11, 14, 21, 22*
for healthy relationships, *63, 64, 66, 68, 69, 70, 72, 75, 77, 79, 80, 83, 85*
for mental/emotional health, *31, 35, 38, 39, 41, 43, 44, 47, 49, 51, 52*

for nutrition, *97, 101, 103, 107, 108, 110*

for personal health, *144, 145, 149, 150, 152, 154, 158, 160, 162, 166, 167*

for physical activity, *122, 124, 125, 130, 131, 135*

for safety and environment, *296, 297, 302, 303, 304, 306, 307, 309, 310, 311, 315, 317, 319, 321*

for sexually transmitted diseases, *280*

for tobacco/smoking, *222, 226, 228, 232*

Recovery (from drugs), 254

Recovery heart rate, 130

Recycling, 320

Red blood cells, 190

Red Cross. *See* American Red Cross

Reducing waste, 320

Refusal skills, 78–80

  abstinence, 80

  definition of, 78

  for drugs/alcohol, 257, 262

  as health skill, *13*, 15

  S.T.O.P. strategy, *79*, 79–80

  against tobacco, 230, *231*, 234–235

Rehabilitation (from drugs), 255

Reinforce, 33

Relationships

  communication skills for, 62–66

  definition of, 62

  family, 67–72

  friends and peers, 73–77. *See also* peer pressure

  healthy. *See* Social health

Relaxation, 48, *48*

Reliability, 74

Reproductive cells, 211

Reproductive system, 206–209

  care of the, *209*

  definition of, 206

  female, 206–208, *207*

  male, 208, *208*, 209

Rescue breathing, 313, *313*

Resilience, 34

Resolving conflicts. *See* Conflict resolution

Respect

  as character trait, 37

  in friendships, 75

  for others' bodies and feelings, *109*

Respiratory system, *178, 179,* 187, 191

Responsibility, *162*

  as character trait, 38, 39

  in the family, 68, *68*

  and good character, *213*

Resting heart rate, 129

Retina, *152*

Reusing items, 320

Rh factor, 190

Risk

  cumulative, 17

  definition of, 16

Risky behaviors, 44

  and abstinence, 44, 80

  and alcohol use, 246

  and cumulative risk, 17

Road safety, 303, *303*

Role models

  definition of, 39

  on television, *40*

Roles (in the family), 68

S

SADD (Students Against Destructive Decisions), *257*

Safety, 296–311

  and the body system, 179–180

  drug, 161

  in exercising, 132–135, *133*

  and first aid, 312–317

  food, 105

  with medicines, 161

  online, *64*

  outdoors, 305–307

  and preventing accidents, 296

  on the road, 303, *303*

  in schools, 303

  in severe weather, 308–311

  on the trail, 306–307

  from violence, 84–85

Safety belts, 11

Saliva, 185, *186*, 274

Salivary glands, *186*

Salt, 106–107

Sartorius, *184*

Saturated fats, 106

Saving money, 158

Saying No, 262. *See also* S.T.O.P. strategy

Scale (for wellness), 7

Scalp problems, 149

School counselors, *59*

Schools

  dealing with bullies, 88

  violence prevention in, 303–304

  Science connections

  alternate energy sources, *319*

  bacteria, *270*

  deafness, *153*

  HIV, *280*

  and teeth and gums, *146*

Sclera (eye), *152*

Scrotum, *208*

Second-degree burns, 316, *316*

Secondhand smoke, 232

Sejnowski, Terrence, 196

Self-concept, 32–35

  definition of, 32

  media influence on, *34*

Self-control, 44

Self-destructive behaviors

  peer influence on, 77

  resiliency as defense against, 34

Self-esteem, 34

Self-help groups, 72

Self-image, 32

Sensory neurons, 192

Separation (of parents), 69

Serving sizes (food), 101–101, 104

Servings per container, 104

Sexual abuse, 71

Sexually transmitted diseases (STDs), 277–281

  AIDS, 278–280

  HIV, 278–280, *280*

  prevention of, 280

Shared interests, 73, 74

Shoes, athletic, *134*

Shopping, 156–158

Short-term goals, 21

Sicknesses. *See* Diseases

Side effects of medicines, 160

Simple carbohydrates, 95

Single-custody families, *68*

Single-parent families, *68*, 88

Situations, understanding, 17

Skeletal muscles, *183, 184*
Skeletal system, *178, 179,*
    181–182, 182
Skin, 147–148, 187, *224*
Skin cancer, 284
Skin cells, 177
Sleep, 196
Small intestine, *186*
Smog, 319
Smoke alarms, 302
Smokeless tobacco, *224, 226*
Smoking. *See* Tobacco
Smooth muscle, *183, 184*
Snacks, 102, 103, 106
Sneezing, *272, 273*
Snowstorms, 310
Snuff, 226
Social development, 205
Social health, 4–6, 62–88
    benefits of physical activity
        on, 122
    and bullies, 88
    and communication, 62–66
    and conflict resolution, 81–87
    and drug abuse, 254
    and family, 67–72
    and friends, 73–77
    inventory of, 6, 26
    and refusal skills, 78–80
Sodium, 106–107
Sound, loudness of, 154
Sources (in advertising), 14
Specialists, health care, 164,
    165. See also specific
    occupations
Sperm, 208, *208,* 209, 211
SPF. *See* Sun protection factor
Spiders, 51
Spinal cord, 192, *193*
Sports, 12, 39. *See also* Outdoor
    safety; Physical activity
    and fitness
Sports gear, 12, 132, *133, 297*
Sports medicine, *141*
Sprains, 317
Standardized Test Practice
    for alcohol and drugs, 265
    for the body system, 199
    for disease prevention, 293
    for growth and development,
        219
    for health/wellness, 29
    for healthy relationships, 91

    for mental/emotional health,
        59
    for nutrition, 117
    for personal health, 173
    for physical activity, 141
    for safety and environment,
        327
    for tobacco/smoking, 239
Staying informed, 13
STDs. *See* Sexually transmitted
    diseases
Steroids, anabolic, 251
Stimulants, 250, 253, 254
Stomach, 183, *184,* 186, *225,*
    290
S.T.O.P. strategy, *79,* 79–80
Strangers, 85
Strength, 123, 125, 138
Strep throat, *273*
Stress
    definition of, 45
    response to, 47, *47*
    sources of, 46
    types of, 46–47
Stress management, 45–49
    as health skill, 13, *13*
    and relaxation exercises, *48*
    strategies for, 48–49
Stroke, 283
Students Against Destructive
    Decisions (SADD), *257*
Substance abuse, 256, 257
Substance abuse counselor, 265
Sugar, 106
Suicide, 51–52
    definition of, 51
    warning signs of, 52
Sun exposure
    and eye health, 151
    and skin cancer, 284
    and skin health, 147–148
Sun protection factor (SPF), 148
Sunblocks, 148, 284
Sunscreen, 148, 284
Support, 75, 76
Support groups, 72, 258
Surgeon General's warning, 236
Surgery, cancer, 284
Sweat glands, *148*
Syphilis, *278*
Systems, body. *See* Body systems

T
T.A.L.K. conflict resolution
    strategy, 83
Tar, 221, *224*
Target heart rate, 130, *130*
Tartar, 145
T-cell, 278, *279*
Tears, 274
Technology, 10
Teeth and gums, 145–147
    brushing/flossing, 146, *146*
    dental visits, 147
    preventing problems with,
        146
    and tobacco, *224,* 226
    and tooth decay, *145*
Television. *See also* Media
    and decision making, *18*
    role models on, *40*
Temperatures (food), 105
Tension headaches, 290
Testes, *203, 208,* 209
Third-degree burns, *316,* 317
Throat, *224*
Thunderstorms, 309
Thyroid gland, *203*
Time management, 49
Time together (families), 69
Time-out, 83
Tinnitus, 153
Tissues, *176,* 177
Tobacco
    addiction to, 223
    and cancer, 284
    chemical dependency on,
        223
    and citizenship, 231
    and the cost of smoking, 233
    harmful effects of, 221–226,
        224–225
    and the media, 228, *228*
    and peer pressure, 77
    pressure to use, 228
    and quiting smoking, 230,
        231, 236
    reasons for use of, *228*
    refusal skills against, *234–235*
    smokeless, *224,* 226
    staying free of, 230–233
    substances in, 221
    teenagers and, 227–229, 236
    warning others about, *233*
    ways of refusing, *231*

Toenails, 150
Tolerance
    definition of, 82
    of medicines, 160
Tooth decay, *145*
Tornadoes, 310–311
Trachea, *191*
Trails, 306–307
Training techniques, 131
Trans fats, 106
Transfusions (blood), 190
Trash, 320
Triceps, *184*
Trustworthiness, 37
Tuberculosis, *273*
Tumors, 284
Type 2 diabetes, 286, *286*
Typhoid, 319

U
Ultraviolet (UV) rays, 147, 148,
    168
Umbilical cord, 212
Unit pricing, 157, *157*
Upper respiratory system, *191*
Urethra, *208, 209*
Urine, 187
U.S. Department of Agriculture
    (USDA), 98
U.S. Food and Drug
    Administration (FDA), 158,
    161
USDA (U.S. Department of
    Agriculture), 98
Uterus, 207, *207*
UV rays. *See* Ultraviolet rays

V
Vaccines, 160, 275, *275*
Vagina, *207*

Values, 17
Vas deferens, *208*, 209
Vegetables, 100, 105
Veins, 189, *189*
Violence, 303–304
    avoiding, 84
    definition of, 84
    strategies for avoiding, 84–85
Viruses, 269, 278, 279
Vision
    color, 170
    problems, 152
Vitamins, 96, *96*
Voluntary health agencies, 165,
    166
Voluntary muscles, 183
Volunteering, 165, *166*, 213

W
Warm-up exercises, 130
Waste disposal, 320
Waste reduction, 320, 322–323
Water
    benefits of drinking, 187
    as nutrient, 97, *97*
    pollution of, 319
    when exercising, 133
Water safety, 305–306
Weapons, 84, 304
Weather emergencies, 308–311
Weather-related injuries,
    134–135
Weight management, 108–111,
    179
Wellness, 7
West Nile Virus, *271*
White blood cells, 190, 274
Whole grains, 105
Withdrawal (from drugs),
    254–255

Words, communication
    through, 63
Writing skills
    for alcohol and drugs, *242,
        249, 253, 256*
    for the body system, *176, 181,
        185, 188*
    for disease prevention, *272,
        282, 286*
    for growth and development,
        202, 206, 210
    for health/wellness, *4, 8, 12,
        16, 20*
    for healthy relationships, *62,
        67, 73, 78, 81*
    for mental/emotional health,
        32, 36, 41, 45, 50
    for nutrition, *94, 918, 102,
        108*
    for personal health, *144, 151,
        155, 159, 163*
    for physical activity, *120, 126,
        132*
    for safety and environment,
        *296, 300, 305, 308, 312,
        318*
    for sexually transmitted
        diseases, *277*
    for tobacco/smoking, *221,
        222, 227, 230*

X
X chromosomes, 211

Y
Y chromosomes, 211

Photo Credits

Physical Activity and Fitness Guidelines

The Surgeon General's Report on Physical Activity and Health, along with the President's Council on Physical Fitness and Sports, identified fitness as a major public health concern. The Physical Fitness Objectives from *Healthy People 2010* for children and adolescents appear below.

Physical Activity in Children and Adolescents

- Increase the proportion of adolescents who engage in moderate physical activity for at least 30 minutes on 5 or more of the previous 7 days.

- Increase the proportion of adolescents who engage in vigorous physical activity that promotes cardiorespiratory fitness 3 or more days per week for 20 or more minutes per occasion.

- Increase the proportion of the Nation's public and private schools that require daily physical education for all students.

- Increase the proportion of adolescents who participate in daily school physical education.

- Increase the proportion of adolescents who spend at least 50 percent of school physical education class time being physically active.

- Increase the proportion of adolescents who view television 2 or fewer hours on a school day.

Physical Fitness Guidelines

Regular physical activity performed on a daily basis reduces the risk of developing illness or disease. Moderate physical activity can be achieved in a variety of ways, and the Centers for Disease Control and Prevention (CDC) have developed this list of examples showing moderate amounts of activity that can contribute to an individual's health.

Physical Activities Arranged by Energy Level and Time

- Washing windows or floors for 45-60 minutes

- Playing volleyball for 45 minutes

- Playing touch football for 30-45 minutes

- Gardening for 30-45 minutes

- Wheeling self in wheelchair for 30-40 minutes

- Walking 1 ¾ miles in 35 minutes (20 min/mile)

- Basketball (shooting baskets) for 30 minutes

- Bicycling 5 miles in 30 minutes

- Dancing fast (social) for 30 minutes

- Pushing a stroller 1 ½ miles in 30 minutes

- Raking leaves for 30 minutes

- Walking 2 miles in 30 minutes (15 min/mile)

- Water aerobics for 30 minutes

- Swimming laps for 20 minutes

- Wheelchair basketball for 20 minutes

- Basketball (playing a game) for 15-20 minutes

- Bicycling 4 miles in 15 minutes

- Jumping rope for 15 minutes

- Running 1 ½ miles in 15 minutes (10 min/mile)

- Shoveling snow for 15 minutes

- Stair walking for 15 minutes

Source: CDC, Physical Activity and Health, A Report of the Surgeon General

Healthy People 2010

Healthy People 2010 is a set of 28 health objectives established for the nation to achieve over the first decade of the new century. The objectives, listed on these pages, were created after the Surgeon General's Report in 2000 identified specific National Health Promotion and Disease Prevention goals. The chapters and lessons in *Teen Health* provide strategies for addressing many of the objectives of Healthy People 2010.

1. **Access to Quality Health Services** Improve access to comprehensive, high-quality health care services.

2. **Arthritis, Osteoporosis, and Chronic Back Conditions** Prevent illness and disability related to arthritis and other rheumatic conditions, osteoporosis, and chronic back conditions.

3. **Cancer** Reduce the number of new cancer cases as well as the illness, disability, and death caused by cancer.

4. **Chronic Kidney Disease** Reduce new cases of chronic kidney disease and its complications, disability, death, and economic costs.

5. **Diabetes** Through prevention programs, reduce the disease and economic burden of diabetes, and improve the quality of life for all persons who have or are at risk for diabetes.

6. **Disability and Secondary Conditions** Promote the health of people with disabilities, prevent secondary conditions, and eliminate disparities between people with and without disabilities in the U.S. population.

7. **Educational and Community-Based Programs** Increase the quality, availability, and effectiveness of educational and community-based programs designed to prevent disease and improve health and quality of life.

8. **Environmental Health** Promote health for all through a healthy environment.

9. **Family Planning** Includes preventing unintended pregnancy.

10. **Food Safety** Reduce foodborne illnesses.

11. **Health Communication** Use communication strategically to improve health.

12. **Heart Disease and Stroke** Improve cardiovascular health and quality of life through the prevention, detection, and treatment of risk factors; early identification and treatment of heart attacks and strokes; and prevention of recurrent cardiovascular events.

13. **HIV** Prevent human immunodeficiency virus (HIV) infection and its related illness and death.

14. **Immunization and Infectious Diseases** Prevent disease, disability, and death from infectious diseases, including vaccine-preventable diseases.

15. **Injury and Violence Prevention** Reduce injuries, disabilities, and deaths due to unintentional injuries and violence.

16. **Maternal, Infant, and Child Health** Improve the health and well-being of women, infants, children, and families.

17. **Medical Product Safety** Ensure the safe and effective use of medical products.

18. **Mental Health and Mental Disorders** Improve mental health and ensure access to appropriate, quality mental health services.

19. **Nutrition and Overweight** Promote health and reduce chronic disease associated with diet and weight.

20. **Occupational Safety and Health** Promote the health and safety of people at work through prevention and early intervention.

21. **Oral Health** Prevent and control oral and craniofacial diseases, conditions, and injuries and improve access to related services.

22. **Physical Activity and Fitness** Improve health, fitness, and quality of life through daily physical activity.

23. **Public Health Infrastructure** Ensure that Federal, Tribal, State, and local health agencies have the infrastructure to provide essential public health services effectively.

24. **Respiratory Diseases** Promote respiratory health through better prevention, detection, treatment, and education efforts.

25. **Sexually Transmitted Diseases** Promote responsible sexual behaviors, strengthen community capacity, and increase access to quality services to prevent sexually transmitted diseases (STDs) and their complications.

26. **Substance Abuse** Reduce substance abuse to protect the health, safety, and quality of life for all, especially children.

27. **Tobacco** Reduce illness, disability, and death related to tobacco use and exposure to secondhand smoke.

28. **Vision and Hearing** Improve the visual and hearing health of the Nation through prevention, early detection, treatment, and rehabilitation.

40 Developmental Assets

Search Institute has identified the following building blocks of healthy development that help young people grow up healthy, caring, and responsible.

External Assets

Support
1. **Family support**—Family life provides high levels of love and support.
2. **Positive Family Communication**—Young person and her or his parent(s) communicate positively, and young person is willing to seek advice and counsel from parents.
3. **Other Adult Relationships**—Young person receives support from three or more nonparent adults.
4. **Caring Neighborhood**—Young person experiences caring neighbors.
5. **Caring School Climate**—School provides a caring, encouraging environment.
6. **Parent Involvement in Schooling**—Parent(s) are actively involved in helping young person succeed in school.

Empowerment
7. **Community Values Youth**—Young person perceives that adults in the community value youth.
8. **Youth as Resources**—Young people are given useful roles in the community.
9. **Service to Others**—Young person serves in the community one hour or more per week.
10. **Safety**—Young person feels safe at home, school, and in the neighborhood.

Boundaries and Expectations
11. **Family Boundaries**—Family has clear rules and consequences and monitors the young person's whereabouts.
12. **School Boundaries**—School provides clear rules and consequences.
13. **Neighborhood Boundaries**—Neighbors take responsibility for monitoring young people's behavior.
14. **Adult Role Models**—Parent(s) and other adults model positive, responsible behavior.
15. **Positive Peer Influence**—Young person's best friends model responsible behavior.
16. **High Expectations**—Both parent(s) and teachers encourage the young person to do well.

Constructive Use of Time
17. **Creative Activities**—Young person spends three or more hours per week in lessons or practice in music, theater, or other arts.
18. **Youth Programs**— Young person spends three or more hours per week in sports, clubs, or organizations at school and /or in the community.
19. **Religious Community**—Young person spends one or more hours per week in activities in a religious institution.
20. **Time at Home**— Young person is out with friends "with nothing special to do" two or fewer nights per week.

Internal Assets

Commitment to Learning
21. **Achievement Motivation**—Young person is motivated to do well in school.
22. **School Engagement**—Young person is actively engaged in learning.
23. **Homework**—Young person reports doing at least one hour of homework every school day.
24. **Bonding to School**—Young person cares about her or his school.
25. **Reading for Pleasure**—Young person reads for pleasure three or more hours per week.

Positive Values
26. **Caring**—Young person places high value on helping other people.
27. **Equality and Social Justice**—Young person places high value on promoting equality and reducing hunger and poverty.
28. **Integrity**—Young person acts on convictions and stands up for her or his beliefs.
29. **Honesty**—Young person "tells the truth even when it is not easy."
30. **Responsibility**—Young person accepts and takes personal responsibility.
31. **Restraint**—Young person believes it is important not to be sexually active or to use alcohol or other drugs.

Social Competencies
32. **Planning and Decision Making**—Young person knows how to plan ahead and make choices.
33. **Interpersonal Competence**—Young person has empathy, sensitivity, and friendship skills.
34. **Cultural Competence**—Young person has knowledge of and comfort with people of different cultural/racial/ethnic backgrounds.
35. **Resistance Skills**—Young person can resist negative peer pressure and dangerous situations.
36. **Peaceful Conflict Resolution**— Young person seeks to resolve conflict nonviolently.

Positive Identity
37. **Personal Power**— Young person feels he or she has control over the "things that happen to me."
38. **Self-Esteem**—Young person reports having a high self-esteem.
39. **Sense of Purpose**—Young person reports that "my life has a purpose."
40. **Positive View of Personal Future**—Young person is optimistic about her or his personal future.